Algae, Man,
and the
Environment

Cyclotella, a diatom found in Onondaga Lake. This stereoscanning electron micro-photograph is enlarged 10,000 times. (Courtesy of Dr. F. E. Round)

Algae, Man,
and the
Environment

Proceedings of an International Symposium
sponsored by Syracuse University and the
New York State Science and Technology Foundation
June 18–30, 1967
Syracuse, New York

Edited by
DANIEL F. JACKSON

Department of Civil Engineering
Syracuse University

SYRACUSE UNIVERSITY PRESS

Manufactured in the
United States of America

CONTENTS

FOREWORD

The algae occupy a unique position among the organisms of the aquatic world. They are ignored and endorsed, maligned and extolled, exterminated and pampered, depending on the viewpoint of the individual and the manner in which they affect his happiness. During the past several decades there have appeared an increasing number of reports on algae and the multitude of problems relating to them. Some of these manifestations include changes in the color of the water, clogging of the sand filters of the water supplier, the supersaturation or depletion of dissolved oxygen, resulting in abundance or death of fish, respectively, and the destruction of recreational areas and replacement of pleasant aquatic environments with malodorous and unsightly ones. On the other hand, algae are an important link in the food chain. All young fish eat algae; thus these food organisms are essential to the economy of any lake or stream.

The major problem concerning algae, then, is how to have the proper kind of algae in the appropriate amounts. Although this appears to be a simple statement and that a solution to it could be obtained readily, such is not the case. Evidence to prove this is the sordid condition of Lake Erie, Oneida Lake near Syracuse, New York, Sodus and Henderson Bays in Lake Ontario, New York, Lake Tahoe, California, and the Great South Bay in Long Island. These are but a few examples. Algal problems know no geographic boundaries. Each of the outstanding aquatic environments mentioned, through the process of eutrophication, becomes green, unsightly, and smelly as the summer season progresses. These changes result in the loss of great recreational areas and in the loss of significant revenue to businesses which cater to the tourist industry.

To cope with the complexities of problems associated with algae, the assistance of not only phycologists but limnologists, chemists, ichthyologists, engineers, economists, geographers, physicians, invertebrate zoologists, political leaders, and others is needed. Fundamental data regarding algal cytogenetics, physiology, and taxonomy are essential if a sound management program regarding algae or other aspects of applied phycology is to be formulated.

To help achieve this goal, an international symposium entitled "Algae, Man, and the Environment" was sponsored by the New York State Science and Technology Foundation and Syracuse University. This was held from June 18 to June 30, 1967, in Syracuse, New York. Seventy-five participants were invited to share in the program, and the formal papers presented at the Symposium are assembled in this book. The book is divided into three unequal sections. The first part is devoted to the fundamental aspects of phycology. The second section is concerned with the applied aspects of phycology, while the last part is devoted to some algal studies in a specific region, namely, New York State.

The underlying theme of the symposium is obvious: the development of ways in which algae can better serve man through fundamental and applied research investigations. The simplest of all green plants, the algae, can be unquestionably either the greatest environmental menace of the late twentieth and early twenty-first centuries, or they can be one of man's greatest natural resources.

It is with pleasure that I acknowledge the assistance I have received from many quarters in the organization of the Symposium and the preparation of this book. Without the financial support of both the New York State Science and Technology Foundation and Syracuse University, neither of these activities would have been possible. Within these organizations, I would like to recognize especially two individuals, Dr. Donald Davenport, of the New York State Science and Technology Foundation, and Dr. Clark D. Ahlberg, vice-president for Administration and Research, Syracuse University. Although neither is a phycologist, their help, interest, and enthusiasm in regard to the Symposium exemplify the type of cooperation which is necessary to solve the environmental problems associated with algae.

Naturally, each of the contributors deserves recognition for his own investigation. There are undoubtedly numerous other individuals who should be publicly recognized, the hidden gears of any well organized book or symposium. To these unnamed workers, I give thanks.

My personal hidden gear, who makes all my activities possible through encouragement and assistance, is my wife, Bettina. To her belongs much of the success for the Symposium and for the preparation of this book.

DANIEL F. JACKSON
SYRACUSE UNIVERSITY

Algae, Man,
and the
Environment

Some Reflections on Four Decades of Phycology, 1927–1967*

HAROLD C. BOLD

Department of Botany
University of Texas
Austin, Texas

Dr. Jackson, participants in the International Symposium on Algae, Man and the Environment, and distinguished guests: I face my task with real humility when I consider the eminence of the phycologists gathered here. Immediately after I had agreed to serve as a speaker at this dinner, I began to consider a number of possibly appropriate topics which would neither interfere with your digestive process after a good dinner nor bring to a still more acute stage what some of you may now be experiencing.

The program of your symposium indicates that you have been considering such a broad spectrum of phycological topics that no dinner speaker could hope to add much of significance. It then occurred to me that the year 1967 represented for me an anniversary since it is the fortieth year during which I have been seriously interested in and involved in phycology. Accordingly, I decided to share with you some reflections on developments in the subject as I have been impressed by them during the last four decades, to assay the present status of phycology, and to make some predictions regarding future developments. My survey will not be *exhaustive*, and I hope it will not prove *exhausting*.

My own career in phycology can be attributed to mere chance, and the career itself almost foundered as soon as it had been launched! I was an undergraduate student forty years ago at a large eastern university, and in the curriculum of the Department of Botany was listed a course called "Botanical Problems." I mention this because we are sometimes deluded into thinking that it was Sputnik which only recently inspired provision in the curriculum for undergraduate research. The details of the situation remain clear to me although it was forty years ago. I had a conference with "the professor," who, undoubtedly harassed by other duties, turned toward the window, perhaps for inspiration, and saw there an old jelly jar in which were the remains of some badly wilted flowers, which jar was

* Banquet address.

at the time green with algae. The professor suggested that I might identify "the alga" that was present. Considering that he was a phanerogamic botanist, I now realize that he was widely read because he knew of Klebs' work and of his monumental book *Die Bedingungen der Fortpflanzung bei einigen Algen und Pilzen*, and he also knew that algae could be grown on silica gel!

Accordingly, at our second conference, he provided me with a copy of Klebs' book, six petri dishes, and a bottle of potassium silicate solution and suggested that I get to work. In my youthful zeal, without any prior reading, I immediately poured some potassium silicate diluted with Knop's solution into the dishes, naively expecting that it would gel, and then attempted to spread a suspension of the algae over the surface. You might well imagine how discouraged I was on the following day to find that the little green flakes of algae had sunk to the bottom and that they had died and become bleached in the silicate. As a matter of fact, it was not until approximately fifteen years later that I finally learned how to make good silica gel plates.

I have one other confession to make in this connection. I did not, in fact, isolate the specific organism which the professor had pointed out to me, which was probably a *Chlamydomonas*; instead, of all things, I isolated an alga which I later reported on in detail as *Chlorococcum infusionum*, and this was the beginning of my interest in the genus *Chlorococcum*, which continues to the present. In retrospect, I do not think that starting a phycological career with the challenge of identifying a species of *Chlorococcum* is the most auspicious way to begin.

I have several more observations regarding this incident. Because the professor, Carlton C. Curtis, who was a first-rate botanist but not a phycologist, could not help me in the identification, he suggested that I might write to Professors Robert Chodat, Gilbert Smith, and F. E. Fritsch, which I did. I recall with gratitude that *all* of them answered promptly and tried to give me helpful guidance and advice. I have remembered this very often during the intervening years when I have been tempted to avoid answering letters of inquiry by students, rationalizing that I was "too busy."

It must be obvious that my appraisal of phycology as it was forty years ago will be from two vantage points: my own experience as a student and the somewhat different viewpoint one develops when he later reviews the past. The current appraisal, moreover, has obviously been affected by my own interests in the field, and, of course, by my nationality.

I would like to comment first regarding phycology courses, which were almost universally called "algology" courses, in those days. Very few American institutions offered courses in phycology, though mycology was widely taught. Most of the courses were based largely on formaldehyde-preserved specimens of algae, collected during previous summers at Woods Hole or at another marine station, or on similarly preserved fresh-water materials and prepared slides. These were supplemented, when the instructor had the opportunity and drive, with fresh collections from the field. Too often, however, it seemed to be (and in some institutions it still seems to be) more convenient to use bleached and preserved algae.

At this point I must pay tribute to the late Professor Tracy E. Hazen, who already by the late 1920's had been offering an excellent course in phycology at Columbia University for two decades. Professor Hazen spared neither expense (I mean personal expense; there were no grants for travel in those days, nor did the university reimburse him) nor effort in trying to collect living specimens of algae. For him this was all the more arduous because he had no car, and he lived in New York City, but he did manage to find a relatively diverse collection of freshwater and marine algae within the city limits! He thought nothing of going to Atlantic City, using subway train, railroad, and taxi, so that he might have living marine algae for his class the following week, and he used other opportunities such as Thanksgiving, Christmas, and Easter vacations to bring back living algae from Bermuda and other *then* relatively far-off places.

One additional bright spot on the horizon of phycological pedagogy in those days was the fact that several field laboratories offered and had offered for some years, summer courses in phycology with field work. This enabled small numbers of interested students to see some living algae in the field. As early as 1889, Dr. James E. Humphrey, of Johns Hopkins University, gave instruction on algae in the form of ten lectures at Woods Hole, and this was followed by a course in marine botany given by Professor Setchell and others each year, beginning in 1890 and continuing to the present. Similarly, a course in algae was first given in 1898 at the Hopkins Marine Station by Dr. Bradley Moore Davis. At Friday Harbor, the first instruction in algae was given by Dr. T. C. Frye in 1904.

I turn now to the matter of phycological text and reference books. The phycological bibles forty years ago were Friedrich Oltmanns' great three-volume work, *Die Morphologie und Biologie der Algen*, its latest edition published in 1923, and West's *Algae*, Vol. I, published in 1916. A "modernized" volume, West and Fritsch's *British Freshwater Algae*, appeared in 1927. Limitations of language made Oltmanns' volumes less accessible to American students than might otherwise have been the case.

With respect to manuals for the identification of algae, the situation was especially unfortunate for American marine algae. Until 1937, the only available work which dealt with East Coast algae was Farlow's very sparsely illustrated *Marine Algae of New England*, which had been published in 1879! It was not until 1937 that William Randolph Taylor's *Algae of the Northeastern Coast of North America* was first published. For the West Coast, there were the admittedly incomplete volumes by Setchell and Gardner, published between 1916 and 1925. The marine green algae, but not the other groups, were treated in F. S. Collins' series (1909). Most helpful then, and still useful today for freshwater algae, were certain volumes of Pascher's *Süsswasserflora* and Rabenhorst's *Kryptogamenflora.*

I would now like to comment briefly on the matter of visual aids in the teaching of phycology. There were available to me, first as a student, and later as a teacher at Columbia University, the beautiful German Kny charts and other German charts illustrating very realistically a number of genera of algae and their morphology. There were no Kodachromes or Ektachromes forty years ago, and so these charts had to suffice in providing students with realistic concepts regarding algae. In this connection, I would like to show you several of the hand-colored lantern slides of the period which were prepared by and for the late Dr. Hazen. These must be between fifty and seventy years old.

Among the mature and active phycologists of forty years ago were Drs. Fritsch in England, Pringsheim at Prague, Setchell and Gardner at Berkeley, Howe at the New York Botanical Garden, Taylor (then still at Pennsylvania), Hazen at Columbia, Smith (then still at Wisconsin), Chodat at Geneva, Kylin at Lund, Svedelius at Uppsala, and Pascher at Prague. Of these, Drs. Taylor and Pringsheim, the latter at eighty-five, continue to be highly productive, an inspiration for all of us.

I turn now to a brief consideration of the types of phycological research in vogue forty years ago. One good index here seemed to be *Biological Abstracts.* The first issue of *Biological Abstracts,* Volume I, Number 1, was published in 1927, although dated December, 1926, and I examined it as well as the numbers for 1927, considering that this would give us some reflection of the nature of phycological research at that time.

The section on Algae in *Biological Abstracts* was then under the editorship of Dr. William Randolph Taylor, and in *boldface* type under the section heading, "Algae," one reads, "Algae (Taxonomy and Morphology)"; one can almost *see* the "only" added after the words "taxonomy" and "morphology," and in my opinion one of the tragedies of phycology has been that students of algal physiology, and later of algal biochemistry, were and are for the most part not primarily interested in the algae themselves. Too many students of algal physiology and biochemistry have seemingly been motivated in exploiting algae as "systems," with little, if any, consideration for algae as organisms and members of populations and communities. The blame, however, is not theirs alone, for too many of us phycologists have been too circumscribed in our own interests. Relatively recently, these unfortunately biased viewpoints have seemed to be disappearing as biochemistry becomes more comparative and evolutionary in its outlook and as phycologists, formerly largely, if not exclusively, taxonomic, morphological, and ecological in viewpoint, have begun to be impressed by the data provided by studies in physiology and biochemistry.

To return to the first issue of *Biological Abstracts*, I thought you would be interested in a few of the papers abstracted there. In spite of the forbidding subtitle (taxonomy and morphology) of the section on algae, somehow the coverage of phycological papers was remarkably broad. Number 46 summarized Mez and Ziegenspeck's "Der königsberger seriodiagnostische Stammbaum" with the following conclusion, as abstracted: "All life is monophyletic with the bacteria as the lowest forms. The flagellates *are not* the source of the algae, but are derived from algal reproductive cells and gave rise to the animal kingdom. Both Rhodophyceales and Phaeophyceales are derived from the Chlorophyceales." These are rather strong pronouncements.

Abstract Number 316 summarizes Czurda's 1926 paper on the culture of conjugate algae in which he reported achieving pure cultures of two desmids as well as of *Zygnema* and *Spirogyra*, the last two triumphs which to my knowledge have not been duplicated until quite recently.

Of historical, as well as current, interest to me was Abstract 350, by Okamura, Oeda, and Miyake, entitled "On the Harmful Action of Deep Fog on *Porphyra tenera*," which concluded that smog damaged the exposed plants of *Porphyra* in Tokyo Bay very severely at low tide because the particles in the smog adsorbed sulfur dioxide.

A very important paper in the field of soil algae and algal physiology is also reviewed in the first issue of *Biological Abstracts*, by Bristol-Roach, entitled "On the Relation of Some Soil Algae to Soluble Carbon Compounds," in which was reported the facultative heterotrophy of the soil alga *Scenedesmus*.

The other numbers of the first volume contain floristic studies (probably based mostly on preserved algae!), a paper by Dr. E. Castle on movement of *Anabaena* and *Oscillatoria* (the mechanism of which we still do not understand forty years later), and a report of the heteromorphic life cycle of the kelp *Macrocystis*. Especially significant from my point of view was the appearance of Number V. of Dr. Pringsheim's series, "Researches on Chlorophyll-Bearing Microorganisms," in which he presented some methods and experiences based on the addition of soil extracts to his medium and in which he first defined various grades of culture.

I was interested to find that botanists of those days, including phycologists, unlike many of us today, were interested in economy, so that a paper by Dr. E. D. Merrill, entitled "An Economical Herbarium Case," is referred to in the algae section. We must remember that there were no grants in those days.

Especially interesting to me was a paper by Guillermond, entitled "New

Researches Concerning the Structure of the *Cyanophyceae*," in which he concluded so many years ago that mitochondria and chloroplasts were lacking in blue-green algal cells. In the same volume of *Biological Abstracts* is a paper by William Beebe considering symbiosis between algae and the three-toed sloth; the author concluded that the algae in the animal's fur "spread a veil of invisibility about the host," this being the basis for the term symbiosis!

Several additional items caught my eye. In one, Dr. Causey concluded that the pyrenoids of *Euglena* arise from mitochondria! Also reviewed were the classical paper by F. E. Lloyd on maturation and conjugation in *Spirogyra longata*, Feulgen's detailed account of the so-called Feulgen procedure, and a paper by Milner entitled "The Stratigraphical Value of Microorganisms in Petroleum Exploration," emphasizing diatoms.

Finally, in the last issue for 1927, Dangeard's report of sexuality in *Bangia*, a phenomenon about which we are still largely in the dark, was abstracted, and another paper on diatoms which makes it clear that in 1927 diatom locomotion had already been a puzzle for more than a hundred years. Surely before another hundred years Dr. Drum, Paul Conger, and others will have solved the puzzle!

Let us now review some of the important developments in the intervening years, that is, in the four decades since 1927. Here again, time does not permit me to make a completely comprehensive summary. To put the matter succinctly one might say: *Phycology has matured or come of age.* With respect to courses, phycology has become a standard member of the university curriculum, in most institutions, and phycologists are sought after and valued as respected members of the faculty. With few exceptions, younger phycologists are availing themselves of the excellent opportunities provided by such culture collections of algae as that at Indiana University, so that they are able to show to their students pigmented living organisms instead of bleached white ones. Even here, human nature being what it is, it seems that many instructors order cultures from the Indiana laboratory, so that they arrive at just about the time they are to be used, without realizing that if they themselves were to culture the algae for at least a little while, they could evoke a wide range of stages which otherwise both they and the students would never see.

Although the availability of unialgal and bacteria-free cultures has had a tremendous impact on the teaching of and interest in phycology, it has one possible disadvantage, namely, that students become accustomed to thinking of organisms as occurring only in unialgal cultures. The antidote for this, of course, is clear. Students should be encouraged to continue their field work and to examine many mixed collections from nature.

With respect to phycological books and manuals, the situation has improved remarkably, with the publication of the comprehensive *Struc-*

ture and Reproduction of the Algae by Fritsch (1935, 1945), the two editions of Smith's *Freshwater Algae of the United States* (1933, 1950), Volume I of Smith's *Cryptogamic Botany* (1938, 1955), and the *Manual of Phycology* (1951), all of which were tremendous syntheses. There have also appeared the smaller, but useful, volumes of Ettl, Fott, Christensen, Chapman, Round, and Dawson. Regrettably, the Fritsch and Smith volumes are no longer sufficiently current, and once again, especially those of us who teach phycology, and students who begin the study of it, feel a void of both *teachable* and comprehensive syntheses.

Of tremendous value to phycology in the Americas have been the second edition of Dr. Taylor's work on the *Algae of the Northeastern Coast of North America* and his treatment of *The Marine Algae of the Tropical and Subtropical Coasts of the Americas*; Smith's *Algae of the Monterey Peninsula*; also the publication of two editions of Dr. Prescott's account, *Algae of the Western Great Lakes Area*; most recently Bourrelly's large volume on the green algae; and Patrick and Reimer's *Diatoms of the United States*.

At this point, I would be remiss were I to omit reference to the two editions of L. H. Tiffany's *Algae—the Grass of Many Waters*, which have no doubt done immeasurable good for our cause in communicating phycology to students and laymen.

There has been great progress too in visual aids and illustrations in phycology. Although helpful in the past, most charts and hand-colored lantern slides have now been supplanted by the excellent collections of transparencies of living algae in various stages of development, and for those who have not prepared their own, the beautiful Kodachromes of Patnode are available commercially; I will describe several of them at this point.

Certainly of tremendous significance in phycology has been the establishment of the great Culture Collections of Algae at Cambridge, Paris, Indiana University, Göttingen, and Prague, and plans to add to these in other countries such as Japan augur well for the future. These great collections are not only maintaining a readily available supply of living organisms for instructional purposes on a continuing basis, but they are also serving to provide reliable stocks of organisms for research. More important still, we now have available depositories for maintaining populations of type organisms as new taxa of algae are described, especially those of microalgae. These living cultures are of paramount importance, and one hopes that provision will be made someday in the International Code of Botanical Nomenclature requiring the deposition of such "type cultures" in a specified Culture Collection when one describes a new taxon.

Among the most important forces in the development of culture techniques and methods, both in instruction and in research, has been the fruitful life and publications of Dr. E. G. Pringsheim. The appearance in 1946 of his book, *Pure Cultures of Algae—Their Preparation and Maintenance*, and his publications on the biphasic soil-water culture method have been the basis for the cultivation of a wide range of organisms which hitherto were only sporadically available. The publications of Provasoli in this area are also of great significance and practical value.

Another important segment of emphasis in phycology during the last four decades, an area which was emphasized especially during the 1930's and still of current interest, is that of life-cycle studies. Progress here has gone hand in hand with improvements and innovations in culture techniques. Although the life cycles of a number of organisms from the several divisions of algae have been at least partially elucidated, we really have very few complete and entirely satisfying accounts of these same life cycles as they occur in nature. Furthermore, there is some reason to believe that many algae are versatile and opportunistic, and that in nature they can take short cuts in their life cycles which, accordingly, are not always as obligate as we imply in our textbooks and in our teaching. This is exemplified in the important work of Føyn on *Ulva mutabilis* and in his earlier work on *Cladophora*.

Do we then at present know all about life cycles in the algae? The answer must certainly be strongly negative. In support of this I cite the fact that relatively few algae have been thoroughly investigated in the field and laboratory with respect to their life cycle, and there are significant gaps even in some of the otherwise excellent accounts published. For example, although the important studies of Drs. Drew-Baker, Hollenberg, and Iwasaki have established beyond doubt the alternation of *Porphyra* with *Conchocelis* and of *Bangia* with *Conchocelis*, the fundamental phenomena of fertilization and meiosis have not been adequately demonstrated for these organisms. Similarly, the life cycle of such a well-known and classical red alga as *Nemalion*, as presented in most textbooks, has of late been questioned, and the germinating carpospores of that organism in my own and other laboratories have thus far failed to yield again the typical *Nemalion* plants from which they came. As a matter of fact, it is now highly questionable whether in fact a haplobiontic life cycle occurs among the red algae!

In a more optimistic vein I would call attention to the penetrating researches of Dr. Von Stosch and his colleagues regarding life cycles of centric diatoms. These studies have indicated clearly that the life cycle is haplobiontic with gametic meiosis and oogamy. How much more there is, however, which needs to be done for both the centric and pennate diatoms with respect to their life cycle and reproduction.

Not unrelated to life-cycle studies have been the contributions to our knowledge of reproductive phenomena and physiologically active substances in algae. In this connection I would remind you of the important contributions of the late G. M. Smith, Ralph Lewin, Levine, Ruth Sager, Buffaloe, Tsubo, Trainor, Regnery, and Gowans and especially those of Wiese and Jones on sexual phenomena and genetics in *Chlamydomonas*. Clearly related to these are the studies of sexual reproduction in *Oedogonium* and on its hormonal control by Hoffman and Rawitscher-Kunkel and Machlis, and the exciting researches of Starr, Darden, and other investigators at Indiana University on volvocalean reproduction and genetics.

Another area not represented forty years ago, but currently providing fruitful information for phycology, is the increasing use of electron microscopy. The data provided by Manton and her associates, by Evans, Gibbs, Bouck, R. M. Brown, Bisalputra, Bowen, Drum, Pankratz, and many others, have given us penetrating insight into a more truly phylogenetic grouping of algal taxa. Thus we see, for example, that the Prasinophyceae of the green algae all possess scaly flagella, and we may cite Dr. Norma Lang's work with *Polytoma* in which her demonstration of a colorless plastid confirmed the relationship of that organism to *Chlamydomonas*. Electron microscopy also has had a significant impact on our understanding of the organization of diatom frustules and of motility in that group.

An interesting aspect demonstrated relatively recently is the antibiotic properties of the algae. Here one may cite the work of Mary Belle Allen, Burkholder and his associates, and the recent studies of Conover and Sieburth on *Sargassum*. The secretion of antibiotics is but a small segment of the larger phenomenon of extracellular secretion by algae, one not considered forty years ago, so far as I am aware, but certainly of tremendous consequence for all organisms present in the same habitat with the algae.

I remember asking a prominent plant physiologist, around 1939, whether he thought anything might possibly diffuse out of his *Chlorella* cells into the medium, and he answered promptly with assurance and vigor, "Of course not." The recent report that up to 40 per cent of the photosynthate of Zooxanthellae in reef corals and bivalves is liberated as glycerol and utilized directly by the corals scarcely supports this denial. Furthermore, Karakashian and his associates have shown that up to 86 per cent of the photosynthate of symbiotic Zoochlorellae leaks out of the algal cells in culture and presumably in their hosts as well. Here we must also recall the unequivocal demonstration of nitrogen fixation and secretion of nitrogenous compounds by certain blue-green algae, and of extracellular enzymes in certain chlorococcalean algae.

Although taxonomy was the earliest aspect of phycology chronologically, and although it is often considered to be static, it is in this area of phycology that perhaps the most significant and dramatic changes have been taking place; these may be discussed as to both method and result. Taxonomic studies necessarily involve prior floristic surveys. While these are in many quarters considered of little significance, such studies are continually uncovering previously undescribed taxa, and they are beginning to give us some preliminary insight into the range of distribution of algae over the surface of the earth. Four decades ago phycological taxonomy was based almost exclusively on morphological attributes, and for many algae and many phycologists it is still so based. It must be clear, however, that morphology itself is the expression of chemical organization and physical forces, and to neglect physiological and biochemical criteria in the classification of organisms is to base classification on an incomplete range of characteristics. Here I am reminded of a statement by an eminent paleobotanist who wrote, "No system [of classification] can be accepted as final as long as a single fact concerning any kind of plant remains unknown."

In many microalgae, in which the range of morphological attributes is relatively limited, physiological and biochemical criteria must of necessity play an increasingly important role. The elucidation of such attributes of algae is in most instances based on the method of axenic culture in the laboratory, a technique which has advanced dramatically through the last four decades.

The herbarium method and comparison of specimens with type specimens, of course, continue to be fundamentally important methods in algal taxonomy. There are two important considerations here, however. Even for those organisms where the method is useful, one can never obtain a complete spectrum of attributes from nonliving organisms! Some seventeen or eighteen years ago I wrote in this connection, "Who among us can with authority or even with reasonable assurance define the generic and specific limits in such a series of organisms as (1) *Chlorococcum, Cystococcus, Hypnomonas*, etc.; (2) and of *Chlamydomonas, Palmella, Sphaerellopsis*, and *Gloeocystis*?" In the same paper I stated, "It well may be that further work in such genera, particularly *Chlorella*, will indicate that the solution of the taxonomy of these forms must be based to some degree on physiological criteria obtained from their study in pure culture." This last statement was seemingly prophetic, as evidenced by the appearance of the important contribution on *Chlorella* by Shihira and Krauss and the valuable papers of Dr. Kessler and his associates on biochemical attributes in *Chlorella* taxonomy.

The culture method is as indispensable in the study of microalgae as it has been for other organisms studied in microbiology. The usual criticism of taxonomy based on cultures is that cultures do not duplicate the "normal" conditions of the environment, a viewpoint which makes a tremendous act of faith in assuming that the environment *is*, indeed, always uniform and "normal." How much more secure and firm a taxonomy can be educed from studies of axenic clonal cultures under a set of rigorously controlled conditions in which the range of variation of genetically determined attributes can be measured and recorded!

Recent studies of the genus *Stigeoclonium* by Dr. Islam and by Dr. Elenor Cox in our own laboratory illustrate this very clearly. Dr. Islam, following traditional methods, produced a comprehensive summary of herbarium-based data regarding *Stigeoclonium*. In a subsequent study of twenty isolates of the genus grown in axenic culture in the laboratory, and in several streams at the same time, Dr. Cox was able to demonstrate two points of fundamental significance. In the first place, many of the attributes on which the taxonomy of the genus *Stigeoclonium* had traditionally been based are unreliable and variable. She found, on the other hand, that the basal system, usually absent from herbarium specimens, is the most reliable and conservative characteristic of the plant, one not readily modified by conditions of culture, and this she confirmed by parallel studies of material grown in the laboratory and in natural bodies of water.

Other examples of the contributions of the culture method to taxonomy are clearly illustrated by Dr. Pringsheim's *Contributions Toward a Monograph of the Genus Euglena*, Dr. Van den Hoek's studies of *Cladophora*, and the several efforts in my own laboratory to contribute to the taxonomy of chlorococcalean and chlorosphaeracean algae.

A large monographic study of the Oscillatoriaceae, part of which I have been privileged to examine before publication, would unite the genera *Oscillatoria*, *Phormidium*, and *Lyngbya* on the basis of the author's conclusion from studies of herbarium specimens that the presence or absence of a sheath is an unreliable attribute. Yet, to my knowledge no one has yet validated this claim in long-continued, axenic cultures of several members of the representative genera. Similarly, in the nostocaceous blue-green algae, the literature implies that akinetes and heterocysts develop only as the plants mature, but my associate, Dr. Kantz, has found that there is a good deal of variation here in relation to the species.

Although I have alluded earlier in this discussion to the serological work of Mez and Ziegenspeck, serological techniques do not seem to have been exploited very much in phycological taxonomy until relatively recently, as in the work of Drs. Richard Lester and R. Malcolm Brown with *Tetracystis* and *Chlorococcum*. It was comforting to find that their serological evidence supported the basic arrangement of taxa which had been deduced previously on the basis of morphological (including ultrastructural) and physiological criteria.

It is evident then that phycology and the taxonomy of many algae are becoming more microbiological at present, and this is none too soon. In a recent book entitled *Three Centuries of Microbiology*, algae are mentioned only once in the text and then in cursory reference; there is no mention of the contributions of E. G. Pringsheim, nor is nitrogen fixation by blue-green algae considered. Our brother microbiologists, apparently on the basis of the past performances of phycologists, have been unwilling to admit us into their fraternity.

Great syntheses, be they taxonomic monographs or edited volumes with multiple contributors to certain phases of biology, make a powerful impact on the development and progress of a science, and this is certainly the case in algal physiology and biochemistry which were summarized relatively recently in the monumental volume edited by Dr. Ralph Lewin. Such syntheses serve to focus our attention on what is known and to bring into sharp relief fruitful pathways for augmentation of our knowledge. In reading and rereading many parts of this important work, I am repeatedly impressed that relatively few algae have been studied physiologically and biochemically and that we have as a result made many extrapolations on the basis of a very small sample. We might perhaps paraphrase the British by saying, "Never have so many broad conclusions been based on so few data."

In reference to ecology and applied aspects of phycology, the present symposium is eloquent evidence of progress which is currently being made with respect to productivity, dispersal of algae by birds and aquatic insects, the role of algae in pollution and waste disposal, algal toxicity, and the relation of algae to allergies and other human health problems.

The important work on algal viruses of Ralph Lewin, and especially on the blue-green algal virus discovered by Safferman and Morris, by Kenneth Smith, Goldstein, R. M. Brown, and Walne are providing highly significant data. In this connection, the recent discovery of the same virus by Padan in Israel is of considerable interest.

Especially important in the maturation of phycology has been the establishment of national phycological societies in America (1946), Great Britain (1951), Japan (1952), France and Czechoslovakia (1955), the Philippines (1956), India (1959), Venezuela (1966), and of the International Phycological Society (1961), through the leadership of Paul Silva. The journals and meetings of these societies, consistently improving in quality, have gone far to enhance communication among phycologists.

Although this summary may have *exhausted* you, I repeat that it has not been comprehensive and exhaustive, and surely each of you will think of important items which I should or could have mentioned. However, I think all of you will agree that in the last four decades considerable progress has been made in phycology.

Do we then know all about everything phycological? Is all our old knowledge obsolete, and must we forget all we used to know and all we learned? I think not, but a number of avenues for future fruitful work occur to me, among others, the following: (1) We still need careful taxonomic studies based on organisms in culture correlated with studies of the same taxa in nature. Perhaps an impossibly optimistic goal, but one which I would like to see us achieve, would be that of having every algal species in unialgal culture in the laboratory. (2) We need more studies of life cycles of a greater diversity of organisms, as these occur not only in the laboratory but also in nature. (3) We must continually broaden our spectra, including data from electron microscopy, comparative physiology, and biochemistry, to augment phycological taxonomy. (4) In my opinion we need better informal communication between graduate students and their supervising phycologist-professors at different institutions here and abroad. In several instances we have found that we are needlessly duplicating each other's work. I would like to explore whether it might be possible for us to exchange graduate students and to develop a visiting graduate student program for a semester at a time. This would certainly enrich graduate student training! (5) We need further exploration regarding genetic interchange among blue-green algae and in the euglenoids. (6) There must be more viruses which grow on algae, and an intensified search for these should be fruitful. (7) With respect to phycological pedagogy and training, we need to have better textbooks, better manuals, and better keys, not only for students, but also for amateurs who are interested in phycology. (8) Perhaps, above all, we need continuing exhaustive summaries of titles of phycological publications, such as those for 1960 and 1961, published by Silva in *Phycologia*, if we are to remain informed about our own discipline.

There have been many contributions to the progress of phycology during the last four decades; all of you present have contributed and are continuing to contribute to this progress, for which I congratulate you. Phycology then has come of age, and you have been the catalysts and instruments of its maturation!

II

Biochemistry and Physiology of Algae: Taxonomic and Phylogenetic Considerations

RALPH A. LEWIN

Scripps Institution of Oceanography
University of California
La Jolla, California

Since there is no adequate fossil record of algal evolution and diversification, theories of algal phylogeny must be based almost entirely on comparative studies and the taxonomy of contemporary types. We are seeking a "natural" classification. The test for such a "natural" classification is its internal consistency: the accuracy by which one can predict unknown features of an organism when one knows its assigned taxonomic position. In constructing such a classification with some phylogenetic implications, we should use evidence from all appropriate fields, biochemistry and physiology no less than morphology and cytology.

The algae are apparently the earliest group of organisms to be classified largely on biochemical criteria. Such a classification was proposed well over a century ago by Lamouroux (1813; see Feldmann, 1958), followed by Agardh and Harvey, who must have been quite dissatisfied with the Linnaean system by which algae were classified according to gross features of thallus construction. Their primary criteria were the algal colors due to accessory pigments which are, of course, the most obvious of the biochemical differences among the Chlorophyta, Rhodophyta, and other divisions. This system, though now considerably modified and extended to embrace certain other groups such as the Cyanophyta, is the one accepted today. It is a sad reflection that Alston, in the chapter "Evolutionary Biology" of his book on Biochemical Systematics (1967), made no reference to the algae. I hope that this article may point out some ways in which phycology has progressed in this direction.

COMPARATIVE BIOCHEMISTRY IN THE "SUPER-KINGDOMS" PROCARYOTA AND EUCARYOTA

The Cyanophyta, together with the bacteria, may be considered to constitute the Procaryota, while nucleate algae, with other plants and all animals, constitute the Eucaryota. In eucaryotic organisms the subcellular systems for heredity, photosynthesis, and respiration are typically delimited in membrane-bound organelles (nucleus, plastids, and mitochondria), whereas in procaryotic cells the systems seem to be more closely integrated with one another. Fundamental differences in nuclear chemistry between the Procaryota and the Eucaryota, reflecting their microscopic dissimilarity, are to be expected, although the proportions of guanine *plus* cytosine in the deoxyribonucleic acid (DNA) of blue-green algae (38–56 per cent in those examined by Edelman, *et al.*, 1966) fall well within the range of algae in general. There is a growing body of evidence to indicate that in the procaryon the DNA is not associated with any special basic protein, whereas in the chromosomes of Eucaryota it is normally organized in close association with histones. Doubtless other biochemical differences, such as the mode of formation and the biosynthetic activities of the ribonucleic acids, will prove to be associated with the absence of a nuclear membrane. The walls of Procaryota are typically composed of mucopolymers which, in at least some blue-green algae (as in many bacteria), contain α-ϵ diaminopimelic acid (Holm-Hansen, *et al.*, 1965), a feature unknown among the Eucaryota. Unknown, too, except in Procaryota, is the storage of poly-β-hydroxybutyric acid, which has been reported not only for many bacteria but also for the blue-green alga *Chlorogloea fritschii* (Carr, 1966) and the apochlorotic cyanophyte *Beggiatoa* (Pringsheim and Wiessner, 1963).

Many of the differences must be correlated with the absence in Procaryota of other kinds of intracellular membranes such as those limiting the plastids, mitochondria, and cell vacuoles. Apparently all Procaryota lack steroids (Levin and Bloch, 1964), which are a common feature of nucleate organisms. (The reported absence of steroids in *Cyanidium caldarium* and *Porphyridium* sp. should certainly be reinvestigated.) Associated with these features are the sensitivity of many Procaryota to such inhibitors as penicillin, streptomycin, and 2,3 dichloro-naphthoquinone and their relative insensitivity to polyene antibiotics which, it is believed, interfere with steroid metabolism in Eucaryota (Hunter and McVeigh, 1961). In blue-green algae the aldolase (which, like that in bacteria, requires —SH and a divalent cation for full activity) seems to be firmly bound to relatively large intracellular particles, whereas in other algae it can be more readily obtained in soluble form (Willard, *et al.*, 1965). It appears that one kind of aldolase, designated as "Type II," is not confined to green flagellates, fungi, and procaryotic organisms, as the limited data of Ruttner (1964) indicated, since the presence of this type of enzyme has now been demonstrated also in members of the Chrysophyceae, Bacillariophyceae, Cryptophyta, and Pyrrophyta, as well as in blue-green algae (Van Baalen, 1965;

Antia, 1967). Perhaps the absence of α-cytochrome may prove to be a more constant distinguishing feature of blue-green algal metabolism (Webster and Hackett, 1966).

Through a variety of organisms such as *Beggiatoa* and less well-known members of the Flexibacterales, the apochlorotic gliding Cyanophyta grade into such bacterium-like organisms as *Cytophaga* (Soriano and Lewin, 1965). Many physiological and biochemical implications of this transition remain to be investigated. Are pteridines, which occur commonly in blue-green algae (Hatfield, *et al.*, 1961), absent among their bacterial allies? Can *Oscillatoria* fix carbon dioxide with the use of energy derived from the oxidation of hydrogen sulphide, as suggested by Nakamura (1938), and as does its apochlorotic counterpart *Beggiatoa*? And can early reports of sulphur granules in blue-green algae (Hinze, 1903; Nakamura, 1937) be substantiated?

Nitrogen fixation seems to be restricted to bacteria and to certain morphologically distinct families among the blue-green algae, notably those with heterocysts (Stewart, this volume), and it might be expected that this faculty would occur in parallel fashion only among their colorless homologues (if they exist).

So far, we have considered the blue-green algae with the bacteria, but there are still some valid physiological arguments supporting the more conventional treatment, in which they are grouped with other algae. Like the latter, but unlike photosynthetic bacteria as presently defined, the Cyanophyta can typically liberate oxygen when illuminated in the presence of carbon dioxide. Again, like the photosynthetic Eucaryota, the Cyanophyta normally possess chlorophyll a (whereas in photosynthetic bacteria its place is taken by bacteriochlorophylls) and bicyclic carotenoids (whereas those of bacteria are acyclic or monocyclic) (Goodwin, 1963). Facultative heterotrophy (reported for *Anabaenopsis* by Watanabe and Yamamoto, 1967) is otherwise almost unknown among pigmented cyanophytes, for some unexplained reason. Thus, at least ecologically, the Cyanophyta behave much like other algae, although cytologically they are clearly closer to the bacteria.

Biochemical studies may help to resolve taxonomic problems such as that presented by *Glaucocystis* and *Cyanophora*, in which blue-green plastid-like bodies within a clearly eucaryotic cell have been identified as blue-green algal symbionts on the basis of examination by electron microscopy (Ueda, 1961; Hall and Claus, 1963, 1967; Lefort, 1965). However, their identity is not quite settled: though they contain C-phycocyanin, they seem to lack other pigments characteristic of cyanophytes, notably the carotenoids echinenone and myxoxanthophyll (Chapman, 1966). Recent biochemical evidence for a separate deoxyribonucleic acid component in the plastids of *Euglena, Chlamydomonas*—and perhaps in those of all algae and higher plants—has reopened the question of the possible evolution of plastids from intracellular (photosynthetic) symbionts, presumably Procaryota of some sort (see review by Sagan, 1967; Bisalputra and Bisalputra, 1967). However, if the presence of two (or more) kinds of DNA in a eucaryotic cell is regarded as evidence for a synthetic origin of the cell, how are we to interpret the presence of two kinds of DNA within a blue-green alga, as reported for *Plectonema boryanum* by Kaye, *et al.* (1967)?

BIOCHEMISTRY IN THE EUCARYOTA: DIVISIONS AND CLASSES

Among the eucaryotic algae, plastid pigment composition, carbohydrate reserves, and cell-wall composition have been used extensively for defining the main divisions and for indicating possible phylogenetic relationships among the classes. For instance, similarities of pigment composition, in particular the absence of chlorophyll b, suggest a possible relationship between the Chloromonadaceae and the Xanthophyceae (Chapman and Haxo, 1966).

The occurrence of mannitol and β-1,3 glucan (laminarin or chrysolaminarin), free or combined, in such structurally dissimilar algae as the Phaeophyceae, Chrysophyceae, and Bacillariophyceae (Beattie, *et al.*, 1961) supports earlier indications of affinity based on their content of fucoxanthin and chlorophyll c. The presence of phycobilins in both the Cyanophyta (Procaryota) and the Rhodophyta (Eucaryota) has led some people to conjecture that these two divisions may be phylogenetically related; but the fact that such pigments have now also been demonstrated among the Cryptophyta (O'hEocha and Raftery, 1959) tends to weaken this argument. It is certainly remarkable that even the protein moieties of phycobilins from blue-green and from red algae may have certain features in common, e.g., the N-terminal methionine and C-terminal alanine in phycoerythrins from algae of either division (O'Carra, 1965; Raftery and O'hEocha, 1965). Sequential amino acid analyses of phycobilins from different algal classes will presumably tell us more about their interrelationships.

Although, in their plastid pigment composition, the Euglenophyta resemble the Chlorophyta, the euglenophytes differ in the absence of cellulose walls and in the storage of paramylum (β-1,3 glucan, like the laminarin of the brown algae) instead of starch (α-1,4 glucan). Vogel (1965) has revealed a further biochemical feature, apparently unique among algae, in *Euglena*. In species of this genus, as in many fungi, lysine is synthesized by a pathway through α-amino-adipic acid; in other algae, including the Cyanophyta, the pathway of lysine synthesis goes through diamino-pimelic acid, as it does also in bacteria.

The distribution and biosynthesis of poly-unsaturated fatty acids in the various algal classes may prove eventually of some taxonomic significance, as suggested by Erwin, *et al.* (1964). A number of analyses have now been published (Lovern, 1936; Hilditch, 1956; Laur, 1965; Klenk, *et al.*, 1963, Erwin, *et al.*, 1964; Chuecas and Riley, 1966) though the available data are still so few that we should hesitate before attempting any generalizations on their phylogenetic significance. In almost all of the green and brown algae examined, the unsaturated fatty acids with 18 carbon atoms predominate over those with 16 or 20, whereas in almost all of the red algae (except the two analyzed by Chuecas and Riley, 1966) those with 20 carbon atoms predominate. This difference may be metabolically correlated in some way with the fact that the Rhodophyta, unlike other algae, can combine glycerol with galactose as floridoside, as well as esterifying it with fatty acids. [A recent report of iso-floridoside in a chrysophyte, *Ochromonas malhamensis* (Kauss, 1967) seems to be the first indication that such compounds may be formed by algae other than Rhodophyta.] A further unusual feature of the lipid metabolism of red algae is the predominance of cholesterol, the common C27 sterol of animals. Fucosterol and sitosterol, which occur among other algal divisions, have been reported in Rhodophyta, but these reports have more recently been questioned (Gibbons, *et al.*, 1967). Another lipid whose distribution may prove to follow taxonomic lines is pristane, which was found in relatively high concentrations in the cells of a diatom, a chrysophyte, and a cryptophyte, but in barely detectable amounts in the green, brown, and red algae examined (Clark and Blumer, 1967).

Sulphated polysaccharides occur commonly among marine red, brown, and green algae, although they are almost unknown among freshwater and terrestrial plants. (*Monodus*, a unicellular Xanthophyte found in soil, is apparently exceptional in this respect.) Percival (1964) has pointed out that in the red algae they are usually based on 1,3 galactans, while in the green and brown algae the sulphate groups are borne on 6-deoxy sugars, respectively L-rhamnose and L-fucose. Algin, which is not sulphated, seems to be confined to the Phaeophyceae.

Certain algae have already been reclassified largely on the basis of biochemical evidence; more examples of this are to be expected as biochemical data accumulate. Thus when siphonaceous algae of the genus *Vaucheria* were found to lack chlorophyll b (Soma, 1960), to store oil but no starch, and to have cell walls consisting largely of β-1,4 glucan (Maeda, *et al.*, 1966), they were accordingly transferred from the Siphonales, in which they had long been classified, to the Xanthophyta. This transfer is supported by the fact that the antherozoid flagella of *Vaucheria* are heterokontous. Largely on the basis of flagellar structure and pigment analyses of pure cultures, the diminutive marine flagellate *Micromonas* (*Chromulina*) *perpusilla* has been reassigned from the Chrysophyta to the Chlorophyta (Manton, 1959).

Although there has been little difficulty in assigning such apochlorotic algae as *Astasia, Prototheca, Gymnodinium cohnii,* and *Nitzschia putrida* to their "correct" classes, more biochemical information is needed to enable us to deal similarly with the vast assemblage of phytoflagellates now relegated, by default, to the Protozoa. Similarly, the apochlorotic, branched filamentous organism, *Saprochaete saccharophila* (von Stosch, 1966), should be examined biochemically for clues as to its taxonomic position, at present highly problematical.

COMPARATIVE BIOCHEMISTRY OF ORDERS WITHIN THE EUCARYOTA

Among red algae, the calcified members of the Cryptonemiales (the Corallinaceae) deposit calcitic skeletons, whereas those of the Nemalionales and Bonnemaisoniales are aragonitic (see Lewin, 1962). (Presumably this difference is attributable to a basic dissimilarity of the organic matrices; see Kitano and Hood, 1965.)

Among brown algae, the Fucales, or at least the Fucaceae (representatives of other familes were not analyzed), are biochemically characterized by a higher content of tocopherols, ten to thirty times that in other seaweeds examined, and by the presence of β, γ, and δ tocopherol, as well as the common α tocopherol (Jensen, 1965).

On the basis of new evidence from biochemistry, as well as from electron microscopy, some new classes and orders are now emerging. Biochemical studies, together with other evidence, have recently contributed to the fragmentation of the old Siphonales (Feldmann, 1958). We are now inclined to distinguish, as separate orders, the Siphonales, which lack the carotenoids siphonein and siphonoxanthin; the Dasycladales, which include algae that accumulate fructosans rather than true starches and whose cell walls are predominantly mannans (Werz, 1964); the Caulerpales, in which the cell walls differ from those of almost all other green plants by lacking cellulose, having instead a β-1,3' xylan (Percival, 1964); and the Codiales, in which the main structural component of the wall (at least, in *Codium*) is a β-1,4' mannan. Mannans, which occur with xylans in the walls of the red alga *Porphyra umbilicalis* (Frei and Preston, 1964), may be a normal component of cell walls in the Bangiales, though this remains to be established.

Enzymological and biochemical studies of the agar-like components in the cell walls of red algae (Yaphe and Baxter, 1956; Stoloff and Silva, 1957) promise to be of increasing value in future rearrangements of the orders and families within the Rhodophyta (see Table I). A separation of the

TABLE I   Predominant carbohydrates in various orders and families of red algae. (Augier, 1953, 1954; Yaphe and Baxter, 1956; Stoloff and Silva, 1957; Majak, Craigie and McLachlan, 1966.)

	Cell Wall Components		Intracellular Reserves	
Rhodophyceae	Agar-agar	Gelan Carragheenin	Floridoside	Mannoglycerate
Bangiales	−	−	+	−
Nemalionales			+	−
Gelidiales	+	−	+	−
Cryptonemiales	−	+	+	+
Gigartinales Furcellariaceae Gigartinaceae Hypneaceae Solieriaceae	−	+	+	− +
Gracilariaceae Phyllophoraceae	+	−	+	− +/−
Rhodymeniales	+/−	−	+	+
Ceramiales	+/−	−	+/−	+

Prasinophyceae from the Chlorophyceae has been put forward, based on cell-wall composition as well as on flagellar structure (Chadefaud, 1960; see Christensen, 1962). More biochemical studies of the Charophyta would be of interest, though the cellulosic nature of their walls is unquestioned.

The recognition of at least two distinct lines in the old Chrysophyceae (Haptophyceae and Chrysophyceae s.s.) is supported by similar evidence, while recent data on pigment composition, taken together with the occurrence of silification of the cell walls, also point to a close affinity between certain chrysophytes (e.g., *Mallomonas*) and the diatoms. It will be of interest to see whether further studies on the organic components of the cell walls support or confute these proposed regroupings.

COMPARATIVE BIOCHEMISTRY OF FAMILIES, GENERA, AND SPECIES IN THE EUCARYOTA

Although most algae do not require exogenous cobalamin, those that do vary considerably in their responses to the different homologues of vitamin B_{12}, and in their various responses they provide clues for the comparative taxonomy of algae (see Table IV in Droop, 1962).

Attempts are being made to classify unicellular green algae of the *Chlorella* type on the basis of biochemical and physiological characters. *Auxanochlorella* must be one of the few genera of photosynthetic organisms to be characterized on such grounds: notably, facultative heterotrophy combined with obligate auxotrophy for thiamine (Shihira and Krauss, 1965). Other species, within the genus *Chlorella*, are being distinguished by such characteristics as accessory carotenoid production, hydrogenase activity, and the ability to grow in light or darkness utilizing various sources of carbon and nitrogen (Soeder, 1962; Shihira and Krauss, 1965; Kessler, 1965, 1967; Gromov, *et al.*, 1965; Andreyeva, 1967). Kessler (1967) has begun to apply some of these methods to the taxonomy of *Ankistrodesmus* and *Scenedesmus*, and I think the time is now ripe to tackle other genera, such as *Chlamydomonas*, in the same way.

PHYSIOLOGY

There are physiological as well as biochemical differences which distinguish members of the two "super-kingdoms," Procaryota and Eucaryota. Thus, some procaryotic cells, blue-green algae as well as bacteria, can tolerate higher temperatures (up to 90°C) even in the vegetative state, whereas among Eucaryota only a few thermophilic fungi can grow at temperatures in the 45–50° range. Presumably the absence of a cell vacuole and the denser protoplasm of blue-green algae are somehow related to the relative insensitivity of these organisms to osmotic changes in the environment. But why are virtually all Phaeophyceae and Florideae marine, and why are there no truly marine Conjugales or Oedogoniales? Is the halophily of the Siphonales and their allies in any way connected with their coenocytic construction? Possibly, further studies of osmotic tolerance, contractile and noncontractile vacuoles, and ion transport may help to answer some of these physiological questions, and perhaps may throw incidental light on algal phylogeny.

Our ideas of algal taxonomy are themselves evolving as more information comes to light and as new means of investigation are developed. Perhaps the taxonomy of algae has changed more in its methodology than has that of any other kind of organism. From emphasis on gross form of the thallus, we have passed through phases in which we have tended to emphasize first color, then more sophisticated features of pigment content, then cytochemistry, and latterly a great deal of chromatography and electron microscopy, especially for the smaller forms in which morphological criteria are less readily apparent. Soon, perhaps, we should pay more attention to the fundamental matter of inheritance, the nucleic acids themselves: but this is a subject for a review to be written several years hence.

ACKNOWLEDGMENTS

I am indebted to several colleagues at this Institution, to some of my fellow symposiasts—notably Drs. C. J. Dawes and C. van den Hoek—and to Drs. Joyce Lewin and B. J. D. Meeuse of the University of Washington, for many helpful suggestions in the preparation of this article.

REFERENCES

Most of the research on which this article is based has been referred to in *Physiology and Biochemistry of Algae*, published by Academic Press in 1962. The majority of the articles listed below were published subsequently.)

Alston, R. E., 1967. "Biochemical Systematics," in *Evolutionary Biology*, ed. by Dobzhansky, *et al.,* New York: Appleton, Century, Crofts, I, 197–305.

Andreyeva, V. M., 1967. "On some problems of the taxonomy of the genus *Chlorella*," (in Russian) *Botan. Zhurn., 52,* 82–86.

Antia, N. J., 1967. "Comparative Studies on Aldolase Activity in Marine Plankton Algae, and Their Evolutionary Significance," *J. Phycol., 3,* 81–85.

Augier, J., 1953. "La constitution chimique de quelques Floridées Rhodomélacées," *Rev. gén. botan. 60,* 257–286.

Augier, J., 1954. "Biochimie et systématique chez les Rhodophycées," *Congr. intern. botan., 8ᵉ Congr.,* Paris, *Sect. 17,* pp. 30–32.

Beattie, A., Hirst, E. L., and Percival, E., 1961. Studies on the metabolism of Chrysophyceae. "Comparative Structural Investigations on Leucosin (chrysolaminarin) Separated from Diatoms and Laminarin from Brown Algae," *Biochem. J., 79,* 531–37.

Beattie, A., and Percival, E., 1962. "The Polysaccharides Synthesized by *Monodus subterraneus* when Grown on Artificial Media under Bacteria-free Conditions," *Proc. Roy. Soc. Edinburgh, B, 68,* 171–85.

Bisalputra, T. and Bisalputra, A.-A., 1967. "The Occurrence of DNA Fibrils in Chloroplasts of *Laurencia spectabilis*," *J. Ultrastructure Res. 17,* 14–23.

Carr, N. G., 1966. "The Occurrence of poly-β-Hydroxybutyrate in the Blue-Green Alga *Chlorogloea fritschii*," *Biochim. Biophys. Acta, 120,* 308–10.

Chapman, D. J., 1966. "The Pigments of the Symbiotic Algae (cyanomes) of *Cyanophora paradoxa* and *Glaucocystis nostochinearum* and two Rhodophyceae, *Porphyridium aerugineum* and *Asterocytis ramosa*," *Arch. Mikrobiol. 55,* 17–25.

Chapman, D. J. and Haxo, F. T., 1966. "Chloroplast Pigments of Chloromonadophyceae," *J. Phycol., 2,* 89–91.

Christensen, T., 1962. "Alger," in *Systematik Botanik,* ed. by Böcher, *et al.,* No. 2; 178 pp.

Chuecas, L. and Riley, J. P., 1966. "The Component Fatty Acids of Some Sea-Weed Fats," *J. Mar. Biol. Assoc. (U.K.) 46,* 153–59.

Clark, R. C., and Blumer, M., 1967. "Distribution of n-Paraffins in Marine Organisms and Sediment," *Limnol. Oceanogr. 12,* 79–87.

Droop, M. R., 1962. "Organic Micronutrients," In *Physiology and Biochemistry of Algae* 141–59.

Edelman, M., *et al.,* 1966. "The Deoxyribonucleic Acids of the Blue-Green Algae," *Plant Physiol. 41,* suppl. x.

Erwin, J., Hulanicka, D., and Bloch, K., 1964. "Comparative Aspects of Unsaturated Fatty-acid Synthesis. *Comp. Biochem. Physiol. 12,* 191–207.

Feldmann, J., 1958. "Remarques sur la systématique actuelle des algues," Uppsala Universitets Årsskrift 6, 59–64.

Frei, E., and Preston, R. D., 1964. "Non-Cellulosic Structural Poly-Saccharides in Algal Cell Walls. I. Xylan in Siphonaceous Green Algae. II. Association of Xylan and Mannan in *Porphyra umbilicalis,*" *Proc. R. Soc.* (B) *160,* 293–327.

Gibbons, G. F., Goad, L. J., and Goodwin, T. W., 1967. "The Sterols of Some Marine Red Algae," *Phytochem. 6,* 677–83.

Goodwin, T. W., 1963. "The Distribution of Carotenoids in Nature and Their Biological Significance," In *Carotine und Carotinoide,* Darmstadt: Steinkopff Verlag, 1–25.

Gromov, B. V., Avilov, I. A., and Skrupskaya, V. A., 1965. "On the physiological criteria for the classification of algae in the genus *Chlorella,*" (in Russian) *Vestnik Leningradskovo Univ. 21,* 112.

Hall, W. T., and Claus, G., 1963, "Ultrastructural Studies on the Blue-Green Algal Symbiont in *Cyanophora paradoxa* Korschikoff," *J. Cell Biol. 19,* 551–63.

——— "Ultrastructural Studies on the Cyanelles of *Glaucocystis nostochinearum* Itzigsohn," *J. Phycol. 3,* 37–51.

Hatfield, D. L., van Baalen, C., and Forrest, H. S., 1961. "Pteridines in Blue-Green Algae," *Plant Physiol. 36,* 240–43.

Hilditch, T. P., 1956. *The Chemical Constitution of Natural Fats,* 3rd. ed., London: Chapman and Hall.

Hinze, G., 1903. "Ueber Schwefeltropfen im Innern von Oscillarien," *Ber. dtsch. bot. Ges. 21,* 394–98.

Holm-Hansen, O., Prasad, R., and Lewin, R. A., 1965. "Occurrence of Diaminopimelic Acid in Algae and Flexibacteria," *Phycologia 5,* 1–14.

Hunter, E. O., and McVeigh, I., 1961. "The Effects of Selected Antibiotics on Pure Cultures of Algae," *Amer. J. Bot. 48,* 179–85.

Jensen, A., 1965. "Tocopherol Determinations in Seaweeds," *Proc. 5th Int. Seaweed Sympos.,* Halifax, 281–86.

Kauss, H., 1967. "Metabolism of Iso-Floridoside (O-α-D-galacto-pyranosyl-(1,1)-glycerol) and Osmotic Balance in the Freshwater Alga *Ochromonas,*" *Nature, 214,* 1129–30.

Kaye, A. M., Salomon, R., and Fridlender, B., 1967. "Base Composition and Presence of Methylated Bases in DNA from a Blue-Green Alga, *Plectonema boryanum,*" *J. Molec. Biol. 24,* 479–83.

Kessler, E., 1965, 1967. "Physiologische und biochemische Beiträge zur Taxonomie der Gattung *Chlorella,*" *Arch. Mikrobiol. 52,* 291–96; *54,* 37–45; *55,* 346–57.

——— "Physiologische und biochemische Beiträge zur Taxonomie der Gattungen *Ankistrodesmus* und *Scenedesmus,*" *ibid., 55,* 320–26.

Kitano, Y., and Hood, D. W., 1965. "The Influence of Organic Material on the Polymorphic Crystallization of Calcium Carbonate," *Geochim. Cosmochim. Acta, 29*, 29–41.

Klenk, E., Knipprath, W., Eberhagen, D., and Koof, H. P., 1963. "Ueber die ungesättigten Fettsäuren der Fettstoffe von Süsswasser-und Meeresalgen," *Z. Physiol. Chem., 334*, 44–59.

Laur, M. H., 1965. "Lipides de quelques Rhodophycées," thesis, Faculty of Sciences, Univ. of Paris, 93 pp.

Lefort, M., 1965. "Sur le chromatoplasm d'une Cyanophycée endosymbiotique: *Glaucocystis nostochinearum* Itzigs," *C. R. Acad. Sci.*, Paris, *261*, 233–36.

Levin, E. Y., and Bloch, K., 1964. "Absence of Sterols in Blue-Green Algae," *Nature, 202*, 90–91.

Lewin, J. C., 1962. "Calcification," in *Physiology and Biochemistry of Algae*, 457–65.

Lovern, J. A., 1936. "Fat Metabolism in Fishes. IX. The Fats of Some Aquatic Plants," *Biochem. J., 30*, 387–90.

Maeda, M., *et al.*, 1966. "Chemical Nature of Major Cell-Wall Constituents of *Vaucheria* and *Dichotomosiphon* with Special Reference to Their Taxonomic Position," *Botan. Mag., 79*, 634.

Majak, W., Craigie, J. S., and McLachlan, J., 1966. "Photosynthesis in Algae. I. Accumulation Products in the Rhodophyceae," *Canad. J. Bot. 44*, 541–549.

Manton, I., 1959. "Electron Microscopical Observations on a Very Small Flagellate: the Problem of *Chromulina pusilla* Butcher," *J. Mar. Biol. Ass. U.K., 38*, 319–33.

Nakamura, H., 1937. "Ueber das Auftreten des Schwefelkügelchens im Zellinnern von einigen niederen Algen," *Bot. Mag. Tokyo, 51*, 529–33.

———— 1938. "Ueber die Kohlensäureassimilation bei niederen Algen in Anwesenheit des Schwefelwasserstoffs," *Acta Phytochim.*, Japan, *10*, 271–81.

O'Carra, P., 1965. "Purification and N-Terminal Analyses of Algal Biliproteins," *Biochem. J., 94*, 171–74.

O'hEocha, C., and Raftery, M. 1959. "Phycoerythrins and Phycocyanins of Cryptomonads," *Nature, 184*, 1047–52.

Percival, E., 1964. "Algal Polysaccharides and Their Biological Relationships," *Proc. 4th Int. Seaweed Sympos.*, Biarritz, 1961, 18–35.

Pringsheim, F. G., and Wiessner, W., 1963. "Minimum Requirements for Heterotrophic Growth, and Reserve Substance in *Beggiatoa. Nature, 197*, 102.

Raftery, M. A., and O'hEocha, C. O., 1965. "Amino Acid Composition and C-Terminal Residues of Algal Biliproteins," *Biochem. J., 94*, 166–70.

Rutter, W. J., 1964. "Evolution of Aldolase," *Federation Proc., 23*, 1248–57.

Sagan, L., 1967, "On the Origin of Mitosing Cells," *J. Theor. Biol., 14*, 225–74.

Shihira, I., and Krauss, R. W., (1965 approx.). "*Chlorella:* Physiology and Taxonomy of Forty-one Isolates," Univ. of Maryland Press, 97 pp.

Soeder, C. J., 1962. "Zur Taxonomie de Gattung *Chlorella*," *Ber. dtsch bot. Ges., 75*, 268–70.

Soma, S., 1960. Chlorophyll in *Vaucheria* as a Clue to the Determination of Its Phylogenetic Position," *J. Fac. Sci. Univ. Tokyo, Sect. 3 (Bot.) 7*, 535–42.

Soriano, S., and Lewin, R. A., 1965. "Gliding Microbes: Some Taxonomic Reconsiderations," *Antonie van Leeuwenhoek, 31*, 66–80.

Stoloff, L., and Silva, P., 1957. "An Attempt to Determine Possible Taxonomic Significance of the Properties of Water-Extractable Polysaccharides in Red Algae," *Econ. Bot. 11*, 327–30.

Ueda, K., 1961. "Structure of Plant Cells with Special Reference to Lower Plant. 6. Structure of Chloroplasts in Algae," *Cytologia, 26*, 344–58.

von Stosch, H. A., 1966. "Eine algologische Seltenheit, *Saprochaete saccharophila,*" *Hessische floristische Briefe 15,* 21–28.

van Baalen, C., 1965. "Aldolase in Blue-Green Algae," *Nature, 206,* 193–95.

Vogel, H. J., 1965. "Lysine Biosynthesis and Evolution," In *Evolving Genes and Proteins,* ed. by Bryson and Vogel, 25–40.

Watanabe, A., and Yamamoto, Y., 1967. "Heterotrophic Nitrogen Fixation by the Blue-Green Alga *Anabaenopsis circularis,*" *Nature, 214,* 738.

Webster, D. A., and Hackett, D. P., 1966. "Respiratory Chain of Colorless Algae, II. Cyanophyta," *Plant Physiol., 41,* 599–605.

Werz, G., 1964. "Unterschiede in der Zusammensetzung von Mannanen aus verschiedenen Dasycladaceen-Arten," *Planta, 60,* 540–42.

Willard, J. M., Schulman, M., and Gibbs, M., 1965. "Aldolase in *Anacystis nidulans* and *Rhodopseudomonas spheroides,*" *Nature, 206,* 195.

Yaphe, W., and Baxter, B., 1956. "Bacterial Enzymes in the Identification of Agar and Carrageenin in Marine Algae," *Proc. 2nd Int. Seaweed Sympos.,* Trondheim, p. 145.

III

Microorganic and Microinorganic Requirements for Algae

CLYDE EYSTER

Department of Biology
Mobile College
Mobile, Alabama

MICROORGANIC

Many algae when grown in artificial medium under bacteria-free conditions do not require the addition of organic growth substances. It is presumed that these algae have requirements for numerous organic growth substances but that they have the ability to metabolize them under normal conditions of growth, and that the microorganic substances need not be provided to the algae by including them in the culture medium. Under natural conditions where bacteria abound it is likely that some organic growth substances may be provided to the algae by the intimately associated bacteria.

Microorganic nutrients required as supplements to the growth medium by some algae are: cobaltamin (vitamin B_{12}), biotin, thiamine, and perhaps others still undetermined. The vitamin B_{12} requirement of algal flagellates is discussed by Hutner and Provasoli (1951). Vitamin B_{12} was required by dinoflagellates grown in pure culture by Provasoli and Pintner (1953) and by Sweeney (1954). Wilson and Collier (1955) reported that *Gymnodinium brevis* grew faster when the vitamin B_{12} was increased from 0.05 μg/100 ml to 0.1 μg/100 ml.

Volvox generally blooms in waters rich in organic matter. Pintner and Provasoli (1959) showed that *Volvox globator* and *Volvox tertius* do not need any preformed organic compound as sources of energy but do require the additon of vitamin B_{12} to the medium.

The Kettering Research Laboratory (Brown, 1967) has cultured about twenty-seven species of algae in the past fifteen years under conditions which were strictly unialgal but did not exclude bacteria. Included in this list have been *Nitzschia closterium, Chlorella pyrenoidosa, Chlorococcum wimmeri, Scenedesmus quadricauda, Nannochloris coccoides, Chlamydomonas reinhardtii, Haemotococcus pluvialis, Gloeocapsa alpicola, Nostoc muscorum, Phormidium luridum, Plectonema boryanum, Porphyridium cruentum*, etc., all of which grew well without the addition of any microorganic nutrient to the medium; *Cosmarium botrytis, Micrasterias americana, Cryptomonas ovata* (variety *palustris*), *Amphidinium* sp., *Porphyridium aerugineum*, which were supplied soil extract; *Euglena gracilis*, which required thiamin and vitamin B_{12}; *Phormidium persicinum*, which required dl-asparagine and vitamin B_{12}; and *Ochromonas danica*, which required biotin, thiamin, arginine, glucose, glutamic acid, glycine, and histidine.

Many algae require vitamins; a detailed tabulation is given by Provasoli (1960), and further reviews on the subject have been written by Lewin (1959) and Droop (1962). The Chlorophyceae and Bacillariophyceae have the lowest proportion of species requiring added vitamins. The great majority of the Dinophyceae and Chrysophyceae need vitamins, and all of the species of the Eugleninae and Cryptophyceae studied thus far require vitamins. The need for vitamins seemingly predominates in algal groups having strong animal tendencies; most species of the algal groups having strong vegetal tendencies (Chlorophyceae, Bacillariophyceae, and probably Cyanophyceae) do not need vitamins.

The data in Table I summarize the vitamin requirements of 154 species of algae. Whereas ninety-eight species require vitamins, fifty-six grow

TABLE I   Vitamin Requirements of Algae*

Algal Group	Number of Species	Do not Require Vitamins	Require Vitamins	B_{12}	Thiamine	Biotin
Chlorophyceae	58	25	33	27	30	0
Eugleninae	9	0	9	8	7	0
Cryptophyceae	9	0	9	7	7	0
Dinophyceae	17	1	16	15	5	4
Chrysophyceae	13	1	12	10	9	3
Bacillariophyceae	37	20	17	14	7	0
Cyanophyceae	10	9	1	1	0	0
Rhodophyceae	1	0	1	1	0	0
Total	154	56	98	83	65	7

* Taken from Provasoli (1960).

without the addition of vitamins to the culture medium. Of the ninety-eight species which require vitamins, eighty-three or 85 per cent need vitamin B_{12}, sixty-five or 66 per cent need thiamine, and seven or 7 per cent need biotin. Only the phagotrophic flagellates (e.g., *Peranema*) seem to require other vitamins.

The quantities of vitamins which need to be added to nutrient media to support the growth of some algae are: vitamin B_{12}, 0.1 µg per liter; thiamine, 0.1 mg per liter; and biotin, 0.5 µg per liter (Provasoli and Pintner, 1960).

Provasoli came to the following conclusions regarding the need of algae for vitamins: (1) no correlation seems to exist between the need of vitamins and the ability of algae to employ various sources of energy; (2) no correlation can be found between environment and the need for vitamins; (3) the need for vitamins seemingly predominates in algal groups having strong animal tendencies, whereas most species of the algal groups having strong vegetal tendencies do not need vitamins; (4) the thiamine requirement is more evident in the Chlorophyceae, while the need for vitamin B_{12} predominates in the other algal groups; (5) both vitamin B_{12} and thiamine are required by the majority of the Euglenineae, Cryptophyceae, and Chrysophyceae; and (6) most Dinophyceae require only vitamin B_{12}.

In the Algal Culture Collection at the University of Indiana numerous algae are brought and maintained under artificial culture by the use of an inorganic medium supplemented with soil or soil extract. The principal effective ingredients of the soil extract are perhaps several microorganic nutrients which have not as yet been fully identified. Here is an area of research where our knowledge of the physiology of microorganic nutrients could be expanded with relatively little effort.

Soil Medium

Soil-water medium is the most useful medium developed by Pringsheim (1946a, 1946b), permitting wide variations suited to the needs of particular species and allowing more normal morphological development. It essentially consists in adding to a suitable vessel, i.e., a test tube, bottle, or pint jar, one part garden loam and nine parts water (or sea water). Depending on the type and pH of the desired medium, $CaCO_3$, peat, pea, or inorganic salts can be added prior to the soil. The vessel is then plugged with cotton and steamed for one hour on each of two consecutive days. Allow the liquid to clear before inoculation.

Soil Extract

Many algae grow well in dilute mineral solutions containing soil extract. Such cultures have an advantage over those in soil-water cultures in that they are free from detritus and debris. The soil extract (Bold, 1942) is prepared by adding one part garden soil to two parts water and steaming in an Arnold sterilizer for one hour on each of two consecutive days. This mixture is allowed to settle and is then decanted; only the clear supernatant is used. As a rule, when employing soil extracts vitamins need not be added. However, biotin, thiamine, and vitamin B_{12} may be used advantageously with some types of soil extract and in some cases can replace it completely. Guillard (1961) recommends the following concentrations:

Thiamin HCl	0.2 mg/liter
Biotin	1.0 μg/liter
B_{12}	1.0 μg/liter

Bristol's Modified Solution has been used widely with success in the cultivation of freshwater algae. The following is essentially modified from Deason and Bold (1960), but differs in that soil extract (to make 5 per cent) is added. Six stock solutions (400 ml in volume) are employed, each one containing one of the following salts in the amount listed:

$NaNO_3$	10.0 g
$CaCl_2$	1.0 g
$MgSO_4 \cdot 7H_2O$	3.0 g
K_2HPO_4	3.0 g
KH_2PO_4	7.0 g
NaCl	1.0 g

To 886 ml of distilled water add 10 ml of each stock solution and 1 ml of each of four micronutrient solutions listed in the next paragraph. Fifty ml of soil extract are then added.

Micronutrients

When soil extracts are used in the media, micronutrients are not usually necessary. However, the following may be used advantageously in some cases with or without soil extract. These have been modified from those presented by Deason and Bold (1960):

Solution 1	(grams per liter)
$FeSO_4 \cdot 7H_2O$	4.98
$ZnSO_4 \cdot 7H_2O$	8.82
$MnCl_2 \cdot 4H_2O$	1.44

Solution 2	(grams per liter)
MoO_3	0.71
$CuSO_4 \cdot 5H_2O$	1.57
$Co(NO_3)_2 \cdot 6H_2O$	0.49

Solution 3	(grams per liter)
EDTA	50.0
KOH	31.0

Solution 4	(grams per liter)
H_3BO_3	11.42

A few algae such as *Spirogyra* grow well in a soil-water medium or in a medium containing soil extract. For algae which thrive in an alkaline medium, a small pinch of powdered $CaCO_3$ is placed in the bottom of the vessel before the soil and water are added. Some algae like *Euglena, Pyrobotrys, Polytomella, Polytoma, Astasia,* and others require additional complex nitrogenous or carbon compounds. In the case of *Euglena* and *Pyrobotrys*, the best results have been obtained by adding one-fourth of a garden pea cotyledon to the basic medium (including $CaCO_3$) before steaming. For the colorless forms, the addition of a barley grain before steaming supplies the necessary carbon source. A few strains such as *Botryococcus* grow best when a pinch of sterile ammonium magnesium phosphate is added after the steaming of the basic medium (including $CaCO_3$), and p-aminobenzoic acid has been shown to be required for *Chlamydomonas moewusii* (Droop, 1962).

Provasoli (1956) has written that "It is not surprising that soil extract has been such a panacea for growing exacting algae, since it contains ammonia, thiamine, and B_{12}," and that "it might be expected that soil with an abundant and varied microflora will give extracts rich in all trace metals chelated by humic acid."

Wilson and Collier (1955) were able to mass-culture *Gymnodinium brevis* in bacterized culture, and found that enrichment of sea water with B_{12} (0.1 μg per 100 ml), a chelating agent, and soil extract were necessary for growth. Good cultures could also be obtained by diluting 100 ml of sea water with 7 to 10 ml of river water or peat extract.

Presumably all algae use vitamin B_{12}, thiamine, and biotin. Those algae which grow in a bacteria-free medium to which these vitamins are not added very likely synthesize them. The question has been posed whether vitamin B_{12} and the other vitamins are endogenously produced by the algae or are accumulated from the environment. Ericson and Lewis (1953) concluded that vitamin B_{12} in seaweeds appeared to have an exogenous origin. They found that 70 per cent of the epiphytic bacteria growing on the seaweeds were vitamin B_{12} producers, and they postulated that the vitamin B_{12} stored in the algae was of bacterial origin. Provasoli (1956) reported that there are a larger number of species with high content of vitamin B_{12} among red seaweeds than among brown algae, and that all of the five species of blue-green algae tested had a very high content of vitamin B_{12}.

There is an interesting report that a sample of sea water containing a red tide of dinoflagellates was very rich in vitamin B_{12}. It is presumed that the bacterial flora of the sea is the main source of vitamin B_{12}. It now remains to be established whether the amount of vitamin B_{12} in sea water is a limiting factor and if it varies seasonally.

Some vitamin B_{12}-rich algae have been shown to be vitamin B_{12} producers. Bacteria-free cultures of three blue-green algae (Robbins, et al., 1951) and of *Chlorella* (Hashimoto, 1954) were found to produce high contents of vitamin B_{12}. The various vitamin requirements are associated with their function as cofactors for various enzyme systems.

MICROINORGANIC

The microinorganic nutrition of algae is reviewed by Wiessner (1962) and by Eyster (1964). Since then there have been reports that boron was essential for the growth of the marine alga, *Cylindrotheca fusiformis* (Lewin, 1965), and that boron was not required by either *Chlorella pyrenoidosa* (Bowen, et al., 1965) or *Chlorella sorokiniana* (Eyster, 1966). A previous report that strontium could replace calcium for the culture of *Chlorella pyrenoidosa* could not be substantiated by Eyster (1966) for the thermotolerant strain, 7–11–05. It should be pointed out here that the thermotolerant strain, 7–11–05, of *Chlorella pyrenoidosa* is now known as *Chlorella sorokiniana* (Shihira and Krauss, 1963). Recently Iwasaki (1967) has shown that the edible seaweed, *Porphyra tenera*, needs boron, manganese, zinc, strontium, rubidium, lithium, and iodine for growth. The iodine effect was remarkable, producing peak growth with 10 μg per liter.

Table II reviews the present information on the algal requirements for microinorganic elements. In artificial culture media in the presence of a strong chelate such as EDTA, the amounts of microinorganic elements required are quite high, which may be 100 to 1000 times the amount required in natural waters where there is an absence of significant amounts of chelate.

Studies of microinorganic elemental requirements for algae may be placed in the following sequence: (1) establish essentiality in a qualitative way showing that growth is significantly less in the absence than in the presence of the element; (2) determine the quantitative requirement of the element to establish a concentration range of the element for optimal physiology; (3) find the role or roles of the element in cellular function; and (4) isolate the enzyme which contains the microinorganic element and perform experiments which will thoroughly elucidate the physiology of the

TABLE II Microinorganic Elemental Requirements for Algae

Element	Optimal Concentration Without Chelate (ppm)	With EDTA* (ppm)	Cellular Function	Known Enzymes with Element
Iron (Fe)	0.05	5	Photosynthesis Respiration	Peroxidase, catalase, cytochromes, cytochrome oxidase, ferredoxin for photosynthesis.
Manganese (Mn)	0.005 0.000005	5	Hill Reaction Krebs Cycle	
Zinc (Zn)	0.001	6	Hydrogen transfer in both respiration and photosynthesis.	Carbonic anhydrase, carboxypeptidase and 7 specific dehydrogenases.
Copper (Cu)	0.001	0.4	Respiration Photosynthesis	Laccase, ascorbic acid oxidase, polyphenol oxidase (tyrosinase), plastocyanin for photosynthesis.
Cobalt (Co)	0.00004		Nitrogen fixation	
Molybdenum (Mo)	0.00001 0.01		Reduce nitrate Nitrogen fixation	Nitrate reductase
Boron (B)	0.1		Nitrogen fixation	
Vanadium (V)	0.1		Photosynthesis	Enzymatic role not yet clarified
Calcium (Ca)	0.05	40	Digestion	Amylases
Chlorine (Cl)	0.3 about 0.001		Nitrogen fixation Photosynthesis	
Sodium (Na)	2		Required by blue-green algae. Exact function not yet determined.	
Silicon (Si)	1		Cell wall constituent in diatoms. Other function indicated.	
Iodine (I)†	0.01		Not known	

* Based on unpublished data by Eyster (1966), for *Chlorella sorokiniana* using 500 mg EDTA per liter of culture.

† Other micro-elements which may be required but which require further verification are bromine, strontium, rubidium, lithium, and arsenic.

enzyme and establish unequivocally the role and irreplaceability of the micro-element in the enzyme.

A specific species of alga has a total nutritional requirement which includes numerous essential elements. It is possible to demonstrate that there will be no growth if any one of the numerous essential elements is removed and withheld from the alga. Further, the rate of growth can be controlled by judicious additions of the element in minimal or short supply. The law of the minimum is an important principle in physiology, stating that regardless of how satisfactory one or more requirements of an organism may be, it cannot survive or flourish unless all requirements are met. As an example of this law and its application, let us suppose that a certain plant is supplied with all physical and chemical requirements in adequate amounts except one essential element (for example, manganese). Regardless of how adequate other minerals and other specific environmental conditions may be, the minimum requirements of the plant have not been met, and it cannot continue to grow.

Elemental requirements for the metabolism and growth of algae are related to cellular functions such as respiration, photosynthesis, and nitrogen fixation. For example, *Nostoc muscorum* requires the following critical concentrations for nitrogen fixation: calcium, 0.3 ppm; boron, 0.1 ppm; and molybdenum, 0.01 ppm (Eyster, 1964). A critical concentration is defined as the minimum concentration which will produce maximum growth. Micro-elemental requirements for photosynthesis include manganese, iron, copper, chlorine, vanadium, etc., in addition to such major elements as carbon, hydrogen, nitrogen, phosphorus, magnesium, and potassium. Iron, manganese, zinc, and copper are known to have various roles in respiration. Much additional research is required to elucidate the functions of sodium, boron, and iodine and to add to our knowledge of the functions of all the other micro-elements. Macro-elements are expected to have multiple functions including micro-elemental roles as enzyme constituents. Magnesium is such an element. Calcium has a double role both as a major element and as a minor element.

Without the use of EDTA in the medium, it is difficult to demonstrate that algae require calcium and copper. The need for all of the metals is accentuated in the presence of EDTA as a chelate. The chelate competes with the algae in the medium for the various metals.

SUMMARY

Some algae require cobaltamin (vitamin B_{12}), thiamine, and biotin as supplements to the growth medium. These vitamin supplements serve as cofactors for various enzyme systems.

Algae have micro-elemental requirements which are related to cellular functions such as respiration, photosynthesis, and nitrogen fixation. Many metal-containing enzymes have already been isolated and purified. These essential micro-elements include iron, manganese, zinc, copper, cobalt, molybdenum, boron, vanadium, calcium, chlorine, sodium, silicon, and iodine. In the future others may be added to this list.

REFERENCES

H. C. Bold, 1942. "The Cultivation of Algae," *Bot. Rev. 8(2),* 69–138.

J. E. Bowen, H. G. Gauch, R. W. Krauss, and R. A. Galloway, 1965. "The Nonessentiality of Boron for *Chlorella," Jour. of Phycology, 1(4),* 151–54.

T. E. Brown, 1967, personal communication.

T. R. Deason and H. C. Bold, 1960. "Phycological Studies—I. Exploratory Studies of Texas Soil Algae," Univ. of Texas Publ. No. 6022, Austin, Tex.

M. R. Droop, 1962. "Organic Micronutrients," Chapt. 8 in *Physiology and Biochemistry of Algae,* ed. by R. A. Lewin, Academic Press, New York, 141–60.

L. E. Ericson and L. Lewis, 1953. "On the Occurrence of B_{12} factors in Marine Algae," *Ark. f. Kemi. 6,* 427–42.

C. Eyster, 1964. "Micronutrient Requirements for Green Plants, Especially Algae," in *Algae and Man,* ed. by D. F. Jackson, Plenum Press, New York, 86–119.

C. Eyster, 1966. "Mineral Nutrient Requirements of *Chlorella* in Continuous Pure Culture," Final Report. Contract AF 41(609)–2414. USAF School of Aerospace Medicine, Aerospace Medical Center, Brooks AFB, Texas.

R. R. L. Guillard, 1961. "Media for Isolation and Maintenance of Marine Algae," the Woods Hole Oceanographic Institution, Woods Hole, Mass., mimeographed.

Y. Hashimoto, 1954. "Vitamin B_{12} in Marine and Freshwater Algae," *J. Vitaminology 1,* 49–54.

S. Hutner and L. Provasoli, 1951. *Biochemistry and Physiology of Protozoa,* ed. by A. Lwoff, Academic Press, New York, 27–128.

H. Iwasaki, 1967. "Nutritional Studies of the Edible Seaweed *Porphyra tenera*—II. Nutrition of *Conchocelis," Jour. of Phycology 3(1),* 30–34.

Joyce C. Lewin, 1965. "Boron requirement of a Marine Diatom," *Naturwissenschaften 52(3),* 70.

R. A. Lewin, 1959. "Phytoflagellates and Algae," in *Handbuch der Pflanzenphysiologie,* ed. by W. Ruhland, Vol. 14, 401–17, Springer, Berlin.

I. J. Pintner and L. Provasoli, 1959. *Proc. Int. Bot. Congress Abstracts II,* 300–301.

E. G. Pringsheim, 1946a. *Pure Cultures of Algae,* Cambridge Univ. Press.

E. G. Pringsheim, 1946b. "The biphasic or soil water culture method for growing algae and flagellata," *Jour. Ecol. 33,* 193–204.

L. Provasoli, 1956. "Growth Factors in Unicellular Marine Algae," in *Perspectives in Marine Biology,* ed. by A. A. Buzzati-Traverso, University of California Press, Berkeley and Los Angeles, 305–403.

L. Provasoli, 1960. "Transactions of the Seminar on Algae and Metropolitan Waters, April 27–29, 1960," U.S. Public Health Service, Robert A. Taft Sanitary Engineering Center, Cincinnati 26, Ohio.

L. Provasoli and I. J. Pintner, 1953. "Ecological Implications of *in vitro* Nutritional Requirements of Algal Flagellates," *Ann. New York Acad. Sci. 56,* 839–51.

L. Provasoli and I. J. Pintner, 1960. "The Ecology of Algae (Pymatuning Symposia in Ecology, Special Publication No. 2)," ed. by C. A. Tryon, Jr. and R. T. Hartman, University of Pittsburgh Press, Pittsburgh, Pa.

W. J. Robbins, A. Hervey, and M. E. Stebbins, 1951. "Further Observations on *Euglena* and B_{12}," *Bull. Torrey Botan. Club 78*, 363–75.

I. Shihira and R. W. Krauss, 1963. "*Chlorella,* Physiology and Taxonomy of Forty-one Isolates," University of Maryland, College Park, Md, 30–31.

B. M. Sweeney, 1954. "*Gymnodinium splendens*, a marine dinoflagellate requiring vitamin B_{12}," *Am. Jour. Botany 41*, 821–24.

W. Wiessner, 1962. "Inorganic Micronutrients," Chapt. 17 in *Physiology and Biochemistry of Algae, loc. cit.*, 267–86.

W. B. Wilson and A. Collier, 1955. "Preliminary Notes on the Culturing of *Gymnodinium brevis* Davis," *Science 121*, 394–95.

IV

Phosphate Metabolism of Green Algae

ADOLF KUHL

Institute of Plant Physiology
University of Göttingen
Göttingen, Germany

Of all chemical elements which are essential for the growth and reproduction of living matter phosphorus plays a very important role. It was found that this role is not restricted to special parts of the general metabolism of organisms but that it covers the whole range of metabolic processes. It is of little surprise, therefore, that since the very beginning of the scientific study of basic metabolic processes, much effort has been spent—and is still being spent—in getting a closer and even intimate knowledge of the role and pathways of this chemical element in metabolism. Since it has been proved experimentally that phosphorus metabolism is essentially connected with the energy transforming systems of living cells, great effort was concentrated on this subject especially (Katchman, 1961a, 1961b).

Experimental work and data dealing with the phosphorus metabolism of algae are innumerable and collected from so many different organisms or parts of them that it is impossible to cover the whole field here. In view of the general theme of our symposium I shall restrict myself to those facts which allow a better understanding of the *physiological* aspects of phosphate metabolism in algae, rather than compile all biochemical reactions in which phosphorylated compounds participate.

REMARKS ON THE METHODS OF STUDY OF PHOSPHATE METABOLISM

Experimental work to elucidate the role of phosphate or phosphorylated compounds in algal metabolism on principle follows two main principles. The first one observes the organisms, reactions and their basic metabolic functions such as growth, reproduction, photosynthesis, or respiration, perhaps at different developmental stages depending on varying phosphate concentrations of the surrounding medium and under the influence of different external conditions (e.g., light of various strengths or wavelengths, darkness, temperature, pH value, influence of other ions, metabolic inhibitors, or organic substrates). This kind of experiment provides many important facts but fails to explain the mode and site of phosphate action. Secondly, one can try to explain the metabolic action of the phosphate ion itself by analyzing its distribution among certain conventional phosphate fractions or phosphorylated compounds extracted from the cells. The results of these experiments, in which the application of radioactive-labeled phosphate is of invaluable importance, allow conclusions as to the phosphate turnover and its probable influence on the over-all cell metabolism.

From algae, as from tissues of higher plants, phosphorylated compounds can be extracted by making use of their different behavior against nonpolar solvents and cold acid (trichloroacetic or perchloric acid are most commonly used). So three main fractions are obtained: phosphatides, acid-soluble phosphates, and acid-insoluble phosphates. A diagrammatic

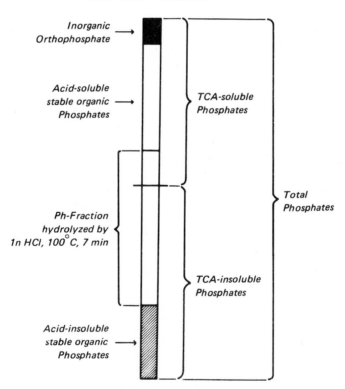

FIG. 1. Diagrammatic representation of conventional phosphate fractions obtained from algae by the Pirson and Kuhl (1958) method.

representation of the phosphate fractions extracted from green algae according to the method of Pirson and Kuhl (1958) is given in Figure 1.

Soluble in cold trichloroacetic acid (TCA) are inorganic ortho- and low molecular polyphosphates, phosphorylated intermediates of carbohydrate metabolism, and nucleotides. Insoluble are ribonucleic acid (RNA), deoxyribonucleic acid (DNA), and high molecular inorganic polyphosphates. A further separation is possible by subjecting the acid-soluble as well as the insoluble phosphates to the hydrolytic action of a 1 Normal hydrochloric acid at 100°C for a seven-minute period (Lohmann, 1931). By this procedure all inorganic condensed phosphates (polyphosphates) are totally hydrolyzed. Some phosphorylated organic compounds of the acid-soluble fraction are hydrolyzed too, at least partially (LePage, 1959).

Because the separation of phosphorus compounds by acid extraction alone is not selective enough, it has been improved by connecting it with ion-exchange, paper, and thin-layer chromatography. For special purposes (e.g., determination of nucleic acids) other extraction and separation methods have been of great value (Lee, *et al.,* 1965; Fitzgerald and Nelson, 1966; Richter and Senger, 1964). For more details see summaries by Albaum, 1952; Lindberg and Ernster, 1956; LePage, 1959; Bieleski and Young, 1963; and Rowan, 1966.

The Metabolism of Phosphate Uptake

In the natural environments of algae—different though they may be— and in the most common nutrient media, phosphorus is present mainly as orthophosphate. Therefore the uptake of phosphate ions from the surrounding medium by these organisms constitutes the basic process of phosphate metabolism. This process is governed to a greater or lesser degree by a variety of factors—light, temperature, pH value, presence of certain ions—but in spite of much investigation their mode of action is far from clear (summaries by Kuhl, 1962a and Rowan, 1966).

In algae the most important effect on the phosphate uptake comes from the action of light. This seems reasonable because phosphorylated compounds are closely involved in metabolic and energy-transforming reactions of photosynthesis (Simonis, 1960). Many experiments with different algae have proved that phosphate uptake and incorporation in certain fractions is greater in light than in darkness (see Figure 2). This can be observed especially after the addition of phosphate to algae grown under conditions of PO_4 deficiency or an insufficient PO_4 supply (Kuhl, 1962b and Kylin, 1964a); but the way by which light accelerates the initial entry of PO_4 into the algal cell is still a matter of discussion. Excluding the up-

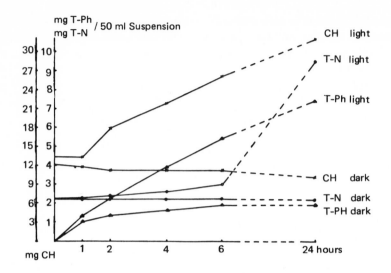

FIG. 2. Behavior of the total phosphate content (T-Ph), carbohydrate content (C-H), and total nitrogen content (T-N) during illumination of 12,000 lux, and in darkness after adding phosphate to P-deficient four-day-old *Chlorella* cultures. All values given in mg/50 ml algae suspension. (Kuhl, 1962b)

take into the apparent free space, the incorporation of ions requires energy. The question if this is supplied by light via the primary photochemical reactions or photosynthesis directly or indirectly by subsequent metabolic reactions at the expense of intermediates or products of the CO_2-assimilation is still without a conclusive answer, though Simonis, *et al.* (1962), Simonis and Urbach (1963), and Overbeck (1963) have done a lot to gather experimental evidence for its decision.

Influences on phosphate uptake exerted by the phosphate- or hydrogen-ion concentration of the surrounding medium, by the presence or absence of organic substances and by different temperatures, can only be mentioned without further explanation. Those affected by potassium or sodium ions are reported by Badour (1959), Simonis and Urbach (1963), Schaedle and Jacobson (1965), and Baumeister and Conrad (1966).

The ability of certain algae to satisfy their phosphorus requirements by the use of condensed inorganic phosphates or organic phosphorus compounds, however, is noteworthy. Galloway and Krauss (1963) have described experiments exploring the usefulness of various phosphate compounds in nutrient media and the manner in which they are absorbed by growing cells. It was shown that inorganic polyphosphates up to a chain length of fifty-five PO_4 units were utilized by *Chlorella* cultures at the same rate as potassium phosphate. This was made possible by an enzyme produced by the cells, and probably associated with the cell wall, which hydrolyzes polyphosphates to orthophosphate. Different marine algae were able to utilize glucose-6-phosphate as a phosphorus source after this ester was hydrolyzed by an extracellular phosphatase to yield phosphate, which was subsequently assimilated (Kuenzler 1965, and Kuenzler and Perras 1965, also cited for further literature).

INCORPORATION OF ORTHOPHOSPHATE INTO ORGANIC PHOSPHATE

After having crossed the outer cell membranes by an active process (perhaps by the formation of a complex with an often discussed but still hypothetical "carrier"), the phosphate ion in algae is incorporated into organic or condensed inorganic phosphates. These energy-requiring (endergonic) reactions are mediated by either the mechanism of *photophosphorylation*, which is restricted to chloroplasts, or phosphorylation coupled with respiration, intimately associated with the mitochondria (*oxidative* phosphorylation). I cannot treat here in detail these two major energy-yielding chains of processes necessary for the life of all green plants, but the following excellent review articles offer much information: Kandler (1960), Bassham (1963), Vernon and Avron (1965), and Hill (1965), on photophosphorylation; Griffiths (1965), and Rowan (1966) on oxidative phosphorylation. By these two basic mechanisms, from adenosine diphosphate (ADP) and orthophosphate, adenosine triphosphate (ATP) is formed.

$$\text{ADP + orthophosphate} \xrightarrow[\substack{\text{photophosphorylation} \\ \text{or oxidative phospho-} \\ \text{rylation}}]{\text{energy}} \text{ATP}$$

This compound occupies a main position because most endergonic reactions in algae metabolism—as in all other living organisms—are coupled to the hydrolysis of the β- or γ-phosphate bond of ATP. The hydrolysis of this "energy-rich" bond is exergonic and therefore provides energy by which the synthesis or breakdown of material of cell metabolism is rendered possible. Many of these innumerable reactions are essentially connected with the transfer of phosphate groups by the catalyzing action of specific enzymes.

A few remarks on the mechanisms of photophosphorylation, which is restricted to organisms with photosynthetic activity, should be allowed. In the study of photosynthesis, the discovery by Arnon, *et al.* (1954) that isolated chloroplasts of higher plants are able to convert *light* energy into *chemical* energy in the form of ATP was of high significance. They found that this reaction depends on the transfer of hydrogen or electrons originating from the splitting of water, which is induced photochemically by light absorbed by chlorophyll systems. With this discovery, earlier proposals by Ruben (1943), and Emerson, *et al.* (1944), found confirmation. These workers suggested that the only function of light absorbed by the chlorophyll system is the formation of "energy-rich" phosphate bonds which may then be utilized to drive all subsequent "dark" reactions of photosynthesis. Although a tremendous scientific effort was concentrated in elucidating the mode and site of ATP-formation in the sequence of these transfer reactions, a final decision still seems impossible (Witt, 1965).

It has long been doubtful whether photophosphorylation, which worked wonderfully in vitro, also occurs in vivo, but experiments with different unicellular green algae reported by Wiessner and Kuhl (1962), Kuhl (1962b), Tanner, *et al.* (1965), Tanner, *et al.* (1966), and Simonis (1966) have strongly supported this possibility.

We can be sure now that ATP originated by this special light reaction may be used by the plant cell to support all energy-requiring metabolic reactions, e.g., photosynthetic CO_2-assimilation, uptake of ions or organic compounds (glucose, acetate), activation of amino acids in protein synthesis, formation of nucleic acids, and even synthesis of inorganic polyphosphates.

The second important mechanism by which algae and many other aerobic organisms yield ATP consists of phosphorylation reactions connected with the oxidation of substrates of the citric acid cycle to carbon dioxide and water. Synthesis of ATP is connected to the electron transport chain of respiration. In this economic way a large part of energy which otherwise would be lost is withheld by the cell. This ATP-bond energy likewise can be used for all endergonic cell reactions already mentioned.

GROWTH AND METABOLISM OF ALGAE UNDER LIMITED PHOSPHORUS SUPPLY

The amount of available phosphorus has often been shown to control strictly the growth of algae populations in their natural environment as well as in laboratory cultures (summary by Kuhl, 1962a). In light of the facts already submitted, this seems quite natural. The ecological importance of different phosphorus compounds promoting algal growth and reproduction in natural waters, therefore, has been studied by many workers under varying aspects and with different methods—partly by measuring the phosphate concentration of the water (for methods see

Schmid and Ambühl 1965, Ambühl and Schmid, 1965) to see whether or not the absence or presence of certain algae or the extent of their propagation can be related to distinct ranges of phosphate concentration, and partly by culture experiments to investigate their phosphate requirements under controlled conditions.

Increased knowledge of phosphorus compounds as ecological factors is highly important, especially nowadays, because the total amount of sewage and the concentration of soluble phosphates in it are steadily increasing in many countries. This is due to the increased use of detergents, water softeners, or other items of modern living. Very often the extremely high concentration of phosphates in sewage effluents are responsible for the uncontrolled growth of algal bloom in lakes and streams, making an effective use of those natural waters impossible. This phenomenon also offers proof that phosphorus is the key element determining the fertilization of natural waters, while nitrogen deficiency is often eliminated by biological fixation of this element (Katchman, 1961a).

A better understanding of these effects is obtained by a study of the growth and general metabolism of algae under conditions of limited phosphate supply or phosphorus deficiency. For this reason experimental data which evaluate the physiological response of algae under such conditions is reported at this time. Most of the data has been obtained using unicellular green algae because of their easy handling, but the general results are representative of many other algae, too (Kuhl and Lorenzen, 1964).

Under P-deficiency the production of dry weight and protein total nitrogen (Figure 3) is lowered, while the carbohydrate content of the cells is significantly higher (Figure 4). Perhaps this accumulation of carbohydrates is responsible for a slight acceleration of respiration. The photosynthetic O_2-production is inhibited (Pirson, *et al.*, 1952). Bergmann (1955) reported a higher oxidative assimilation of glucose in P-deficient *Chlorella* and an accumulation of fat.

After the addition of phosphate to such cultures ("recovery technique"), photosynthetic O_2-production increased, reaching the rate of normal-grown algae within a short time. This is proof that the photosynthetic apparatus itself has not undergone severe damages, at least during the early stages of deficiency. Endogenous respiration (already slightly higher than in normal algae) is further accelerated very markedly. Experiments reported by Kylin (1964b, 1964c) with phosphate-deficient *Scenedesmus* cells gave proof that other metabolic reactions are also markedly influenced by the action of phosphate ions. It turned out that P-deficient cells (0.2–0.3 mg P/g fresh weight of algae as compared with 3–5 mg P/g for normal cells) took up much more sulphate from the medium than did cells growing in the presence of phosphate ions. The presence of phosphate

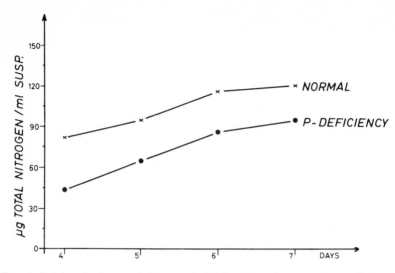

FIG. 3. Uptake of nitrogen (total organic N) by *Chlorella pyrenoidosa* cells between the fourth and seventh days after inoculation. Both suspensions were grown at 25°C under continuous fluorescent light (10^4 lux) and aerated with air enriched with 2 per cent CO_2.

Normal = complete nutritional media (Kuhl, 1962b); phosphate concentration 5×10^{-3} Mol/1.

P-Deficency = phosphate concentration 5×10^{-5} Mol/1.

Algal Strain: 211–8b. (Algal culture from the Institute of Plant Physiology, University of Göttingen)

also blocks to a large extent the incorporation of sulphate into different S-fractions as indicated by the total sulphate content of the cells. Possible explanations for these inhibiting effects of phosphate on sulphate uptake may be, besides others, the competition for absorption sites or an influence on the sulphate-activating system (PAPS–adenosine–3'–phosphate–5'–phosphosulphate).

Growing algae at different phosphate concentrations has clearly revealed the existence of distinct ranges in which they tolerate this anion. According to the excellent work of Rohde (1948) it is possible to group freshwater algae into three categories on the basis of whether or not they are able to grow in phosphate concentrations below, around, or above 20 μg per liter. Representatives for the low concentration range are *Dinobryon divergens*, or *Uroglena americana*; an example of the medium range is *Asterionella formosa*, and for the high, *Scenedesmus quadricauda*. Most of the planktonic algae fall into the low or medium range, so that their growth may not be limited to low range by PO_4-concentration alone, but can be suppressed too by concentrations in excess of an upper limit.

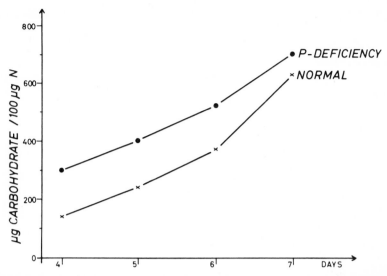

FIG. 4. Carbohydrate content of *Chlorella pyrenoidosa* grown in normal or P-deficient media. Carbohydrate determined by arthrone reagent; for other details see legend, Fig. 3.

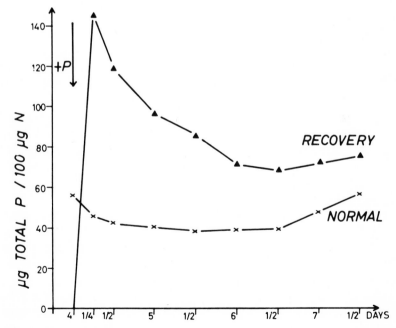

FIG. 5. Total phosphate content of *Chlorella pyrenoidosa* cells grown in (a) complete nutrient medium (see legend, Fig. 3; Normal); (b) P-deficient medium (see legend, Fig. 3). To the latter suspension (recovery) phosphate was added up to a final concentration of 5×10^{-3} Mol/l on the fourth day (indicated by arrow).

A very striking effect in respect to the rate and extent of phosphate incorporation into P-deficient cells has been observed in many experiments with different algae. Phosphorus-starved algae, when provided with phosphate, take up this anion at a great rate and to the extent that the total P concentration inside the cells is far above that actually used, especially in the light. In P-deficient *Chlorella* this "excess" phosphorus is accumulated almost exclusively in the acid-insoluable fraction of polyphosphates (Figure 5 in comparison to Figure 6). The amount of total

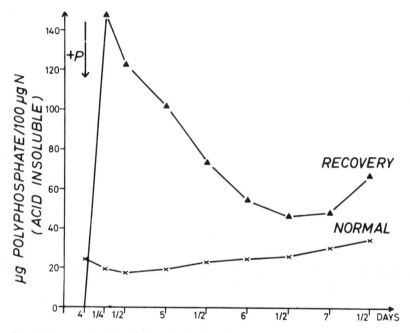

FIG. 6. Content of acid-insoluble polyphosphate in *Chlorella pyrenoidosa* cells. See legend, Fig. 5, for experimental conditions.

phosphate found in P-depleted cells four hours after the addition of phosphate was nearly sixty times higher compared to the previous amount.

CONDENSED INORGANIC PHOSPHATES

A large part of the phosphorus compounds in algae cells consists of inorganic polyphosphates. These condensed phosphates are important for the general metabolism of all microorganisms, and with a very few exceptions their occurrence is restricted to these organisms. A thorough treatment would be too comprehensive (refer for this to general reviews by Schmidt, 1951, Wiame, 1958, Kuhl, 1960, 1962, Langen, 1965, and Harold, 1966), but the most interesting facts cannot be omitted without leaving this survey incomplete.

Inorganic condensed phosphates are classified by their molecular structure. Closed-ring molecules following Thilo (1959) should be called *metaphosphates*, while the terminus *polyphosphate* should be used only for compounds with an open-chain structure. Almost all condensed phosphates found in microorganisms are of the latter type.

$$HO-\overset{\overset{\displaystyle O}{\|}}{\underset{\underset{\displaystyle H}{|}}{P}}-O-\left[\overset{\overset{\displaystyle O}{\|}}{\underset{\underset{\displaystyle H}{|}}{P}}-O\right]_n-\overset{\overset{\displaystyle O}{\|}}{\underset{\underset{\displaystyle H}{|}}{P}}-OH$$

Polyphosphates are labeled "seven-minute phosphates," which means that they are completely hydrolyzed within seven minutes by 1 N HCl at 100°C (Figure 1). This property is used for their quantitative determination.

Polyphosphates have been extracted from algae by different methods. The smaller part is soluble in cold trichloroacetic acid (TCA-soluble) while the greater part is extractable only by alkaline or neutral salt solutions at different temperatures. Kanai, *et al.* (1965) could clearly separate four fractions by successive extraction of *Chlorella*. To differentiate between so many fractions by chemical means is reasonable because in many cases they also differ in their physiological behavior. With histological techniques, the location of distinct polyphosphate granules (volutin-granules) inside the cell is possible. These granules change in number and size according to nutrient conditions, a fact which proves their active participation in cell metabolism (Stich, 1953, 1955; Hase, *et al.*, 1963).

Polyphosphates extracted from the cell can further be separated by paper chromatography and ion-exchange chromatography (Aoki and Miyachi, 1964). Mostly a mixture of polyphosphates with different condensation numbers (n-values) are found, the majority of which have high n-values. More special analytical methods to differentiate between inorganic polyphosphates are described by Heinerth, 1958, Matsuhashi, 1963, and Rössel, 1963. Recently Correll (1966) investigated polyphosphate isolated from Chlorella with a somewhat surprising result: he found that it must contain subunits which are cylic and which contain both imidodiphosphate linkages and phosphate anhydride linkages. The same author has spent much effort in the investigation of a ribonucleic acid-polyphosphate complex isolated from different algae (Correll and Tolbert, 1962, Correll and Tolbert, 1964, and Correll 1965). The detailed descriptions of the isolation and properties of this complex together with some speculations about its possible metabolic role are of great interest for the general understanding of the biology of inorganic polyphosphates.

The earlier literature concerning the biosynthesis of polyphosphates by algae is reviewed by Kuhl (1960, 1962a). Taking in account all the experimental data, it is sure that algae, beside their ability to synthesize polyphosphates in the dark at the expense of energy released by oxidative phosphorylation, can use light energy to synthesize the energy-rich phosphate groups of polyphosphates from orthophosphate; probably in connection with the mechanisms of photophosphorylation. This light-promoted synthesis of polyphosphate, especially, takes place under conditions by which other energy-requiring reactions of the cell metabolism (e.g., assimilation of carbon-dioxide, or acetate, glucose, or nitrate) are inhibited. The rate of polyphosphate-synthesis is extremely high shortly after the addition of phosphate to P-deficient algae. Under these conditions algae incorporate large amounts of orthophosphate into polyphosphate with high condensation numbers (Kuhl, 1962b). The synthesis of polyphosphates in the light and the synthesis in the dark are markedly influenced by the absence or presence of some cations (K^+; Mg^{++}; Mn^{++}) in the surrounding medium (Badour, 1959).

THE METABOLIC FUNCTIONS OF INORGANIC POLYPHOSPHATE

Hoffman-Ostenhof and Weigert (1952) considered the biological functions of the condensed inorganic phosphates to be the storing of energy and phosphate.

According to the equation:

$$ATP + (PO_3^-)_n \rightleftharpoons ADP + (PO_3^-)_{n+1}$$

polyphosphate should act as reservoir for high-energy phosphate under conditions where ATP is available in excess. This theory was supported by experiments of Meyerhof, et al. (1953), and Yoshida (1955), which proved that the P—O—P bonds of the polyphosphate molecule are so-called energy-rich phosphate bonds. The discovery of enzymes in some microorganisms that reversibly can transfer phosphate from ATP to polyphosphate (Ebel and Dirheimer, 1957, Kornberg, 1957, Hoffmann-Ostenhof and Slechta, 1958) seems to support the proposed the function of polyphosphate as an energy donor.

Another enzyme using inorganic polyphosphate to phosphorylate glucose without the mediation of ATP was first demonstrated in *Mycobacterium phlei* by Szymona (1962). It seems to be an inorganic polyphosphate: D–glucose–6–phosphotransferase (Szymona and Ostrowski, 1964), which acts very similar to an enzyme extracted by Dirheimer and Ebel (1962) from *Corynebacterium xerosis*. More recent experiments, however, are in contrast to the theory that the principal functions of polyphosphate is the storage of energy (for reference see: Harold, 1966).

It seems more likely that inorganic polyphosphates play an important role as source of phosphorus in special synthetic reactions and certain developmental stages during the growth of especially unicellular algae (Baker and Schmidt, 1963, 1964a, and 1964b, Miyachi, *et al.*, 1964, Harold, 1966). Polyphosphates as cell constituents therefore enable many algae to continue to grow for a certain time even if the external phosphorus is depleted and therefore the polyphosphates are an ecological factor for the growth of algae under natural conditions.

CONCLUDING REMARKS

Ending this comprehensive treatment of the phosphate metabolism of green algae I am well aware that I was only able to concentrate on some topics of this wide field of scientific interest and that I had to leave aside many very interesting and important problems. In spite of this, I hope that I was able to show to you clearly the importance of physiological research as a help in solving the problems which algae pose for man and his environment.

REFERENCES

Albaum, H. G., 1952. Metabolism of Phosphorylated Compounds in Plants," *Ann. Rev. Plant Physiol., 3,* 35–58.

Ambühl, H., and Schmid, M., 1965. "Die Bestimmung geringster Mengen von Gesamtphosphor im Wasser von Binnenseen," *Schweiz. Z.Hydrol., 27,* 184–92.

Aoki, S., and Miyachi, S., 1964. "Chromatographic Analyses of Acid-Soluble Polyphosphates in *Chlorella* Cells," *Plant and Cell Physiol., 5,* 247–50.

Arnon, D. I., Whatley, F. R., and Allen, M. B., 1954. "Photosynthesis by Isolated Chloroplasts—II. Photosynthetic Phosphorylation, the Conversion of Light into Phosphate Bond Energy," *J. Am. Chem. Soc., 76,* 6324–329.

Baker, A. L., Schmidt, R. R., 1963. "Intracellular Distribution of Phosphorus During Synchronous Growth of *Chlorella Pyrenoidosa,*" *Biochim. Biophys. Acta 74,* 75–83.

———, 1964a. "Further Studies on The Intracellular Distribution of Phosphorus During Synchronous Growth of *Chlorella pyrenoidosa,*" *Biochim. Biophys. Acta 82,* 336–42.

———, 1964b. "Polyphosphate Metabolism During Nuclear Division in Synchronously Growing *Chlorella*," *Biochim. Biophys. Acta 82*, 624–26.

Badour, A. S. S., 1959. "Analytisch-chemische Untersuchung des Kaliummangels bei *Chlorella* im Vergleich mit anderen Mangelzuständen," Dissertation, University of Göttingen.

Bassham, J. A., 1963. "Photosynthesis: Energetics and Related Topics," in *Advances in Enzymology*, Vol. 25, ed. by F. F. Nord, New York: Interscience Publishers, pp. 37–117.

Baumeister, W., and Conrad, D., 1966. "Über Beziehungen zwischen Natriumversorgung und dem Phosphathaushalt bei *Scenedesmus obliquus* (Turp.) Kuetz," *Ber. dtsch. Bot. Gesellschaft, 79*, 15–26.

Bergmann, L., 1955. "Stoffwechel und Mineralsalzernährung einzelliger Grünalgen—II. Vergleichende Untersuchungen über den Einfluss mineralischer Faktoren bei hetertropher und mixotropher Ernährung," *Flora*, (Jena), *142*, 493–539.

Bieleski, R. L., and Young, R. E. , 1963. "Extraction and Separation of Phosphate Esters from Plant Tissues," *Analyt. Biochem.*, *6*, 54–68.

Correll, D. L., 1965. "Ribonucleic Acid-Polyphosphate from Algae—III. Hydrolysis Studies," *Plant & Cell Physiol. 6*, 661–69.

———, 1966. "Imidonitrogen in *Chlorella* Polyphosphate," *Science 151*, 819–21.

Correll, D. L. and Tolbert, N. E., 1962. "Ribonucleic Acid-Polyphosphate from Algae— I. Isolation and Physiology," *Plant Physiology*, *37*, 5, 627–36.

Dirheimer, G., and Ebel, J.-P., 1962. "Mise en evidence d'une polyphosphate-glucose-phosphotransferase dans *Corynebacterium xerosis*," *Compt. Rend. 254*, 2850–52.

Ebel, J. P., et Dirheimer, G., 1957. "Relations métaboliques entre polyphosphates inorganiques et adénosine diet triphosphates," *Compt. rend. soc. biol. 151*, 979–81.

Emerson, R. L., Stauffer, J. F., and Umbreit, W. W., 1944. "Relationship between Phosphorylation and Photosynthesis in *Chlorella*," *Am. J. Botany*, *31*, 107–20.

Fitzgerald, G. P., and Nelson, Th. C., 1966. "Extractive and Enzymatic Analyses for Limiting or Surplus Phosphorus in Algae," *Journ. of Phycol.*, *2*, 1, pp. 32–37.

Galloway, R. A., and Krauss, R. W., 1963. "Utilization of Phosphorus Sources by *Chlorella*," in "Studies on Microalgae and Photosynthetic Bacteria," *Plant Cell Physiol.*, Tokyo, pp. 569–75.

Griffiths, D. E., 1965. "Oxidative Phosphorylation," in *Essays in Biochemistry*, Vol. I, ed. by P. N. Campbell and G. D. Greville, New York: Academic Press, pp. 91–120.

Harold, F. M., 1966. "Inorganic Polyphosphates in Biology: Structure, Metabolism, and Function," *Bact. Rev.*, *30*, 772–94.

Heinerth, E., 1959. "Zur Papierchromatographie der kondensierten Phosphate," *Zeitschr. f. analyt. Chem. 166*. Bd. 1. Heft, Springer Verlag.

Hill, R., 1965. "The Biochemist's Green Mansions: The Photosynthetic Electron-Transport Chain in Plants," in *Essays in Biochemistry*, Vol. I, ed. by P. N. Campbell and G. D. Greville, New York: Academic Press, pp. 121–51.

Hoffmann-Ostenhof, O. und L. Slechta, 1957–58. "Transferring Enzymes in the Metabolism of Inorganic Polyphosphates and Pyrophosphates," *Proc. Intern. Symposium Enzym Chem. Tokyo and Kyoto 2*, 180–98. London: Pergamon Press, 1958.

Hoffmann-Ostenhof, O., and Weigert, W., 1952. "Über die mögliche Funktion des polymeren Metaphosphats als Speicher energiereichen Phosphats in der Hefe," *Naturwissenschaften 39*, 303–304.

Kandler, O., 1960. "Energy Transfer Through Phosphorylation Mechanisms in Photosynthesis," *Ann. Rev. Plant Physiol.*, *11*, 37–54.

Katchman, B. J., 1961a. "Phosphates in Life Processes," in *Phosphorus and its Com-*

pounds, Vol. II, ed. by J. R. van Wazer, New York: Interscience Publishers, pp. 1281–343.

———, 1961b. "Phosphates in Biological Macromolecular Syntheses and Energy Mechanisms," *ibid.*, pp. 1345–427.

Kornberg, S. R., 1957. "Adenosine Triphosphate Synthesis from Polyphosphate by an Enzyme From *Escherichia coli*," *Biochim. Biophys. Acta 26*, 294–300.

Kuhl, A., 1960. "Die Biologie der kondensierten anorganischen Phosphate," in *Ergebnisse der Biologie*, Vol. 23, ed. by H. Autrum, Berlin: Springer, pp. 144–86.

———, 1962a. "Inorganic Phosphorus Uptake and Metabolism," in *Physiology and Biochemistry of Algae*, ed. by R. A. Lewin, New York: Academic Press, pp. 211–29.

———, 1962b. "Zur Physiologie der Speicherung kondensierter anorganischer Phosphate in *Chlorella*," *Vortr. Botan. hrsg. Deutsch. Botan. Ges.* (N.F.), *1*, 157–66.

Kuhl, A., and Lorenzen, H., 1964. "Handling and Culturing of *Chlorella*," in *Methods of Cell Physiology*, Vol. I, ed. by Prescott, New York: Academic Press, pp. 159–87.

Kuenzler, E. J., 1965. "Glucose-6-Phosphate Utilization by Marine Algae," *J. Phycol., 1*, 156–64.

Kuenzler, E. F., and Perras, J. P., 1965. "Phosphatases of Marine Algae," *Biol. Bull., 128*, 271–84.

Kylin, A., 1964a. "An Outpump Balancing Phosphate-Dependent Sodium Uptake in *Scenedesmus*," *Biochem. Biophys. Res. Comm., 16*, 479–500.

———, 1964b. "Sulphate Uptake and Metabolism in *Scenedesmus* as Influenced by Phosphate, Carbon Dioxide, and Light," *Physiol. Plant., 17*, 422–33.

———, 1964c. "The Influence of Phosphate Nutrition on Growth and Sulphur Metabolism of *Scenedesmus*," *ibid.*, 384–402.

Langen, P., 1965. "Vorkommen und Bedeutung von Polyphosphaten in Organismen," *Biol. Rdsch.* (Jena), *2*, 145–52.

Lindberg, O., and A. L. Ernster, 1956. "Determination of Organic Phosphorus Compounds by Phosphate Analysis," in *Methods of Biochemical Analysis*, Vol. III, ed. by D. Glick, New York: Interscience Publishers, pp. 1–22.

Lohman, K., 1931. "Darstellung der Adenylpyrophosphorsaure aus Muskulatur," *Biochem. Z., 233*, 460–69.

Lee, G. F., Clesceri, N. L., and Fitzgerald, G. P., 1965. "Studies on the Analysis of Phosphates in Algal Cultures," *Int. J. Air Water Pollution, 9*, pp. 715–22.

Le Page, G. A., 1959. "Analysis of Phosphorylated Intermediates," in *Macrometric Techniques*, ed. by Umbreit, Burris, and Stauffer, Minneapolis: Burgess Publishing Co., pp. 268–87.

Matsuhashi, M., 1963. "Die Trennung von Polyphosphaten durch Anionenaustausch-Chromatographie," *Hoppe-Seyler's 333*, 28–34.

Meyerhof, O., Shafas, R., and Kaplan, A., 1953. "Heat of Hydrolysis of Trimetaphosphate," *Biochim. et Biophys. Acta 12*, 121–27.

Miyachi, S., Kanai, R., Mihara, S., Miyachi, Sh., and Aoki, S., 1964. "Metabolic Roles of Inorganic Polyphosphates in *Chlorella* Cells," *Biochim. Biophys. Acta, 93*, 625–34.

Overbeck, J., 1963. "Untersuchungen zum Phosphathaushalt von Grünalgen—VI. Ein Breitrag zum Polyphosphatstoffwechsel des Phyloplanktons," *Ber. dtsch. Bot. Gesellschaft, 76*, 276–86.

Pirson, A., 1955. "Functional Aspects in Mineral Nutrition of Green Plants," *Ann. Rev. Plant Physiol., 6*, 71–114.

Pirson, A., and Kuhl, A., 1958. "Über den Phosphathalt von Hydrodictyon I," *Arch. Mikrobiol., 30*, 211–25.

Pirson, A., Tichy C., and Wilhelmi, G., 1952. "Stoffwechel und Mineralsalzernährung einzelliger Grünalgen—I. Vergleichende Untersuchungen an Mangelkulturen von *Ankistrodesmus," Planta, 40,* 199–253.

Richter, G., and Senger, H., 1964. "Extraktion und chromatographische Auftrennung der Nukleinsäuren aus Photosynthese-Organismen," *Biochim. Biophys. Acta, 87,* 502–505.

Rössel, T., 1963. "Die chromatographosche Analyse von Phosphaten—II. Die Dünnschichtchromatographie der kondensierten Phosphate," *Zeitschr. f. analyt. Chem. 197, 3.* Heft, Springer Verlag.

Rowan, K. S., 1966. "Phosphorus Metabolism in Plants," in *Intern. Rev. Cytol.,* Vol. 19, New York: Academic Press, pp. 301–90.

Ruben, S., 1943. "Photosynthesis and Phosphorylation," *J. Am. Chem. Soc., 65,* 279–82.

Schaedle, M., and Jacobsen, L., 1965. "Ion Absorption and Retention by *Chlorella pyrenoidosa*—I. Absorption of Potassium," *Plant Physiol., 40,* 214–20.

Schmid, M., and Ambühl, H., 1965. "Die Bestimmung geringster Mengen von Phosphation im Wasser von Binnenseen," *Schweiz. Z. Hydrol., 27,* 172–83.

Schmidt. G., 1951. "The Biochemistry of Inorganic Pyrophosphates and Metaphosphates," in *Phosphorus Metabolism,* Vol. I, ed., by McElroy and Glass, Baltimore: Johns Hopkins University Press, pp. 443–75.

Simonis, W., 1960. "Photosynthese und lichtabhängige Phosphorylierung," in *Handbuch der Pflanzenphysiologie,* Vol. V, ed. by W. Ruhland, Berlin: Springer, pp. 966–1013.

———, 1966. "Problems of Photosynthetic Phosphorylation in Vivo by Unicellular Algae (*Ankistrodesmus*)," in *Currents in Photosynthesis,* pp. 217–25.

Simonis, W., and Urbach, W., 1963. "Untersuchungen zur lichtabhängigen Phosphorglierung bei *Ankistrodesmus braunii*—IX. Beeinflussung durch Phosphatkonzentrationen, Temperatur, Hemmstoffe, Na$^+$-Ionen und Vorbelichtung," in *Microalgae and Photosynthetic Bacteria,* Tokyo, pp. 597–611.

Stich, H., 1953. "Der Nachweis und das Verhalten von Metaphosphaten in normalen, verdunkelten, und trypaflavinbehandelten *Acetabularien," Z. Naturforschg. 8b,* 36–44.

———, 1955. "Synthese und Abbau der Polyphosphate von *Acetabularia* nach autoradiographischen Untersuchungen des P^{32}-stoffwechels," *ibid., 10b,* 282–84.

Szymona, M., 1962. "Purification and Properties of the New Hexokinase Utilizing Inorganic Polyphosphate," *Acta Biochimica Polonica IX,* 165–81.

Szymona, M. and Ostrowski, W., 1964. "Inorganic Polyphosphate Glucokinase of *Mycobacterium phlei," Biochim. Biophys. Acta 85,* 283–95.

Tanner, W., Dächsel, L., and Kandler, O., 1965. "Effects of DCMU and Antimycin A on Photoassimilation of Glucose in *Chlorella," Plant Physiol., 40,* 1151–56.

Tanner, W., Loos, E., and Kandler, O., 1966. "Glucose Assimilation of *Chlorella* in Monochromatic Light of 658 and 711 mμ," in *Currents in Photosynthesis,* pp. 243–51.

Thilo, E., 1959. "Die kondensierten Phosphate," *Naturwissenschaften, 46,* 367–73.

Vernon, L. P., and Avron, M., 1965. "Photosynthesis," *Am. Rev. Biochem., 34,* 269–96.

Wiame, J. M., 1958. "Accumulation de l'acide phosphorique (Phytine, Polyphosphates)," in *Handbuch der Pflanzenphysiologie,* Vol. IX, ed. by W. Ruhland, Berlin: Springer, pp. 136–48.

Wiessner, W., and Kuhl, A., 1962. "Die Bedeutung des Glyoxylsäurezyklus fur die Photoassimilation von Acetat bei autotrophen Algen," in *Vortr. Botan. hrsg. dtsch. Botan. Ges. (N.F.), 1,* pp. 102–108.

Yoshida, A., 1955. "Studies on Metaphosphate—II. Heat of Hydrolysis of Metaphosphate Extracted from Yeast Cells," *J. Biochem.* (Tokyo), *42,* 165–68.

V

Nitrogen Input into Aquatic Ecosystems

WILLIAM D. P. STEWART

Department of Biological Sciences
University of Dundee
Dundee, Scotland

Lund (1965), in his excellent review of the ecology of freshwater phytoplankton, writes, "Nitrogen and phosphorus can still be considered as two of the major elements governing primary productivity." Dr. Kuhl has presented the picture for phosphorus; I shall try to complement his work by talking about nitrogen. According to the law of mass action, "the mass of the substances entering a chemical reaction is the same as the mass of the products of the reaction." This can be applied to nitrogen transformations in lakes just as it can to chemical reactions in the laboratory. Thus, for convenience nitrogen transformations can be pigeonholed into three main categories: (1) the input of nitrogen, (2) the chemical interrelations going on in the lake, (3) the outflow of nitrogen from the system. It is my responsibility to consider the first of these—nitrogen input—for subsequent reactions are dependent in the first instance on the nitrogen which enters, or has entered, the ecosystem. This paper is in no way intended to be a comprehensive review of the field, rather it is a summary in which aspects of particular interest to the writer are emphasized.

Nitrogen entering a lake comes from many sources, the incidence and importance of each depending on the particular lake under investigation. It is probably a fair statement that there is no lake in which complete measurements of all sources of nitrogen input are available. Thus generalizations only can be made. The main sources of nitrogen input can be listed as follows: (1) nitrogen from rainfall, rivers and streams; (2) nitrogen from agriculture and urbanization; (3) nitrogen from natural ecosystems; and (4) nitrogen from *in situ* nitrogen fixation.

NITROGEN FROM RAINFALL, RIVERS, AND STREAMS

Rainfall is a consistent contributor of combined nitrogen, but the magnitude of its contribution varies greatly depending on the geographical location of the area under study. For example, it is higher over industrial areas such as central Europe than over non-industrial regions. Carroll (1962), from a study of over sixty stations in Northern Europe, reports an average rainfall contribution of 0.31 mg/l. and 0.06 mg/l. of nitrate- and ammonium-nitrogen, respectively. Comparable values for the United States are 0.7–4.7 mg/l. and 0.05–2.2 mg/l., respectively. In less precise but perhaps more readily understood terms, Goldschmidt (1954) suggests an average annual contribution from rainfall of 4–10 lb. nitrogen acre/annum, but as emphasized, there are wide variations. For example, Drover and Barrett-Lenard (1956) record values of 0.6–3.7 lb. nitrogen/acre/annum in Western Australia.

The origin of rainfall nitrogen is still uncertain. Air pollution contributes, but this is a localized effect. Classical chemistry textbooks emphasize the importance of electrical discharges in the atmosphere, but increasing evidence suggests that this plays only a minor role, for there is little direct correlation between the frequency of lightning discharges in the atmosphere and the combined nitrogen content of rainwater. Hutchison (1944) contends that the combined nitrogen in the air results mainly from ammonia released by biological degradation of organic matter on Earth and then partly oxidized in the atmosphere to nitrate. Wilson (1959) postulates that the oceans are an important source of atmospheric combined nitrogen. He observed that New Zealand snow, occurring above the level of higher plant vegetation, has an abnormally high level of organic nitrogen and is devoid of nitrate and nitrite (classical products of electrical discharges in the atmosphere). Having ruled out other sources of this nitrogen, he considers that it originates from the surface layer of the ocean, which is whipped up into foam and carried into the atmosphere. The high nitrogen content of these surface waters can be accounted for by the presence of plankton and their debris. Considering that the oceans cover about four-fifths of the Earth's surface, this may be an important source of atmospheric combined nitrogen. Recent work on the production of organic aggregates by sea foam (see Riley, et al., 1964, 1965; Wangersky, 1965) supports Wilson's view. Of particular interest are the findings of Jones and Stewart (1969) who, using ^{15}N, observed that soluble extracellular products of marine algae form nitrogen-containing aggregates around inorganic nuclei suspended in solution.

Thus, the source of combined nitrogen in rainfall is uncertain, but its contribution (an average 4–10 lb./acre/annum) is not. Such rainwater falling on the Earth picks up additional nitrogen in two main ways. Firstly, in situ nitrogen fixation may occur in the streams and rivers, and secondly, nitrogen is accumulated from the land over which the rain, the streams, and the rivers pass.

In situ nitrogen fixation in streams has been studied by the writer. He showed (1969) that, in streams which originate from Yellowstone hot springs and which have midstream temperatures varying from 70–90°C at source to 28°C at base, two distinct nitrogen-fixing algal floras are present. In the larger, more rapidly flowing streams a flora dominated by *Mastigocladus* (probably *Mastigocladus laminosus*) fixes nitrogen at temperatures up to 54°C with a maximum at 42.5°C. The former temperature is the highest at which nitrogen fixation by an alga has been recorded, and the evidence for fixation confirms previous laboratory studies on *Mastigocladus* (Fogg, 1951; Schneider, *et al.*, 1960). In the smaller streams where greatest plant biomass occurs at 46–55°C (Brock, 1967), *Calothrix* comprises the dominant nitrogen-fixing vegetation and fixes nitrogen at temperatures up to about 46°C (see Figure 1). In midstream at temperatures of 50°C or higher *Calothrix* is absent, but it does persist upstream,

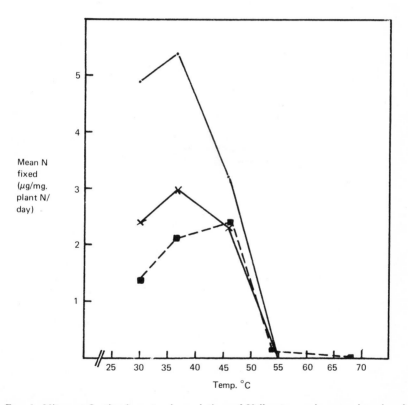

FIG. 1. Nitrogen fixation by natural populations of Yellowstone microorganisms in relation to temperature in three streams. ·—· = Pool A; x—x = Mushroom Spring; samples incubated at the temperatures from which they were collected. ■—■ = White Creek; samples collected at 48°C and incubated at the temperatures indicated on graph.

together with *Nostoc*, as a black band which occurs along the edge of the streams where the temperature range is 24–40°C. There, these algae fix nitrogen slowly and probably contribute additional combined nitrogen which is used by the midstream floras growing at high temperatures (50–90°C). According to R. A. Lewin (personal communication), many flexibacteria require amino acids for growth, and the extracellular products of the nitrogen-fixing algae may be a source of these in this particular ecosystem. Chemical analyses of the waters support the ^{15}N data. They show that ammonia and nitrate levels of the water increase considerably from top to bottom of the stream (a distance of approximately fifty meters), although the phosphate and sulphate levels show little variation (Table 1).

TABLE 1   Concentrations of various inorganic nutrients in a stream originating from a Yellowstone hot spring (after Stewart, 1969)*

Nutrient ($\mu g/1$)	Source (Temp. 70°C)	Downstream (Temp. 28°C)
Ammonia	12	26
Nitrate	1	8
Phosphate	2,000	2,000
Sulphate	18,000	16,900

* This stream, known as Mushroom Spring, is about 30 cm. wide × 10 cm. deep at source, but increases in width and decreases in depth further from the source. pH is 8.2–8.4, and *Calothrix* is the only common heterocystous algal component of the midstream flora.

Input from Agriculture and Urbanization

The main source of biologically fixed nitrogen in the world as a whole is that made available by the leguminous crops such as peas, clover, and soy beans, which bear nitrogen-fixing nodules on their roots. In the agriculturally advanced countries of the world, where cheap synthetic fertilizer is readily available, the contribution of biological fertilizer decreases, for synthetic fertilizer tends to replace, rather than supplement, the biological type.

Biologically fixed nitrogen, when used as the main source of nitrogen fertilizer, contributes about 100–200 lb. nitrogen/acre/annum (Stewart, 1966); synthetic fertilizer is applied at about the same rate. The quantities which find their way in to our lakes, however, are quite different. Biologically fixed nitrogen is retained in the soil over a long period as it gradually decomposes, and the loss by leaching is probably about 10–25 lb. nitrogen/acre/annum. Synthetic-fertilizer nitrogen, on the other hand, is rapidly washed out, and indeed more than half the application may quickly find its way into the lakes. This is particularly so in the more northerly parts of the hemisphere where fertilizer nitrogen tends to be applied by the farmer before the frozen sub-soil has thawed after winter. The contribution of fertilizer nitrogen to lakes will become increasingly important in the future, not only as synthetic fertilizer replaces biological fertilizer, but as liquid synthetic fertilizer, because of its ease of transportation and lower cost, replaces solid synthetic fertilizer. For example, during the period 1954–1965, the consumption of liquid fertilizer in the United States increased approximately 374-fold (Smith, 1967), and this upward trend will continue.

If the land surrounding lake edges is habitable and is not under agricultural development, the chances are that urbanization exists there. The impact of urbanization varies markedly from area to area, but the tendency is towards high-density populations. These, at least in the West, live on protein-rich diets, obtaining produce from all over the world. The more affluent the society, the greater the concentration of nitrogen and, ultimately, the greater the nitrogen pollution of the lakes.

NITROGEN FROM NATURAL ECOSYSTEMS

The wetlands and natural vegetation surrounding our lakes tend to be regarded simply as extensions of the lake with nitrogen input depending on wash-off or leachates from more elevated terrain. Such wetlands provide a rich nutrient source as decomposition of plant material occurs, but they may also contribute "new" nitrogen by *in situ* nitrogen fixation. Characteristic nitrogen-fixing plants of these areas, particularly in Europe, are the nodulated, non-leguminous angiosperms *Alnus glutinosa* and *Myrica gale*, two out of well over two hundred such species. The presence of root nodules can generally be verified readily—I cannot remember examining field material of *Alnus* or *Myrica* which was not nodulated. *Alnus* nodules are distinct coralloid masses occurring at, or just below, soil surface. They are perennial structures, often as large as tennis balls, and have a brownish-orange thick cork covering. Their endophyte is an actinomycete (Becking, *et al.*, 1964; Gardner, 1965). *Alnus* nodules were suspected of fixing nitrogen as early as 1892 (Nobbe, *et al.*), but despite this, and despite the work of higher-plant physiologists (see Bond, 1963, 1967; Stewart, 1966), limnologists have until recently neglected their contribution, even though *Alnus* is frequently one of the commonest trees around lake edges. For example, almost every second tree round Lake Windermere in England is *Alnus glutinosa*—a tree which in dense stands fixes about 200 lb. nitrogen/

acre/annum (Virtanen and Miettinen, 1963). High-density stands of *Alnus* seldom occur around lake edges; nevertheless, the contribution of these plants when present must be appreciable, for about 90 per cent of the nitrogen fixed annually is rapidly transported out of the nodules to the remainder of the plant, including the leaves (Stewart, 1962) (Table 2). At

TABLE 2   Data on the transfer of biologically fixed nitrogen from *Alnus glutinosa* root nodules to the remainder of the plant (after Stewart, 1962).

Period*	Mean N fixed/plant (mg.)†	Mean N transferred from nodules to rest of plant (mg)‡	N transferred as % of N fixed
9–21 June	1.17	1.03	88
21 June–3 Jul.	2.45	2.23	83
3–15 Jul.	3.40	3.12	92
15–27 Jul.	5.72	5.27	92
27 Jul.–8 Aug.	12.34	10.93	89
8–20 Aug.	24.29	22.53	93
20 Aug.–1 Sept.	30.51	29.50	96
1–13 Sept.	27.42	27.42	98
13–25 Sept.	4.64	4.64	100
25 Sept.–7 Oct.	1.70	1.81	106

* Data are for 1st-year plants grown in combined-nitrogen-free water culture in the greenhouse in Scotland in 1960. Ten plants were sampled at each harvest.
† Calculated by subtracting the mean nitrogen per plant including nodules at each sampling from the corresponding figure at the following sample.
‡ Calculated by subtracting the mean nitrogen per plant less nodules at each sampling from the corresponding figure at the following sample.

leaf fall these leaves drop directly into the lake. The importance of *Alnus* plants is emphasized by the work of Goldman (1961). He studied the productivity of a California lake where *Alnus tenuifolia* occurred on one bank but not on the other. He noted that the leaves of *Alnus* had nitrogen contents about four times greater than those of associated non-nitrogen-fixing species. He also showed that in the presence of *Alnus* the ammonia levels in the stream water were twice as high as where *Alnus* was absent and that primary productivity of the lake was highest on the side where *Alnus* grew. Such data provide strong evidence that nitrogen fixation by *Alnus* plants helps increase the productivity of the lakes around which these trees occur.

Myrica gale, the other plant in question, is a characteristic species of acid wetlands in many areas, including Britain. The root nodules characteristically bear white upwardly-growing nodule rootlets. These may be aerating in function and an adaption to the plant's environment, but such rootlets also occur on other *Myrica* species from a variety of habitats. *Myrica*, like *Alnus*, continues to nodulate (Stewart, 1963a) (Table 3) and

TABLE 3   Growth and nodulation data for *Myrica gale* plants growing in the presence of ammonium-nitrogen (after Stewart, 1963a)*

NH$_4$-N/1. of culture solution	Total dry weight/ plant (mg.)	Dry weight of nodules/ plant (mg.)	Nodule number/ plant	Nodule weight as % of total plant weight
0	1257	84	122	7.3
10	2085	106	115	5.3
50	2458	97	84	4.0
100	2025	78	59	3.7
150	1737	50	41	3.5

* Data are for 13-week-old plants grown in a greenhouse in Scotland in 1960. Each value above is the mean for 15 plants.

to fix nitrogen (Stewart and Bond, 1961) in the presence of combined nitrogen levels far in excess of those encountered in nature so that it can be assumed that if these plants are actively growing they will also be fixing nitrogen. The annual contribution by *Myrica gale* is uncertain, for no data on *in situ* fixation rates are available. Bond (1951), however, on the basis of greenhouse studies, considers that this may be of the order of 8 lb nitrogen/acre/annum. *Myrica*, and *Alnus* in particular, should be regarded as important sources of combined nitrogen. To disregard them may lead to a serious underestimation of the nitrogen input to lakes around which these plants grow.

In Situ Nitrogen Fixation in Lakes

The contribution of *in situ* nitrogen fixation to the productivity of lakes is one of the most important but until recently the least readily investigated. Various workers suggested that it probably played a role (Sawyer, *et al.*, 1945; Ruttner, 1953; Hutchinson, 1957), but only in the 1960's did the accurate measurement of *in situ* fixation become reality. Then, the ^{15}N method which previously had been used routinely in physiology and biochemistry laboratories was adapted by measuring *in situ* nitrogen fixation in lakes (see Dugdale and Neess, 1960; Dugdale and Dugdale, 1962). They studied in particular the relationship between the abundance of *Anabaena* and nitrogen fixation, observed a direct correlation, and provided evidence to substantiate this relationship. They observed, for example, that fixation was light-dependent, that it increased with increasing light intensity, and that boiled control samples showed no ^{15}N incorporation. Like Stewart and Bond (1961) for *Alnus*, they noted that low levels of ammonium-nitrogen, although partially inhibiting nitrogen fixation, resulted in a greater over-all quantity of nitrogen being fixed because of the greater over-all yield of nitrogen-fixing organisms which resulted (Dugdale and Dugdale, 1963). In Sanctuary Lake, Pennsylvania, where seasonal variation was measured, maximum *in situ* fixation occurred in late August when the nitrogen fixed per day amounted to 6 per cent of the total nitrogen present. In Lake Mendota, however, lower values (0.2 per cent) were usually found by Goering and Neess (1964). Similar studies have been carried out in Lake Windermere, England, by G. E. Fogg and A. J. Horne (unpublished), who also observed a direct correlation between the abundance of *Anabaena* and nitrogen fixation.

Despite the important contribution made by the ^{15}N method, it has some limitations. It is expensive, in terms of the cost of ^{15}N-labeled molecular nitrogen and in terms of necessary equipment such as the mass spectrometer; it is somewhat tedious, and the data are not generally available until twenty-four to forty-eight hours from the start of the experiment.

Recently this writer has investigated the possibility of using acetylene reduction to measure indirectly the nitrogen fixation by algae in aquatic ecosystems. The application of the acetylene reduction technique suggested itself when Dilworth (1966) and Schöllhorn and Burris (1966, 1967) reported that the nitrogen-fixing enzyme (nitrogenase) extracted from cell-free extracts of *Clostridium pasteurianum* could reduce not only nitrogen gas to ammonia (a $6e^-$ reduction) but also acetylene gas to ethylene (a $2e^-$ reduction). The ability of *Azotobacter* and root nodules to do likewise has been demonstrated (Koch, *et al.*, 1967; Sloger and Silver, 1967; Hardy, *et al.*, 1967), and other evidence from cell-free extracts has confirmed that the nitrogenase shows great versatility and can reduce a variety of compounds including hydrogen cyanide (Hardy and Knight, 1967a).

Stewart, Fitzgerald, and Burris, using samples from lakes and pure cultures of blue-green algae, have demonstrated acetylene reduction in the blue-green algae. The ability to reduce acetylene is restricted to known nitrogen-fixing species. *Anacystis nidulans*, as can be seen from Table 4, shows no such capacity. The standard system was to expose algal samples generally containing 0.5–5 mg protein in 1.0 ml of combined-nitrogen-free culture medium (Gorham, *et al.*, 1964) to acetylene in 5.0 ml bottles fitted with serium caps. After a thirty-minute incubation period, the reaction was terminated by the injection of 0.2 cc of 50 per cent trichloro-

TABLE 4   Acetylene-reduction by pure cultures of
various blue-green algae*

Algae	Sample	mμmoles ethylene produced/mg. protein/min.
Anabaena cylindrica[†]	1	4.13
	2	5.45 (4.15)
	3	2.96
Anabaena flos-aquae[†]	1	1.21
	2	1.36 (1.30)
	3	1.33
Anacystis nidulans[‡]	1	0.00
	2	0.00 (0.00)
	3	0.00
Mastigocladus laminosus[†]	1	1.28
	2	1.75 (1.41)
	3	2.20
Tolypothrix tenuis[†]	1	1.17
	2	0.75 (0.91)
	3	0.80

* Algae grown in batch culture then 1.0 ml. samples incubated for 30 mins. under a gas phase initially containing 10 per cent acetylene (purified grade) and 90 per cent argon. CO_2 was supplied as 10 mg/l. $NaHCO_3$. During incubation, light intensity, 320 f.c. continuous; temp., 30°C.
† Culture medium was combined-nitrogen-free modification of Allen and Arnon's (1955).
‡ Alga originally grown in combined-nitrogen-containing medium, Kratz and Myers (1955), but transferred to combined-nitrogen-free medium 24 hours before tests were carried out.

acetic acid, and samples of the gas phase analyzed for the presence of ethylene by gas chromatography. The method compares favorably with the ^{15}N method in that: (1) it is much more sensitive, thus extremely small samples of test material can be used; (2) it is rapid, and the exposure period can be reduced to about five minutes if a large test sample/gas volume ratio is employed. Also the results can become available within about three minutes of terminating an experiment. This is particularly advantageous, especially as certain algal blooms persist for only very short periods and as their composition frequently changes throughout the day; (3) it is inexpensive, the only major piece of equipment required being the gas chromatograph—a satisfactory model can be purchased for about $1200; 4) it is a simple, practical method and the gas chromatography analysis, unlike mass spectrometer analysis requires no particular skill, and can be routinely run by a well-trained technician.

Studies on lake samples freshly collected from Lake Mendota in June and July 1967, confirm the data from laboratory culture (Table 5). They show that samples containing heterocystous blue-green algae reduce acetylene; there is no evidence of reduction by the Chlorophyceae, by the Euglenophyceae, or by non-heterocystous blue-green algae. The lack of acetylene reduction by algae such as *Cladophora* implies indirectly that nitrogen-fixing bacteria are not important; otherwise ethylene production would also have been detected in these samples.

TABLE 5   Acetylene reduction by algae from three Wisconsin lakes.

Alga	Lake	mμmoles ethylene produced/mg. protein/min.*
Anabaena sp.[†]	Wingra	0.10
Aphanizomenon flos-aquae	Monona	0.77
Calothrix sp.[‡]	Mendota	0.01
Cladophora sp.	"	0.00
Euglena sp.	"	0.00
Gloeotrichia echinulata	"	0.36
Hydrodictyon sp.	"	0.00
Microcystis aeruginosa	"	0.00
Nostoc sp.	"	1.62
Oscillatoria sp.	"	0.00
Ulothrix sp.	"	0.00

* Each value is the mean of triplicate determinations.

† The Lake Wingra algae are characteristically pale green and unhealthy in appearance. It is probable that much higher acetylene reduction rates will be obtained with *Anabaena* blooms from other areas.

‡ Epilithic *Calothrix* association which occurs just above the splash zone. Other non-heterocystous Myxophyceae were intermingled with the *Calothrix*.

The positive evidence for *Aphanizomenon* requires comment because negative data were obtained in a previous test for nitrogen fixation using ^{15}N-labeled gas (Williams and Burris, 1952). A possible explanation of the discrepancy between the two sets of data is that an alga which may be capable of reducing acetylene may be incapable of fixing nitrogen. If this is the case, it will be the first time that the direct relationship between acetylene reduction and nitrogen fixation has been found not to hold. Such a relationship has been established from extensive biochemical studies on bacterial cell-free extracts (see Hardy and Knight, 1967b) as well as with symbiotic systems and with blue-green algae. For example, ammonium-nitrogen (a well-known inhibitor of nitrogen fixation) also inhibits acetylene reduction in *Anabaena flos-aquae* (Table 6).

Secondly, it is conceivable that nitrogen-fixing and non-nitrogen-fixing strains of *Aphanizomenon* exist. This could be a satisfactory explanation,

TABLE 6 Acetylene reduction by ammonia-grown and molecular
nitrogen-grown cells of *Anabaena flos-aquae*.*

Nitrogen Source	Sample	mμmoles ethylene produced/ mg. protein min.
NH$_4$Cl[†]	1	0
	2	<.001
	3	<.001
N$_2$[‡]	1	5.72
	2	5.60
	3	4.70

* Tischer's strain (see Davis, Tischer, and Brown, 1966).
† Protein per sample, 0.65 mg; 100 mg. NH$_4$-N/1.
‡ Protein per sample 0.56 mg.

for non-nitrogen-fixing strains are known of all major nitrogen-fixing groups. However, tests using acetylene reduction on a unialgal culture of the original strain used by Williams and Burris showed ethylene production.

Thirdly, it is possible that in the present studies, associated bacteria and not the algae were fixing nitrogen. This is conceivable, but does not explain why *Aphanizomenon* samples from the lake showed acetylene reduction, whereas *Cladophora* samples collected at the same time did not, unless nitrogen-fixing bacteria are specifically associated with *Aphanizomenon* colonies or perhaps some nitrogen-fixing association of *Aphanizomenon* and bacteria exists. This would imply also that a nitrogen-fixing system resulted when a laboratory bacterium contaminated the pure culture of *Aphanizomenon* since it was used by Williams and Burris (1952). Thus, contamination by nitrogen-fixing bacteria cannot be ruled out, but it is much easier to explain the data if one accepts that *Aphanizomenon* itself carries out the reduction. In this writer's opinion, it is a virtual certainty that this is so, and further studies to confirm this are in progress using both acetylene and ^{15}N$_2$.

From the point of view of *in situ* nitrogen fixation in lakes, it is immaterial which organism fixes nitrogen. What is important is that there is now evidence that *Aphanizomenon* blooms fix nitrogen. Such data may go a long way towards explaining the prominence of *Aphanizomenon* as a bloom former in eutrophic lakes, as well as helping us to understand why the percentage nitrogen content of *Aphanizomenon* is high relative to known non-nitrogen-fixing algae such as *Microcystis* and *Oscillatoria* (see Lund, 1965).

Finally, in relation to the acetylene reduction method, the question arises: Can it be used to measure quantitatively nitrogen fixation *in situ*?

The available data to date suggests that it can: acetylene reduction by whole cells increases linearly over test periods of one hour (Figure 2), so that acetylene does not appear to exert any inhibitory effect on the alga. The ethylene produced may alter the metabolic rate, however, if it accumulates in high quantities, but in quantitative studies using short exposure periods and small test samples in relation to gas volume we have never had any evidence that the levels of ethylene produced affected the metabolic rate of the test organisms. Secondly, the nitrogenase enzyme is saturated in *Anabaena* by partial pressures of acetylene of approximately 10 per

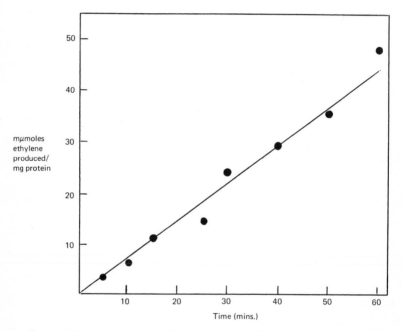

Fig. 2. Ethylene production with time by a pure culture of *Anabaena flos-aquae.*

cent, or more (Figure 3) and as the nitrogenase reduces the acetylene preferentially over nitrogen, small air leaks will not seriously affect the quantitative data obtained. This is in contrast to ^{15}N studies, where slight air leaks seriously affect the ^{15}N-labeling of the gas phase and the subsequent nitrogen-fixation rates obtained. What is required now is a comparison of the rates of acetylene and nitrogen reduction by similar test samples incubated under similar conditions except for the nitrogen or acetylene in the gas phase. One can then calculate from the rate of ethylene production the rate at which nitrogen fixation is occuring. Experiments on this aspect are currently in progress. Despite some reservations which obviously must

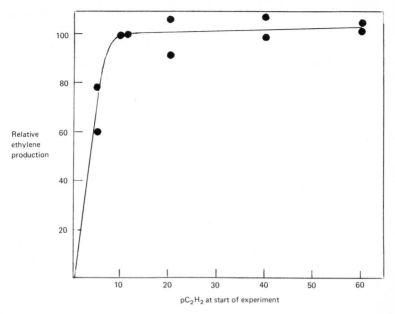

FIG. 3. Ethylene production by *Anabaena flos-aquae* in relation to partial pressure of acetylene CO_2 supplied as bicarbonate (0.01 gm. $NaHCO_3/1$.) 1.0 ml. reaction mixture, 4.0 cc. gas phase. No account taken of dissolved acetylene in calculating the above partial pressures. Argon used as balance.

be made at present, it seems probable that the acetylene reduction technique will eventually replace the ^{15}N method as a means of measuring *in situ* fixation rates in lakes, in the sea, and in terrestrial ecosystems. This is not because the ^{15}N method is bad, but because the acetylene method is so very good.

The shortage of accurate data on *in situ* algal fixation is surpassed only by the almost complete lack of quantitative data on bacterial nitrogen fixation. Heterotrophic nitrogen fixation has been disregarded largely because workers have accepted that nitrogen-fixing forms are inefficient users of carbohydrate, fixing one to twenty-five mg. nitrogen per gram of carbohydrate consumed. Thus the quantities of soluble carbohydrate necessary for intense nitrogen fixation are rarely available, and there is intense competition for that which is available, not only by nitrogen-fixing forms but by non-nitrogen-fixing forms as well. In the few studies where heterotrophic fixation has been assessed (for example those of Kusnetsov, 1959) the contribution by heterotrophic bacteria relative to that by algae is negligible.

The role of photosynthetic bacteria is a different proposition, however, for unlike their heterotrophic counterparts most, if not all, photosynthetic bacteria tested in pure culture in the laboratory have been shown to fix nitrogen. Thus, the pertinent questions are: How widespread is the distribution of photosynthetic bacteria in lakes, and do they fix nitrogen *in situ* when they occur?

Their distribution depends on two major factors—anaerobic conditions and light. They are limited, therefore, to ecological niches which satisfy these requirements. They occur in the anaerobic sediments of shallow lakes, and are prominent in deeper waters only if anaerobic conditions prevail at depths where light still penetrates. Such a situation is found in certain Norwegian lakes which have been formed in the past by the uppermost reaches of fjords, becoming isolated from the sea and resulting in lakes which have an anaerobic bottom layer of sea water on top of which is an aerobic layer of fresh water (Holtan, 1965). If light penetrates to the anaerobic zone, photosynthetic bacteria frequently occur in profusion in its uppermost layer, presumably because intense bacterial development prevents the penetration of light to lower depths. The bacterial genera found include *Pelodictyon, Rhodospirillum,* and *Rhodomicrobium* species. Similar-type lakes with distinct zones of photosynthetic bacteria are well known in other areas as well (see Kondrat'eva, 1965).

Studies in cooperation with the Norwegian Water Research Laboratory Blindern, Oslo, were carried out on one such lake south of Oslo in June, 1966 to determine whether *in situ* nitrogen fixation was occurring. The data in Table 7 clearly show the delineation into an anaerobic and aerobic

TABLE 7   Distribution of green photosynthetic bacteria and nitrogen-fixing capacity at various depths in a Norwegian lake.

Depth (m.)	Dissolved oxygen (mg./l.)	Dissolved sulphide (mg./l.)	Relative Light absorption (770 mμ)*	Atom % excess ^{15}N/ sample.[†]
0	9.90	0	5	−0.001
2	9.90	0	0	−0.001
4	8.72	0	0	—
6.5	0.37	0	7	0.001
7.0	0	18.22	100	0.019
7.5	0	16.80	—	0.005
8	0	27.20	55	—
12	0	23.39	13	0.002

* This value which is taken as an indication of abundance of green photosynthetic bacteria was obtained by filtering 50 ml. aliquots from various depths on to Millipore filters (grade HA) and extracting the pigments using a methanol-acetone mixture (7 : 2).

[†] Each value is the mean of duplicate determinations.

zone, with hydrogen sulphide replacing oxygen below 6.5 meters. Light penetration was not detectable below 7.0 meters. Green photosynthetic bacteria closely related to *Chlorobium* but belonging to the genus *Pelodictyon* (N. Pfennig, personal communication) predominate in the 7.0-meter zone, and nitrogen fixation as measured *in situ* by ^{15}N uptake also occurs largely in this layer. The rate of ^{15}N uptake is low, but this is probably a reflection of the low lake temperature (7.0°C at 7.0 meters at the time of sampling) due to the late breakup of the ice in the spring of 1966. According to J. Ormerod and H. Holtan (personal communication), of the Norwegian institute, the layer of photosynthetic bacteria persists throughout summer so that higher fixation rates probably occur as the lake warms up. The data also point out how extensive investigations of lakes must be if all important sources of fixed nitrogen are to be accounted for. If *in situ* nitrogen fixation in this lake had been assessed solely on the basis of surface phytoplankton (the dominant forms were *Peridinium* sp., *Dinobryon divergens, Tabellaria fenestrata* and pennate diatoms), the conclusion would have been that *in situ* nitrogen fixation was of no importance at that particular time.

The availability of biologically fixed nitrogen to other organisms must be considered. Such nitrogen becomes available to secondary producers by grazing, and nitrogen may also be released by cell autolysis—these are obvious sources. On autolysis proteolytic bacteria break down cell protein to ammonia, which is readily utilized by phytoplankton. An outstanding point concerns the availability of the organic intermediates between whole cells and ammonia, and also the organic nitrogen compounds liberated extracellularly during healthy growth of blue-green algae. Several studies on the nature of these extracellular nitrogenous products have been made (Watanabe, 1951; Fogg, 1952; Stewart, 1963b), and it appears that a large proportion of the extracellular nitrogen is liberated in the form of polypeptides, though small quantities of free amino acids are also liberated. Studies on the utilization of organic nitrogen compounds by algae are few, but there is evidence that both freshwater and marine representatives can utilize certain organic nitrogenous compounds as their sole source of nitrogen (Algeus, 1948; Belmont and Miller, 1965; Pintner, *et al.*, 1963; Van Baalen and Marler, 1963). Studies by Jones and Stewart (1969) are of interest in this connection. They investigated the availability of the extracellular nitrogen produced by *Calothrix scopulorum*, a marine nitrogen-fixing alga, to other organisms. There is nothing to suggest that, though the data were obtained with a marine species, they will not apply equally to algae from freshwater habitats.

The procedure used was to grow the algae exponentially under a gas phase containing $^{15}N_2$ and then to separate the alga and medium by filtration. The aseptic filtrate containing ^{15}N-labeled extracellular products was then used as a culture medium for the growth of other non-nitrogen-fixing organisms, and after several day's growth the test organisms were harvested and analyzed for ^{15}N enrichment by mass spectrometry. Data presented in Table 8 shows that members of the Chlorophyta,

TABLE 8   The ^{15}N enrichment of various organisms grown in the presence of ^{15}N-labeled extracellular products of *Calothrix scopulorum* (after Jones and Stewart, 1969).

Organism*	Atom per cent excess ^{15}N[†]
Algae:	
Chlorella marina	0.086
Dunnaliella tertiolecta	0.048
Synechocystis sp.	0.045
Porphyridium cruentum	0.060
Fungi:	
Cercospora salina	0.154
Stachyobotris alba	0.170
Trichothecium roseum	0.130
Bacteria:	
Mixed culture	0.133

* Algal strains obtained from the Westfield College, London, culture collection and were bacteria-free. Bacteria-free fungal cultures were obtained from Dr. G. J. F. Pugh, University of Nottingham. The bacteria were isolated from a natural population of *Calothrix scopulorum*.
† Each value is the mean of triplicate determinations. Atom per cent excess ^{15}N in extracellular nitrogen was 0.741.

Rhodophyta, the fungi, and bacteria all become labeled with ^{15}N, the heterotrophic organisms being most highly labeled. Thus, uptake occurs, and there is evidence that such extracellular nitrogen may act as the sole nitrogen source for the growth of *Chlorella* (Figure 4), although growth on extracellular nitrogen alone is slow compared with that on nitrate-nitrogen. Other evidence (see Jones and Stewart, 1969) implies that such uptake is due largely to active uptake by the various test organisms, but that passive uptake and adsorption also occur. Algal cell surfaces thus seem ideal ecological niches for the growth of bacteria and other epiphytes, for there they obtain not only the extracellular products of the organisms on which they grow but also organic material adsorbed from other sources. As can be seen from Table 9, ^{15}N-labeled extracellular products are taken up even when combined nitrogen is present in the medium, so that in nature it can be expected that non-nitrogen-fixing organisms will directly remove the extracellular nitrogenous material. As the production of extracellular

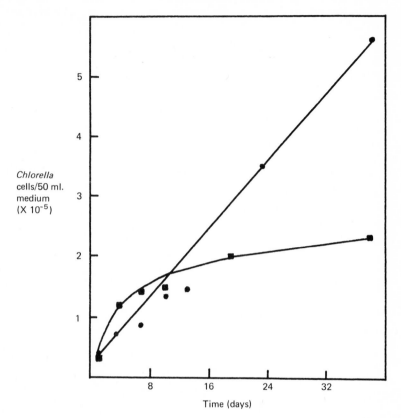

Fig. 4. Growth of *Chlorella marina* in medium initially free of combined nitrogen.
●—● = medium inoculated with *Calothrix*; ■—■ = No *Calothrix* added.

TABLE 9 ^{15}N-labeling of *Chlorella marina* grown in the presence of ^{15}N-labeled extracellular products of *Calothrix scopulorum* and nitrate-nitrogen.*

Days after inoculation	Atom per cent excess ^{15}N in *Chlorella*[†]
1	0.185
3	0.112
6	0.054
10	0.014

* Alga grown in 25 aliquots of medium which initially contained 1.0 gm./l. of unlabeled nitrate-nitrogen and 0.856 mg. extracellular nitrogen/l. labeled with 0.741 atom per cent excess ^{15}N. Inoculum contained 42 μg. nitrogen.

† The decrease in labeling from the one-day stage onward implies exhaustion of the utilizable ^{15}N-labeled products and continued growth on unlabeled nitrate-nitrogen. With the mass spectrometer used at Westfield College, London, all these values can be considered as showing a significant uptake of ^{15}N.

nitrogen seems to be a characteristic of algae, whether nitrogen-fixing or not (Fogg, 1961, 1966), it is probable that cross-utilization of the extra-cellular products of various species occurs in mixed blooms prior to the breakdown of these extracellular products to ammonia by proteolytic bacteria.

Finally, in relation to *in situ* nitrogen fixation, there is the question of what happens to the bloom-forming species once the bloom disappears. Cell autolysis occurs, but there must also be some means of survival until the next bloom. Many blue-green algae have perennating organs in the form of spores or akinetes, but other common bloom-formers such as *Microcystis* and *Oscillatoria* do not. The fact that nitrogen fixation is a reductive process suggested that perhaps nitrogen-fixing blue-green algae could grow and fix nitrogen under reducing conditions. A typical set of data for *Anabaena flow-aquae* is shown in Figure 5. It is seen that this

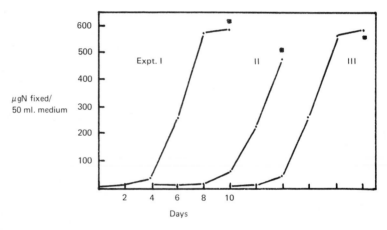

Fig. 5. Growth of *Anabaena flos-aquae* supplied with H_2S (0.1 gm/l of Na_2S. $9H_2O$) donor. The above graphs represent data for three concurrent experiments. Each point is the mean of duplicate determinations except at the fifth harvest in Experiments I and II, when one of the duplicates was used as inoculum for the following experiment. The graphs for the second and third experiments are displaced in this figure for clarity. Aerobic controls (■) were harvested after ten days for comparison.

alga grows readily under reducing conditions and that total yield is of the same order as when the alga grows aerobically. This finding is not new for the blue-green algae. Nakamura (1938) noted the growth of *Oscillatoria* in the presence of hydrogen sulphide and reported that sulphur accumulates in the cells, while Setlik (1957) reported the anaerobic growth of *Oscillatoria, Symploca,* and *Mastigocladus.* Thus, perhaps the question as to what happens to bloom-formers without perennating structures is not so enigmatical. These organisms may exist under the reducing or anoxic conditions of lake sediments, probably growing anaerobically and heterotrophically there. Heterotrophic growth and nitrogen fixation is known to occur in certain blue-green algae (Fay, 1965; Watanabe and Yamamoto, 1967). Even if these algae do not actually multiply on the lake bottom, they may exist, as the diatom *Melosira* does, in what Lund (1965) terms a "physiological resting stage." A period of bottom growth may also be advantageous, perhaps allowing these algae to accumulate essential nutrients which are in short supply in the surface waters. More data are required on the occurrence of blue-green algae in the benthos to determine whether this theory, based on physiological data from the laboratory, is substantiated by field observation. It is through the concerted efforts of ecologists and physiologists that this problem can be resolved. Such a multidisciplinary approach applies to studies of lakes in general.

REFERENCES

Algeus, S., 1948. *Physiol. Plant, 1*, 236.
Allen, M. B., and Arnon, D. I., 1955. *Plant Physiol., 30*, 366.
Becking, J. H., De Boer, W. E., and Houwink, A. L., 1964. *Anton v. Leeuwenhoek, 30,* 343.
Belmont, L., and Miller, J. D. A., 1965. *J. Exp. Bot., 16*, 318.
Bond, G., 1951. *Ann. Bot., 15*, 447.
Bond, G., 1963. *Symp. Soc. Gen. Microbiol., 13,* 72.
Bond, G., 1967. *Ann. Rev. Plant Physiol., 18,* 107.
Brock, T. D., 1967. *Science, 158*, 1012.
Carroll, D., 1962. Geol. Surv. Water Supp. Pap., 1535-G.
Davis, E. B., Tischer, R. G., and Brown, L. R., 1966. *Physiol. Plant, 19*, 823.
Dilworth, M. J., 1966. *Biochim. Biophys. Acta, 127*, 285.
Drover, D. P., and Barrett-Lenard, I. P., 1956. *J. Aust. Inst. Agric. Sci., 22*, 193.
Dugdale, V. A., and Dugdale, R. C., 1962. *Limnol. Oceanogr., 7*, 170.
———, 1963. *ibid., 10*, 53.
———, and Nees, J. C., 1960. In: *Trans. Sem. Algae Met. Wastes*, U.S.P.H.S., Cincinnati.
Fay, P., 1965. *J. Gen. Microbiol., 39*, 11.
Fogg, G. E., 1951. *J. Exp. Bot., 2*, 117.
———, 1952. *Proc. Roy. Soc. B., 139*, 372.
———, 1962. In: *Physiology and Biochemistry of Algae*, ed. by R. A. Lewin, New York: Academic Press, p. 475.
——— 1966. *Oceanogr. Mar. Biol. Rev., 4*, 195.
Gardner, I. C., 1965. *Arch. Mikrobiol., 51*, 365.
Goering, J. J., and Neess, J. C., 1964. *Limnol. Oceanogr., 9*, 530.
Goldman, C. R., 1961. *Ecology, 42*, 282.
Goldschmidt, V. M., 1954. *Geochemistry*, London: Oxford University Press.
Gorham, P. R., McLachlan, J., Hammer, U. T., and Kim, W. K., 1964. *Ver. Internat. Verein. Limnol., 15*, 796.

Hardy, R. W. F., and Knight, E., Jr., 1967a. *Fed. Proc., 26*, 725.

———, 1967b. *Progress in Phytochemistry*, p. 387. London: John Wiley.

Hardy, R. W. F., Knight, E., Jr., and Jackson, E. K., 1967. *Bact. Proc.*, 112.

Holtan, H., 1965. *Nature, 207*, 156.

Hutchinson, G. E., 1944. *Amer. Sci. 32*, 178.

———, (1957). *A Treatise on Limnology I. Chemistry, Physics and Geography*, John Wiley, New York.

Jones, K., and Stewart, W. D. P., 1969. *J. Mar. Biol. Assoc. U.K.* (in press).

Koch, B., Evans, H. J., and Russell, S., 1967. *Plant Physiol., 42*, 466.

Kondrat'eva, E. N., 1965. *Photosynthetic Bacteria*, translated from Russian by Israel Program for Science Translations.

Kratz, W. A., and Myers, J., 1955. *Amer. J. Bot., 42*, 282.

Kusnetsov, S. I., 1959. *Die Rolle der Mikroorganismen im Stoffkreislauf der Seen*, Berlin.

Lund, J. W. G., 1965. *Biol. Revs., 40*, 231.

Nakamura, H., 1938. *Acta Phytochim., 10*, 271.

Nobbe, F., Schmid, E., Hiltner, L., and Hotter, E., 1892. *Landw. Vers. Sta., 41*, 138.

Pintner, I. J., and Provasoli, L., 1963. In: *Marine Microbiology*, ed. by C. H. Oppenheimer, Illinois: C. C. Thomas.

Riley, G. A., Wangersky, P. J., and Van Hemert, D., 1964. *Limnol. Oceanogr., 9*, 546.

Riley, G. A., Van Hemert, D., and Wangersky, P. J., 1965. *Ibid., 10*, 354.

Ruttner, F., 1953. *Fundamentals of Limnology*, Toronto: University of Toronto Press.

Sawyer, C. N., Lackey, J. B., and Lenz, R. T., 1945. *Rept. Gov. Comm., Madison Wis.*, 92 pp.

Schöllhorn, R., and Burris, R. H., 1966. *Fed. Proc., 25*, 710.

———, 1967. *Proc. Nat. Acad. Sci., 58*, 213.

Sloger, C., and Silver, W. S., 1967. *Bact. Proc.*, 112.

Setlik, I., 1957. *Ceskosl. biol., 6*, 424; *Biochim. Biophys. Acta, 24*, 434.

Schneider, K. C., Bradbeer, C., Singh, R. N., Wang, L. C., Wilson, P. W., and Burris, R. H., 1960. *Proc. Nat. Acad. Sci., U.S., 46*, 726.

Smith, A. M., 1967. *Comm. Fert. Plant. Fd. Indust.*, April, 1967, 25.

Stewart, W. D. P., 1962. *J. Exp. Bot., 13*, 250.

———, 1963a. *Zeit. Allg. Mikrobiol., 3*, 152.

———, 1963b. *Nature, 200*, 1020.

———, 1966. *Nitrogen Fixation in Plants*, London: The Athlone Press of the University of London.

———, 1969. *Phycologia* (in press).

———, 1968. *New Phytol.* (in press).

Stewart, W. D. P., and Bond, G., 1961. *Plant and Soil, 14*, 371.

Van Baalen, C., and Marler, J. E., 1963. *J. Gen. Microbiol., 32*, 456.

Virtanen, A. I., and Miettinen, J. K., 1963. In: *Plant Physiology*, ed., F. C. Steward, *3*, p. 539. New York: Academic Press.

Wangersky, P. J., 1965. *Amer. Sci., 53*, 358.

Watanabe, A., 1951. *Arch. Biochem. Biophys., 34*, 50.

———, and Yamamoto, Y., 1967. *Nature, 214*, 738.

Williams, A. E., and Burris, R. H., 1952. *Amer. J. Bot., 39*, 340.

Wilson, A. T., 1959. *Nature, 184*, 99.

VI

Light and Temperature: Some Aspects of Their Influence on Algae

F. E. ROUND

Department of Botany
The University
Bristol, England

Pigmented algae photosynthesize and thereby utilize light energy in the conversion of carbon dioxide and water into more complex organic molecules; these biochemical processes are greatly influenced by temperature. However, such topics are extensive and have been reviewed elsewhere. I therefore propose to deal with the effects of these two ecological variables on other aspects of the biology of the algae; however, to some extent all these aspects are linked to photosynthesis, and in many it is difficult to distinguish between the photosynthetic effect and the secondary light-induced phenomenon. Light is involved in the life of an alga from the point of settling of the zygote throughout its developmental history to the stage of the reformation of a zygote. It affects polarity, morphogenesis, and phototropism; it is effective in tactic movements of vegetative cells and in movements of chromatophores. Rhythmic aspects of algal metabolism, movement, and reproduction may be phased by light, and light influences the distribution of algae in time and space. Temperature is concerned more with rates of processes but is also involved in the distribution of species in nature.

Sporulation

Most of the evidence for light and temperature effects on this phase of the life history are derived from laboratory experiments and show the need for a shift in one or other of these factors to induce sporulation. To what extent these shifts are necessary in nature is unknown. Species of *Oedogonium* and *Vaucheria*, which in the laboratory require low light or darkness to produce spores (Klebs, 1896), are repeatedly subjected to such a regime in nature, and even the considerable temperature shifts required by some species are provided in the natural environment. Sporulation in some species is correlated with an endogenous diurnal rhythm, but not in all algae since continuous illumination inhibits sporulation in *Melosira nummuloides* (Bruchmeyer-Berkenbusch, 1955), and it is a characteristic of endogenous rhythms that they continue in constant light.

High light and high temperatures inhibit spore formation in *Melosira nummuloides*. At low light intensities the cell diameter at which auxospore formation occurs is higher (18.5 μ at 300 lux) than at higher light intensity (16.5 μ at 2400 lux). This indicates that the metabolic balance affected by light intensity and reflected in the cell size must reach a critical stage before sporulation occurs. Increase in light period from five to fifteen hours (1500 lux) increased the cell diameter at which auxospores formed from 16μ to 17–18μ. Constant light reduced the size; e.g., at 500 lux (21°C) it was 14+μ and at 1500 lux (21°C) it was 12μ. (Bruchmeyer-Berkenbusch, 1955). In *Lithodesmium*, which is an oogamous diatom, von Stosch (1954) found that continuous illumination produced cells which gave rise almost entirely to female gametes, weak daylight alternating with darkness produced only male gametes, and strong light alternating with darkness induced both male and female gametes.

GERMINATION

The establishment of a new generation of algae involves either the movement of a motile, usually flagellate, zoospore or planozygote to a substrate followed by withdrawal of the flagella and cleavage of the cell. Oogamous species forming nonmotile zygotes merely omit the directed motile stage and commence with cleavage.

Light generally acts on motile zygotes inducing a negative phototaxis resulting in swimming away from the water surface. This is obviously advantageous in forms which are attached to basal underwater substrata. The extent of this reaction is unknown—does it apply, for example, to epiphytic species or to unattached species. If this reaction is similar to the negative phototaxis of vegetative cells, then it probably has the same action spectrum as positive phototaxis (Halldal, 1958), but we have no information about the mechanism involved. This negative phototaxis appears to be exhibited almost immediately after copulation of the gametes, e.g., in *Cymopolia* (Hammerling, 1944), which prior to this moment are positively phototactic. This could be due to a sudden change in the ionic balance within the cells—Halldal (1958) found that experimentally changing the Mg:Ca ratio from >6:1 to <6:1 changed the phototaxis of *Platymonas* from positive to negative. The planozygotes are also reported to remain motile for a longer period of time in the dark. Cleavage of the eggs of members of the Fucales *Dictyota* and *Laurencia* is determined by unidirectional light—

the first cleavage plane being formed perpendicular to the direction of the incident light and the rhizoid growing from the face away from the light source.

Zygotes of *Acetabularia* can be kept in the dark for months, and this appears to prevent germination. Planozygotes kept in the dark retain their motility for several days, whereas in the light they soon settle. Cysts can also be kept in the dark for long periods, and this prevents the formation of gametes until they are brought into the light—*Acetabularia mediterranea* and others all require light to produce swarming of gametes. Nor does copulation occur in the dark in these species or in *Chlamydomonas*. Spores of *Ulothrix* (see also the section on photoperiodism), *Enteromorpha*, and *Ulva* also require light for germination. There is evidence from a study of the growth of sporelings of *Plumaria elegans* that the damaging effect of intense light is prevented by the screening effect of phycoerythrin (Boney and Corner, 1962).

High temperature is necessary to induce germination of some spores, e.g., the zygospore of *Chlamydomonas* (37°C), *Chlorococcum* (37°C), *Chlorogonium* (40°C) (Strehlow, 1929), and *Nostoc* akinetes (30°) (Harder, 1918). Low temperature is also said to be operative for some species. The action of light and temperature on algal spores is aking to the breaking of dormancy in seeds.

CHROMATOPHORE MOVEMENT (PHOTOTAXIS)

One of the most noteworthy subjects for this aspect of light-induced movements is *Mougeotia*, which has an elongate plate-like chromatophore; in high light intensity this chromatophore moves so that the edge is towards the light. In moderate intensities it turns the face towards the light, but at intermediate light intensities orientates at an angle to the light. At intensities between 15–20,000 lux the chromatophores turn from the flat to the edge (profile) position. Dark pretreatment and high concentration of CO_2 result in a lowering of the light intensity required to cause the chromatophores to turn.

Twenty thousand lux is a very low intensity for natural populations and if these natural populations behave in the same way as experimental material, then they are therefore likely to remain in the profile position.

Boch and Haupt (1961) showed that the photoreceptor for positive chloroplast movement in *Mougeotia* was in the cytoplasm and not in the chloroplast—phytochrome is involved with the molecules orientated in a screwplane around the cell. The negative phototaxis (i.e., turning from plane to profile) is not effected through the same photoreceptor system but through another pigment absorbing with a maximum around 470mμ. In *Vaucheria*, however, although the photoreceptor is located in the cytoplasm, the action spectra of positive and negative phototaxis is similar (Fischer-Arnold, 1903).

When *Mougeotia* is darkened there is no rearrangement of the chloroplast; this does not apply, however, to *Mesotaenium*, another member of the Conjugatophyceae.

In *Melosira*, bright sunlight causes the chromatophores to move to the poles of the cells (Peteler, 1939), but in *Biddulphia titiana* the chromatophores collect around the nucleus (karystrophy). This effect could be produced if only a part of the cell were illuminated (Höfler, 1962).

Chromatophore Size

The chloroplast of *Mougeotia* not only moves within the cell but also contracts or expands according to the light intensity. In intense light the chloroplast contracts after it has completed the movement. Contraction also occurs during prolonged periods of darkness, but this is a gradual process and therefore might simply be due to long-term removal of substances from the chloroplast. Another genus of the Conjugatophyceae, *Spirogyra*, has been reported (Gessner, 1930) to change its chloroplast size, reducing the breadth of the chromatophore by a half in bright sunlight. This may, however, merely be a change of shape from a flat to an elliptical or spherical shape in section. This aspect of chromatophore study has been relatively neglected since its early description in *Melosira* by Schmitz (1882) and then by Schimper (1885), who noted that in *Striatella* the plastids shorten in high light or on darkening. The *Melosira* chromatophore is a lobed disc during daytime, but at night or in bright sunlight the lobes are retracted, i.e., a similar reaction to that described for *Striatella*. According to Peteler (1939) these changes in *Melosira* can be induced by dark breaks during the light period and by light breaks during the dark period. The retraction of the lobes is a slow process (eight to ten hours) both during natural or under artificial darkening, whereas the extension of the processes can be very rapid, e.g., ten minutes in direct sunlight. This suggests that the processes are not just simple reversals and that the extension is perhaps linked with the onset of photosynthesis. Whether or not there is an endogenous rhythm in this system is unknown, and further investigation is needed.

Photokinesis

Photokinesis is defined as rate of movement affected by light. The speed at which hormogones of *Nostoc* move increases considerably between 5–

100 m candles, but the increase is much less above this value (Harder, 1918–20). Reversal of direction of movement occurred with a sudden lowering of intensity while increases did not reverse the direction, but there is some confusion about this. However, no such increases in velocity could be detected for *Oscillatoria formosa* (Burkholder, 1934).

Positive kinesis has also been defined as cessation of movement when light is cut; negative kinesis is cessation of movement when light is switched on. Diatoms do not react immediately to darkness but take up to four hours to stop, after which no movement was found (Nultsch, 1950). Movement in the dark was dependent to some extent on the pretreatment—low light intensity reduced dark movement and so did 500 lux, while 1000–2000 lux was optimal. Conversely, the time lag before movement started on transfer from dark to light was shortest at 1000–2000 lux, less at lower intensities, and inhibited by 5000 lux.

Experiments with *Phacus pleuronectes* and *Euglena gracilis* showed almost no variation in rate of movement at different light intensities and a shock reaction only when light was reduced, but not when increased (Mast and Gover, 1922). Temperature affects movement; Haudingsfeld (1943) found 20°–28°C optimum for *Navicula radiosa*. Below 20°C there was little movement, and at 8°C none. These upper temperatures are considerably higher than those at which there is active movement in nature. It may be significant that Eaton (1967) found that *Navicula radiosa* tended to be a summer form, and there may be a link between temperature, motility, and maintenance in the epipelic habitat where lack of motility would result in burial and/or washing away.

The action spectrum for photokinesis of *Phormidium* was measured by Nultsch (1962), and it was shown to be sensitized by the phototsynthetic pigments.

PHOTOTAXIS

Some species, e.g., *Oscillatoria splendida*, are negatively phototactic, while *Oscillatoria formosa* can arrange its filaments at right angles to the incident beam. *Oscillatoria sancta* moves towards the light in a looping path which involves a series of reversals in direction—what actually causes these reversals is not known (Burkholder, 1934).

In experiments with diatoms Nultsch (1950) found a positive topophototaxis (movement along a light gradient) at illuminations over 10 lux. All these movements involve a series of reversals (as in Cyanophyta) and the simplest system is found in forms which travel along a straight path, e.g., *Navicula*, where in positive phototaxis the distances traversed after reversals are longer in the direction towards the light source. Since reversals also occur autonomously, then light in some way alters the incidence of these. *Amphora* undergoes a looping movement similar to *Oscillatoria sancta*. *Nitzschia* has a more complex system, or rather series of movements, e.g., a series or arcs in which the angle is inclined slightly to the direction of the light at each reversal. A similar pathway, but without the reversals, gives a circular movement overlapping towards the light. These two movements appear to be related to the morphology of the cell. A modification of the first type occurs if the cell undergoes a swinging movement towards the light at some reversals. The operative wave lengths are 500–530 mμ, but positive topotaxis was also found in the U.V. at 398 mμ.

Phobophototaxis (a shock reaction on passing across a light/dark boundary) in diatoms occurs as a cell moves over a boundary between light and dark, causing a premature reversal into the light zone. Cells may reverse as soon as a tip passes into the dark zone, but it is more common when the cell has moved half to two diatom lengths into the dark. Only rarely is there no reaction or just a slowing down. Phobophototaxis in Cyanophyta normally results in the reversal of movement, or rather as Haupt (1966) puts it, a premature reversal in movement since autonomous reversal also occurs. This effect in diatoms and Cyanophyta is best illustrated by using a so-called light trap, i.e., a strongly illuminated region. As each filament enters this region it is unaffected by the increase in light, but when it tries to leave, it immediately passes into a region of lower illumination, and this stimulus causes reversal into the light trap.

In topophototaxis of *Anabaena*, Drews (1959) showed that curvature of filaments can be induced by unilateral illumination, the illuminated side becoming concave, i.e., retarded. *Anabaena* moves without rotating around its axis, whereas genera such as *Oscillatoria* and *Phormidium* do rotate, and so no curvature occurs. In these genera topophototactic accumulation in the light is caused by filaments moving towards the light, continuing this motion plus a stimulation to reversal in those moving away from the light. This is a statistical effect since autonomous reversals also occur about every ten minutes.

Such systems almost certainly operate in nature, since there is usually a concentration of these forms on the surface of sediments in a disjunct manner corresponding with areas which have been covered or uncovered. It would also presuppose a concentration of these forms in the light zone, however, and this is not true of all species, e.g., *Arthrospira* in Abbotts Pond, England, is confined to the less well-illuminated region (Moss, personal communication).

The topic and phobic reactions appear to operate through different photoreceptor systems since the optimum light needed for topotaxis is low (50–200 lux) and high for phobotaxis (5000–10,000 lux). Topophototaxis seems to be related to absorption by the phycobilins and phobophototaxis to both chlorophyll and phycobilin absorption.

The same range of light intensities are operative in diatom phobo- and topophototaxis, except in *Nitzschia stagnorum* which was indifferent to topophototaxis and showed negative phobotaxis above 2500 lux. Blue light below 550 mμ was the only region operative in these taxes.

Unfortunately, these phototactic responses are not a fixed feature of the cells but can be varied by growth in different media. *Euglena gracilis* is inactive in Ross media at pH 3.0, but is positively phototactic in a less concentrated medium at pH 7.0; *Platymonas subcordiformis* varies between negative and positive phototaxis depending on the Mg : Ca ratio, while the addition of potassium induces positive phototaxy. It is also of interest that when the sign of the orientation has been fixed by the ionic balance it cannot be altered by light intensity. This suggests that in nature where changes from positive to negative occur during the day the ionic system must be balanced. A rather neglected study of *Lepocinclis texta* by Brucker (1954) showed that at all light intensities this organism was positively phototactic, and negative reactions were never recorded. He approached the problem from a study of the threshold light intensities necessary to produce a phototactic aggregation. Dark adapted material reacted when illuminated with 0.75 mc., while material in bright daylight required 20–21 mc. to produce the same effect. Material exposed to light of less than 50 lux acted in the same way as in darkness. These data suggest that photosynthetic activity is responsible for the decreased sensitivity after a period in bright light. Also experiments carried out from 6.00 to 20.00 hours showed a clear fall in sensitivity from 6.00 to midday, a period of low sensitivity around midday, followed by a steady rise (Figure 1). This was correlated with carbon dioxide uptake, and experiments in gas streams showed a similar decreasing sensitivity as the carbon dioxide concentration was increased. Decrease in cell concentration increased the sensitivity, presumably again due to the effect on carbon dioxide concentration. Despite this rhythm during the day, Brucker could not detect any endogenous rhythm. He reports similar results with *Chlamydomonas gracilis, C. variabilis, C. media,* and *Euglena viridis.*

Brucker's results seem to contradict Pohl's (1948) data on *Euglena gracilis*, since for this latter species the phototactic sensitivity rose to a maximum around midday and then decreased (Figure 2). It is notable that both increase and decrease in sensitivity occur unrelated to light intensity since the former starts prior to transfer into the light and the latter during full light intensity. In the dark *Euglena gracilis* clumps and is difficult to detach from the culture flask, thus suggesting some form of dark secretion. The apparent contradiction between the *Lepocinclis texta* and *Euglena gracilis* data may be an actual variation in sensitivity or the result of differing experimental conditions; e.g., if the light intensity was sufficient in Pohl's experiments then they would accumulate most at midday, even

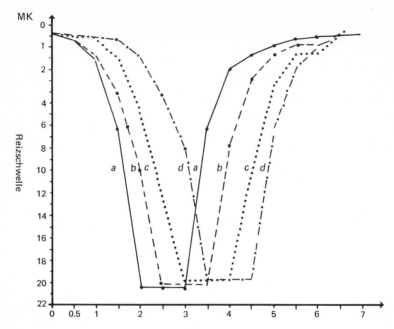

FIG. 1. Changes in the phototactic response of *Lepocinclis texta* to light from 7.00 hrs to 20.00 hrs showing that a higher light intensity is necessary to induce an effect during the midday period. From Brucher, 1954.

though a higher light intensity may be necessary at midday than at earlier or later times.

Chlorophyll is inactive in flagellate phototaxis, and Halldal (1958) showed that pigments absorbing light around 490 mμ act as the receptor

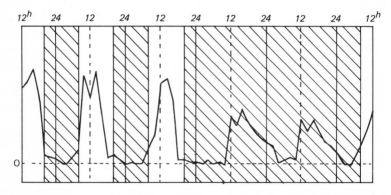

FIG. 2. The phototactic sensitivity of *Euglena gracilis* in alternating 12 hr. light/12 hr. dark periods and in constant dark. Dark periods are crosshatched. From Pohl. 1948.

for phototaxis (*Prorocentrum* was the only exception with absorbtion at 570 mμ). Thus it appears that carotenoids are active as the photoreceptor. Colorless *Euglena* mutants studied by Gossel (1957) had a principal absorption maximum at 410 mμ, and it may be that the photoreceptor does actually absorb at this wavelength. If ATP is involved in flagellar activity, as is now generally assumed, then in these colorless forms the ATP is generated by a process other than photosynthesis.

Phototaxis in nature is less easy to perceive, although an early worker, Strasburger, noted phototactic movements of *Volvox*, etc. Most of the studies have been of vertical migration of phytoplankton; Cowles and Brambel (1936) investigated the diurnal movements of *Gonyostomum semen* and found an aggregation in the 0–1 m. surface layer from 5.00 to 13.00 hours, after which the flagellate moved downwards so that peak cell numbers were at 2–3 m. at 17.00 hours, and at 21.00 hours actual depletion of the 0–015 m. had occurred (Figure 3). Taking into account experimental work such as that of Pohl, it is not surprising that the *Gonyostomum* was already abundant on the surface under conditions of low light intensity at

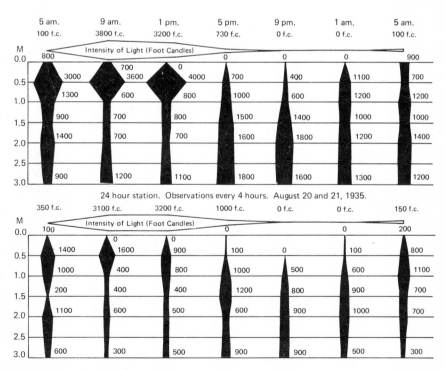

FIG. 3. The daily vertical migration of cells of *Gonyostomum semen* in a bog pond. From Cowles and Brambel, 1936.

5.00 hours since motility commences before dawn; in fact at 1.00 A.M. there is some evidence of upward movement. Downward movement commences when light intensity is very high, suggesting a reduction in phototactic sensitivity or swimming rate. These data were obtained in summer when there were marked gradients of temperature oxygen and carbon dioxide down the water column which may have affected the distribution, although it was concluded that light was the major factor. In a similar study of the chrysophyte *Chrysococcus diaphanus*, similar fluctuations were recorded when other variables (e.g., temperature) were either more uniform down the depth profile or not varying diurnally, e.g., oxygen (Figure 4) (Happey and Moss, 1967). *Chrysococcus* is only weakly motile, and

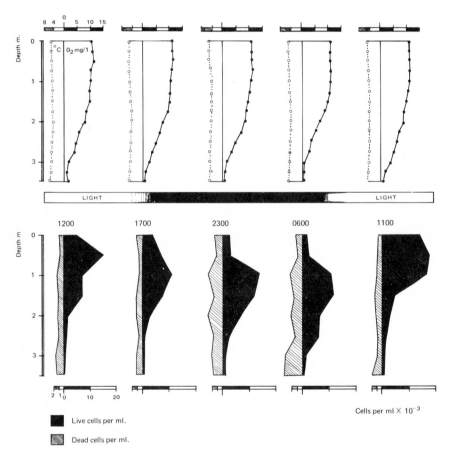

FIG. 4. The vertical distribution of temperature, oxygen and *Chrysococcus diaphanus* cells over a 24-hr. period. From Happey and Moss, 1967.

thus surface phototactic aggregation was possible only when circulation of water was minimal as measured by the oxygen depletion at the base of the water column. This occurred for about six weeks during December and January (Figure 5).

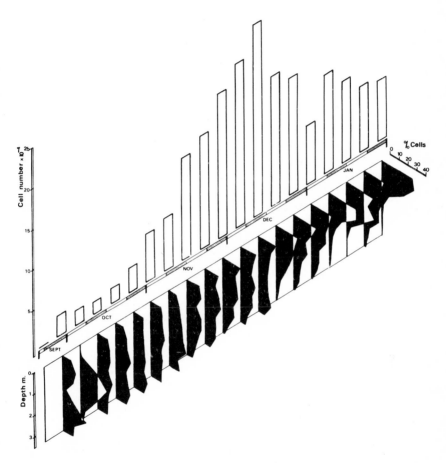

FIG. 5. The vertical distribution of populations of *Chrysococcus diaphanus* cells over a five-month period. Total number of cells in the upper histogram and vertical distribution in the lower graph expressed as percentages of total cell numbers at each depth. From Happey and Moss, 1967.

In spite of the increased degree of vertical mixing in marine habitats, phototactic aggregation at the surface has frequently been recorded. Hasle (1950, 1954) recorded such movements for *Ceratium furca*, *C. fusus*, *Peridinium triquetrum*, and *Prorocentrum micans*. There were clearly more cells in the surface waters at sunrise than at 2.15 hours, and the decline occurred as in freshwaters between 11.15 and 15.00 hours. But the pattern is more difficult to plot because of tidal movements of cells. The dangers of too few observations in this type of work are illustrated by Wheeler's conclusion (1966) that *Exuvaiella baltica* is negatively phototactic on finding this flagellate abundant at the surface at 7.50 hours and lower in the water column at 16.10. The choice of these two times for almost any of the phototactic flagellates would lead to erroneous conclusions.

Phototactic movements of benthic algae have been recorded by several workers (see references in Round and Palmer, 1966) and it is a "feature" of these rhythms that they are only conspicuously expressed in the light. Shading of the habitat prevents the upward migration in both *Euglena obtusa* (Palmer and Round, 1965) and in *Hantzschia virgata*, var. *intermedia* (Palmer and Round, 1967). This upward movement is a phototactic response, and it is quite clear that it is not a constant reaction throughout the daylight hours since exposure after 16.30 hours in the tidal situations where these observations were made produced only small or in some instances no vertical migration. Also few cells (*Euglena*) or no cells (*Hantzschia*) appear at the surface of sediments during nighttime, even in constant light. Re-burrowing of the cells on artificial darking may be an active process or merely the result of loss of motility and therefore fairly rapid sinking since the sand and water is constantly moved by small animals.

That the response is more than a simple reaction to light is shown by the fact that a few cells of *Euglena obtusa* migrate upwards when samples are placed in the dark during daytime, suggesting that light is essential to direct the movement but that a rhythm of motility is also present (Round, 1966). No such rhythm of motility can be detected during the night.

Davies (personal communication) found a distinct rhythm of motility in freshwater *Euglena* spp. in alternating light/dark and only erratic motility in continuous light or dark.

Hantzschia appears to switch from a late afternoon "up" phase to an early morning "up" phase as the tides move through the day, and morning exposure of the habitat re-starts as afternoon exposure is decreasing (Figure 6). Palmer and Round (1967) proposed a theory to cover the apparent switch based on a system in which there are two potentially upward migratory periods, one of which is suppressed during darkness (Figure 7). This may simply be suppression of motility since it seems as though many of these upward migration rhythms can start in the dark and then continue more strongly in a uni-directional form after dawn.

Temperature has little effect on the vertical-migration rhythm of *Euglena obtusa* from 5°–14°C, but at 2°C the rhythm is inhibited.

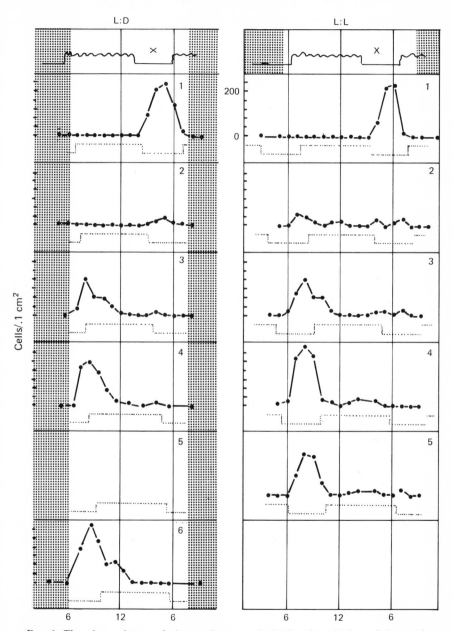

Fig. 6. The phase change of the persistent vertical-migration rhythm of *Hantzschia virgata* in alternating light-dark periods (L:D) and in constant light (L:L). Stippling indicates dark periods. X = time of collection of sample. Depression in dotted lines represent times of low tide in nature on days when rhythm was studied in the laboratory. Cell counts expressed in percentages of the highest on each day. From Palmer and Round, 1967.

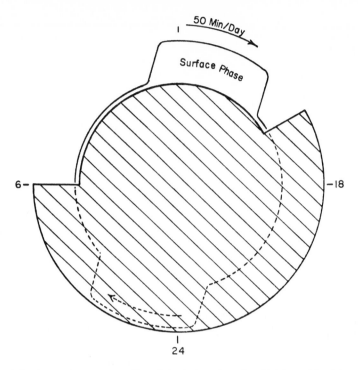

FIG. 7. Diagrammatic representation of the interaction of a 24.8 hour binodal vertical-migration rhythm. Surface phases represented by bulges in the disc. Shaded area represents nighttime, and cut out are daytime. From Palmer and Round, 1967.

2°C reduced but did not completely inhibit the rhythm of the diatoms, and 20°C had virtually no effect on them (Round and Palmer, 1966) (Figure 8). Transference from 2°C to 12°C caused a shift in the phase of the rhythm. The evidence suggests that the vertical migration starts up immediately after the perturbation; similar phase shifts by a single shock were reported by Bruce and Pittendrigh (1958). Although the phase is shifted the period is unaffected.

Two lines of evidence indicate that these migration rhythms are more than simply rhythms of phototaxis which can only be operative during the daytime. Firstly, the rhythms of freshwater stream and pond algae (Round and Happey, 1965; Round and Eaton, 1966) both show upward migration starting well before dawn; therefore, the system is "switched on" prior to illumination. Secondly, the rhythm of *Hantzschia* moves through the day even under constant laboratory conditions; i.e., it is "switched on" at different times each day irrespective of light conditions.

Constant light is not harmful to *Euglena* or the diatoms of the intertidal

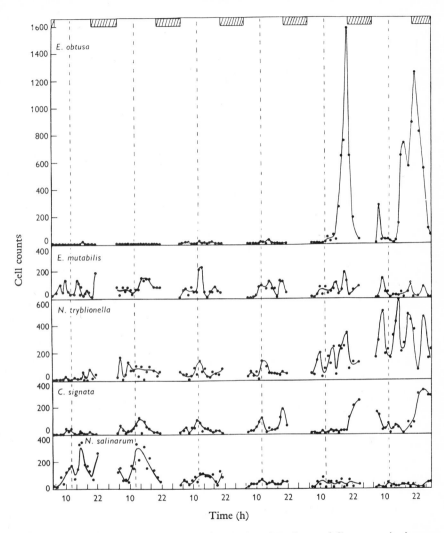

FIG. 8. Six cycles of the vertical-migration rhythm of *Euglena* and diatom species in constant light and at 2°C until the end of the fourth cycle, then transferred to 12°C. Cross-hatched areas indicate natural dark periods. From Round and Palmer, 1964.

zone, but it does greatly disrupt the rhythm of stream and pond diatoms, apparently preventing their downward movements. This may be related to the natural habitat conditioning of the organisms, since those of the intertidal zone are accustomed to periods of exposure at the surface whereas the stream and pond algae are not. However, the species which actually move beneath the surface sediments impose upon themselves a period of darkening. Thus it can be argued that constant light prevents this burrowing either by stimulating movement of the freshwater forms or by preventing an active downward movement, if indeed such a directional movement exists.

Constant darkness had the least effect on stream diatoms, disturbed those of pond diatoms, and almost completely suppressed those of the intertidal region. This suggests that different populations have different innate motility systems; the stream diatoms seem to have a clear rhythm of motility, the pond diatoms have only a slight innate rhythm (this is what causes the upward movement to start before dawn), and the intertidal forms have a motility rhythm which is confined to the short period of time during which they normally appear on the surface.

When *Euglena obtusa* is brought into the laboratory and its vertical migration rhythm studied, it has frequently been found to have a series of peaks superimposed on the general upward-downward migration cycle in both natural daylight and under constant light conditions. The minor peaks occured at 1–1½-hour intervals (Figure 9) and were synchronized to within fifteen minutes in replicate samples. This is not an effect of the pretreatment within the natural habitat since samples taken on different days— therefore under different tidal regimes—show exactly the same effect. In addition, as shown in Figure 9, samples exposed to the light at different times show an immediate upward movement at about the same rate fol-

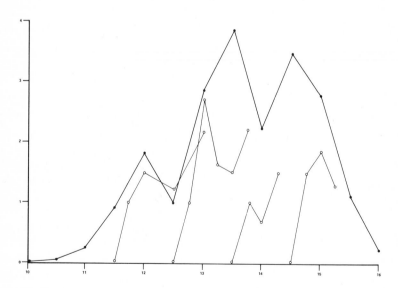

Fig. 9. The vertical-migration of *Euglena obtusa* in constant light (continuous line) and when removed from darkness at different times (open circles).

lowed by a drop in numbers. This kind of evidence suggests a drop in photosensitivity after a period in full light followed by a recovery. Whether or not this is due to a change of pH, as might be expected from Brucker's study of *Lepocinclis*, or other factors is unknown. Some diatoms also appear to lose the ability to stay at the surface in nature, although they, too, sometimes recover; likewise, in constant conditions in the laboratory some species have a conspicuous series of peaks, e.g., *Nitzschia tryblionella* (Round and Palmer, 1966).

PHOTOTROPISM

Growth curvature towards a light source is only likely to occur in multicellular algae and possibly amongst stalked diatoms. *Bryopsis* exhibits phototropism in that the side branches grow towards the light source, blue but not red light being operative. Phototropism of two other siphonaceous algae, *Derbsia Lamourousii* (Feldmann, 1938) and *Acetabularia calciculus* (Nasr, 1939), has been briefly recorded.

PHOTOPERIODISM

The effect of day length on some algae has been demonstrated under varying experimental conditions, but its effect in nature is relatively unknown. Indirect evidence of its importance for the seasonal growth of plankton was obtained by Grim (1950), who showed that the species most abundant in spring, e.g., *Asterionella formosa* and *Synedra acus*, var. *angustissima*, grow best in the laboratory with light periods of 8–12 hours, whereas late-spring/early-summer species, e.g., *Fragilaria crotonsis*, grow best with 14–16 hours of light. Undoubtedly day length is effective, but disentangling this effect from the other ecological variables is difficult. Long-day *Ulva lactuca* and short-day *Ulva thurettii* plants have been recorded by Føyn (1955), the former growing in Scandinavia and the latter in southern Europe. The former is anisogamous, and the latter is ogamous, and in view of von Stosch's (1954) work on *Lithodesmium*, there may be a connection between reproductive morphology and day length.

The rate of mitosis in the diatoms *Biddulphia sinensis* and *Coscinodiscus granii* is dependent on the alternation of light/dark periods, presumably connected via general metabolism. Huling (1960) studied the effects of various photoperiods on cell division of *Euglena gracilis,* var. *bacillaris* and found a greater number of divisions during the dark period whatever time it was imposed. Cell division was inhibited by short light periods and stimulated when they were increased from 2–8 hours.

Hygen (1948) found that although the biflagellate zooids of *Ulothrix flacca* produced under different photoperiods were identical, they behaved differently. The long-day zooids fused to form globular zygotes while the short-day zooids were asexual and germinated immediately, growing into new filaments. The zygotes left in long days increased in size and wall thickness but did not germinate unless frozen. Young zygotes could be induced to germinate, however, by transferring them to a short-day regime. Hygen used this information to explain the seasonal cycle of *Ulothrix* in northern climates. Zygotes germinate in spring (short days) after freezing; zooids formed soon afterwards (short days) germinate immediately, thus vegetatively propagating the alga. Later in summer (long days) the zooids act as gametes and form zygotes which will not germinate during long days but remain dormant until spring, during which time the dormancy is broken by freezing.

True photoperiodic effects (i.e., definite morphogenetic effects produced by changes in day length) have been reported mainly from higher plants. Almost all the early work on algae has been concerned with the effect of day length on spore formation, and some results are purely growth effects. Dring (personal communication) has shown a genuine photoperiodic effect in the production of the conchosporangia of *Porphyra tenera* studied in *in vitro* culture. The *Conchocelis* phase forms sporangia under short-day conditions, and interruption of the sixteen-hour dark period by one hour of light was sufficient to inhibit sporangia production. Also, exposure to eight short-day cycles followed by long days induced the formation of as many sporangia as were formed after twenty-five short days. These results are sufficient to indicate a true photoperiodic response and not merely an effect on growth. The critical day length for this spore formation in the *Conchocelis* phase—about eleven to twelve hours—was clear and appeared to be temperature stable between 15–25° C, indicating the existence of an accurate and temperature-compensated timing mechanism. Dring considers that the preliminary evidence suggests that this timing mechanism is associated with an endogenous rhythm. This photoperiodic effect on *Porphyra tenera* was suggested by Iwasaki (1961) but was not subjected to testing with light breaks. Iwasaki points out that the experimental results in artificial day lengths exactly parallel the behavior in nature when the *Conchocelis* phase grows in the long-day season and the leafy thallus in the short-day, and the transition between the two is almost exactly at the equinox.

Photomorphogenesis

There are several reports in the literature of the effect of light on the morphology of algae with the production of "sun" and "shade" forms.

Tetraspora lubrica, for example, forms long thin strands in shade and dense glomerate thalli in high light intensity (Boch, 1950). Such effects result in taxonomic problems since in the absence of cultural studies the same species is often placed in two different taxa. Jaag (1945), however, equally showed the danger of relying on cultural studies since an increase in light intensity, at least among the Cyanophyta, can alter the morphology of a form which would be allocated to *Tolypothrix distorta,* var. *pencillata,* to that of *Scytonema julianum.* In such an instance there is obviously only a single taxon involved, but the expression of its morphology is controlled by ecological variables to yield a series of ecotypes. The problematical aspect is what the generic designation should be. In 1894 Héribaud reported some strange effects of light on diatom morphology. He found that at fifteen meters below lake surface the diatoms were more elongate and had more widely spaced striae than the same species in shallow water, and also at high altitudes (i.e., at high light intensity) the striae were closer together. The matter requires reinvestigation.

The well-known "loss" of chlorophyll in the mass mutations of colored *Euglena* spp. to apochlorotic mutants is in a sense a photomorphogenetic effect and is produced by ultraviolet light and high temperature (Grenson, 1964).

ENDOGENOUS RHYTHMS

Endogenous rhythms are those functionings of organisms which are relatively independent of environmental changes. These are not then a direct effect of changing light and temperature regimes. Temperature, however, is a factor which has stimulated much interest since variation of this factor over a wide range has only very slight effects on the rhythm, which has in fact been termed "temperature independent." There is a certain degree of variability in this. The vertical migration rhythm in *Euglena obtusa* (Figure 10) has a $Q_{10} = 1.0$ between $5°-15°$ and $Q_{10} = 0.94$ between $15°-18.5°C$ (Palmer and Round, 1965), whereas the induced luminescence rhythm in *Gonyaulax polyedra* has a Q_{10} of 0.86. Q_{10} of less than unity seems to be confined to algae. It is assumed, as yet without direct proof, that a "biological clock" is the underlying mechanism. Naturally some biochemical basis is thought to be involved, but it does not show the *usual* temperature sensitivity. In fact, it "runs faster" at lower temperatures which is only explicable "on the basis of a biochemical temperature compensating mechanism" (Sweeney, 1962).

Some of the most interesting data on this problem have been obtained using the bioluminescence of dinoflagellates, which involves an actual

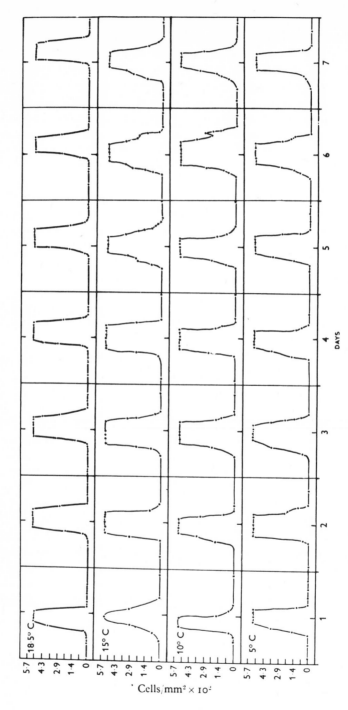

FIG. 10. The effect of various constant temperatures on the vertical-migration rhythm in *Euglena obtusa*. Light intensity (98 ft.-c) was identical at each temperature. From Palmer and Round, 1965.

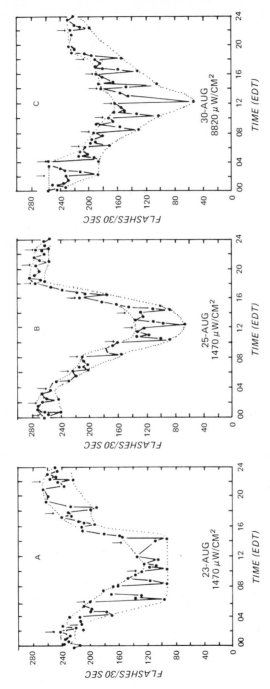

FIG. 11. The effect of light inhibition on the flashing rates of populations of bioluminescent dinoflagellates. The lower curves connect the flashing rates after 15 min. exposure to light. Start of exposure indicated by arrows. The upper dashed line connects rates after complete recovery. They all show proportionately greater inhibition of flashing during daylight hours. From Kelly and Katena, 1966.

light output coupled to an endogenous rhythm. In experimental systems a diurnal rhythm of luminescence is exhibited by *Gonyaulax* at low light intensities (500–1500 lux) but is suppressed at higher light intensity (Sweeney and Hastings, 1957). Light can be used to "entrain" this rhythm of luminescence, though immediately the "entraining" regime ceases the rhythm reverts to its natural period (Hastings and Sweeney, 1958). Recently Clarke and Kelley (1965) have shown that this rhythm also occurs in nature—flashing being much greater during the night, and although the organisms were not identified it is almost certain that they were dinoflagellates. This was followed up by work on the flashing of single cells of dinoflagellates taken directly from the sea by Kelly and Katona (1966) in which luminescence was shown to be exhibited by six species previously not known to be luminescent, and also that the decreased rate of flashing during daytime is inhibited further by exposure to short periods of light. This inhibition is proportionally greater during daytime than nighttime (Figure 11). Thus light superimposes some degree of control on an already existing endogenous rhythm.

Alternating light/dark conditions are not involved in the timing mechanism in *Gonyaulax* except to impart an added precision to it since in continuous illumination the rhythm continues, though usually with a period slightly other than twenty-four hours. The effect of high light in causing arhythmicity has been mentioned above, and this is also a characteristic of the rhythm of luminescence of *Gonyaulax*. Such behavior indicates a complex effect of light on endogenous rhythms. This lack of rhythm at high light intensities has been shown to be a property of individual cells (Sweeney, 1960; Sweeney and Hastings, 1960) and not merely an effect on the population.

ECOLOGICAL EFFECTS

The interplay between light and temperature effects in lakes led Findenegg (1943) to suggest four types of organisms associated with different seasons: (1) low light/low temperature (winter); (2) low light/high temperature (autumn); (3) high light/low temperature (spring); and (4) high light/high temperature (summer). One of the few observational and experimental studies of these factors is that of Rodhe (1948), who showed that *Melosira islandica*, subspecies *helvetica*, grew best at 5°C, although initial growth was greater at 10°C and 20°C; it is a spring and autumn form in Lake Erken. *Synura uvella* behaved like *Melosira*. He found that Chlorococcales (*Ankistrodesmus, Scenedesmus, Chlorella,* and *Coelastrum*) grew best at 20°–25°C, and they are frequently found in abundance in summer.

There seems little doubt that it is illumination increase which initiates the growth of many forms in spring, especially those which start or complete the spring cycle under ice cover (Lund, 1965). Rodhe's data (1948) also suggests that temperature is probably the important factor in the summer growth of Chlorococcales; the same is possibly true of Cyanophyta in temperature lakes and throughout the year in tropical lakes. Ukeles (1961) showed that different algal groups have differing temperature requirements. Many apparently aberrant occurrences are noted in the literature, however, and these may be related to a temporary imbalance in the environment (cf. the rapid growth of *Melosira* at 20°C, but if allowed to continue it proved fatal). Some of the apparently naive statements in the literature regarding seasonal occurrences and relationships to physical factors are clearly valid, but it will require intensive studies to prove them. Thus, in a detailed study, Canter and Lund (1966), showed with over twenty years of data that the desmid populations were clearly correlated with the spring/summer increase in temperature rather than with day length or radiation. Planktonic populations are almost certainly some of the most complex to study since vertical turbulence transports the cells through an ever changing series of light and temperature regimes, necessitating a complex integration of all the factors. At least the effect of changing depth can be considerably reduced if a population living on the surface is selected for study, e.g., the epipelon.

The gross effect of light limiting the depth penetration of the epipelic algal community in lakes was shown by Round in 1961, but there was not sufficient evidence to show any shading effects of planktonic growth on this community, although the later peaks of epipelic growth at the lowest depths may be influenced by this. The effect of shading by overhanging trees at the shallowest station was also detected together with the restriction of certain species to certain depths. There was no doubt about the absence of some otherwise common species at the shallowest stations in Windermere (e.g., *Surirella, Stenopterobea, Diploneis, Gyrosigma, Neidium, Nitzschia sigmoidea, N. acicularis, Navicula radiosa*), while these very same species were somewhat better represented at one meter in the sheltered Blelham Tarn stations. Among the flagellates, *Gymnodinium aeruginosum* and *Cryptomonas* spp. were more abundant at four to six meters. There are several early records of depth restrictions of epipelic algae, and the whole field requires further intensive study. In spite of the absence of many diatom species from one meter in Windermere, the total cell count at this station was higher than at any other, and there is no evidence of lack of growth during the coldest/least-illuminated months, but merely a steady rate of growth during the period from December to the end of May. The decline from this peak occurs during a high light/high temperature period, and its relationship to these factors is not clear. It is possible that nutrients, especially nitrate, become limiting. The smallest populations occurred in November, and this again may be the combined effect of low light and temperature, although in the previous months the population was decreasing while nutrients were increasing, and it is possible that some other limiting factor must be sought.

In a more detailed study of epipelic diatoms, Eaton (1967) came to the conclusion that at no time during the year is temperature alone the controlling factor, though it may at some times accelerate or decelerate growth. He also found that the major species also grew over the whole range of daylengths and only a few minor species might possibly be affected by day length. Comparison of the populations with total incident illumination yielded little evidence for light control except for possible acceleration and deceleration growth at certain times, while the summer growth in particular was more susceptible to nutrient levels.

Moss (personal communication) has shown that light extinction caused by plankton absorption can explain the decreasing epipelic algal production with depth. The interplay between phytoplankton production and light penetration is probably a more important factor than nutrient depletion in the seasonal depth development of the epipelic community in small bodies of water.

The ideal situation for the analysis of temperature and light effects on algae is in springs where temperature and nutrients are constant and light is the major variable. In cold water ($10° \pm 0.5°$ C) springs near Bristol the lowest light intensity is in November. This coincided with the lowest population of epipelic diatoms in 1963, after which a rise in numbers immediately commenced. In 1964 in one spring the lowest cell count was again reached in November, while in a second spring the fall in population continued until the end of January. In both springs the diatom population reached a peak in late April and then slowly declined until November. This was associated with shading, as the leaf canopy at these sites suddenly reduced the light intensity to a quarter of its early April figure. This dramatic reduction in incidence light did not in fact induce a catastrophic drop in the diatom population such as occurs when, for example, silica becomes limiting, but rather a steady decline in numbers as light slowly decreases under the tree cover throughout summer. Theoretically this is exactly what one might expect since light is affecting general metabolism and reduction is not likely to be lethal, whereas removal of silica removes an absolute requirement from the habitat. Even more striking is the very rapid increase which occurred in the springs during each winter when the cell counts increased by five-fold amounts over a period of one–two months, while light only increased very slightly (of the order of 20–30 gm. cal./cm²/day) showing quite clearly that neither high light intensities nor high temperatures are necessary for epipelic diatom growth. The decline in numbers to the very low November cell counts has been attributed above to the decreasing light intensity, but one other factor has to be considered—flow rate—which increases drastically in the autumn and will certainly increase the depletion of the population. In fact, the very low populations in November extend into January in one year, coinciding exactly with the periods of high flow. It is therefore almost certain that this, coupled with a slower rate of growth at low light intensities, is responsible for the reduction in the population. In view of the fact that growth is rapid immediately as the flow rate drops, although light is still low, then one can hypothesize that even the decline in numbers during late summer is merely caused by the increased flow rate, and that in the absence of this variable factor the epipelic diatom growth in these springs would in conditions of steady flow fluctuate only slightly during the year—high populations coinciding with periods of maximum radiation and only slightly reduced populations coinciding with the lowest light. In fact, neither light nor temperature would be drastically limiting growth (I am grateful to Dr. J. W. Eaton for allowing me to use the above data which he will analyze in greater detail and publish elsewhere). In this context it is interesting that Hughes and Lund (1962) showed that *Asterionella formosa* produced larger cell crops under intermittent low light conditions than under higher continuous light when phosphorus was supplied at 0.9 g./ml. At higher phosphate concentrations it was possible to produce almost identical crops, though the low, intermittent light cultures were always slightly ahead. Studies of epiphytic diatoms in springs (Tippet, personal communication) suggest a fairly steady seasonal production on some hosts, e.g., the liverwort, *Chiloscyphus polyanthus*, which forms a fairly stable host. But more variable populations, as might be expected, occur on angiosperm hosts which themselves have a more pronounced seasonal development. Even on *Chiloscyphus*, however, there is a seasonal population change of some epiphytic diatom species, a change which may be related to light. Clearly the introduction of another variable—host development—into an otherwise almost monotonous environment immensely complicates attempts to correlate algal growth and light intensity.

Castenholz (1966) found evidence from an experimental and ecological study of epilithic marine diatoms that their seasonal ecology is at least partially determined by day length and light intensity.

Production of large algal crops at low temperature and light intensity is well known in polar regions, and Bunt (1965) found that, at levels as low as eight ft.c. and around $0°C$, 20 per cent of the net photosynthetic activity at light saturation was still possible. This is admittedly under more extreme light and temperature conditions than in Rodhe's experimental work or in the above quoted work on springs, but it does re-emphasize the general characteristic of diatoms to function at these extremes. The other important aspect is the relatively low rate of population loss, or put another way the high stability of habitat conditions, which enables large populations to develop. Again the balance between rate of production, influenced by light, and temperature, and loss from the habitat, is of overwhelming importance. If coupled with this stability there is also dark adaption, as shown for marine phytoplankton (Steemann-Nielsen and Hansen, 1959), and reduced respiration in low light intensities, as shown for an estuarine planktonic community (Patten, 1963), then the enormous polar populations are not as exceptional as often supposed. Bunt (*et al.*, 1966) found that respiration of the antarctic cryophilic species *Fragilaria sublinearis* was restricted at lower temperatures and it also "grows slowly at light intensities well below its normal compensation intensity," the temperature optimum for photosynthetic processes being appreciably lower than the optimum for respiration. In spite of this faculty, Bunt could not detect heterotrophy. Steemann-Nielsen and Hansen (1959) found that "shade" plankton has a higher photosynthetic rate than surface "sun" plankton. They believed that temperate winter plankton behaved as "shade" plankton, and almost certainly the same is true of cryophilic algae.

Another extreme situation in which the effect of light and temperature can be studied is the high altitude lake. Recently an important paper by Rodhe, *et al.* (1966), records the inversion of the normal trophogenic zones with the bulk of algae and greatest production as measured by C^{14}-techniques in the deeper layers. It is suggested that this reversal is due to the greater penetration of ultraviolet radiation into these extremely clear lakes. Under ice they found significant uptake of C^{14} even where the estimated energy flux was only 9.6 cal./cm^2/day. As in the experiments of Bunt, *et al.*, on a cryophilic alga, so Rodhe, *et al.*, could not establish any significant heterotrophy even under dark winter conditions under the ice.

Thus, evidence from temperate lakes and from specialized habitats, springs, sea ice, and high altitude lakes indicates that, though light and temperature may alter the rates of processes, they in themselves are unlikely to be limiting except under extreme conditions. As long as a stable niche is available—and this is a feature of benthic habitats under ice—the slow rates of growth, coupled with adaptive mechanisms, are quite ample to produce very large populations.

Lest it be thought that all diatoms are adapted to low temperatures, mention should be made of their distribution in hot springs, which has been recorded for many sites (Hustedt, 1938–39; Broch and Broch, 1966; and Stockner, 1967). Stockner found diatoms up to 45°C (a confirmation of several earlier reports), and he concluded that the negligible growth in winter was due to a lack of light allowing respiration and grazing losses to exceed production. Broch and Broch determined the optimum temperature for biomass in the hot springs of Yellowstone, and in Iceland they measured chlorophyll content, nucleic acid, and protein, and found optimal amounts in sites at temperatures from 48–56°C. As they suggest, and fitting with evidence quoted above, light is unlikely to be a limiting factor, but temperature is.

Temperature resistance is an important ecological parameter and one that has been only slightly studied. Biebl (1962) found that intertidal tropical algae can resist temperatures down to −2°C but will not tolerate freezing. For subtidal tropical algae, on the other hand, the limit is between +5°C to 14°C (compared with −2°C to +3°C for subtidal temperate species). Both Biebl and Scholm (1966) found that the resistance of subtidal forms was up to 30°–35°C. This degree of adaptation is only slightly greater than the highest sea temperatures in the regions studied. Schölm also showed that species from greater depths were susceptible to lower temperatures, suggesting a fine degree of temperature adaptation. Parker (1960) found that the growing tips of *Fucus vesciculosus* were most resistant to low temperatures and also that there is a degree of seasonal adaptation since this alga could withstand −30°C in summer and −45°C to −60°C in winter. Freezing of *Fucus* down to −40°C does not impair its photosynthetic ability which immediately resumes on thawing (Kanwisher, 1957).

REFERENCES

Biebl, R., 1962. "Temperaturresiztenz tropischer Meeresalgen," *Bot. Mar., 4,* 241–54.

Boch, G., and Haupt, W., 1961. "Die Chloroplastendrehung bei *Mougeotia,* III. Die Frage der Lokalisierung des Hellrot-Dunkelrot Pigmentsystems in der Zelle," *Planta, 57,* 518–30.

Boney, A. D., and Corner, D. S., 1962. "The Effect of Light on the Growth of Sporelings of the Intertidal Red Alga *Plumaria elegans* (Bonnem.), Schm.," *Jour. Mar. Biol. Ass. U.K., 42,* 65–92.

Brock, T. D., and Brock, M. L., 1966. "Temperature Optima for Algal Development in Yellowstone and Iceland Hot Springs," *Nature, Lond., 209,* 733–34.

Brucker, W., 1954. "Beiträge zur Kenntnis der Phototaxis gruner Schwärmzellen," *Arch. Protistenk., 99,* 294–327.

Bruckmeyer-Berkenbusch, H., 1955. "Die Beeinflussung der Auxosporenbildung von *Melosira nummuloides* durch aussenfaktoren," *Arch. Protistenk., 100,* 183–211.

Bruce, V. G., and Pittendrigh, C. S., 1958. "Resetting the *Euglena* Clock with a Single Light Stimulus," *Am. Naturalist, 92,* 295–306.

Bunt, J. S., 1965. "Measurements of Photosynthesis and Respiration in a Marine Diatom with the Mass Spectrometer and Carbon-14," *Nature, Lond., 207,* 1373–75.

Bunt, J. S., Owens, O., and van H., and Hoch, G., 1966. "Exploratory Studies on the Physiology and Ecology of a Psychrophilic Marine Diatom," *J. Phycol.*, 2, 96–100.

Burkholder, P. R., 1934. "Movement in the Cyanophyceae," *Quart. Rev. Biol.*, 9, 438–59.

Canter, H. M., and Lund, J. W. G., 1966. "The Periodicity of Planktonic Desmids in Windermere, England," *Verh. int. Verein. theor. angew. Limnol.*, 16, 163–72.

Castenholz, R. W., 1964. "The Effect of Daylength and Light Intensity on the Growth of Littoral Marine Diatoms in Culture," *Physiol. Plant.*, 17, 951–63.

Clarke, G. L., and Kelly, M. G., 1965. "Measurements of Diurnal Changes in Bioluminscence from the Sea Surface to 2000 Meters Using a New Photometric Device," *Limnol. Oceanogr.*, 10 (Suppl), R54–R56.

Cowles, R. P., and Brambel, C. E., 1936. "A Study of the Environmental Conditions in a Bog Pond with Special Reference to the Diurnal Vertical Distribution of *Gonyostomum semen*," *Biol. Bull. Mar. Biol. Lab., Woods Hole*, 71, 286–98.

Drews, G., 1959. "Beiträge zur Kenntnis der Phototaktischen Reaktionen der Cyanophycean," *Arch. Protistenk.*, 104, 380–430.

Eaton, J. W., 1967. "Studies on the Ecology of Epipelic Diatoms," Ph.D. thesis, Univ. of Bristol.

Feldmann, J., 1938. "Sur le phototropisme du *Derbesia Lamourousii* Solier," *Rev. Algol.*, 9, 145–47.

Findenegg, I., 1943. "Untersuchungen über die Ökologie und die Produktions-Verhältnisse des Planktons im Kärntner Seengebiet," *Int. Rev. Hydrobiol.*, 43, 366–429.

Fischer-Arnold, G., 1963. "Untersuchungen über die Chloroplastenbewegung bei *Vaucheria sessilis*," *Protoplasma*, 56, 495–520.

Føyn, B., 1955. "Specific differences Between Northern and Southern Populations of the Green Alga *Ulva lactuca*," *Publ. Staz. Zool. Napoli*, 27, 261–70.

Gessner, F., 1930. "Gestaltänderung an *Spirogyra*-chromatophoren," *Mikroskopie f. Naturfr.*, 8, 1–10.

Gössel, I., 1975. "Über des Aktionsspektrum der Phototaxis chlorophyllfreier Euglenen und über die Absorption des Augenflecks," *Arch. Mikrobiol.*, 27, 288–305.

Grenson, M., 1964. "Physiology and Cytology of Chloroplast Formation and Loss in *Euglena*," *Internat. Rev. Cytol.*, 16, 37–59.

Grim, J., 1950. "Versuche zur Ermittlung der Produktionskoeffizienten einiger planktophyten in einem flachen See," *Biol. Zbl.*, 69, 147–74.

Halldal, P., 1958. "Action Spectra of Phototaxis and Related Problems in Volvocales, *Ulva* gametes, and Dinophyceae," *Physiol. Plant*, 11, 118–53.

Hämmerling, J., 1944. "Zur Lebensweise, Fortpflanzung und Entwicklung verschiedener Dasycladaceen," *Arch. Protistenk.*, 97, 7–56.

Harder, R., 1918. "Über die Bewegung der Nostocaceen," *Z. Bot.*, 10, 177–242.

————, 1920. "Über die Reaktionen freibeweglicher pflanzlicher Organismen auf plötzliche Änderungen der Licht-intensitat," *ibid.*, 12, 353–462.

Hasle, G. R., 1950. "Phototactic Vertical Migration in Marine Dinoflagellates," *Oikos.*, 2.

————, 1954. "More on Phototactic Diurnal Migration in Marine Dinoflagellates," *Nytt. Mag. Bot.*, 2, 139–47.

Hastings, J. W., and Sweeney, B. M., 1955. "A Persistent Diurnal Rhythm of Luminescence in *Gonyaulax polyedra*," *Biol. Bull. Mar. Biol. Stat.*, Woods Hole, 45, 440–58.

Heidingsfeld, I., 1943. "Phototakische Untersuchungen an *Navicula radiosa*," Diss. Breslau, ref. in Nultsch (1956).

Haupt, W., 1966. "Phototaxis in Plants," *Int. Rev. Cytol.*, 19, 267–97.

Héribaud, J., 1894. "De l'influence de la lumiere et de l'altitude sur la striation des valves des Diatomees." *C.R. Acad. Sci.*, Paris, 1894, 1–3.

Höfler, K., 1962. "Karystrophe durch Säurewirkung bei *Biddulphia titiana*," *Ber dtsch. Bot. Ges.*, *LXXU*, 206–10.

Hughes, J. C., and Lund, J. W. G., 1962. "The Rate of Growth of *Asterionella formosa* Hass. in Relation to its Ecology," *Arch. Mikrobiol.*, *42*, 117–29.

Huling, R. T., 1960. "The Effects of Various Photoperiods on the Population Increase of *Euglena gracilis* v. *bacillaris* Pringsh," *Trans. Amer. Microsc. Soc.*, *79*, 384–91.

Hustedt, F., 1938–39. "Systematische und ökologische Untersuchungen über die Diatomeen-flora von Java, Bali und Sumatra nach dem Material der Deutscher Limnologischen Sunda-Expedition," *Arch. f. Hydrobiol.*, *Suppl. Bd.*, *15*, *16*.

Hygen, G., 1948. "Fotoperiodiske reaksjoner hos alger," *Blyttia*, *6*, 1–6.

Iwaskaki, H., 1961. "The Life Cycle of *Porphyra tenera in vitro*," *Biol. Bull. Mar. Biol. Lab.*, *Woods Hole*, *121*, 173–87.

Kanwisher, J., 1957. "Freezing and Drying in Intertidal Algae," *ibid.*, *113*.

Kelly, M. G., and Katona, S., 1966. "An Endogenous Diurnal Rhythm of Bioluminescence in a Natural Population of Dinoflagellates," *ibid.*, *131*, 115–26.

Klebs, G., 1886. "Über die Organisation der Gallerte bei einigen Algen und Flagellaten," *Untersuch. aus d. bot. Inst.*, *Tübingen.*, *2*.

Lund, J. W. G., 1965. "The Ecology of Freshwater Phytoplankton," *Biol. Rev.*, *40*, 231–93.

Mast, S. O., and Gover, M., 1922. "Relation Between Intensity of Light and Rate of the Loco-motion in *Phacus pleuronectes* and *Euglena viridis*," *Biol. Bull. Mar. Biol. Lab.*, *Woods Hole*, *43*, 203–209.

Nasr, A. H., 1939. "On the Phototropism of *Acetabularia caliculus*," *Rev. Algol.*, *11*, 347–50.

Nultsch, W., 1956. "Studien über die Phototaxis der Diatomeen," *Arch. Protistenk.*, *101*, 1–68.

———, 1962. "Über das bewegungsverhalten der Diatomeen," *Planta*, *58*, 22–33.

Palmer, J. D., and Round, F. E., 1965. "Persistent, Vertical-Migration Rhythms in Benthic Microflora. I. The Effect of Light and Temperature on the Rhythmic Behavior of *Euglena obtusa*," *J. Mar. Biol. Assn.*, *U.K.*, *45*, 567–82.

———, 1967. "Persistent, Vertical-Migration Rhythms in Benthic Microflora. VI. The Tidal and Diurnal Nature of the Rhythm in the Diatom *Hantzschia virgata*," *Biol. Bull. Mar. Biol. Lab.*, *Woods Hole*, *132*, 44–55.

Parker, J., 1960. "Seasonal Changes in the Cold Hardiness of *Fucus vesiculosus*," *ibid.*, *119*, 474–78.

Patten, B. C. 1963. "Information Processing Behaviour of a Natural Plankton Community," *Am. Biol. Teachers*, *25*, 489–501.

Peteler, K., 1939. "Amöboide Formveränderungen der Diatomeen Plastiden," *Protoplasma*, *32*, 9–19.

Pohl, R., 1948. "Tagesrhythmus in phototaktischen Verhalten der *Euglena gracilis*," *Z. Naturf.*, *3B*, 367–74.

Rodhe, W., 1948. "Environmental Requirements of Fresh-Water Plankton Algae," *Symb. Bot. Upsaliens.*, *10*, 149 pp.

Rodhe, W., Hobbie, J. E., and Wright, R. T., 1966. "Phototrophy and Heterotrophy in High Mountain Lakes," *Verh. Int. Verein, Limmol.*, *16*, 302–13.

Round, F. E., 1961. "Studies on Bottom-Living Algae in Some Lakes of the English Lake District. VI. The Effect of Depth on the Epipelic Algae Community," *J. Ecol.*, *49*, 245–54.

———, 1965. "Persistent, Vertical-Migration Rhythms in Benthic Microflora. V. The Effect of Artificially Imposed Light and Dark Cycles," *Proc. Vth Int. Seaweed Symp.*, 197–203.

Round, F. E., and Eaton, J. W., 1966. "Persistent, Vertical-Migration Rhythms in Benthic Microflora. III. The Rhythm of Epipelic Algae in a Freshwater Pond," *J. Ecol.*, *54*, 609–15.

Round, F. E., and Happey, C. M., 1965. "Persistent, Vertical-Migration Rhythms in Benthic Microflora. IV. A Diurnal Rhythm of the Epipelic Diatom Association in Non-Tidal Flowing Water," *Br. Phycol. Bull*, *2*, 463–71.

Round, F. E., and Palmer, J. D., 1966. "Persistent, Vertical-Migration Rhythms in Benthic Microflora. II. Field and Laboratory Studies on Diatoms from the Banks of the River Avon," *J. Mar. Biol. Assn., U.K.*, *46*, 191–214.

Schimper, A. W. F., 1885. "Untersuchungen über die chlorophyllkörper und die ihnen homologen Gebilde," *Jb. wiss. Bot.*, *16*, 1–247.

Schmitz, F., 1882. "Die chromatophoren der Algen," *Verh. Naturviss. Ver. Rheinland u. Westfalen*, *40*, 1–76.

Schölm, H., 1966. "Untersuchungen zur Wärmeresistenz von Tiefenalgen," *Bot. Mar.*, *9*, 54–61.

Steemann-Nielsen, E., and Hansen, U. K., 1959. "Light Adaptation in Marine Phytoplankton Populations and its Inter-Relation with Temperature," *Phys. Plant.*, *12*, 353–70.

Stockner, J. G., 1967. "Observations of Thermophilic Algal Communities in Mount Rainier and Yellowstone National Parks," *Limnol. Oceanogr.*, *12*, 13–17.

Sweeney, B. M., 1960. "The Photosynthetic Rhythm in Single Cells of *Gonyaulax polyedra*," *Cold Spring Harbor Symp. Quant. Biol.*, *XXV,* 145–48.

———, 1962. "Rhythms," in *Physiology and Biochemistry of Algae*, ed. by Lewin, 687–700.

Sweeney, B. M., and Hastings, J. W., 1957. "Characteristics of the Diurnal Rhythm of Luminescence in *Gonyaulax polyedra*," *J. Cellular Comp. Physiol.*, *49*, 115–28.

———, 1948. "Rhythmic Cell Division in Populations of *Gonyaulax polyedra*," *J. Protozool.*, *5*, 217–24.

———, 1960. "Effects of Temperature upon Diurnal Rhythm," *Cold Spring Harbor Symp. Quant. Biol.*, *XXV.*, 87–104.

Von Stosch, H. A., 1954. "Die Oogamie von *Biddulphia mobiliensis* und der bisher bekannten Auxosporenbildung bei den Centrales," *Congr. Int. Bot. 8ᵉ Paris, Sect. 17*, 58–68.

Ukeles, R., 1961. "The Effect of Temperature on the Growth and Survival of Several Marine Algal Species," *Biol. Bull. Mar. Biol. Lab., Woods Hole*, *120*, 255–64.

Wheeler, B., 1966. "Phototactic Vertical Migration in *Exuviaella baltica*." *Bot. Mar.*, *9*, 15–17.

VII

Phytoplankton Photosynthesis

SHUN-EI ICHIMURA

Tokyo Kyoiku University
Botanical Institute, Faculty of Science
Tokyo, Japan

From an ecological point of view the studies of the production of organic matter by green plants have a twofold aim. One is to contribute to our knowledge about the geochemical cycle in the biosphere at large, and the other is to make clear the dynamic status of primary production occurring in a given ecosystem. In aquatic environments, the reproduction of organic matter is performed mainly by planktonic microalgae.

Numerous studies have been carried out on the photosynthesis of microalgae in pure cultures kept under optimal laboratory conditions. A great deal of knowledge about the mechanism of photosynthesis has thus been accumulated by plant physiologists, biochemists, and biophysicists. The subject of interest for aquatic ecologists, on the other hand, is the productive behavior of planktonic algal species or their communities under field conditions.

This paper attempts to summarize recent studies on phytoplankton photosynthesis and discusses their ecological significance as the process of primary production.

Physiological processes occurring in phytoplankton are affected by environmental factors which change not only diurnally and seasonally but also climatically and spatially. The effect of the environment on phytoplankton photosynthesis has been studied in various ways. The rate of photosynthesis is usually determined by measuring the amount of oxygen produced or carbon dioxide consumed by photosynthesis. In ecological studies or in field experiments, Winkler's titration method is commonly used for measuring oxygen and the carbon-14 technique for carbon dioxide uptake. Since the Winkler technique gives errors of $\pm$ 0.02 mg. $O_2/l.$, it can be applied only to waters rich in phytoplankton. Besides producing oxygen by photosynthesis, phytoplankton consumes oxygen by respiration. To measure the rate of photosynthesis accurately, therefore, we have to know the concurrent rate of respiration.

Compared with the oxygen method mentioned above, the carbon-14 method developed by Steemann-Nielsen (1952) has the advantage of being not only more accurate but also applicable to waters poor in phytoplankton. Moreover, the values obtained by the carbon-14 method represent approximately the net rate of photosynthesis. In some environments, especially in oligotrophic or severely polluted waters, the rate of photosynthesis measured by the oxygen method has given a much larger value than that measured by the carbon-14 method. Comparison of the two methods has been made by many workers, but the real cause of the discrepancy still remains a matter of dispute.

On surveying the literature on phytoplankton photosynthesis, one often encounters a difficulty in comparing the data reported by different authors because the rate of photosynthesis is expressed in reference to different units of phytoplankton biomass such as dry weight, cell volume, cell number, chlorophyll concentration, etc. At present no suitable conversion factor has been worked out to make these different expressions comparable with each other. Standardization of the method of expressing the rate of photosynthesis of phytoplankton is deemed highly relevant at present.

Another problem is in the method of measuring the light intensity under which the photosynthesis of phytoplankton proceeds. In ecological studies, light intensity is usually expressed in terms of "lux" or "cals/ cm²/ min." Lux is usually used as the unit when the light intensity is measured by a photometer with a selenium photocell whose spectral response resembles that of the human eye. Considering the sensitivity of the selenium photocell to the infrared range, which is not effective for photosynthesis, it is possible to convert approximately lux into cal./cm.²/min. and vice versa. However, the action spectrum of photosynthesis of phytoplankton may not be the same in all species, and the spectral energy distribution also differs according to the light source used. Even expressed in terms of the same unit, therefore, different data appearing in the literature cannot always be compared accurately with each other.

It must also be noted that the photosynthetic response to environmental factors differs according to physiological conditions and the previous history of the phytoplankton.

The foregoing are matters that must be borne in mind in describing the photosynthetic characteristics of phytoplankton. For further details on these problems reference is made to the following papers: Steeman-Nielsen (1952), Strickland (1960), Thomas (1961), and Lund and Talling (1957).

In the present article special consideration is focused on two cardinal problems: (1) characteristics of the photosynthesis-light curve, and (2) the photosynthetic rate. For general problems on phytoplankton production, reference is made to the papers by Gessner (1955, 1959), Vinberg (1960), Steemann-Nielsen (1960, 1965), Strickland (1965), Ryther (1965), Yentsch (1963), and Lund (1965).

CHARACTERISTICS OF THE PHOTOSYNTHESIS-LIGHT CURVE

The dependency of the rate of photosynthesis on light intensity is usually expressed by the photosynthesis-light curve, whose form is different according to plant species and environmental factors. It offers an important clue to ecologists for characterizing the physiological condition of phytoplankton.

The photosynthesis-light curve for a given sample assumes different forms according to the modes of expression of light intensity and the rate of photosynthesis. Yentsch and Lee (1966) have pointed out that the procedure of "normalization" of the photosynthesis-light curve with respect to the maximum rate (P_m) may suggest a misleading interpretation of the responses of natural phytoplankton. They have also remarked that the "normalized" curves are not suitable for comparing the photosynthesis-light responses of different phytoplankton photosyntheses.

According to the results obtained by Ryther (1956) for cultures of fourteen species of marine planktonic algae—including green algae, diatoms, and dinoflagellates—the shapes of the photosynthesis-light curves were remarkably similar for the species belonging to the same taxonomic group but strikingly different for the species of different groups.

Under natural conditions, the photosynthesis-light curve differs with phytoplankton taken from different habitats. As has been well known by plant ecologists, the photosynthesis pattern of terrestrial plants can be classified into sunny and shady types. The sunny form shows higher rates of photosynthesis in bright light than the shady form, whereas the reverse is true at low light intensities. Several investigators have also observed similar photosynthesis patterns in natural phytoplankton, and the patterns have been shown to be dependent mainly on the light conditions, partly on some other factors such as temperature and nutrient conditions of the phytoplankton habitat.

The typical photosynthesis-light curves for natural phytoplankton are those obtained by Ryther and Menzel (1959) in the Sargasso Sea off Bermuda. The samples were taken from surface waters and from depths to which 10 per cent and 1 per cent, respectively, of the surface light penetrated. Under winter conditions, when the water was isothermal and mixed to below the euphotic zone, phytoplankton from all three depths showed the same photosynthesis-light curves. In summer, when the water and plankton were stratified, three distinct curves were obtained with phytoplankton from the three depths. The curves shifted from the sunny form in the surface phytoplankton to the shady form in deeper phytoplankton. This finding suggests that the differentiation of the photosynthesis-light curve of phytoplankton has resulted from the difference of light conditions in the habitat.

Steemann-Nielsen and Hansen (1959) have examined the photosynthesis-light curves in marine phytoplankton from different oceans. They have found that phytoplankton from the deeper layer of the euphotic zone always showed the shady form and that the curve of the surface phytoplankton differed greatly with the latitude and season.

The vertical and regional differences of photosynthesis-light curves have also been found in freshwater phytoplankton. The sunny form is usually shown by the surface phytoplankton in eutrophic waters, and the shady form is observed with the samples from oligotrophic waters or from deeper layers in the euphotic zone.

The shape of the photosynthesis-light curve, especially that for the surface phytoplankton, apparently varies according to the season. Steemann-Nielsen and Hansen (1961), who followed the change of photosynthesis-light curves throughout the year in Danish waters, have found that the curves for all surface samples tested were of shady form in winter and of sunny form in summer, and that the slope of the curves at low light intensities were not determined solely by the light conditions but probably also to some extent by temperature and by composition of species. Similar results were obtained in freshwaters by the present author (1960).

The dynamic aspect of the process of differentiation of the photosynthetic pattern is complicated by the fact that in nature a number of physiological processes in phytoplankton are affected by changes in various environmental factors, and that the natural phytoplankton population often consists of a large variety of photosynthetic microorganisms. To get causal insight into the phenomenon of variation of photosynthetic character of phytoplankton population we have to choose waters in which the species composition is as simple as possible, showing certain regularities in its annual change. Complementary to investigations made in the field, laboratory experiments should be performed under controlled conditions with unialgal cultures of typical planktonic species obtained from the field. In this respect a series of experiments performed by Talling at Windermere may be regarded as a model.

Light

Differentiation of the photosynthesis pattern of phytoplankton caused by the change of light environment was first demonstrated by Talling (1966) in Windermere. He made a series of observations at short intervals between the 12–29 May. In the early period of observation the lake showed a marked thermal stratification which dwindled in the middle of the observation period owing to the cool and windy weather. During the remaining period, a strong stratification redeveloped rapidly. In the early and last phases of strong stratification, the photosynthesis-light curves shown by the sample taken from the surface layer was of a typical sunny form, whereas those shown by the samples taken from the depths of five and ten m. were of the shady form. He considered that the development of these differences was due mostly to the restricted circulation of phytoplankton in the strata of the vertical light gradient. This observation also suggested that the change in photosynthetic pattern occurs within a short period of one week at the most. With natural phytoplankton, the rate of physiological redifferentiation has been observed by the present author (1960) in freshwater phytoplankton. The first experiment was undertaken with phytoplankton having the sunny type of photosynthetic pattern. The sample waters from the surface layer of a eutrophic lake were taken in large glass bottles and kept under controlled sunlight in a greenhouse. Then, the change in photosynthetic responses to varying light intensities of the phytoplankton of each sample was observed. It was found that the photosynthetic pattern began to change after one day, and in four days it became that of the typical shady type under the light of 3–10 per cent of sunlight but not under that of 30 per cent. Another experiment was performed with the samples from the depths of zero, two, four, and six m. in a strongly stratified lake. The measurement performed soon after the sampling showed that the photosynthesis pattern was of the typical sunny form in the surface sample, and it changed progressively into those of the shady form in the samples of two, four, and six m. depths. The sample waters were taken in 2-l. flasks and exposed to 8000 lux in a growth chamber at 20°. After two days, the photosynthesis pattern of the samples from two and four m. depths were transformed completely into the sunny form. From these experiments it can be deduced that the change of photosynthetic behavior of natural phytoplankton takes place in a fairly short period, and the effect of previous light history of phytoplankton upon its photosynthetic pattern does not persist for a long period after the algae are transferred to different light environments. This was also ascertained by the experiment made with marine phytoplankton by Steemann-Nielsen and Park (1964). According to their results, when the surface phytoplankton was enclosed in glass bottles and suspended at a depth where the light intensity was about 5 per cent of the surface light, it took three days for the phytoplankton to change their photosynthetic behavioɪ to the shady type.

Thus the shape of the photosynthesis-light curve, which reflects the previous photic history of a phytoplankton, changes rather rapidly when the phytoplankton is transferred to a new light condition. Talling (1966) has reported that when natural phytoplankton were exposed to strong illumination their photosynthetic activity showed a decline in less than twenty-four hours, and that in one experiment using a surface sample, storage in darkness caused an increase of the activity. In another experiment using surface and deeper samples, however, dark storage did not appreciably change the photosynthesis-light curves of the plankton. Steemann-Nielsen, *et al.* (1962), observed with *Chlorella vulgaris* that the cells grown under weak light gave a shady type curve, while those grown under high light intensity showed a sunny type curve. When the cells were transferred from strong light to low light conditions, or vice versa, they changed their photosynthesis-light curve to those corresponding to the new light condition within about seventeen hours. When *Chlorella* grown in strong light were kept in the dark for thirty-six hours, the shape of photosynthesis-light curve changed gradually, whereas the curve of the sample transferred to low light intensity changed to the shady type after only seventeen hours. Yentsch and Reichert (1963) observed a significant effect of dark treatment on the photosynthetic behavior of a marine flagellate, *Dunaliella euchlora*, grown at 20° under light of 800 ft-c. After transfer to darkness, the photosynthetic capacity of the sample increased rapidly, showed a plateau from about the twentieth to the fiftieth hour, and thereafter decreased gradually. Yentsch and Lee (1966) obtained similar results with cultures of *Nannochloris atomus*. In their experiment it was noticed that when "normalyzed," the shapes of the photosynthesis-light curve remained identical throughout the course of dark incubation.

Temperature

The effect of temperature on the shape of the photosynthesis-light curve has been studied by many workers, both with unialgal cultures and with natural populations. It is well known that at low light intensities the rate of photosynthesis is not affected by temperature, while at higher light intensities the rate increases with the temperature. The mode of change of the rate of photosynthesis with temperature varies from one species to another, however. At saturating light intensities an average temperature coefficient of 2.1 has usually been reported for natural populations. The shape of the photosynthesis-light curve is shifted to the sunny type at higher temperatures. In some species, very high light intensities caused a depression of the photosynthetic rate at low temperatures (Tamiya, *et al.*, 1953).

Under natural conditions, the shapes of the photosynthesis-light curve of algal population are of the sunny form near the surface and of the shady form in the depths; the sunny form tends to predominate in summer, and the shady form in winter. In aquatic environments, the diurnal fluctuation of temperature is small, and within the euphotic zone the vertical gradient of temperature is also minor. Thus, the temperature effect on the rate of photosynthesis is, in general, more manifest in different seasons and different latitudes. This was illustrated by the results obtained by Talling (1957) with freshwater diatoms in some English lakes. He observed that when the *in situ* temperature increased from 5° to 20° the light saturated rate of photosynthesis (P_{max}) was enhanced markedly and that there was a linear relation between log P_{max} and temperature. A linear relation also held between temperature (C) and the lowest light intensity at which the photosynthesis rate becomes light-saturated. Talling suggested that the most significant source of variation of the photosynthesis-light curve was the temperature. Steemann-Nielsen, *et al.* (1961), had examined the shape of the photosynthesis-light curves for phytoplankton collected from the sound off Helsingør throughout the year, and they suggested that the shape of the curve is determined not exclusively by the light conditions at the habitat, but that it is also dependent on the temperature *in situ* and on the composition of species. The present author drew the same conclusion from the data obtained with freshwater phytoplankton in a eutrophic lake.

Under field conditions, however, the situation is often more complicated and unpredictable than that stated above. As has been pointed out by Talling (1966), the temperature relation of the seasonal changes of photosynthetic behavior of phytoplankton is often obscure. Factors other than temperature, such as the concentration of nutrients in the water and the physiological conditions of algal cells, also vary seasonally to affect the photosynthesis behavior of the plankton. Verduin (1956) has observed that a natural phytoplankton population living in a lake water of 0° to 3° shows as high a rate of photosynthesis per unit of plant volume as does the population living in 18° to 23° environment. Steemann-Nielsen and Hansen (1959) found that the shape of the photosynthesis-light curves shown by the samples of surface phytoplankton obtained from temperate and Arctic regions during the summer season were reasonably identical. The difference in temperature in the two cases was about 10°, and although the light intensities were comparable, the day length in the temperate region was shorter than that in the Arctic region. They assumed that in the Arctic the influence of the low temperature on the shape of the curve is counteracted by higher enzymic activities of the plankton. In Tokyo Bay, which has a definite horizontal gradient in nutrient concentration and a uniform temperature distribution throughout, the present author (1967) found that the seasonal differentiation in the photosynthesis-light curve results from the variation of water temperature in the eutrophic coastal waters, and that the main factor determining the shape of the curve in oligotrophic oceanic waters appears to be the variation of the nutrient concentration.

When the photosynthesis of algae at different temperatures under optimal light conditions is measured at the temperature under which they have previously been cultured, the photosynthesis-light curves show different shapes corresponding to the respective culture temperatures. If the photosynthesis of algae is measured at a temperature different from that of the culture, however, the shape of the curve rapidly shifts towards the one characteristic of the alga grown continuously at that given temperature. This has also been ascertained with natural phytoplankton.

Nutrients

The photosynthetic behavior of phytoplankton is also dependent on the nutrient conditions of the water. According to Edmondson's experiment in a small pond, the effect of the addition of phosphate on the photosynthetic behavior of phytoplankton appeared three days after treatment. The present author (1958) observed that the shady type photosynthesis-light curve of phytoplankton obtained from an oligotrophic lake transformed to the sunny form within a day after the addition of phosphate and nitrate. Such a nutrient dependence is often observed in a lake during nutrient-deficient seasons. Depletion of nutrients frequently appears in the later phase of the population maximum even in eutrophic lakes, generally in summer and in autumn. The deficiency of nutrients in the water transforms phytoplankton photosynthesis of the sunny type to that of the shady type. During the season of nutrient deficiency, application of fertilizers enhances the rate of phytoplanktonic photosynthesis, transforming the shape of the photosynthesis-light curve from a shady to a sunny form. These results indicate that the photosynthetic behavior of natural phytoplankton is not exclusively dependent on the genetic character peculiar to the species but is determined also by the physio-ecological condition of the phytoplankton.

Ecological Interpretation of the Photosynthesis-Light Curve

The differentiation of the photosynthesis-light curve in natural phytoplankton has usually been interpreted as being a result of the physiological adaptation of algae to different light conditions in their habitats. Of interest in this connection are the two composite photosynthesis-light curves presented by Verduin (1956). One curve represents the data obtained during the autumn months, and the other was for the data collected during spring. In the former, the light saturation occurred at a light intensity of about one-fifth of full sunlight, whereas the latter showed a broad plateau of the curve extending from one-quarter to three-quarters of full sunlight. The maximal photosynthetic rate was larger in the autumn samples than in the spring samples, but the inhibition of photosynthesis by strong light was more marked in the former than in the latter. Based on the shapes of these curves, Verduin inferred that the autumn plankton population arising under the relatively poor light of autumn uses the dim light more effectively and that they are more sensitive to strong light than the spring population.

When the rate of photosynthesis of natural phytoplankton is expressed in terms of the per unit amount of chlorophyll, the sunny form curve usually gives a much larger value at light saturation than that of the shady form, while the initial slopes of both curves are approximately identical. These two shapes of curves are comparable, respectively, to those of algae grown in the laboratory under high and low light intensity. It is a well-known fact that algae grown under a low light intensity, as compared with those grown under strong light, are smaller in cell size and richer in chlorophyll content and show lower assimilation numbers and lower saturation intensities (I_{max}). The former are of the so-called shady type and the latter the sunny type. If the rates of photosynthesis are plotted against the cell number or dry weight of cells, the slope of the curves at lower light intensities are different in the two types of cells, the shady form showing a steeper rise of the curve. The light-saturated rates of photosynthesis (P_{max}) are similar in the two types, but light saturation occurs at lower intensities in the shady type. Verduin (1956) and Steemann-Nielsen and Hansen (1959) have reported for natural phytoplankton that at low light intensities the photosynthetic rate per unit dry weight of cells is much higher in the shady plankton than in the sunny one. If the rate of photosynthesis is plotted against the chlorophyll content, the photosynthesis-light curves of the sunny and shady forms show the same slopes at lower light intensities. This is due to the higher chlorophyll content in shady forms than in sunny forms.

Under natural conditions, however, the studies of these problems are beset with several difficulties, such as those in exact determination of dry weight or quantity of (actively functioning) chlorophyll in plankton cells. In addition the natural phytoplankton population consists of physiologically different algae. It has been observed that the photosynthesis-light curve of deteriorated phytoplankton in deeper layers of the euphotic zone was quite similar to that of the shady form. Yentsch and Lee (1966) have suspected that the variation in the shape of the photosynthesis-light curve for natural phytoplankton is due more to some physiological stress than to the adaptation to the conditions of the habitat.

The photosynthesis-light curve is of basic significance in estimating primary productivity in waters by the indirect method in which the primary production in a column of water is assessed by the photosynthesis-light curve and the illumination measured in the water.

For further information about the indirect method, reference is made to the papers by Manning and Juday (1941) and Ryther and Yentsch (1957). Concerning the photosynthesis-light curves observed with natural phytoplankton and its ecological significance in relation to primary production, see the papers by Talling (1955), Ryther and Menzel (1959), and Ichimura, *et al.* (1962).

RATE OF PHOTOSYNTHESIS IN NATURAL PHYTOPLANKTON

Photosynthetic Rate

As mentioned in the preceding section, the rate of photosynthesis under light of saturating intensity is a good index for the photosynthetic activity of phytoplankton in natural waters, and it is often used for the assessment of the fertility of waters.

The rate of photosynthesis is often expressed in terms of the quantity of carbon assimilated per unit time per unit quantity of the photosynthetic organisms, for example, C mg./ hr./ Cmg., but in practice it is difficult to measure the photosynthetic cell carbon in mixed natural populations without including the carbon having nothing to do with photosynthesis. A factor which is often used as a denominator in expressing the rate of photosynthesis is the quantity of chlorophyll contained in phytobiomass. There are still problems, however, concerning the methodology to be used in measuring the quantity of chlorophyll. The problem as to whether a definite relation exists between the rate of photosynthesis and the quantity of chlorophyll measured is also a matter of discussion. An excellent review on these problems has been made by Strickland (1960).

There have been many reports on the rate of photosynthesis of natural phytoplankton, and some of them were summarized by Verduin (1959), Odum, *et al.* (1958), Strickland (1960), Talling (1961), and Ichimura and Aruga (1964). The rate of photosynthesis varies considerably with the change of conditions under which it is measured and also with the difference in species as well as in the physiological condition of the phytoplankton population. According to Strickland (1960), the values collected from the literature are usually in the range of 1–10 mg./ hr. per milligram of chlorophyll under optimal light conditions and lie mostly in the range of 2 to 6. Talling (1966) observed in his work on English lakes that throughout the period of maximum growth of phytoplankton population the level of photosynthetic activity in terms of mg. O_2/mg.chl./hr. was approximately 6, and that much higher values were obtained during the early spring season when phytoplanktonic cells, although low in concentration, started to proliferate actively.

As has been reported earlier by the present author (1964), the photosynthetic rate under saturating light shown by ordinary natural phytoplankton in both freshwater and marine environments is in most cases below 5 and scarcely exceeds 10 mg. C/ mg.chl./hr. On rare occasions, values higher than 20 mg. C were recorded, which seems to have been because of incomplete extraction of the pigments. On the other hand, too low values are obtained when pigments other than chlorophyll, such as pheo-pigments, in detritus are included in the assay of chlorophyll. In Japanese lakes, the photosynthetic activity per chlorophyll of actively growing surface phytoplankton is 2–6 mg. C/hr. in eutrophic lakes, 1–2 mg. C/hr. in mesotrophic lakes, and 0.1–1 mg. C/hr. in oligotrophic lakes.

The photosynthetic activity of natural phytoplankton, however, fluctuates considerably according to the season, day length, and depth, a fact which should be taken into account in comparing the activities of phytoplankton taken from various environments.

Diurnal Changes of Photosynthetic Activity

Variation of illumination during the day affects not only the photosynthetic activity but also other physiological states of phytoplankton. The results of photosynthetic measurements with surface phytoplankton made under natural conditions usually show a characteristic diurnal change. The highest photosynthetic activities are measured in the morning hours; then the activities decline towards midday, and again increase, attaining a second maximum in the afternoon. Talling (1966) has reported that the photosynthetic activities of the surface phytoplankton in English lakes sampled between 0900–1000 hours were by 40–100 per cent higher than the activities of the samples taken between 1200–1300 hours. Despite such a change, no significant changes were found in the concentration of cells or chlorophyll. No doubt, the mode of diurnal changes of the photosynthetic activity of natural phytoplankton differs with the difference of depth, which is dependent on the intensity of incident light and on the transparency of water. A typical example of the diurnal changes with regard to depth was reported by Jenkin (1937).

These patterns of diurnal changes cannot be accounted for simply by photosynthesis-light curve and daily changes of illumination, since diurnal variation of the photosynthetic ability occurs in the phytoplankton itself. Recently, similar diurnal fluctuations in the specific photosynthetic activity of natural phytoplankton were observed in various waters. In these investigations, phytoplankton was taken at certain intervals throughout the day, and its photosynthetic rate was measured under optimal light conditions. Doty and Oguri (1957) reported that the photosynthetic activity of marine phytoplankton taken from surface water of the equatorial region showed a daily periodicity with a range of variation of around five- to sevenfold. The maximum photosynthetic activity appeared during the few hours before midday, and the minimum activity at around 1900 hours. Yentsch and Ryther (1957) observed a diurnal variation of photosynthetic activity in surface phytoplankton, from Woods Hole, but the range of variation was only twofold. In the water of the Pacific at 18° N, Shimada (1958) found a three- to fourfold difference in the photosynthetic capacity of phytoplankton, with a maximum at the 0600 to 0800 hours and a minimum at 1600 hours. Such a diurnal variation of photosynthetic activity has also been observed for freshwater phytoplankton by several workers.

These diurnal variations in photosynthetic activity appear to be due to an endogenous rhythm in phytoplankton, which is probably related to the diurnal change of illumination. This possibility was tested experimentally by Doty (1959). He found that the magnitude of diurnal variation of photosynthetic activity decreased with increasing latitude from the equatorial region northwards and was less pronounced or absent at higher latitudes. He suggested that the shortening of the twilight period and the lessening of variation in day length could be the main causes for the pronounced diurnal fluctuation of the activity observed at the Equator. Lorenzen (1963) has reported that the largest values of daily variation in photosynthetic activity of freshwater phytoplankton seemed to occur when the daylight period approached twelve hours, and that when the day length was similar, the magnitude of variation was probably due to the difference in the total amount of incident radiation.

Diurnal variation in the chlorophyll content in phytoplankton cells was observed under natural conditions by Yentsch and Ryther (1957), Shimada (1958), and Yentsch and Scagel (1958) in marine waters, and Ichimura (1960) in freshwaters. Yentsch and Ryther (1957) assumed that the daily periodicity in the photosynthetic capacity of phytoplankton may be at least partially explained on the basis of the change of their chlorophyll content caused by changing light conditions. However, the results obtained by Verduin (1957) and Holmes, *et al.* (1957), seem to speak against this explanation. Talling (1966) reported that in English lakes the diurnal rhythm of potential photosynthetic activity was usually absent or less than 25 per cent, and the diurnal changes in the quantity of photosynthetic pigments also appeared to be very small or absent.

Depression of photosynthetic activity during the afternoon is probably caused by physiological stress after strong illumination. It is well known that under natural conditions the rate of phytoplankton photosynthesis is often reduced near the surface of the water, and the extent of this depression depends on the physiological as well as the environmental conditions. The reduction of the photosynthetic rate is most marked at the surface or on overcast days. The phenomenon of light inhibition of photosynthesis has been observed widely both in freshwaters and in the sea. Goldman, *et al.* (1963), found a strong inhibition and a decrease in photosynthetic activity caused by high light intensities in the twenty-four-hour Antarctic summer daylight. The inhibition, however, could be reduced by exposing the plankton to the light passing through neutral density filters.

Since the diurnal fluctuation in potential photosynthetic activity occurs to some appreciable extent only in the phytoplankton of the surface layer where the phytoplankton mass is usually poor, the total primary production in the plankton community seems to be only slightly influenced by the diurnal fluctuation mentioned above. This was confirmed experimentally by Ichimura (1960) and Lorenzen (1963). If, however, the photosynthetic rate is measured for comparing the fertility or productivity of different waters, the periodicity of photosynthetic activity should be kept in mind at the time of water sampling and during the incubation period. This consideration is also of importance when the photosynthesis-light expressed in a relative unit is transformed to that of the absolute unit.

Changes in Photosynthetic Rate of Phytoplankton with Depth

The variation of photosynthetic rate with depth is primarily determined by the relation between photosynthesis and the vertical gradient of light intensity in the water. The general features of the vertical changes of photosynthetic activity have been obtained from mathematical calculation models and from experiments in the field or laboratory. The former approach has been developed by Tamiya, *et al.* (1953), Talling (1957), Ryther and Yentsch (1957), and Steele (1962), and these mathematical models have been reviewed by Vollenweider (1966). In the indirect method, the vertical change in the photosynthetic rate is calculated by combining the formulas for photosynthesis-light curves and for light attenuation in water. To achieve this, it is important to have pertinent knowledge of all the factors involved.

A more direct approach has been made by measuring the photosynthesis in bottles filled with unialgal material or sample water taken from a given depth. Bottles are exposed for a few hours to either natural light at various depths in the water or artificial light in incubators with neutral filters. There is usually a good agreement between the results obtained in the field experiments and those calculated by mathematical models. The investigations of Talling (1960), using a well-defined algal material, showed that the photosynthetic behavior of phytoplankton deduced from laboratory experiments agreed fairly well with those observed in the sea. It may be said, therefore, that the change in photosynthetic rate as a function of depth is determined by light attenuation which in turn is dependent on weather and various factors affecting light penetration.

The mode of variation of photosynthetic rate with depth is well illustrated by the figure of the photosynthesis-depth profile presented by Jenkin (1937) which has been corroborated by many investigators for various waters. In general, some inhibition of photosynthesis occurs at higher light intensities near the surface layer, while the maximum photosynthetic rate appears somewhat below the surface where the light intensity is about 0.1–0.3 ly./min. (Strickland, 1960), 24,000–27,000 lux (Talling, 1960), or 0.03–0.06 cal./cm.^{2}/min. (Jenkin, 1937). Below this layer of maximum photosynthesis, the organic matter production wanes with increasing depth, and the photosynthetic rate is proportional to the light intensity. The layer at which the maximum photosynthetic rate is measured is usually deeper on sunny days or in clear waters than on cloudy days or in turbid waters. This has well been illustrated in the figures presented by Steemann-Nielsen (1954), Edmondson (1956), and Yentsch (1963). Diurnal variation of photosynthetic rate as it changes with the depth has also been studied by many researchers in various waters.

As has been shown by Talling (1957, 1965), the phenomena described above are most clearly observed in unstratified and almost isothermal natural waters where the phytoplankton population is distributed evenly within the euphotic zone. In stratified waters, on the other hand, the actual depth profiles of the photosynthetic rate measured *in situ* generally differ from the profiles obtained with uniform algal materials suspended in respective depths in the waters.

The shape of the depth profiles of photosynthetic activity in stratified waters is determined not only by the relation between the photosynthetic rate and light attenuation in the water but also by many other factors such as population density and species composition with different physiological features at various depths. Scrutiny of these points is of importance for quantitative estimation and analysis of photosynthetic productivity in the water. In this respect, noteworthy studies have been made by Talling (1957, 1965, 1966), Ohle (1964), Elster (1966), and Findenegg (1966).

Seasonal Variation in Photosynthetic Rate of Phytoplankton

Seasonal changes in the photosynthetic rate of phytoplankton in various waters have been studied, but the data reported are difficult to explain in coherent terms. The photosynthetic rate is determined by both external and internal factors, and their combined effect varies considerably from water to water and from season to season. One of the few phenomena in which the observations made by different workers coincide with one another is that in the north temperate zone, in which the light-saturated rate of photosynthesis per unit quantity of population shows a regular seasonal variation with two maxima, one in spring or early summer and the other in autumn. In general, the photosynthetic rate begins to increase in March, rapidly reaching a high level in early summer, and after a temporary decrease during midsummer, increases again in early autumn, showing a high level in mid-autumn. In eutrophic waters the level of autumnal peak is usually almost the same as that of the spring peak, but in most other kinds of waters the autumnal peak is generally lower than the spring one. During the whole winter season the photosynthetic rate usually shows a very low value. An exception is the phytoplankton living under poor nutritional conditions, in which the potential photosynthetic activity is more or less constant throughout the year. Gessner (1949) and Ichimura (1958), who measured the potential photosynthetic activity of the phytoplankton population as a whole, observed that it remained almost constant throughout the year, except for two spells in late summer and late winter. The low potential activity in these two spells seems to correspond to the time of alteration in the species composition of the phytoplankton. The difference between the actual and the potential photosynthetic rate may be attributed partly to nutrient depletion and partly to the deterioration of the phytoplankton.

For tropical freshwaters characterized by high temperature and intense illumination, Talling (1965) observed that there was relatively little variation in the maximum light saturation rate of photosynthesis per unit quantity of chlorophyll-a.

The seasonal variation of photosynthetic rate is subject to the influence of multifarious geographical and biological factors, a fact which makes it difficult to interpret the seasonal variation of the photosynthetic rate in an articulate manner, and the accumulation of quantitative data useful in predicting the seasonal variation in various aquatic environments is deemed highly relevant.

The author wishes to express his gratitude to Professor Hiroshi Tamiya for his kind help in preparing this manuscript.

REFERENCES

Doty, M. S., 1959. "Phytoplankton Photosynthetic Periodicity as a Function of Latitude," *J. Mar. Biol. Ass. India, 1*, 66–68.

Doty, M. S., and Oguri, M., 1957. "Evidence for a Photosynthetic Daily Periodicity," *Limnol. Oceanogr., 2*, 37–40.

Edmondson, W. T., 1956. "The Relation of Photosynthesis by Phytoplankton to Light in Lakes," *Ecology, 37*, 161–74.

Edmondson, W. T., and Edmondson, Y. H., 1947. "Measurements of Production in Fertilized Salt Water," *J. Mar. Res., 6*, 228–45.

Elster, H. J., 1966. "Absolute and Relative Assimilation Rates in Relation to Phytoplankton Populations," in *Primary Productivity in Aquatic Environments*, ed. by Goldman, Univ. California Press, 79–103.

Findenegg, I., 1966. "Factors Controlling Primary Productivity, Especially with Regard to Water Replenishment, Stratification, and Mixing," *ibid.*, 107–109.

Gessner, F., 1949. "Der Chlorophyllgehalt im See und sein photosynthetische Valenz als geophysikalische Problem," *Schweiz. Zeit. Hydrol., 11*, 378–410.

———, 1955. *Hydrobotanik 1, Energiehaushalt*, Deutscher Verlag der Wissenschaften, Berlin.

———, 1959. *Hydrobotanik 11, Stoffhaushalt*, Deutscher Verlag der Wissenschaften, Berlin.

Goldman, C. R., Mason, D. T., and Wood, B. J. B., 1963. "Light Injury and Inhibition in Antarctic Freshwater Phytoplankton," *Limnol. Oceanogr., 8*, 313–22.

Holmes, R. W., Schaefer, M. B., and Shimada, B. M., 1957. "Primary Production, Chlorophyll and Zooplankton Volumes in the Tropical Eastern Pacific Ocean," *Inter-Amer. Trop. Tuna Comm. Bull., 2*, 129–69.

Ichimura, S. 1960. "Diurnal fluctuation of chlorophyll content in lake water. *Bot. Mag. Tokyo, 73:* 217–224.

———, 1960. "Photosynthetic pattern of natural phytoplankton relating to light intensity." *Bot. Mag. Tokyo, 73:* 458–467.

———, 1967. "Environmental Gradient and Its Relation to Primary Productivity in Tokyo Bay," *Records of Oceanogr. Works in Japan, 9*, 115–28.

Ichimura, S., and Aruga, Y., 1958. "Some Characteristics of Photosynthesis of Freshwater Phytoplankton," *Bot. Mag. Tokyo, 71*, 261–69.

Ichimura, S., and Aruga, Y., 1964. "Photosynthetic Nature of Natural Phytoplankton in Japanese Waters," *Recent Research in the Field of Hydrosphere, Atmosphere and Nuclear Geochemistry*, Tokyo.

Ichimura, S., Saijo, Y., and Aruga, Y., 1962. "Photosynthetic Characteristic of Marine Phytoplankton and Their Ecological Meaning in the Chlorophyll Method," *ibid.*, 75 212–20.

Jenkin, P. M., 1937. "Oxygen Production by the Diatom *Coscinodiscus excentricus* Ehr. in Relation to Submarine Illumination in the English Channel," *J. Mar. Biol. Ass., 22*, 301–43.

Lorenzen, C. J., 1963. "Diurnal Variation in Photosynthetic Activity of Natural Phytoplankton Populations," *Limnol. Oceanogr., 8,* 56–62.

Lund, J. W. G., 1965. "The Ecology of the Freshwater Phytoplankton," *Biol. Rev., 40,* 231–93.

Lund, J. W. G., and Talling, F. R., 1957. "Botanical Limnological Methods with Special Reference to the Algae," *Bot. Rev., 23,* 489–583.

Manning, W. C., and Juday, R. E., 1941. "The Chlorophyll Content and Productivity of Some Lakes in Northeastern Wisconsin," *Trans. Wisc. Acad. Sci. Art and Lett., 33,* 363–93.

Odum, H. T., McConnell, W., and Abbott, W., 1958. "The Chlorophyll 'A' of Communities," *Publ. Inst. Mar. Sci. Univ. Tex., 5,* 65–96.

Ohle, W., 1964. "Interstitiallösungen der Sedimente, Nährstoffgehalt des Wassers und Primärproduktion des Phytoplanktons in Seen," *Helgol. Wiss. Meeresunters, 10,* 411–29.

Ryther, J. H., 1956. "Photosynthesis in the Ocean as a Function of Light Intensity," *Limnol. Oceanogr., 4,* 492–97.

Ryther, J. H., 1965. "Geographic Variations in Productivity," in *The Sea, 2,* ed. by Hill, pp. 347–80.

Ryther, J. H., and Guillard, R. R. L., 1959. "Enrichment Experiments as a Means of Studying Nutrients Limiting to Phytoplankton Production," *Deep Sea Res., 6,* 65–69.

Ryther, J. H., and Menzel, D. W., 1959. "Light Adaptation by Marine Phytoplankton," *Limnol. Oceanogr., 4,* 492–97.

Ryther, J. H., and Yentsch, C. S., 1957. "The Estimation of Phytoplankton Production in the Ocean from Chlorophyll and Light Data," *ibid., 3,* 281–86.

Shimada, B. M., 1958. "Diurnal Fluctuation in Photosynthetic Rate and Chlorophyll-a Content of Phytoplankton from Eastern Pacific Waters," *ibid., 3,* 336–39.

Steele, J. H., 1962. "Environmental Control of Photosynthesis in the Sea," *ibid., 7,* 137–50.

Steemann-Nielsen, E., 1952. "The Use of Radioactive Carbon (C^{14}) for Measuring Organic Production in the Sea," *J. Cons. Int. Explor. Mer., 18,* 117–40.

———, 1954. "On Organic Production in the Oceans," *J. Cons. Int. Explor. Mer., 19,* 309–28.

———, 1960. "Productivity of the Oceans," *Ann. Rev. Pl. Physiol., 11,* 341–62.

———, 1965. "Productivity, Definition and Measurement," in *The Sea, 2,* pp. 126–64.

Steemann-Nielsen, E., and Hansen, V. K., 1959. "Light Adaptation in Marine Phytoplankton Populations and Its Interrelation with Temperature," *Physiol. Plant., 12,* 353–70.

Steemann-Nielsen, E., and Hansen, V. K., 1961. "Influence of Surface Illumination on Plankton Photosynthesis in Danish Waters (56°N) Throughout the Year," *Physiol. Plant., 14,* 595–613.

Steemann-Nielsen, E., Hansen, V. K., and Jørgensen, E. G., 1962. "The Adaptation to Different Light Intensities in *Chlorella vulgaris* and the Time Dependence on Transfer to a New Light Intensity," *Physiol. Plant., 15,* 505–17.

Steemann-Nielsen, E., and Park, T. S., 1964. "On the Time Course in Adapting Low Light Intensities in Marine Phytoplankton," *J. Cons. Int. Explor. Mer., 24,* 19–24.

Strickland, F. D. H., 1960. "Measuring the Production of Marine Phytoplankton," *Bull. Fish. Res. Bd. Can., 122,* 1–172.

———, 1965. "Production of Organic Matter in the Primary Stages of the Marine Food Chain," in *Chemical Oceanography, 1,* ed. by Riley & Skirrow, pp. 477–610.

Talling, J. F., 1957. "Photosynthetic Characteristics of Some Freshwater Plankton Diatoms in Relation to Underwater Radiation," *New Phytol., 56,* 29–50.

———, 1957. "The Phytoplankton Population as a Compound Photosynthetic System," *ibid.,* 133–49.

———, 1960. "Comparative Laboratory and Field Studies of Photosynthesis by a Marine Planktonic Diatom," *Limnol. Oceanogr., 5*, 62–77.

———, 1961. "Photosynthesis Under Natural Conditions," *Ann. Rev. Plant Physiol., 12*, 133–54.

———, 1965. "The Photosynthetic Activity of Phytoplankton in East Africa Lakes," *Int. Rev. Ges. Hydrobiol., 50*, 1–32.

———, 1966. "Photosynthetic Behavior in Stratified and Unstratified Lake Population of a Planktonic Diatom," *J. Ecol., 54*, 99–127.

Tamiya, H., Hase, E., Shibata, K., Mituya, A., Iwamura, T., Hihei, T., and Sasa, T., 1953. "Kinetics of growth of *Chlorella*, with Special Reference to Its Dependence on Quantity of Available Light and on Temperature," in *Algal Culture from Laboratory to Pilot Plant,* Carnegie Inst. Publ. No. 600, 204–32.

Thomas, W. H., 1961. "Physiological Factors Affecting the Interpretation of Phytoplankton Production Measurements," in *Proc. Conf. Primary Production Measurement, Marine and Freshwater,* ed. by Doty, U.S. Atomic Energy Commission, TID-7633, 147–62.

Verduin, J., 1956. "Energy Fixation and Utilization by Natural Communities in Western Lake Erie," *Ecology, 37*, 40–50.

———, 1957. "Daytime Variation in Phytoplankton Photosynthesis," *Limnol. Oceanogr., 2*, 333–36.

———, 1959. "Photosynthesis by Aquatic Communities in Northwestern Ohio," *Ecology, 40*, 377–83.

Yentsch, C. S., and Lee, R. W., 1966. "A Study of Photosynthetic Light Reactions, and a New Interpretation of Sun and Shade Phytoplankton," *J. Mar. Res., 24*, 319–37.

Yentsch, C. S., and Reichert, C. A., 1963. "The Effects of Prolonged Darkness on Photosynthesis, Respiration, and Chlorophyll in the Marine Flagellate, *Dunaliella euchlora*," *Limnol. Oceanogr., 8*, 338–42.

Yentsch, C. S., and Ryther, J. H., 1957. "Short-term Variation in Phytoplankton Chlorophyll and Their Significance," *ibid., 2*, 37–40.

Yentsch, C. S., and Scagel, R. F., 1958. "Diurnal Study of Phytoplankton Pigments. An *in situ* Study in East Sound, Washington." *J. Mar. Res., 17*, 567–83.

VIII

Photosynthesis of *Cladophora* Under Unnatural Conditions

KENNETH G. WOOD

Department of Biology
State University College
Fredonia, New York

The "light and dark" bottle method for measuring primary production has been in use for forty years. Various attempts have been made to relate the results of such studies to performances under completely natural conditions. Verduin (1959) reported that the rates under natural conditions were distinctly higher than those obtained with a community enclosed in a bottle. Hepher (1962) commented on several sources of error such as bacterial respiration and increase in algal populations in the light bottles during the experiment. During exposures of less than three hours, Hepher felt that such errors would be negligible. Verduin (1960), however, showed that bacterial respiration may be important even for three-hour exposures. Wetzel (1965) reviewed the use of this method with aquatic macrophytes and periphyton. The method was felt to be unsuitable for aquatic macrophytes because oxygen produced during photosynthesis may be stored in internal lacunae of the plants. For rheophylic periphyton, restriction of water movement may affect metabolism. Patten, *et al.* (1964), studied the precision of the method using oxygen measurements. They reported that when B.O.D. bottles were filled with river water and kept under various conditions the standard error of the mean within groups was 0.01. The method seems quite precise—the introduction of biological specimens seem to cause the problems.

During one of the numerous discussions at this conference I was asked why I was studying *Cladophora.* My answer was: Because it is there. *Cladophora* is the major problem algae affecting recreational use of the lower Great Lakes. This paper represents my initial contacts with the algae and deals primarily with methodology and recognition of problems. As yet I have not dealt at all thoroughly with the effects of light, CO_2 level, temperature, stirring, micronutrients, or chlorophyll content.

121

METHODS

Samples of filamentous algae were placed in 16-ounce prescription bottles with flat sides. The bottles were filled with membrane-filtered water from Lake Erie. The water was equilibrated with air before use. Tests were performed under fluorescent light and also under full sunlight. By use of a light meter that responded to visible light, the fluorescent light was found to equal 36 per cent of the light measured outdoors. The bottles were placed in a white enameled pan, with flowing water for control of the temperature.

All rates of photosynthesis and respiration are based on the ash-free dry weight of the algae. *Cladophora* contained an average of 15.4 per cent ash in the dry weight. This value is probably high, as some minerals from the substrate adhered to the holdfasts. *Ulothrix* contained 25 per cent ash, and *Spirogyra* contained 4 per cent ash in the dry weight.

Van Slyke Method for CO_2

Carbon dioxide was measured by a modification of the Van Slyke method (Wood, 1963.), which consists of stirring an acidified 5 ml. sample of water under vacuum in a special apparatus so that dissolved gases are extracted. The pressure of the extracted gases is measured at constant volume and temperature before and after alkaline absorption. The total inorganic CO_2 content of the water is proportional to the drop in pressure during alkaline absorption. The method is accurate to within one per cent (95 per cent confidence level) in testing water from Lake Erie. The usual limit of error is about $\pm$ 10 μmoles/liter, with occasional chaotic error of up to $\pm$ 40 μmoles/liter.

Note that the method measures total inorganic CO_2 and does not distinguish between free CO_2, bicarbonate, or carbonate. The manometric Van Slyke apparatus used for these determinations was manufactured by A. H. Thomas Company, Philadelphia, Pennsylvania.

Data from fifteen experiments in which the Van Slyke method and the isotope method were used simultaneously were analyzed for this study. The method of calculation for each method will be described using an experiment with *Cladophora* from June 7, 1967. By the Van Slyke method the CO_2 content of the bottle decreased from 1754 μmoles/liter to 1702 μmoles/liter during 5.93 hours under fluorescent light. The bottle contained 0.0166 grams of algae as ash-free dry weight, in a volume of 0.250 liters. Therefore, the rate of removal of CO_2 from the bottle was:

$$52 \, \mu\text{moles/liter} \times 0.25 \text{ liters} \div 0.0166 \text{ grams of algae}$$
$$\div 5.93 \text{ hours} = 132 \, \mu\text{moles/gm/hr}.$$

This represents the net photosynthesis at 15.5°C. Dark bottle respiration at 26°C was 61 μmoles/gm/hr.

Isotopic Carbon Method

In some experiments the carbon-14 method was used simultaneously with the Van Slyke method. In this manner it was possible to obtain independent estimates of photosynthetic activity: the Van Slyke determinations reveal the amount of CO_2 that was added or removed from the water, and the carbon-14 method reveals the amount of CO_2 taken up by the algae.

Although the Van Slyke method can be given absolute value by analysis of standard solutions of sodium carbonate, the question of absolute values in carbon-14 tracing is rather difficult. The use of dried specimens on planchets, as done in the present study, involves uncertainties of "geometry" which affect the efficiency of detection. In addition, the specific activity of the carbon-14 stock solution is specified to within only 5 per cent by the supplier. Despite this uncertainty, the carbon-14 method has been very useful in the detection of chaotic error in the Van Slyke determinations. In future studies it is planned to employ two additional methods, liquid scintillation counting and gas phase counting, in the hope of resolving these uncertainties in the radioactive tracer method.

The samples were counted in a windowless Ridl preflush flow system using P-10 gas. The efficiency of the machine was determined as 30.3 per cent by counting a standard Beta source. The standard source, however, was of different "geometry" than the 2.43 cm. diameter steel planchets used for the algae. To avoid this problem, barium carbonate precipitates were produced on identical planchets, and the carbon-14 counts were extrapolated to zero thickness activity. Jitts and Scott (1961) made a similar study in which they produced the precipitates in flasks for later collection on membrane filters. To avoid this loss in the present study, small amounts of barium hydroxide were placed directly on tared planchets. Some water was added to partially dissolve the powder, and then 0.794 ml. of radioactive solution was pipetted onto the planchet. The planchets were then dried under a heat lamp and counted at a later date (from one to seventeen days later). Four different dilutions were used: 1 μc/150 ml., 1 μc/ 220 ml., and 1 μc/312 ml. Counts from all dilutions were prorated to a dilution of 1 μc/220 ml., and the $\log_{10}$ count was plotted against the density of precipitate in mg/cm².

As the delivery volume of the pipette was 0.974 ml., the zero-thickness activity at 100 per cent efficiency would be 2.22×10^6 (dpm per μc) $\div$ 220 ml. $\times$ 0.974 ml. = 9828 dpm.

The semilogarithmic interpretation of the data is based on simple application of the absorption law:

$$N = No\ e^{\frac{-\mu t}{2}}$$

Where   N = the count obtained
Where   No = the count at zero thickness
Where μ = the absorption coefficient for $BaCO_3$
Where   t = the weight of precipitate in mg/cm²
Where   e = the natural logarithm base

In this instance the absorber does not lie on top of the source, but rather it is mixed uniformly with the source. For thin samples (0 to 3 mg/cm²) it may be assumed that all the activity of the source is concentrated at the center of mass. Hence t/2 is used in the above equation. When the data was plotted, the slope yielded a coefficient of absorption (μ/2) of 0.16. This is close to a value of 0.15 calculated from data by Jitts and Scott (1961) and of 0.14 from Chase and Rabinowitz (1962).

Seven high values at less than 1 mg/cm² were ignored. These were perhaps influenced by use of the windowless detector method or are the result of errors in weighing the planchets at low values of t. Four low values at less than 1 mg/cm² of t were also ignored. Three of these were caused by the use of $Ba(OH)^2$ that was exposed to the air for two days. It had perhaps already formed $BaCO_3$, hence it could not fix the ^{14}C into a stable form.

The zero-thickness extrapolation of the data was antilog 3.567, or 3690 cpm. This represents an efficiency of 37.5 per cent if the extrapolation is valid and if the activity of the ampoules is correct.

A similar relationship was demonstrated for another purpose using dried *Cladophora* on planchets (Figure 1). These data will be discussed in more detail later. A curve drawn by eye through selected points yielded a μ/2 value of 0.19. This is taken as evidence that the algae absorb the Beta rays in a similar fashion to $BaCO^3$. In the absence of a more exact study it seems best to assume that the previously given exponential equation will describe the self-absorption of the algae, using the coefficient (μ/2) of 0.16.

Therefore, all planchets were weighed before and after adding the algae and drying at 105°C, and the t value in mg/cm² was computed. Counts were then corrected on the basis of an efficiency of counting of 37.5 per cent.

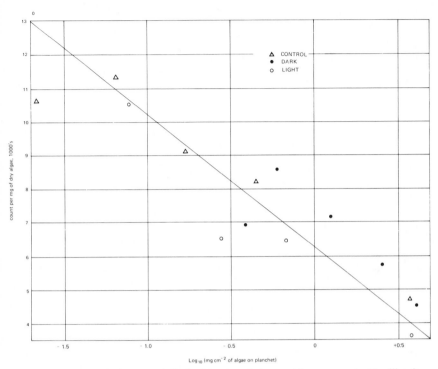

FIG. 1. Photosynthetic rates of Cladophora in relation to biomass per bottle, illumination, and duration of experiment.

Although the planchets could be dried at 105°C before being weighed, they could not be ashed. An average value of 15.4 per cent ash was used to express all values on the basis of ash-free dry weight.

For a sample calculation using the isotope method additional data must be presented. During the experiment described for the Van Slyke method, one ampoule of 10 μc of carbon-14 was added to 2007 ml. of Lake Erie water. This water contained 1754 μmoles per liter of total CO_2 after the addition of the isotope. Therefore, the amount of CO_2 associated with each distintegration per minute was:

$$\frac{1.754 \times 2007}{2.22 \times 10^7} = 1.586 \times 10^{-4}\,\mu\text{moles.}$$

The raw count of the algae on the planchet for the experiment was 21342 cpm. The planchet contained 4.25 mg/cm² of dried algae. Therefore, the self-absorption factor becomes $e^{0.16 \times 4.25} = 1.97$. Assuming that only 37.5 per cent of the activity leaving the sample was detected, the true activity becomes

$$\frac{21342 \times 1.97}{0.375} = 112.120$$

The rate of carbon uptake then becomes

$$\frac{112120 \times 1.586 \times 10^{-4}}{0.0166/gm \times 5.93 \text{ hrs}} = 181 \ \mu\text{moles/gm/hr.}$$

This value is in error by the dark uptake of isotope. Isotope uptake in the reverse direction was the equivalent of 4 μmoles/gm/hr. Therefore the corrected uptake rate becomes 177 μmoles/gm/hr.

Note that this value was 1.34 times greater than the corresponding Van Slyke determination. From 8 tests, however, a mode was found at about 1.05. This ratio is more nearly in agreement with the results of Ryther and Menzel (1965) than with those of McAllister, *et al.* (1961), or of Steemann-Nielsen (1965). The latter workers found that the carbon-14 method measured only a portion of net photosynthesis, whereas Rhyther and Menzel found that this measured the amount of carbon fixed and retained by the algae.

Although the absolute value of the present ratio has little meaning until the uncertainties of efficiency and self-absorption are resolved, it is helpful to have two simultaneous determinations by independent methods.

The isotope method and the carbon-14 determinations depend upon the evaluation of multiple planchets. Various weights of algae were used in an attempt to select an optimum amount for study. This resulted in considerably more scatter than is anticipated in future experiments. On the basis of these tests it is suggested that the planchets be prepared as follows. At the end of the experiment filter the water to remove the algae. Rinse the algae with fresh water. To five tared planchets add approximately equal amounts of algae so that the dried thicknesses will be about 2 mg/cm^2. Dry under a heat lamp. Any remaining algae is to be dried and weighed separately. The total dry weight of algae will be the sum of the dry weights on the planchets plus any remainder. The specific Beta activity of the algae will be the average of counts per mg from the five planchets, corrected for self-absorption and for efficiency of counting.

RESULTS

Effect of Elevated CO_2 Content

Strands of *Cladophora* three to four inches in length were collected at Port Credit, Ontario, at 900 hours, May 6, 1967. The algae were stored in darkness or dim light until 1300 hours, May 7, when tests were performed. Membrane-filtered water from Lake Erie was enriched with CO_2 gas to give various initial total CO_2 contents of 1587, 1757, and 1916 μmoles/ liter. Individual Van Slyke analyses were performed on each bottle immediately before the addition of the algae. After two to three hours, the CO_2 content was again measured and the photosynthetic rate was calculated. As the initial CO_2 was increased from 1587 to 1916 μmoles/liter, the net photosynthesis increased from 511 to 1010 μmoles/gm/hr. Respiration also seemed to increase with increasing CO_2 content of the water, from 103 μmoles/gm/hr at 1617 μmoles/liter to 154 at 1889 μmoles/liter.

Effect of Reduced CO_2 Content

To test the effect of reduced CO_2 content on net photosynthesis, algae were allowed to deplete the CO_2 content of the bottle while the uptake was being measured. *Ulothrix* was used in the first experiment. It was collected from the shore of Lake Erie on May 15 at 900 hours, and the experiment was begun at 1400 hours. The algae had an ash-free dry weight of 33.5 mg, and it was placed in a volume of 481 ml. in a prescription bottle under fluorescent lights. The temperature was 11–14°C. Samples of 6 ml. were withdrawn at intervals for CO_2 tests, and the volume was replaced with original water. CO_2 added in this manner was taken into account when the photosynthetic rates were calculated.

The algae were kept under constant illumination for a period of twenty-four hours. During this time the CO_2 content in the bottle decreased from 1698 μmoles/liter to 554 μmoles/liter. The pH at the end of the experiment was 10.4, and only 33 per cent of the original CO_2 content remained.

Initially, the rate of carbon uptake of *Ulothrix* was rather low, but then it began a steady increase to a maximum rate of 1225 μmoles/gm/hr during 4 to 6.2 hours of illumination. The rate declined to 647 μmoles/gm/hr during 8 to 9 hours. However, during the subsequent 10 hours while the CO_2 content decreased from 54 per cent to 39 per cent, the rate of photosynthetic removal averaged 850 μmoles/g/hr.

Although the photosynthetic rate then became erratic, it is evident that reasonably high rates were maintained in the presence of less than half of the original CO_2 content. The effect of "fatigue" and of unnatural photoperiod cannot be separated from the effect of the CO_2 supply. Possible enhanced bacterial growth could also affect the results.

A similar experiment was performed with *Spirogyra* at 12°C. The algae was collected from an outdoor fish tank on May 17 at 1600 hours and tested at 2100 hours. The rate of net photosynthesis was 449 μmoles/gm/hr during 0 to 12.6 hours, and 450 μmoles/gm/hr during 14.6 to 18.9 hours. The low rate of 102 at 13.5 hrs must be an error in measurement, as it is based on a CO_2 difference of only 19 μmoles/liter. Apparently the photosynthetic rate of *Spirogyra* remained unaltered, while the CO_2 content of the water decreased to 56 per cent of its original value. There was some evidence of "pulses" in the response of the algae during this unnatural photoperiod. After 37 hours of constant illumination, only 28 per cent of the total CO_2 content remained in the water. At this time the water was replaced with fresh water containing 1700 μmoles/liter of CO_2. The plants no longer seemed capable of photosynthesis, however, and CO_2 was excreted in the light at a rate of 175 μmoles/gm/hr. This was over twice that of dark respiration (66 μmoles/gm/hr).

In an experiment with *Cladophora* on May 25, using a biomass of 93.3 mg, ash-free dry weight, net photosynthesis was 398 μmoles/gm/hr during 0 to 5 hours, and 309 μmoles/gm/hr during 5 to 18 hours. Over this period of time the total CO_2 in the bottle decreased from 1845 to 1458 to 654 μmoles/liter. Thus while the total CO_2 decreased by two-thirds, the photosynthetic rate decreased by only one-third. Steemann-Nielsen (1965) used this ability of algae to "soak up" CO_2 to calibrate the isotope method, assuming total removal from an acidified medium.

Excretion of Metabolites

In a review of primary productivity measurements Wetzel (1966) pointed out that up to 10 per cent of the assimilation products may be excreted as glucose during active photosynthesis. Of course these carbohydrates could not be measured by the Van Slyke analysis as it detects only inorganic carbon. An experiment was set up, therefore, in which water from the previous experiments was used. The water was aerated, tested for total inorganic CO_2 content, inoculated with coliform bacteria, and retested for CO_2 after four days.

It was found that water from 37 hours of photosynthesis gained CO_2 in the amount of 65 μmoles/liter during the four days. Water from the twenty-four hours of respiration gained 69 μmoles per liter. The control water (aged Milliporer-filtered Lake Erie water), however, gained 108 μmoles/liter over the same period. Thus the water exposed to the plants seemed to contain less metabolizable carbon than the control water.

In a companion experiment on June 6, 1967, 4 grams fresh weight of *Cladophora* were placed in a 488 ml. bottle with 27 μcuries of carbon-14, and left for forty-eight hours. The bottle was placed on a window ledge in northern light. At the end of two days, at 1600 hours, the algae was removed and divided into three portions. Of these, one portion was immediately killed, placed on planchets, and dried. Another portion was placed in a dark bottle, and a third portion was placed in a light bottle under fluorescent lights. At the end of eighteen hours the remaining two portions were placed on planchets, and the activity of all was determined using a gas-flow proportional counter at an efficiency of 37.5 per cent. The planchets were weighed before addition of the algae, and after drying in an oven at 105°C they were weighed with the algae. Thus the counts could be related to the density of algae on the planchets as shown in Figure 1.

In this figure, the logarithm of the algal density is plotted against the uncorrected count per mg. Although the data show considerable variation, it seems that points from the experiment in the light lie below the dark and control points. This suggests that tagged carbon was lost in the light but not in the dark. Evidently the two methods for study of excretion have given opposite results.

Inhibition of Photosynthesis from
Crowding in the Bottles

A study was undertaken to determine the optimum duration for the photosynthetic studies and, also, the optimum amount of algae to use in each bottle. Four bottles were used in each experiment, each containing different amounts of *Cladophora* with ash-free dry weights of from 0.02 to 0.3 gm. The algae was collected from Lake Erie on May 24, 1967, at 1200 hours and tested under fluorescent lights at 1500 hours. A portion of the algae was kept until 1400 hours on May 25, when it was tested in full sunlight at 27°C.

In the first experiment photosynthetic rates were determined for a five-hour period under fluorescent light. The small volume used for the Van Slyke analysis was replaced in each bottle with fresh water, and the same bottles were used for an additional thirteen hours. Over the weight-range of 0.02 to 0.3 gm of algae per bottle, the photosynthetic rates (in μmoles/gm/hr) were 1239 to 620 for 2 hrs in sunlight, 605 to 110 for 5 hrs under fluorescent light, and 600 to 60 for 15 hrs under fluorescent light.

It is remarkable that for each test the rate of photosynthesis increased with decreasing biomass in the bottle. This effect may be due to blockage of light by the biomass or to self-inhibition. Lefevre (1964) discusses such autoantagonism, which he relates to concentration of excretion products. These results may explain the low values for the photosynthetic rates of *Cladophora fracta* in Lake Ontario reported by Jackson (1966). Jackson used an estimated 0.45 gm/dry wt of biomass in his bottles and obtained a

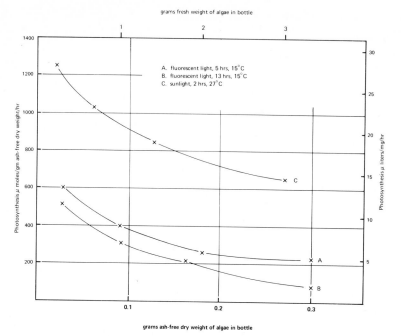

Fig. 2. Self-absorption of ^{14}C by algae.

maximum rate of apparent photosynthesis of 4.00 μliters O_2/mg ash-free dry weight/hr. This equals 179 μmoles/gm/hr, and forms a point that would fall between curves A and B of Fig. 2. Other aspects of this study, however, also show causes for such low rates. Temperature and light seemed to be limiting factors in the present laboratory study as the rate of photosynthesis was approximately doubled in sunlight at a temperature 12°C higher than that in the laboratory. Unfortunately, the effects cannot be separated.

Experiments of longer duration show reduced rates of photosynthesis. With an increase in biomass, hence with increase in utilization of nutrients, nutrients were probably limiting in this experiment.

Seasonal Variation

All of the *Cladophora* from Lake Erie was collected at Point Gratiot, Dunkirk, New York. It was taken from the wave zone of that rocky shore. The strands in early May were quite short, and it was necessary to scrape the rocks to obtain sufficient material. Specimens were then placed in a small dish and carefully checked to remove any clumps of rock attached to the holdfasts. This material had a photosynthetic uptake of 985 μmoles/ g/hr at 22°C. On May 25 similar collections had an uptake of 609 μmoles/ g/hr.

Collections from Lake Ontario taken on May 6 were previously shown to have photosynthetic rates of 511 to 1010 μmoles/g/hr. These plants were three to four inches in length and quite in contrast to the plants at Point Gratiot, which were about one inch in length at that time.

The above-mentioned tests were performed under fluorescent light, at about 36 per cent of sunlight as measured by a Weston cell. When the *Cladophora* was placed in the sun on May 24, a rate as high as 1239 μmoles/g/hr was obtained at 25°C. No inhibition from high light intensity was observed at that time.

On June 7 some of the plants at Point Gratiot had attained a length of two to three inches. These were of a paler green color than the shorter plants in the same area. These pale green plants had a photosynthetic rate of 132 to 139 μmoles/g/hr, as measured by the Van Slyke method. Simultaneous measurements by the isotope method yielded similar low rates of 177 to 195 μmoles/g/hr. On June 8 an attempt was made to carefully select the best green plants from Point Gratiot. Estimates of photosynthesis from this material ranged from 261 to 347 μmoles/g/hr.

The *Cladophora* plants had attained a length of three to four inches by July 10. The plants were being continually moved back and forth in the surf, the ends of the filaments were torn, and many had no cell contents. The plants had also developed what appeared to be a main axis that was darker in color. This was the result of a twisting effect that had wound the filaments together in a tight, central core. Many sand grains were trapped in this region. Animal inhabitants included midge larvae, oligochaetes, crane-fly pupae, and Protozoa.

On July 10 and 13 the middle sections of these plants were tested. The plants were squeezed flat and sections of length about 1½ inches were cut from the center of the length. Under fluorescent light on July 10 these specimens were tested for the effect of biomass per bottle on photosynthetic rate. The experiment was repeated on July 13 in full sunlight. In preparing the plants, no serious attempt was made to separate individual filaments. Thus the distribution in the bottle was clumped.

On July 10 the highest rates were obtained with a biomass of 30.5 mg ash-free dry weight in the bottle. This rate was 346 μmoles/gm/hr, as measured by the Van Slyke method, or 319, as measured by the isotope method. With less biomass in the bottle, inhibition was presumably due to excess light even under fluorescent light, for the rate at 15.8 mg/bottle was 319 to 305 μmoles/gm/hr. At a higher biomass the rate was depressed slightly due to excess shading (59 mg; 284 μmoles/gm/hr).

In full sunlight on July 13 the low biomass bottle yielded a Van Slyke–carbon-14 ratio of 0.75, and the 73.9 biomass bottle yielded a ratio of 1.88. These ratios are far from unity; hence the results are suspect. The remaining tests of July 13 yielded ratios close to unity and also show an inhibition at low biomass. With 40.7 mg in the bottle the rate was 162 to 169 μmoles/g/hr, whereas with 160.8 mg in the bottle the rate was 304 to 312 μmoles/gm/hr.

These results show that in July sunlight had become inhibiting, and best results were obtained with some shading or by using reduced light. The biomass per bottle is thus seen as an index of shading. It was found that 160 mg/bottle in the sun resulted in about the same rate of photosynthesis as 16 mg/bottle under fluorescent light (36 per cent of sunlight).

On July 19 experiments were conducted with the proximal portions of the plant. These were much greener in color. Animal life could be avoided, and if the holdfasts were cut away the filments could be disassociated and all sand grains removed. This eliminated the problem of clumped distribution. All filaments were exposed equally to the light. In the sunlight extreme inhibition was observed. The rates of photosynthesis were so low that error became a serious problem in the Van Slyke measurements. Positive values were obtained with the Van Slyke at biomasses of 6.6 and 14.6 mg in the sun. The carbon-14 method yielded more reliable data indicating rates of 59 and 89 μmoles/gm/hr at these low levels of biomass. At a biomass of 30.3 mg the Van Slyke measure was negative, and the carbon-14 method gave a rate of 149 μmoles/gm/hr. Under fluorescent light the same material had a photosynthetic rate of 318 to 452 μmoles/gm/hr with a biomass of 20.9. Clearly the effect of inhibition by high light has been demonstrated for the plant in July, whereas such inhibition was absent during May.

Summary

Measurements of photosynthesis of *Cladophora* require careful interpretation. The maximum photosynthetic rate was found to decrease remarkably between the months of May and July. During May the maximum rate was over 1200 μmoles/g/hr, and it occurred in full sunlight. During July the maximum rate was about 400 μmoles/g/hr, and it occurred at reduced light intensity. Response to full sunlight over this time varied from strong utilization in May to inhibition during July. The minimum rate in sunlight was 59 μmoles/gm/hr using approximal portions of the plant.

The initial CO_2 level seemed important, for the rate of photosynthesis during May was doubled when the initial CO_2 content was increased from 1587 to 1916 μmoles/liter. Nevertheless *Cladophora* and other algae were capable of removing a large fraction of the total CO_2 from the bottles without great diminution of photosynthetic rate.

The effect of short-term physiological condition was shown by *Ulothrix* in an experiment in which the photosynthetic rate began at 345 μmoles/g/-hr. During the subsequent four hours the rate increased to 1225 μmoles/-g/hr. The possible excretion of organic carbon was investigated by two methods. The results were uncertain and further studies are needed.

Both the Van Slyke method and the carbon-14 method yielded reliable data. The Van Slyke method is needed to determine the dilution of the isotopic carbon. It also reveals the respiration rate in the dark bottle.

The *Cladophora* from Lake Erie was identified as *Cl. glomerata* (L.) Kutz var. *glomerata* by Dr. C. van den Hoek.

REFERENCES

Chase, G. D., and Rabinowitz, J. L., 1962. *Principles of Radioisotope Methodology*, Minneapolis: Burgess.

Hepher, B., 1962. "Primary Production in Fish Ponds and Its Application to Fertilization Experiments," *Limnol. Oceanogr., 7*, 131–36.

Jackson, Daniel F. 1966. *Photosynthetic Rates of Cladophora fracta from Two Sites in Lake Ontario Under Natural and Laboratory Conditions*, Univ. Michigan, Great Lakes Res. Div. Pub. No 15, 44–50.

Jitts, H. R., and Scott, B. D., 1961. "The determination of Zero- Thickness Activity in Geiger Counting of ^{14}C Solutions Used in Marine Productivity Studies," *Limnol. Oceanogr., 6*, 116–23.

LeFevre, Marcel, 1964. "Extracellular Products of Algae," in *Algae and Man*, ed. by Jackson, New York: Plenum Press, pp. 337–67.

McAllister, C. D., *et al.*, 1961. "Measurements of Primary Production in Coastal Sea Water Using a Large-Volume Plastic Sphere, *Limnol. Oceanog. 6*, 237–58.

Patten, B. C., *et al.*, 1964. "Some Experimental Characteristics of Dark and Light Bottles," *J. Cons. Int. Explor. Mer., 28*, 335–53.

Ryther, J. H., Menzel, D W., "Comparison of the ^{14}C Technique with Direct Measurement of Photosynthetic Carbon Fixation," *Limnol. Oceanogr., 10*, 490–491.

Steemann-Nielsen, E., 1965. "On the Determination of the Activity in ^{14}C-Ampoules for Measuring Primary Production," *Limnol. Oceanogr., Supp. 10*, R247–52.

Verduin, J., 1959. "Photosynthesis by Aquatic Communities in Northwestern Ohio," *Ecology, 40*, 377–83.

———, 1960. "Phytoplankton Communities of Western Lake Erie and the CO_2 and O_2 Changes Associated With Them,"*Limnol. Oceanogr., 5*, 372–380.

Wetzel, R. G., 1965. "Techniques and Problems of Primary Productivity Measurements in Higher Aquatic Plants and Periphyton," in *Primary Productivity in Aquatic Environments*, ed. by C. R. Goldman, Mem. Ist. Ital. Idrobiol., 18 Suppl., Berkeley: Univ. Calif. Press, pp. 251–67.

Wood, Kenneth G., 1963. "Gasometric Determinations of Carbon Dioxide in Natural Waters in Relation to pH and to the Activities of Plants," *Verh. internat. Verein. Limnol., 15*, 322–29.

IX

Biology of the Filamentous Conjugating Algae

ROBERT W. HOSHAW

Department of Biological Sciences
University of Arizona
Tucson, Arizona

In the twentieth century, man has been changing the balance of nature at an ever-increasing rate. In an eloquent and timely statement, René Dubos (1966) summarized man's predicament with regard to his changing environment: "One of the most painful dilemmas of our times is that we still regard nature as the ultimate source of beauty and other fundamental blessings, yet exploit and despoil it for the sake of wealth and power." Exploitation takes the form of dams, nuclear plants, highways, and housing developments, all of which serve to modify the earth's surface and to reduce its value as a natural habitat for all types of plant and animal life. To further enhance his environment, man has even learned to produce climatic modification, using improved methods of cloud seeding. Although these changes benefit man himself, they also drastically endanger the once harmonious relationship of man, algae, and the environment.

As man continues to manipulate his environment and to change the balance of nature, phycologists should be alert to the changing fate of many algal species. Certainly, modern techniques of algal culture permit species to be isolated and maintained for later study. Just as archaeologists conduct salvage operations to remove artifacts from an area facing large-scale land development, phycologists should conduct salvage operations by intensifying field collections in selected areas of the world before habitats are destroyed for many algal species. This proposal presents major difficulties, of course, some of which are related to our lack of knowledge about the cultivation and long-term preservation of algae (Starr, 1963). In addition, the trend away from investigations in organismic biology often makes it difficult to obtain sufficient financial support for projects which lack glamor. However, the continuing changes in the environment seem to make such a task imperative.

In light of this critical situation, this paper is an attempt to present a summary of both past knowledge and present experimental work on the species of the green algal family Zygnemataceae. Only four genera of the Zygnemataceae are considered here in detail: *Mougeotia, Sirogonium,*

Spirogyra, and *Zygnema.* The paper focuses first on the place of these algae in their natural environment (where, unfortunately, many habitats have already been eliminated) and second on the experimental studies in which these algae have been involved during the last twenty years. Where it is of historical significance, investigations prior to the last twenty years are cited to provide continuity with more recent investigations. Species of *Spirogyra* have been observed and investigated far more than all other species combined, while investigations on the three remaining genera, *Zygnema, Mougeotia,* and *Sirogonium,* have proceeded in this order with decreasing frequency. Since 1962, several species of these four genera have been under investigation in the Phycological Laboratory at the University of Arizona. The data reported in this paper for *Sirogonium,* an alga superficially similar to *Spirogyra,* originates exclusively from studies in this laboratory. Hopefully, the information in this paper provides a comprehensive fund of data on a family of algae which is one of the many threatened by man's ceaseless efforts to transform his surroundings.

THE FILAMENTOUS CONJUGATING ALGAE

The algae designated by this title belong exclusively to the Zygnemataceae, although filamentous conjugating species also occur among the desmids. According to Transeau (1951), members of the Zygnemataceae are the most numerous and generally distributed of the filamentous green algae. Opinions vary, however, as to their classification. Transeau's monograph on the family lists 534 species in thirteen genera, while a more recent monograph by Randhawa (1959) contains descriptions for 580 species. Descriptions of species continue to appear regularly in the literature. Although both Transeau and Randhawa recognize thirteen genera for the Zygnemataceae, Bourrelly (1966) recognizes only twelve, placing *Hallasia reticulata,* a species of questionable status, in *Zygnemopsis.* Other species of doubtful status are those of *Pleurodiscus, Entransia,* and the three species of *Sirocladium* which possess features of *Mougeotia* and *Sirogonium.* Gauthier-Lièvre (1965) considers the Zygnemataceae of Africa in thirteen genera. A revised classification by Yamagishi (1963) proposes thirteen genera for the family, but the genera listed include only eight of those also described by Transeau and Randhawa.

Long-term studies of clonal cultures, essential to clarify the taxonomic status of many zygnematacean species, would also undoubtedly bring to light a variety of biological phenomena peculiar to these organisms. Although members of the Zygnemataceae are abundant and widely distributed in nature, the difficulties encountered in their cultivation have limited

TABLE 1. Strains of the Zygnemataceae in Five Culture Collections Maintaining Algae

Culture Collection	Number of Strains Maintained					
	Mougeotia	*Sirogonium*	*Spirogyra*	*Zygnema*	*Zygnemopsis*	*Zygogonium*
A. Cambridge University, England (The Botany School, 1966)	1	0	8	6	1	0
B. Charles University, Prague (Baslerová and Dvořáková, 1962)	1	0	0	7	0	0
C. Göttingen University, Germany (Koch, 1964)	2	0	1	5	0	1
D. Indiana University, Bloomington (Starr, 1964)	1	1	16	7	0	0
E. Museum National d'Histoire Naturelle, Paris (Bourrelly, personal communication)	2	0	4	4	0	0
Totals	7	1	29	29	1	1

the number of strains available for experimental study. Table 1 lists those strains maintained in five major culture collections. (Certain of these strains are identical and occur in one or more of the collections.)

Certain strains tabulated in Table 1 have been used in experimental studies reported in this paper. The species to which these strains belong and the letter designation (see Table 1) of the culture collections which maintain them are as follows:

Sirogonium melanosporum	(D)
Spirogyra pratensis	(A, D)
Zygnema circumcarinatum	(A, B, C, D)
Zygnema peliosporum	(A, B, C, D)
Zygnema sp.—LB 921 and LB 922	(D)

As a prelude to present-day experimental studies on strains of the Zygnemataceae, the classic investigations on the Zygnematales by Viktor Czurda in Czechoslovakia provide an extensive fund of information, extending from the growth of pure cultures (Czurda, 1926a, 1926b) to a consideration of the systematics of the order Zygnematales (Czurda, 1932). His investigations extended over most of two decades, beginning in 1922 with two accounts on the nuclear cytology of *Spirogyra* (Czurda, 1922a, 1922b). Much of his experimental study was directed toward a better understanding of sexuality and its control in the Zygnemataceae (Czurda, 1925, 1930, 1931, 1933, 1937). His strains of the heterothallic species, *Zygnema circumcarinatum* and *Z. peliosporum*, are still maintained in four of the five culture collections named in Table 1.

Distribution and Occurrence of the Zygnemataceae

World-wide Distribution

No continent, with the exception of Antarctica, is without some representative of the Zygnemataceae (Table 2). The distribution of the ubiquitous *Spirogyra* is so extensive that Fritsch (1907) states, "Probably no feature of the fresh-water flora of the tropics has played such a part in producing the universal impression of similarity with that of temperate regions as the excessive abundance of *Spirogyra*." Numerous species of *Spirogyra* and *Mougeotia* have been collected on every continent except Antarctica, and according to Randhawa (1959), species of *Zygnema* have been reported for all inhabited continents except South America (where certainly it must

TABLE 2. Geographical Distribution of the Zygnemataceae on the Major Continents (Data from Randhawa, 1959, except Africa from Gauthier-Lièvre, 1965)

Continent	Debarya (8)*	Entransia (1)	Hallasia (1)	Mougeotia (121)	Mougeotiopsis (1)	Pleurodiscus (1)	Sirocladium (3)	Sirogonium (16)	Spirogyra (338)	Temnogametum (12)	Zygnema (126)	Zygnemopsis (38)	Zygogonium (23)
Africa	1			43				4	159	6	53	14	13
Asia	4			46			3	11	176	4	56	21	6
Australia	1			7				1	16		5		2
Europe	1		1	42	1			1	98		37	3	1
North America	3	1		53	1			7	145		44	7	4
South America				15		1		3	33	3	7		3

* The number in ( ) refers to the number of species in each genus. This number is a total compiled from both Randhawa and Gauthier-Lièvre.

occur). The reported distribution of some genera is limited (*Temnogametum*, a tropical and subtropical genus; *Hallasia*, reported only from Denmark; *Sirocladium*, from India alone; *Pleurodiscus*, from Puerto Rico; and *Entransia*, from Canada); however, the geographical limits of these genera are likely to be extended as additional collections are examined. Two reasons are suggested for the limitations in the reports of the distribution of some Zygnemataceae. First, similarity among species is often so close that, unless reproductive stages are present, they are indistinguishable from one another. This similarity is illustrated in the following pairs of genera: *Debarya* and *Mougeotia, Temnogametum* and *Mougeotia, Hallasia* and *Zygnemopsis*, and *Pleurodiscus* and *Zygogonium*. Secondly, reproductive stages may not be found in nature because of their rarity or because of limited field collecting; fortunately, these stages can sometimes be induced by employing modern culture techniques. Because of the problems just mentioned, any geographical distribution of the Zygnemataceae must be tentative until additional field collections are made from the vast areas heretofore neglected by phycologists.

Habitats

The Zygnemataceae occupy a great variety of freshwater habitats extending from the cold, swift-flowing streams of the Scandinavian countries to the warm, stagnant pools of the tropics (Fritsch, 1907; Comère, 1913; Transeau, 1934; Chapman, 1964). Exceptions to the above habitats provide evidence of further variety; among the lesser known species, *Zygogonium erecitorum* is found in shallow waters and on moist, acid soils and peat, and *Sirocladium* is found only on damp soils in India. Yet there is little doubt that most species of the four genera under discussion show a decided preference for stagnant pools, ponds, and ditches. This preference for stagnant water, especially by *Spirogyra*, may be one reason for the success of these species in the tropics (Fritsch, 1907).

Although it is generally agreed that most of the Zygnemataceae are found in lentic habitats, there are some species existing in lotic environments. Israelson (1949) reported instances of *Spirogyra lapponica* and *Zygnema melanosporum* forming luxuriant, green meadows on rocks and boulders of waterfalls, cataracts, and rapid streams in Sweden. He further stated that other species of *Spirogyra*, *Mougeotia*, and *Zygnema* are common in these streams, but only in the vegetative condition. Sexual reproduction in these lotic environments was limited to *Spirogyra lapponica* and *Zygnema melanosporum* and occurred only in areas periodically laid bare by the rising and falling water level. It is of interest that *S. lapponica* is no longer found in one of its major habitats, the cataracts of Älvkarleö, following the control of the water level by artificial means. Taylor (1928) commonly found *Mougeotia*, *Spirogyra*, and *Zygnema* in the streams and lakes of Alpine regions in British Columbia; other authors report these genera from mountain streams and creeks of North Carolina and other cold, fast-flowing rivers (Whitford and Schumacher, 1963; Round, 1965). Whitford and Schumacher suggested that some species of *Mougeotia* and *Spirogyra* are entirely lotic in nature, probably because of their higher oxygen and mineral demand, a requirement not fulfilled in lentic environments. Laboratory experiments by Whitford (1960) showed that an unidentified species of *Mougeotia* and another of *Spirogyra* grow better in running water than in still water. In lotic environments, however, species of the four genera (with the exception of *Spirogyra lapponica* and *Zygnema melanosporum*) are rarely seen in the sexual state.

Within specific freshwater habitats, species occur in varied locations. *Spirogyra varians* forms large surface blooms (Palmer, 1959), while *S. adriata* forms long belts along the rocky shores of large lakes. *Spirogyra adriata* is reported growing at depths of ten meters, and *Mougeotia parvula* may extend to a depth of fifteen meters (Fritsch, 1931). In her studies on Lake Windemere, Godward (1937) reported *Mougeotia* occurring to a depth of 0.75 meters, *Zygnema* to 1.5 meters, and *Spirogyra* to 2.5 meters, where she found them attached to stones or epiphytic on higher plants.

The species receiving most consideration here are primarily inhabitants of hard-water environments (Prescott, 1962); however, certain species of the four genera exist in other environments where the algae may be indicative of a variety of conditions. For example, *Spirogyra crassa* and *S. decimina* are indicators of alkaline bog lakes, while *Mougeotia parvula* and *Spirogyra communis* show a preference for organic (polluted) waters (Godward, 1937; Palmer, 1959). Prescott (1962) has reported *Mougeotia* and *Zygnema* from soft-water seepage lakes, but the collections always contained only sterile material.

A notable exception to the freshwater habit of zygnematacean species is the occurrence of *Spirogyra salina*, a brackish-water species, described by Aleem (1952, 1961) as growing and reproducing in waters in France at a salinity of 1.5 per cent. This species was found as a component of the periphyton or as free-floating masses.

Periodicity

According to Transeau (1916), there are two diverse points of view concerning the cause of algal periodicity. He discusses the view of Copeland, who believes that internal rather than external conditions govern the phenomenon of conjugation, and the view of Fritsch, who emphasizes changing environmental conditions, i.e., light, temperature, and concentration of medium, as the factors controlling germination, vegetative development, and reproduction. After seven and one-half years of continuous field observations, Transeau concluded that, although changes in the environment accelerate or retard the reproductive period, the length of the vegetative period in the Zygnemataceae is probably definite under normal conditions. He found for the Zygnematales and Oedogoniales six natural groups which are delimited on the basis of periodicity. These groups are listed below with the zygnematacean representatives observed during his study.

Winter annuals—*Spirogyra tenuissima* and *S. inflata.*
Spring annuals—*Zygnema stellinum, Z. leiospermum, Z. insigne, Spirogyra varians, S. catenaeformis, Mougeotia scalaris, M. robusta,* and *Debarya decussata.*
Summer annuals—*Spirogyra ellipsospora, S. nitida, S. irregularis, S. setiformis,* and *Mougeotia sphaerocarpa.*
Autumn annuals—None.
Perennials—*Mougeotia genuflexa* and *Zygnema pectinatum.*
Ephemerals—None.

Environmental factors play a decisive role in algal periodicity. Whitford and Schumacher (1963) suggested that light, the only variable in some springs and seeps in North Carolina, was responsible for succession within the algal flora. There *Mougeotia* sp. was replaced by *Spirogyra* sp. in areas of higher light intensities. They also found that, as the water in brooks warms to above 15°C, species of *Mougeotia* and *Spirogyra* replace other filamentous forms. Although most algae diminish in the summer, *Spirogyra* may remain in these same brooks throughout the summer in sunny locations. They further stated that *Mougeotia* spp. attained their optimum growth at 10–15°C, *Zygnema* spp. at 15–20°C, and *Spirogyra* spp. above 20°C. These observations seem to implicate temperature as a deciding factor in the composition of the algal flora in a given location at a given time. The lack of algal periodicity in bogs and swamps is probably caused by the uniform conditions in these habitats, whereas certain species lack periodicity even in a changing environment. For instance, Brown (1908) reported *Spirogyra varians* growing and reproducing under varied conditions and at all seasons of the year. Nipkow (1962) concluded from his germination studies on twenty-six zygnematacean species that zygotes of different ages often germinate simultaneously in the natural habitat, indicating a periodicity which comes about only by coincidence.

In the main, zygnematacean species have a marked seasonal periodicity of sexual reproduction which is dominant in the spring in the temperate regions (Smith, 1950). Following a sexual period, these species usually disappear during the summer. Fritsch and Rich (1907) suggest four causes for this summer decrease: (1) increased light intensity and duration; (2) increased water temperature with accompanying decrease in dissolved gases; (3) increased salt concentration resulting from higher temperatures and lack of rain; and (4) increased abundance of higher plants. However, Transeau (1916) found that the periods of highest concentration of dissolved substances occur in the spring and fall rather than in the summer, corresponding to periods of greatest rainfall and increased surface runoff of water into ponds, lakes, and streams. He believed that reproduction is governed mainly by internal conditions, with a definite length inherent to the vegetative period. For example, in *Spirogyra* and probably in *Zygnema* Transeau determined the length of the vegetative stage to be approximately equal to a constant (65) divided by the specific surface (cell surface area divided by cell volume) times the temperature (°C). Jost (1953) questioned Transeau's theory, suggesting more laboratory investigations on the role of nitrogen concentration in the medium and on its effect on reproduction. Before satisfactory conclusions are drawn on algal periodicity, additional data must be obtained from combined field and laboratory studies.

Associations

Filaments of zygnematacean species often serve as substrates for sessile organisms, particularly for diatoms and aquatic fungi. Fritsch (1931) pointed out that the filaments of the Zygnemataceae are more immune to epiphytes than are other algae because of their mucilaginous covering, with *Mougeotia* the most susceptible member of the family. In some cases the appearance of epiphytes is due to a change from aging of the host; e.g., old filaments lose their mucilaginous material and then become colonized by many epiphytes.

Sparrow (1960) lists a total of 125 species of aquatic Phycomycetes as parasites, saprophytes, or epiphytes on *Mougeotia*, *Spirogyra*, and *Zygnema*. These associations often result in physiological and morphological abnormalities or in death of the infected filaments. Investigations of chytrid infections in six species of *Spirogyra* (including *S. varians* and *S. nitida*) showed that variations in temperature, pH, and age of culture promote an increase or a decrease in the amount of fungal parasitism (Barr and Hickman, 1967). For example, certain spring species of *Spirogyra* which do not grow well at 30°C become heavily parasitized by *Rhizophydium* when cultured at this temperature. Aleem (1952) reported that a fungus attack caused the disappearance of *Spirogyra salina* from its brackish-water habitat.

Role in Nature

Although little information is available on the role that members of the Zygnemataceae play in nature, it can be postulated that such an abundant and cosmopolitan algal family must be of importance in maintaining the balance of nature in the freshwater habitats of the world. Several investigators (Biswas, 1936; Dineen, 1953; Delaney, 1954; Prescott, 1962) have noted the importance of the Zygnemataceae as a major source of food for snapping turtles, snails, mosquito larvae, large and small fish, aquatic insects, and amphipods. Smaller algal forms such as desmids and diatoms grow and reproduce in shaded portions of ponds and pools formed by large mats of *Spirogyra* and *Mougeotia* (Anderson and Walker, 1920). During growth or decay, these algae add gases and nutrients which may be beneficial to other organisms. On the other hand, masses of *Spirogyra*, *Mougeotia*, and *Zygnema* often clog artificial waterways and foul filter systems of large reservoirs (Palmer, 1959). Our present state of understanding concerning the role of the Zygnemataceae in their ecosystems indicates the need for further investigations to determine their beneficial or harmful effects.

Introduction to the Experimental Study of the Zygnemataceae

In the four sections to follow, the discussions deal primarily with investigations of laboratory cultures. Algae are now cultivated and manipulated in controlled environments with increasing frequency by many types of biologists, and it is the continuing responsibility of the phycologist to collect, isolate, and characterize additional algal strains for use by the scientific community. At present, culture collections, along with individual laboratories, serve as important sources of experimental organisms. Another source is dried mud or soil samples often used by phycologists to isolate strains into clonal cultures. Currently, we have in storage 325 dried mud samples, most of which were collected in the United States and Mexico. Of the Zygnematacean species, *Spirogyra* is known to occur in 111 samples, *Zygnema* in 31, *Mougeotia* in 21, and *Sirogonium* in 8. Although it would be difficult to isolate and maintain all strains of the Zygnemataceae found in these samples, isolations can be made as needed for experiments on a particular species.

The information on experimental studies presented here concerns the areas of cytology, morphology, and physiology. The literature accumulated in these areas reveals little data from experiments which are based on the use of newer physical and chemical methods. The use of such methods not only would expand our knowledge of these organisms but also would clarify the validity of data already accumulated. In preparing the present paper, three theses (Jost, 1953; Allen, 1958; Gauch, 1966) have been cited frequently because important data from these publications are not generally available in scientific journals. Both Jost and Gauch investigated *Zygnema circumcarinatum*, the only heterothallic species in the Zygnemataceae on which substantial experimental study has been conducted. Allen's studies concentrate on the cytology, morphology, and physiology of *Spirogyra pratensis*.

Culture Techniques and Growth

The development of the soil-water culture technique by Pringsheim (1946a) ushered in a new era of algal investigations in the laboratory. Using this method, investigators now isolate many species of the Zygnemataceae and either grow them in unialgal cultures for experimental purposes or simply maintain them until techniques for purification and a defined culture medium can be developed. In addition to the paper by Pringsheim mentioned above, several other useful discussions dealing with general methods of algal culture have been published—Bold, 1942; Pringsheim, 1946b; Brunel, *et al.*, 1950; Lewin, 1959; Myers, 1962; and Wurtz, 1964.

Media

In spite of the discouraging statements of Chamberlain (1932) and Johansen (1940) that members of the Zygnemataceae are difficult to cultivate, many species are now maintained in culture in our laboratory and in culture collections throughout the world. The soil-water culture technique has been used in our laboratory to grow and maintain several species for cytological, morphological, and physiological investigations (Thomas, 1963; Rickert, 1963; Crow, 1964; Dennis, 1965; Waer, 1966). However, not all members of the Zygnemataceae grow well in soil-water medium; this problem is especially encountered in the larger species of *Spirogyra*, including *S. crassa* and *S. rectispira*.

Autoclaved soil-water supernatant has also been employed with limited success in culturing members of the Zygnemataceae. In this medium Czurda (1933) cultivated sixteen species of *Spirogyra*, although two of them grew poorly, and two others exhibited no growth at all. *Spirogyra pratensis* grows poorly in autoclaved soil-water supernatant (Allen, 1958) but flourishes in steamed soil-water medium. The limitations in the use of soil-water medium and soil-water supernatant for experimental studies result from its unknown composition and its bacterial flora.

Myers (1962) has provided general considerations concerning the construction of media. These are as follows: (1) the source of the major elements and the total salt concentration; (2) a suitable nitrogen source; (3) the pH, both initial and the changes that can occur due to algal metabolism; (4) the need and availability of trace elements; (5) the need for organic growth factors such as B_{12}, thiamine, or biotin; and (6) the stability of the medium. Table 3 gives the content of four media in which members of the Zygnemataceae have been successfully grown. Czurda (1932) stated that most *Spirogyra* species grow best in a liquid medium, while species of *Mougeotia* and *Zygnema* grow best on agar. His greatest difficulty was experienced in growing the larger species, *Spirogyra crassa* and *S. bellis*, regardless of medium or substrate. This same difficulty has been experienced in our laboratory during attempts to cultivate *S. crassa* and *S. rectispira* in soil-water, Godward medium, or Czurda medium. While unialgal cultures of *Mougeotia* and *Zygnema* grow in either Czurda or Godward medium,

TABLE 3.   Composition of Four Media for Growing Zygnematacean Species

Inorganic Salts	mg/liter			
	Czurda (1926a)	Czurda (1932)	Godward (1942)	Bristol (Starr, 1964)
KNO₃	200	100	250	
NaNO₃				250
Na₂SO₄			58	
MgSO₄ · 7H₂O	10	10	80	75
K₂HPO₄	20	10	28	75
KH₂PO₄				175
Ca (NO₃)₂			20	
CaSO₄	4	5		
CaCO₃			10	
CaCl₂ · 2H₂O				25
NaCl				25
K₂SiO₃			2.7	
FeSO₄ · 7H₂O	5	5		5
Total concentration in mg/liter	239	130	448.7	630

they commonly produce a more luxuriant growth in soil-water. Reichart (1963) reported comparable growth of *Spirogyra majuscula* in either defined medium or soil-water.

Axenic cultures of the Zygnemataceae are difficult to obtain because of a lack of motile cells and the presence of bacteria in the outer cell wall layer. Czurda (1926a) was the first investigator to cultivate axenic cultures of the Zygnemataceae in defined media, but his isolates of *Spirogyra varians*, *Zygnema circumcarinatum*, and *Z. peliosporum* were difficult to maintain (Czurda, 1926b, 1930). Agarized Czurda medium with the addition of Chu's microelement solution (1942) was used by Jost (1953) to cultivate Czurda's strains of *Z. circumcarinatum*. This heterothallic alga utilizes ammonia as a nitrogen source almost as well as it utilizes nitrate, growing best at a nitrogen concentration of 45 mg/liter regardless of the source. By contrast, *Spirogyra varians* is not able to utilize ammonia as well as it utilizes nitrate (Czurda, 1926a). Attempts by Czurda (1926a) and Gauch (1966) to demonstrate heterotrophism in *Spirogyra* and *Zygnema* were unsuccessful.

This review of investigations reveals that the nutritional requirements of the Zygnemataceae have barely been explored. Before these organisms can serve extensively as experimental material, nutritional studies are urgently needed. Axenic cultures grown in a defined medium are required as a basis for nutritional and growth experiments which can yield reproducible data.

Culture Vessels

The choice of a culture vessel is determined by the quantity of alga desired, the nature of the experiments to be performed, and the ease with which the container can be handled. Numerous sizes and shapes of vessels from half-pint milk bottles and test tubes to large Erlenmeyer flasks and aquaria have been used for culturing members of the Zygnemataceae. Soil-water in a pyrex test tube has proved effective for the initial isolation of a single short filament. Once a clone has been established, it can be transferred to a half-pint milk jar containing soil-water medium and covered with a small petri dish. A 250-ml Erlenmeyer flask is frequently large enough to grow cultures in a defined liquid medium. For agar cultures a petri dish, slanted test tube, or a slanted Erlenmeyer flask can be used, the selection depending on the frequency of culture transfer and the amount of material needed with a similar history.

Light

Laboratory cultures are often grown under banks of cool-white fluorescent lights with an intensity varying from about 2000–6000 lux. Two light cycles commonly used are 12:12 hour light-dark and 16:8 hour light-dark. Allen (1958) found that *Spirogyra pratensis* deteriorates under a continuous light of about 5000 lux but gives optimum growth on a 16:8 hour light-dark cycle. Single filaments of *Zygnema circumcarinatum* on agar show optimum growth at about 1600 lux and die at 6000 lux, while filaments of *Zygnema* sp. (LB 921 and LB 922) grow at the higher light intensity (Gauch, 1966). Reichart (1963) demonstrated that a 14:10 hour light-dark cycle is best for growing a synchronous culture of *Spirogyra majuscula*.

Temperature

The Zygnemataceae can be cultivated under a wide range of temperatures. Most strains grow well in soil-water at a temperature of about 20°C. A species of *Mougeotia* from the Sahara Desert (Puiseux-Dao and Levain, 1963) grows well at 25–29°C, and *Sirogonium melanosporum* from the Sonoran Desert in Mexico shows optimum growth at 24–27°C. Two large species of *Spirogyra* which are maintained in our laboratory, *S. crassa* and *S. rectispira*, require temperatures near 16°C. *Zygnema circumcarinatum* was reported by Jost (1953) to reach a growth peak at 18–24°C, with limited growth at 8°C and 28°C. While this species dies during exposure to 5°C or 35°C for more than twenty-four hours, short exposures (under sixty minutes) to 40°C do not kill all cells in a culture. Since *Z. circumcarinatum* shows rapid growth within a narrow temperature range, it would be of value to determine whether other species respond in a similar manner.

pH

General data on pH, especially with reference to induction of conjugation at high pH values, have appeared in the literature. Working with nineteen species of *Spirogyra*, most of which were grown in autoclaved soil-water medium, Czurda (1933) determined a pH range for optimum growth and conjugation for each species. The average pH was 6.7 for maximum vegetative growth and 7.9 for conjugation. According to Czurda (1933), *Zygnema circumcarinatum* grows best between pH 6.5–7.0, a range which agrees well with the findings of Jost (1953), who reported optimum growth in this species at pH 6.30 and 7.05; slow growth at pH 5.25 or 8.70; and the death of filaments at pH 4.10 or 9.20.

Measurement of Growth

Most growth studies of the Zygnemataceae have been semi-quantitative because the common methods of determining cell quantity used with unicellular algae (i.e., hemacytometer cell counts, optical density measurements, the use of aliquots to determine dry weight, and cell volume by centrifugation) are not readily applicable to filamentous algae. Since cell width remains relatively constant in some but not all healthy clonal cultures, and since there is a definite relationship between rate of cell division and elongation, two measurements have been used to indicate the growth rate: (1) a measurement of increase in filament length (Jost, 1953), and (2) a measurement of cell number increase (Gauch, 1966). Jost used a camera lucida and a map measurer to determine the total increase in length of filaments growing in a wavelike fashion on agar plates. He expressed growth rate in terms of increase per original mm of length per hour, whereas Gauch, working also with *Zygnema circumcarinatum*, expressed the growth rate from cell counts in doublings per day. Discussions of these methods for computing growth rates are found in the reports by Myers (1962) and Wurtz (1964).

THE SEXUAL CYCLE

Almost every biologist has observed, and in many cases studied in detail, some stage of the sexual process (conjugation) of an alga belonging to the Zygnemataceae. Although reviews on the subject of algal sexuality (Smith, 1951a; Coleman, 1962) make little reference to the Zygnemataceae, an investigator can find considerable information on sexuality in this family (Czurda, 1932; Fritsch, 1935; Smith, 1950; Transeau, 1951; Randhawa, 1959).

Since numerous difficulties still prevent an investigator from using fully defined conditions when studying the Zygnemataceae, the information presented in this section will not always include all conditions associated with a particular response. The reader must therefore refer to original sources in most cases. Unialgal cultures of the Zygnemataceae have proved to be of some value in confirming and extending our knowledge of sexuality. However, the difficulties of maintaining axenic cultures, coupled with the lack of techniques for the stimulation of the phases of sexuality, have discouraged many investigators from using strains of the Zygnemataceae as experimental material. As yet, manipulations like those now employed to control sexuality in other algal groups have not been defined for the Zygnemataceae. Not until axenic cultures grown in defined media and maintained in a controlled environment are available can quantitative data from reproducible experiments be obtained.

Definition of Terms

Before discussing the conjugation process, it is appropriate to clarify some of the terminology used. While the characteristics of scalariform and lateral conjugation are generally known, some confusion often results from the use of certain terms related directly to sexual events. The following three groups of definitions should be helpful in understanding these events:

Isogamy: Sexual reproduction resulting from the fusion of gametes similar in form and in behavior. [e.g., *Zygnema circumcarinatum* (scalariform conjugation), *Mougeotia genuflexa* (lateral conjugation)]

Physiological Anisogamy: Sexual reproduction resulting from the fusion of gametes similar in form but different in behavior, i.e., relative to gamete movement. [e.g., *Spirogyra majuscula* (scalariform conjugation), *Zygnema fanicum* (lateral conjugation)]

Anisogamy: Sexual reproduction resulting from the fusion of gametes unequal in size and different in behavior. [e.g., *Sirogonium melano-sporum* (scalariform conjugation), *Spirogyra pratensis* (lateral and scalariform conjugation)]

Physiological Isogamy with Morphological Anisogamy: Sexual reproduction resulting from the fusion of gametes different in form but similar in behavior, i.e., relative to gamete movement. [e.g., *Mougeotia heterogama* (scalariform conjugation)]

Homothallism: The condition in which sexual reproduction occurs in clonal cultures.

Heterothallism: The condition in which sexual reproduction occurs only when plus and minus strains or male and female strains are mixed.

Male Gamete: Gamete which moves from its gametangium into the female gametangium during anisogamy and physiological anisogamy.

Female Gamete: Gamete which remains in its gametangium during anisogamy and physiological anisogamy.

Mating Types: Strains of heterothallic species with isogamous sexual reproduction.

The Conjugation Process and Sex Determination

The conjugation process has been observed for well over 100 years, but only during the last forty years has there been an understanding of the events involved. DeBary (1858) interpreted conjugation as representing the beginning of a sexual process, while Bennett (1884) stated that if lateral conjugation occurs, it cannot be termed sexual. According to present knowledge, the conjugation process involves the fusion of gametic material from paired cells or from adjacent cells in filaments. Usually all or some part of the gametic material of the two gametes moves into or through a tube produced by one or both of the cells. These conjugating cells are typically from filaments of the same species, but Andrews (1911) figured an interesting conjugation between *Spirogyra crassa* and *S. communis*, species of markedly different characteristics.

The current use of clonal cultures maintained in controlled environments enables the investigator to follow closely all of the events of conjugation. Because the occurrence of these events is not predictable in most cases and because there are few characterized heterothallic strains in the Zygnemataceae, it is difficult to record a timed sequence of events such as Starr (1954) recorded for the desmid *Cosmarium turpinii*.

Heterothallism has been demonstrated for two or three species of *Zygnema*. Czurda (1930) identified *Z. circumcarinatum* and *Z. peliosporum* as heterothallic, the former being isogamous and the latter physiologically anisogamous. Strains of the plus and minus mating types of Z. *circumcarinatum* are still maintained by the culture collections at Bloomington, Cambridge, and Prague. Only the culture collection at Prague can provide cultures of the male and female strains of Z. *peliosporum*. Cultures of an unidentified species of *Zygnema* (Culture No. LB 921 and LB 922) maintained at Bloomington conjugate only when the filaments of the two strains are mixed. This conjugation is of the physiologically anisogamous type. Gauch (1966) designated LB 921 as the female strain and LB 922 as the male strain, inferring the occurrence of heterothallism from data obtained on backcrosses of germling strains to parental strains. Evidence is available, however, which places heterothallism of both Z. *circumcarinatum* and Z. *peliosporum* in doubt. Gauch (1966) figured a lateral conjugation for the strains of Z. *circumcarinatum* isolated originally by Czurda, and Fritsch and Rich (1927) figured a lateral conjugation for Z. *peliosporum* from a natural collection of this species. The limited data of Gauch on *Zygnema* sp. (LB 921 and LB 922) is probably not sufficient to characterize this species as heterothallic. Until additional studies are made, the presence of heterothallism in the Zygnemataceae should remain open to question.

Although investigators have evidence for the presence of heterothallism in a limited number of species of Zygnemataceae, the actual occurrence of heterothallism appears to be rare. Fritsch (1935) predicted that species with only scalariform conjugation should in some cases exhibit heterothallism. Transeau (1951) listed 400 species of the Zygnemataceae with only scalariform conjugation. Table 4 shows the types of sexual reproduction in the four genera considered here. The search for heterothallic species in the Zygnemataceae certainly should continue because of their greater value in experimental studies in genetics and physiology as well as in phycology.

Apparently all strains of *Mougeotia, Sirogonium,* and *Spirogyra* tested

TABLE 4. Types of Sexual Reproduction in Four Genera of the Zygnemataceae (After Transeau, 1951)

No. of Species with Each Type of Conjugation

Genus	Scalariform	Lateral	Scalariform and Lateral
Mougeotia	86	2	4
Sirogonium	12	0	0
Spirogyra	200	16	51
Zygnema	70	3	9
Totals	368	21	64

to date are homothallic; however, with over 300 species of *Spirogyra* described, there are undoubtedly many species not yet examined for sex-determination. All clonal cultures of *Sirogonium* observed in our laboratory are homothallic. The study of sex-determination in *Mougeotia* has been limited because the induction of its conjugation in culture has been fraught with difficulties. If an evolutionary relationship is assumed between the unicellular saccoderm desmids and the Zygnemataceae, as suggested by Fritsch (1935), Transeau (1951), and Yamagishi (1963), it is of interest that heterothallic strains have been characterized for *Mesotaenium* (Starr and Rayburn, 1964), *Spirotaenia* (Hoshaw and Hilton, 1966), but not for *Cylindrocystis*, a presumed ancestor of *Zygnema*.

Stages of the Conjugation Process

Since stages of conjugation for *Mougeotia, Spirogyra,* and *Zygnema* are the most familiar to biologists, *Sirogonium*, a lesser known organism, has been selected here as the model for conjugation (Figures 1–12). Unless otherwise mentioned, our discussions of conjugation refer to the scalariform type. Two major stages involving numerous morphological and physiological events are recognized here for the completion of conjugation: (1) sexual differentiation and (2) syngamy.

SEXUAL DIFFERENTIATION   The morphological and cytological events involved in the shift from the vegetative to the sexual condition are readily observable, and in the early literature there are many excellent descriptions of the beginnings of sexual differentiation (Lloyd, 1924, 1926a, 1926b, 1928; Saunders, 1931). However, very little is known about the underlying mechanisms which stimulate these events. For example, what stimulates filaments to align in a parallel manner and to become agglutinated in mucilage? An answer to this and many other questions about the conjugation process remains obscure.

A conspicuous exception to the usual parallel alignment occurs in *Sirogonium*, in which only a limited number of cells exhibit sexual differentiation (Figure 5). Conjugation is initiated through the random contact of filaments. The filaments of *Sirogonium* lack mucilaginous wall material, but a mucilaginous ring forms in this region of contact.

Vegetative cells function directly as gametangia with the production of a single gamete per cell. Czurda (1925) found in *Spirogyra* that gametangial cells are differentiated from the young cells of a recent cell division. A similar observation was made by Allen (1958) during her study of *Spirogyra pratensis*, a species commonly exhibiting lateral conjugation. She observed the onset of conjugation in newly formed cells in two–three days after the filaments were transferred to the surface of water agar. In *Sirogonium melanosporum* a progametangial cell (Figure 2) divides to form a gametangial cell and a sterile vegetative cell. Information is lacking, however, on the stimulus which promotes any of these cell divisions preparatory to the formation of gametangia. Reichart (1962) using the plasmolyzing agents, glucose, sucrose, and lutrol, has demonstrated for *Spirogyra majuscula* and *S. maxima* that the protoplasts of cells form two plasmolysis types. Cells with angular protoplasts following plasmolysis are in a state of conjugation readiness, while those with convex (roundish) ones remain in the vegetative condition. He found that germlings must have more than eight cells to produce angular protoplasts upon plasmolysis.

As yet, no mechanism has been confirmed to explain the formation of papillae by gametangial cells (see later discussion on hormonal control of conjugation). Saunders (1931) pointed out that the first-formed papilla stimulates the opposite papilla to arise at the place of contact. From her studies on *Spirogyra* she observed that the two papillae are in contact from the moment of their formation, and as these papillae grow, the filaments are pushed apart. Nevertheless, papillae are not always formed by both cells. In *S. majuscula* Reichart (1962) found normal conjugation tubes on single filaments not in contact with other filaments. Transeau (1951) listed a group of twenty-one species of *Spirogyra* whose cells have plane end walls and conjugation tubes formed exclusively by male gametangia. Papillar formation is shown for *Sirogonium melanosporum* in Figure 2. While *S. melanosporum* produces a conjugation tube, this structure is lacking in certain species of the genus, e.g., *S. sticticum*. Little is known about the biochemical events associated with cell-wall modification during the development of papillae into a conjugation tube. Reports differ regarding the involvement of the inner and outer cell wall (Czurda, 1925, 1930; Jost, 1953). Both the biochemical and morphological phenomena involved in the formation of the conjugation tube require additional study.

The final event of sexual differentiation involves the formation of gametes which are usually amoeboid in nature. In all genera except *Mougeotia* the entire protoplast forms the gamete. Exceptions to the amoeboid form occur in *Sirogonium* and *Spirogyra*. *Sirogonium melanosporum* produces spherical gametes (Figure 6) which are not amoeboid in their appearance or movement. Several species of *Spirogyra* with filaments of a large diameter ($>100\mu$) produce roundish to spherical gametes. *Spirogyra crassa* and *S. rectispira* are known to be in this category, and recently *S. maxima* has been reported to produce roundish to spherical gametes (Symons, 1965).

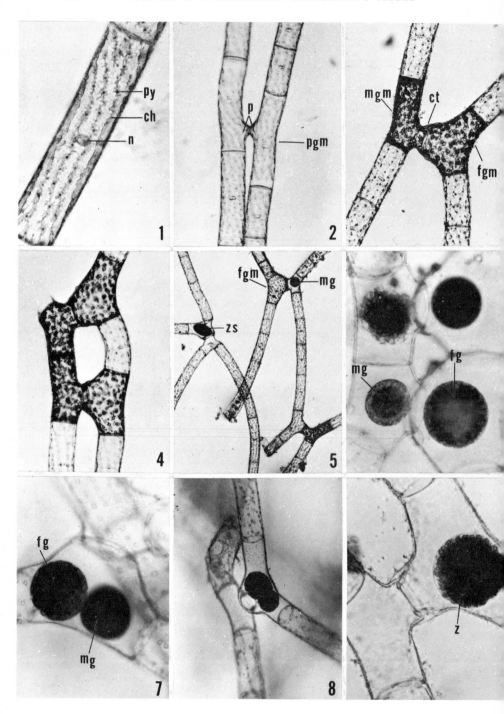

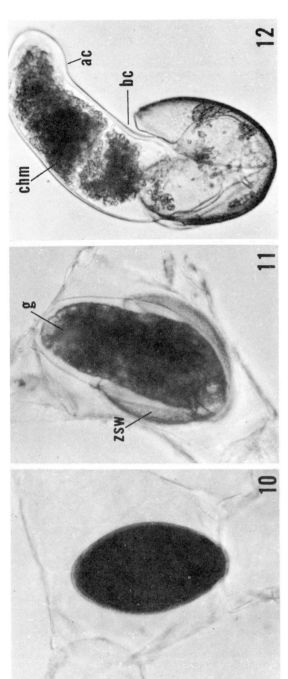

FIG. 1-12. *Sirogonium melanosporum.* FIG. 1. Vegetative cell stained with I₂ KI; n = nucleus; ch = chloroplast; py = pyrenoid, X 257. FIG. 2. Filaments showing a genuflexion and progametangial development; pgm = progametangium; p = papillae, X 120. FIG. 3. Single conjugation; fgm = female gametangium; ct = conjugation tube; mgm = male gametangium, X 115. FIG. 4. Double conjugation; note vegetative cell between female gametangia X 117.

FIG. 5. Filaments with a variety of sexual stages in a 4-week-old culture; zs = zygospore; fgm = female gametangium; mg = male gametangium, X 44.

FIG. 6. Double conjugation with gametes; mg = male gametes; fg = female gamete, X 212. FIG. 7. Female gametangium with male and female gametes immediately following movement of male gamete through conjugation tube; mg = male gamete; fg = female gamete, X 247. FIG. 8. Partial fusion of gametes in female gametangium, X 121. FIG. 9. Zygote 30 min. after syngamy; z = zygote, X 263.

FIG. 1-9. Reproduced at 79% of original photographs.

FIG. 10. Mature zygospore in female gametangium, X 247. FIG. 11. Emergence of germling from zygospore; zsw = zygospore wall; g = germling, X 340. FIG. 12. Two-celled germling; bc = basal cell; ac = apical cell; chm = chloroplastic material, X 329. (From Hoshaw, 1965).

The contraction of the protoplast to form a single gamete undoubtedly involves a variety of physico-chemical mechanisms. Klebs (1896) has pointed out that during the early stages of conjugation the osmotic pressure of gametangial cells decreases due to a sugar-starch conversion reaction. This enzymatically controlled reaction apparently proceeds more rapidly in the male gametangium than in the female gametangium, with the male gamete usually the first to differentiate. Both male and female gametes have a high starch and oil content, indicating a marked change in the metabolic pathways. As the osmotic pressure is lowered in gametangia, the diffusion pressure deficit of the cell sap decreases with the resultant loss of water from the protoplast. This loss can be partly associated with the action of contractile vacuoles (Lloyd, 1926a, 1926b). Similarly, Allen (1958) observed the expulsion of water by contractile vacuoles in *Spirogyra pratensis* as the male gamete moves into the female gametangium during lateral conjugation. In *Mougeotia*, *Spirogyra*, and *Zygnema* most cells have the potential to form gametes, but in *Sirogonium* only a limited number of cells form gametangia and produce gametes as shown in Table 5.

TABLE 5.   Occurrence of Gametangial Cells and Conjugation Types in
Sirogonium

Species	Gametangial Cells %	Double Conjugation %	Cross Conjugation*
S. melanosporum	9.0	1.8	Rare
S. phacosporum†	8.7	1.5	Rare
S. sticticum	15.0	1.4	Rare

* Male and female gametangia occur side by side in the same filament and produce a scalariform conjugation with an adjacent filament.
† Species designation tentative until data from chromosome studies are available.

The gametangia in *Sirogonium* typically occur as single or double pairs of conjugating cells, less than 2 per cent occurring as double pairs.

Syngamy   Prior to syngamy the gametes must be stimulated to move. Gametic movement is amoeboid except in species forming distinctive roundish or spherical gametes. A view of gametic movement and fusion in *Spirogyra* is recorded in a film entitled "Algae," which was produced by the Audio-Visual Center at Indiana University, Bloomington, Indiana. In *Sirogonium melanosporum* the gametic material flows rapidly through the conjugation tube as a stream of small particulate and globular material. Upon entry into the female gametangium, this male gametic material reorganizes into a spherical male gamete (Figure 7). It is possible to induce the movement of the mature male gamete in *S. melanosporum* by tapping the male gametangium; yet if the gamete is not mature, no amount of physical manipulation will induce the gametic material to flow.

Syngamy occurs in the conjugation tube or in the female gametangium. When two gametes come in contact prior to fusion, gamete fusion is either immediate or nearly so. Allen (1958) found that during lateral conjugation in *Spirogyra pratensis* the male and female gametes remain in contact briefly prior to fusion. In laboratory cultures the male gamete of *Sirogonium melanosporum* is in contact with the female gamete for less than one minute before fusion begins (Figure 7). Figure 8 shows gametic fusion, which requires two–three minutes, and Figure 9 shows a newly formed zygote.

Events usually occur rapidly following the formation of a zygote. In *Spirogyra pratensis*, Allen (1958) observed the beginnings of a cellulose wall around the zygote about one hour after syngamy. She also reported that the gamete protoplasts do not mix in the young zygote, the two nuclei remaining in their respective cytoplasms. However, Godward (1961) reported nuclear fusion (karyogamy) in the zygote of *Spirogyra crassa* occurring by the end of the first day, with meiosis beginning immediately after this nuclear fusion.

Formation of Zygospores and Their Germination

The conjugation process, along with zygospore formation and germination, comprises a complete sexual cycle. When conjugation is complete, the zygotes develop into thick-walled spores (zygospores). A zygospore develops as many as five walls, with the median wall variously sculptured and pigmented in shades of blue, yellow, and brown. Little is known about the development of these wall layers or about their sculpturing and pigmentation. Allen (1958) reported for *Spirogyra pratensis* that the original cellulose wall of the young zygospore becomes the outer wall about a week after zygote formation and that a second cellulose wall with a chitin-like substance develops internal to the original wall. She found that a third and innermost wall of cellulose is produced before germination. To date, wall characteristics have been studied primarily as an aid to the identification of species.

That zygospore maturation involves far more than the synthesis of walls is evidenced by the metabolic activity associated with the disappearance of chlorophyll and by the accumulation of numerous, large oil globules. In mature zygospores of *Sirogonium melanosporum* the photosynthetic lamellae of the chloroplast exhibit a grana-like appearance, and pyrenoids may be misshapen and disorganized. Of considerable genetic importance from the standpoint of cytoplasmic inheritance is the disappearance or disorganization of the male chloroplast(s) in the zygospore. This phenomenon was followed in *Spirogyra* (Chmielevsky, 1890; Tröndle, 1907; Allen, 1958) and in *Zygnema* (Kurssanow, 1912). Male chloroplast disappearance in *Sirogonium* is difficult to detect since the chloroplasts fragment in both the male and female gametangia during the formation of gametes. Chloroplast fragments in *Spirogyra*, as described by Tröndle (1907), form groups of orange carotenoid granules. Similar granules seen in *Sirogonium melanosporum* are assumed to be the remains of fragmented male chloroplasts.

Zygospores produced by clonal cultures under controlled conditions often show reduced germination when compared with those collected in nature. The drying of zygospores appears to be a requirement for germination as shown in laboratory studies on *Sirogonium melanosporum*, *Spirogyra pratensis* (Allen, 1958) and *Zygnema circumcarinatum* (Gauch, 1966). However, even in these laboratory studies germination did not exceed 10 per cent. By contrast, Nipkow (1962) found for *Spirogyra maxima* that zygospores from natural collections stored at 4–6°C gave over 50 per cent germination after three years.

Meiosis occurs in the zygospore, preceding the emergence of a single uninucleate germling. The most recent investigation of meiosis has been conducted by Godward (1961) for *Spirogyra crassa*. After a ten-year search,

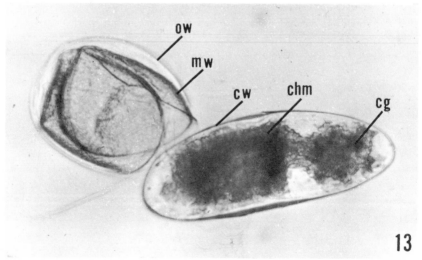

13

Fig. 13. Germling cell with empty zygospore of *Sirogonium melanosporum*; ow = outer wall; mw = median wall; cw = cell wall (formerly inner wall of zygospore); chm = chloroplastic material; cg = carotenoid granules, X 350. Reproduced at 97% of original photograph.

she found that meiosis occurred early in the process of zygospore formation, even before the wall matured. In *Sirogonium melanosporum* the
innermost wall of the zygospore becomes the wall of the one-celled germling (Figure 13). Within the protoplast of the first germling cell typical
chloroplast number and structure is found in *Spirogyra* and *Zygnema*.
By contrast, the young germling of *Sirogonium melanosporum* (Figure 12)
does not form organized chloroplasts until about the six-celled stage. This
delayed organization of chloroplast material into ribbonlike chloroplasts
poses an interesting problem in organellar development.

Environmental Control of the Conjugation Process

Since the early work of Klebs (1896), who included *Spirogyra* in his
studies, investigators have experienced more failures than successes in
their attempts to control conjugation. In some cases, clonal cultures show
continuous conjugation without inductive treatments, but the manipulation
of environmental factors, especially of the nutrient level, is known to accelerate the shift from the vegetative to the reproductive condition. The
following discussion considers six environmental factors with data concerning their effect on conjugation. These data must be interpreted with
care for the following reasons: (1) only two heterothallic strains have been
studied; (2) most strains investigated are maintained in unialgal rather
than axenic culture; (3) many strains are not grown and manipulated in
chemically defined media; and (4) facilities and equipment do not always
permit the maximum control of environmental factors. It is imperative
that future studies on conjugation and its control involve improved culture techniques.

INDUCTION OF CONJUGATION   According to Smith (1950), "The factors
inducing conjugation are not wholly connected with changes in the external environment, and fruiting cannot be induced at will by altering the
conditions of illumination, temperature, and mineral content of the surrounding water." This statement expresses the present state of our knowledge on the conjugation process. Smith was probably referring to the
statement by Czurda (1930) on the internal conditioning of cells which
Czurda referred to as an inner *"physiologischen Zustand."* In the light of
our current understanding of cell physiology, it is quickly recognized that
the external environment acts only as a "switch" to turn on the multitude
of chemical reactions which lead ultimately to observable cytological and
morphological phenomena. In reality, conjugation is controlled directly by
the environment within the cell protoplast and only indirectly by the external environment in which the cell exists.

Conjugation in homothallic strains usually proceeds slowly over a period of several days or weeks. In *Sirogonium melanosporum*, cells genuflex, and the sexual response is initiated, but at least a month is required to obtain a quantity of zygospores. In the heterothallic *Zygnema circumcarinatum*, zygotes form as early as twenty-two hours after the mating types are mixed (Hoshaw, unpublished). To obtain such a rapid response, it is critical for cultures of the two mating types to have undergone identical past histories, especially regarding age and growth rate. Similar observations concerning past history and its effect on conjugation in these same strains are made by Czurda (1930), Jost (1953), and Gauch (1966).

NUTRIENT LEVEL　Conjugation is often stimulated by transferring filaments from growth media to dilute media or to media lacking nutrients. Water agar (1.0–1.5 per cent) can provide a suitable surface for conjugation. Despite these positive statements on the nutritional control of conjugation, a predictable response requires the use of axenic cultures and a defined medium. In his study, Jost (1953) defined the optium nitrogen level for conjugation in *Zygnema circumcarinatum*. Using a modified Czurda medium, he substituted sodium nitrate or ammonium chloride for potassium nitrate as the nitrogen source. When mating types were mixed on the nutrient agar surface (pH 7.0), the greatest number of zygospores was observed at nitrate or ammoniacal nitrogen concentrations of 45 and 60 mg/liter. He observed no zygospores when nitrogen was omitted from the medium or when nitrogen concentrations were above 60 mg/liter. Gauch (1966) obtained consistent conjugation in his C-medium, which, except for a greater sulfate ion concentration, is the same medium used by Jost.

LIGHT　Light apparently controls conjugation. Klebs (1896) concluded that light is the primary factor for inducing conjugation in *Spirogyra*, and Coleman (1962) has even referred to light as the most universal inducer of sexuality in algae. Reports from field observations refer to the occurrence of conjugation at night in *Zygnema* (Kurssanow, 1912; Dohrer, 1940) and *Spirogyra* (Transeau, 1951).

Little quantitative data is available on the relationship of light to conjugation. Simple experiments can be designed to determine the role of light as an environmental factor, but the lack of predictable zygote formation has discouraged most investigators. The study on *Spirogyra pratensis* by Allen (1958) is one of the most recent to consider the effect of light intensity and daylength (Figure 14). She found that the beginning of conjugation related directly to the light intensity with a quantitative relationship between light intensity and conjugation. According to her data,

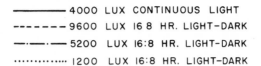

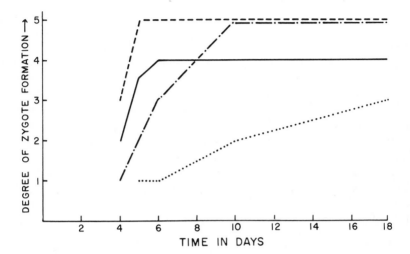

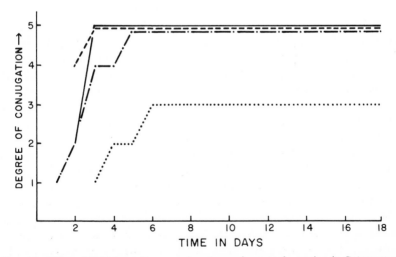

FIG. 14. Effect of light intensity on conjugation and zygote formation in *Spirogyra pratensis*. Culture information: (1) 6-week soil-water cultures; (2) conjugation medium of water agar; (3) light continuous or a 16:8 hr light-dark cycle; and (4) temperature of 20–23° C. (Redrawn with permission from Allen, 1958)

continuous illumination favors early conjugation but has a depressing effect on zygote formation.

Very little data is available on the effect of day length on conjugation. Again studies by Allen (1958) suggest a quantitative relationship between conjugation and the length of the light period. Over a ten-day period, she determined that a 16:8 hour light-dark cycle stimulated conjugation sooner and promoted greater zygote formation than 12:12 hour or 8:16 hour light-dark cycles.

TEMPERATURE   The cost of adequate controlled-environment facilities may be a factor which has contributed to the paucity of temperature studies on conjugation. While the factors of nutrient level, light, pH, and carbon dioxide are more easily manipulated, distinctly separate experimental units are normally required for the control of temperature. Observations of natural collections suggest that conjugation occurs over a wide temperature range, although this range undoubtedly varies for individual species. Temperature effects can be observed in *Sirogonium melanosporum*, in which conjugation accelerates when cultures are transferred from temperatures of $22 \pm 2°C$ to $26 \pm 2°C$, and in *Zygnema cruciatum* (Prasad and Godward, 1963), in which zygospores are produced in cultures maintained at $16-24°C$, but not in those maintained at $11-14°C$.

pH   The enhancement of conjugation at higher pH values as noted by Czurda (1933) has been discussed earlier in the paper. He found the optimum pH range was higher for conjugation than for growth in nineteen species of *Spirogyra* and two of *Zygnema*, including *Z. circumcarinatum*, reporting an optimum range starting at values greater than pH 7.0. Uni-algal soil-water cultures of *Spirogyra pratensis* supported more rapid conjugation when the medium was initially more alkaline (Allen, 1958). Although a relationship is suggested between conjugation and pH, conclusive evidence must come from additional studies of axenic cultures grown in defined media.

CO_2 The exposure of cultures to a CO_2-enriched atmosphere as described by Starr (1964) has failed to induce conjugation in *Spirogyra pratensis* (Allen, 1958) or in *Zygnema circumcarinatum* (Gauch, 1966). Prasad and Godward (1963) found no stimulation of conjugation for *Z. cruciatum* in a CO_2-enriched atmosphere. Starr's CO_2 technique has failed to increase conjugation in several species of the four genera manipulated in our laboratory. This failure is of interest because of the successful application of the technique to desmid species, including those of *Closterium, Cosmarium,* and *Spirotaenia*. Allen (1958) used NaOH to reduce the CO_2 in the atmosphere surrounding cultures of *S. pratensis*. Noting that conjugation was greatly decreased, she suggested a quantitative relationship between photosynthesis and conjugation.

Hormonal Control of Conjugation

Recent investigations and discussions of hormonal substances in the algae center primarily on *Chlamydomonas* (Smith, 1951a, 1951b; Raper, 1952, 1957; Coleman, 1962). A notable exception is the study by Rawitscher-Kunkel and Machlis (1962) on *Oedognium*, in which they defined four hormonal steps and one physical mechanism for sexual reproduction in a heterothallic, nannandrous species of this organism. Several references have already been made in the present essay to the stages of conjugation, and questions have been posed regarding the stimuli responsible for the onset of the major events. By way of review, these events include filament alignment, papillar development, conjugation tube formation, and stages from gamete formation to fusion.

Although there are several speculations on the chemical stimulation of conjugation (Kniep, 1928; Fritsch, 1935; Transeau, 1951), specific experiments designed to show the hormonal integration of the process in *Spirogyra pratensis* (Allen, 1958) and in *Zygnema circumcarinatum* (Jost, 1953) have yielded negative results. Brandham (1967) has observed that the early stages of conjugation in *Cosmarium botrytis* are controlled by one or more substances with the functions of hormones. In 1964, four experiments were designed in our laboratory to seek evidence for the hormonal control of conjugation in *Z. circumcarinatum* (Hoshaw and Haberman, unpublished). Even though these experiments were preliminary, they are reported here to suggest that hormonal substances may integrate the events of conjugation and to stimulate more extensive studies.

Each of the four experiments was designed to provide a different chemical stimulation on the filaments being used: (1) filaments of each strain were placed separately in a supernatant prepared from the growth medium of the opposite strain; (2) filaments of each strain were placed separately in the supernatant of filaments from a conjugating culture of the two strains; (3) filaments of each strain were placed separately in intracellular fluid of filaments from a conjugating culture of the two strains; and (4) filaments of each strain were placed in a dialyzing membrane and then suspended in a culture of the opposite strain or in a conjugating culture of the two strains. Only experiments of type (2) and (3) produced circumstantial evidence for hormonal control of conjugation. Even though experiments of types (1) and (4) failed to show evidence of hormonal control, they should not be excluded in future experimentation. A discussion and summary of the procedure and results for experiments of types (2) and (3) are presented here.

EXPERIMENTAL PROCEDURE   Prior to the experimentation, strains were mixed in dilute Godward medium. [Godward medium plus 2 ml/liter trace elements (Stein, 1958) and diluted 1:9.] These mixed cultures were examined to formulate a model for comparing normal conjugation with hormonally-induced conjugation in a single strain. Conjugation began within twenty-four hours, and the following events were interpreted from circumstantial evidence: (1) strain 43 produced large, knob-shaped papillae before papillar formation began in strain 42; (2) gametes usually entered the large papillae before small papillae formed on strain 42; (3) strain 42 simultaneously formed gametes and small papillae, the latter contacting the larger papillae; and (4) a conjugation tube formed, and isogamy followed.

For experimental purposes small masses of filaments of each strain were inoculated into flasks of Godward medium plus Stein's trace elements. Healthy material of identical history, essential for obtaining conjugation, was produced in about two weeks. Filaments were then transferred to dilute Godward medium to induce conjugation.

ZYGOTE FORMATION   In experiments of types (2) and (3), zygotes were produced by strain 43 alone when filaments of this strain were placed either in a supernatant from a conjugating, mixed culture or in the intracellular fluid from the filaments of a conjugating, mixed culture. Zygotes which appeared both abnormal and normal were produced during both types of experiments. Sexual differentiation was completely lacking in strain 42 when it was handled in the same manner as strain 43. Because the experiments were not continued beyond zygote formation, evidence on zygote viability is unavailable.

MODEL FOR HORMONAL ACTION   Evidence obtained from types (2) and (3) experiments suggests that strain 43 is the active strain and strain 42 the inactive strain. On this basis it is possible to describe a model for the probable relationship of hormonal substances to morphological events. On the hormonal level, a series of steps is mediated by extracellular substances produced by both strains prior to papillar formation in strain 43. After papillae form in strain 43, this strain excretes an extracellular substance which has local action due to low concentration and/or absorption by adjacent filaments. During normal conjugation, this substance elicits papillar formation in strain 42 but under experimental conditions elicits papillar formation in strain 43 alone. In this way two papillae form and meet to produce a conjugation tube. According to this model, it should be possible to find papillae (presumably on strain 43) on unpaired (non-conjugating) filaments in a mixed culture. Such an observation has been made on numerous occasions.

From an evolutionary viewpoint, the primitive state of heterothallism in Z. circumcarinatum is illustrated by the fact that strain 43 conjugates with itself when given the proper hormonal substances. Thus it can be postulated that the ancestor of the presently known species (*Z. circum-carinatum*) was a homothallic organism similar to strain 43 which has now developed control mechanisms mediated through substances elaborated by the evolving strain 42. This speculation is of interest because of the overwhelming preponderance of homothallic species characterized in the genus *Zygnema* and because of the questionable status of those shown to be heterothallic.

The Nucleus and Chromosomes

During the last twenty years many investigators have amassed a large quantity of data on algal cytology, with the Zygnemataceae receiving their share of the attention. Most prolific of these investigators is the English phycologist, Dr. M. B. E. Godward, who has devoted much of her research effort to this group. She has recently edited and partially authored a treatise entitled *The Chromosomes of the Algae* (Godward, 1966a). Since this treatise, which is readily available, provides an extensive discussion of *Spirogyra* and more limited discussions of *Zygnema* and *Mougeotia*, most of the attention here will be focused on *Sirogonium*, a genus not treated in her publication. Godward does refer briefly to *Sirogonium* in earlier reports (1950a, 1950b) by mentioning the presence of satellite chromosomes and the variation of nucleolar number.

Three unique features contribute to cytological interest in the Zygnemataceae: (1) the frequent lack of a single centromere; (2) the presence of a stainable material, called the nucleolar substance, which is intimately associated with the chromosomes during the division cycle; and (3) the complex internal structure of the nucleolus.

Growth and Sampling of Cultures

Cytological examination requires young, repidly growing cultures which provide many dividing cells. Several experiments to determine mitotic peaks for strains growing on several light-dark cycles have revealed a peak in the dark portion. In an early study on *Spirogyra*, Karsten (1918) concluded that light inhibits the mitotic process. From her study on *Spirogyra pratensis*, Allen (1958) found a mitotic peak with 4.8 per cent dividing cells one hour after the beginning of the dark period of a 16:8 hour light-dark cycle (Figure 15). When she transferred cultures to continuous light, no mitotic peak occurred. Waer (1966) obtained results similar to

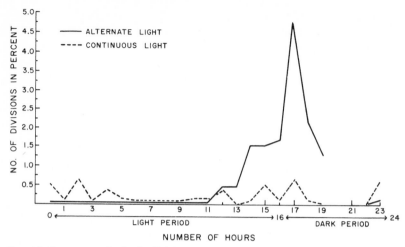

FIG. 15. Frequency of mitotic divisions in *Spirogyra pratensis* maintained on a 16:8 hr light-dark cycle in a light intensity of 4000 lux and in continuous light at 7000 lux. (Redrawn with permission from Allen, 1958)

those of Allen but for *Sirogonium melanosporum*. The mitotic peak for his cultures occurred one hour after the onset of the dark period on a 12:12 hour light-dark cycle with 16.9 per cent dividing cells.

Cytological Methods

FIXATION   Godward (1966b) discussed fixatives which can be used successfully in studies of algal chromosomes. For our chromosome studies on *Sirogonium*, however, two lesser known fixatives have been employed to facilitate the spreading of chromosomes and to reduce the masking effect of chloroplast material. The first, described by Jackson (personal communication), consists of methanol–ethanol–chloroform–acetone–propionic acid (4:2:2:1:1), and the second, by Freytag (1964), is composed of concentrated HCl–50 per cent ethanol–clorox (2:2:1).

STAINING   Algal cytology, and indeed cytology in general, received a much needed stimulus with Godward's (1948, 1950a) description of the iron–alum–acetocarmine method. This method is rapid and can be used with a number of fixatives. Most failures in its application are probably due to poor technique, although species differ markedly in their staining requirements. In the Zygnemataceae, the use of iron–alum–acetocarmine or iron–alum–propiocarmine stains is complicated by the presence of a densely-staining nucleolar substance which completely or partially obscures the chromosomes. This problem is particularly acute in species with many dot chromosomes.

Fortunately, the Feulgen technique does not stain the nucleolar substance. This technique typically involves the hydrolysis of fixed material with 1N HCl at 60°C; however, the recent report by Decosse and Aiello (1966) recommending the substitution of 5N HCl at room temperature has proved successful in studies on the chromosomes of several species of *Sirogonium*. A recommended schedule for the Feulgen technique routinely used in our laboratory which incorporates this new procedure is as follows:

(1) Fix filaments in concentrated HCl–50 per cent ethanol–chlorox (2:2:1) for three–five minutes. (Freytag, 1964).
(2) Transfer filaments to 70–95 per cent ethanol until removal of chlorophyll is complete.
(3) Hydrolyze filaments in 5N HCl for twenty-five to thirty minutes at room temperature (Decosse and Aiello, 1966). Time may vary with the species.
(4) Rinse filaments in distilled water.
(5) Stain filaments with Schiff's reagent (Darlington and La Cour, 1950) for twenty-five to thirty minutes. Time may vary with the species.
(6) Rinse filaments in distilled water.
(7) Mount filaments in forty-five per cent propionic acid and examine. Prior to examination spread chromosomes by placing a cork on the cover glass and strike with a hammer. (The slide and cover glass should be placed between paper toweling.)

Despite several reports of negative results with the Feulgen technique (Oura, 1953; Allen, 1958; Meyer, 1966), investigators should be encouraged to consider it more frequently when details of chromosome morphology and accurate chromosome counts are desired.

Nuclear Cytology

INTERPHASE NUCLEUS The single interphase nucleus is a conspicuous organelle readily observed with the light microscope. Prior to division, this nucleus enlarges, and depending on the staining technique employed during cytological examination, it exhibits one or more of three structural features: nucleoli, nucleolar-organizing tracks, and chromocenters.

Nucleoli and nucleolar-organizing tracks are observable in nuclei stained by the iron–alum–acetocarmine or iron–alum–propiocarmine method. Nucleolar number appears to vary widely among the species, ranging from one in some species to as many as eight in an unidentified *Mougeotia* (Prasad and Godward, 1962). Two nucleoli represent the maximum reported for *Zygnema* (Godward, 1966b); as many as four occur in *Sirogonium melanosporum*; and at least four have been reported in *Spirogyra* (Godward, 1956; Godward and Newnham, 1965). In 1947, Godward identified the complex organization within the nucleolus of *Spirogyra* as nucleolar tracks. Other investigators have identified this same type of nucleolar organization in *Spirogyra pratensis* (Allen, 1958), in *Zygnema* and *Mougeotia* species (Prasad, 1958), and in *Sirogonium melanosporum*.

Chromocenters and the fine strands which connect them are not only observable in nuclei stained by the above methods, but they are the only visible structures in an interphase nucleus treated with the Feulgen technique. Their size is apparently related to the ultimate size of chromosomes in *Spirogyra* (Godward, 1950a) and in *Sirogonium*, i.e., species forming large chromosomes possess large chromocenters, while species forming dot chromosomes possess small chromocenters.

NUCLEOLAR SUBSTANCE   Geitler (1935b) was the first to refer to stainable, granular material occurring in the prophase of mitosis as nucleolar substance. This material, which apparently is found in species of all four genera, stains readily with aceto- or propiocarmine. Figures 16 and 18 show the stained nucleolar substance in *Spirogyra crassispina* and *Sirogonium melanosporum* and reveal the difficulty of studying chromosome number and morphology in material stained with propiocarmine. Nucleolar substance is the product of nucleolar breakdown, and according to Godward (1953) this breakdown may be gradual or abrupt. During a third method, the nucleolus loses its organization and becomes associated with the nucleolar-organizing regions of nucleolar-organizing chromosomes during early to mid prophase. In a comparison of the ultrastructure of the intact nucleolus in *Spirogyra britannica* and *S. ellipsospora* with that of the nucleolar substance, Godward and Jordan (1965) found the two to be of similar structure.

Generally, the nucleolar substance remains in close association with the chromosomes throughout the division cycle; however, little is known about the reorganization of nucleoli following division. In *Sirogonium melanosporum* the formation of the nucleoli results from a fusion of several partially-organized masses of nucleolar substance. Godward (1953) suggested from her extensive work on *Spirogyra* that each nucleolus is organized by a nucleolar-organizing chromosome.

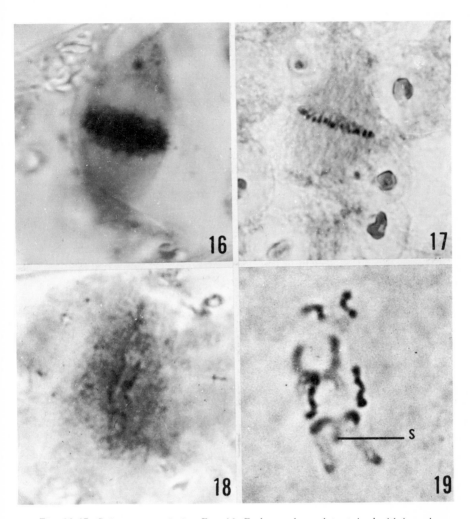

FIG. 16–17. *Spirogyra crassispina*. FIG. 16. Early anaphase plate stained with iron-alum propiocarmine showing the dense mass of nucleolar substance which surrounds and obscures the chromosomes, X 3300. FIG. 17. Metaphase plate showing dot chromosomes as they appear when stained by the Feulgen technique and counterstained with propiocarmine, X 3300. (Courtesy Richard D. Waer)

FIG. 18–19. *Sirogonium melanosporum*. FIG. 18. Early anaphase stained with iron-alum-propiocarmine showing chromosomes surrounded by dense nucleolar substance, X 1650. FIG. 19. Early anaphase showing parallel separation and waviness of chromosomes as they appear when stained by the Feulgen technique and counterstained with propiocarmine. Note satellite(s) of partially separated chromatids, X 2300.

Chromosomes

The presence of nucleolar substance led a number of early investigators to conclude erroneously that chromosomes in the Zygnemataceae are of nucleolar origin. An historical account of these early investigations is found in a paper by Doraiswami (1946). Although several early investigators had postulated that chromosomes did not originate from the nucleolus, it was not until the advent of the Feulgen technique that Geitler (1935a), Suematsu (1936), and Doraiswami (1946) could demonstrate the origin of chromosomes from chromatin material.

Most species investigated have chromosomes 2.0 μ or less in length, and Figure 17 shows the dot chromosomes of *Spirogyra crassispina*. By contrast, large metaphase chromosomes occur in *Spirogyra triformis* (up to 9 μ) (Godward, 1950a) and in *Sirogonium melanosporum* (up to 5.5 μ). For *Spirogyra*, Godward (1954) described the following sizes of metaphase chromosomes: (1) large with diffuse centromere, (2) medium and small with either diffuse or localized centromere, (3) medium with localized centromere, and (4) small or dot-like with no observable centromere. To date, only types (1) and (4) have been characterized in *Sirogonium*. *Sirogonium melanosporum* forms large chromosomes (Figure 19), while all other species of this genus which have been examined possess the dot type, numbering up to 100 in those strains investigated.

Godward (1966b) listed nucleolar-organizing chromosomes for eighteen species of *Spirogyra*, with numbers ranging from one in a haploid strain of *S. pratensis* (Allen, 1958) to four in *S. majuscula* and *S. submargaritata*. Likewise, nucleolar-organizing chromosomes are found in species of *Sirogonium* with either large or dot chromosomes. Figure 19 shows two of the six chromosomes in *S. melanosporum* as the nucleolar-organizing type.

Investigators have focused considerable attention on the centromeric organization in the Zygnemataceae, concluding that while some species possess a single localized centromere, others are polycentric or have a diffuse centromere. To date, Godward (1966b) has found no evidence for a centromere in the Zygnematales from her electron microscope studies. Yet in *Sirogonium melanosporum* the parallel separation of chromatids to form new chromosomes, along with the waviness of these chromosomes (Figure 19), suggests the presence of more than one centromeric region (Hoshaw and Waer, 1967). Further, the absence of U-, V-, or J-shaped chromosomes during anaphase is also indicative that more than one centromere may be present. Only the satellite and secondary constrictions of each nucleolar-organizing chromosome lag during chromosomal movement. Thus, the nature of the centromere, or even its presence, remains open to question. Additional evidence on this question may be obtained through the continuation of electron microscopic examination of more species. Only then can a conclusion be drawn regarding the presence of several centromeres (polycentricity) or the activity of the whole chromosome as a centromere (diffuse centromere).

Polyploidy

All attempts to induce polyploidy in the Zygnemataceae with colchicine have yielded negative results (Allen, 1958; Godward, 1966b). On the other hand, an excellent example of natural polyploidy in laboratory cultures of *Spirogyra pratensis* is reported in detail by Allen (1958). Following the establishment of a clonal culture of this species, she observed the occurrence of a variety of filaments which were referred to as a species complex. Three distinct strains were identified by filament width; these could be arranged in a polyploid series based on evidence from cytological studies. She then defined three groups based on filament width as follows: (1) filaments 15.0–19.5 μ in diameter with eleven–fifteen chromosomes; (2) filaments 21.0–25.5 μ with twenty-six–thirty chromosomes; and (3) filaments 27.0–33.0 μ with fifty-six–sixty chromosomes. From these data she concluded that these strains are produced by increases in ploidy involving euploid steps to give haploid, diploid, and tetraploid strains of variable filament width.

Another chromosomal phenomenon awaiting clarification in certain species is the basic nuclear condition of ordinary vegetative cells. It has not been determined whether homologous pairs of chromosomes occur in *Spirogyra triformis* (six chromosomes; Godward, 1954), *S. subechinata* (four chromosomes; Godward, 1954), or *Sirogonium melanosporum* (six chromosomes). It has long been thought that vegetative cells are haploid; Godward (1961) confirms that meiosis in *Spirogyra crassa* is zygotic, providing cytological evidence that zygnematacean species should be considered functionally haploid. Recently she has suggested the occurrence of chromosome duplication in vegetative cells if more than one nucleolar-organizing chromosome is present (Godward, 1966b).

The Chloroplast, Pyrenoid, and Karyoid

When the criterion for classification is general chloroplast morphology, members of the Zygnemataceae fall into three groups: (1) those with a single, platelike axile plastid, e.g., *Mougeotia* and *Mougeotiopsis*; (2) those with globose to stellate plastids, e.g., *Zygnema* and *Zygnemopsis*; and (3) those with ribbonlike, usually spiraling plastids, e.g., *Sirogonium* and *Spirogyra*. Species providing information on the subjects of phylogeny, chloroplast inheritance, and pyrenoid origin and function may be of interest to the experimentalist. Included in these categories are the following species: (1) those with a greater-than-expected number of chloroplasts, e.g., *Mougeotia prona* and *M. victoriensis* (Transeau, 1951); (2) those with unusual chloroplast morphology, e.g., *Mougeotia robusta*, in which the plastid is sometimes deeply cleft (Transeau, 1951), and *M. heterogama*, in which the chloroplast of the female cell has three-five pyrenoids and that of the male usually has two pyrenoids (Geitler, 1958); and (3) those lacking pyrenoids, e.g., *Mougeotiopsis calospora* (Transeau, 1951). Although these organisms would be useful experimentally, they are not available in the major culture collections. This fact draws attention to the importance of isolating and making available cultures of organisms which, although not of special interest to the isolator, may be of interest to other investigators.

Chloroplast Structure

MODIFICATION IN CULTURE   That chloroplasts are subject to variation brought about by cultural conditions is well known, but the specific conditions responsible for a particular variation are not generally understood. In *Spirogyra pratensis*, media with sequestrene and iron promote an increase in the length and width of the chloroplasts for a short time (Allen, 1958), and in *Zygnema circumcarinatum*, a light intensity of 6000 lux causes an increase in chloroplast number per cell (Gauch, 1966).

Culture conditions apparently have an effect on the direction of spiraling of the plastids in *Spirogyra*. In *Spirogyra majuscula* collected by Butterfass (1957b), the plastids were observed to spiral to the left, the normal direction; in laboratory cultures of the same species, however, spiraling to the right sometimes occurred. Butterfass suggests that conditions allowing this reverse spiraling may not occur normally in nature.

ULTRASTRUCTURE   The ultrastructure of the chloroplasts of the Chlorophycophyta has been studied by several investigators (Ueda, 1961; Gibbs, 1962b; Weier, Bisalputra, and Harrison, 1966). Grana, structures typical for higher plants, have been reported in some species (Ueda, 1961; Weier, *et al.*, 1966), but their presence in members of the Zygnemataceae is uncertain. Grana have been reported in *Spirogyra majuscula* (Butterfass, 1957a), but Dawes (1965) made no mention of grana in his ultrastructural study on *Spirogyra*. Puiseux-Dao and Levain (1963) reported that grana are not found in an unidentified *Mougeotia* cultivated under favorable conditions; in a later paper, Puiseux-Dao (1964) showed thylakoids with a grana-like aspect. Grana are lacking in mature vegetative cells of *Sirogonium melanosporum*, but grana are found in zygospores (Figure 26) and in two-celled germlings. The conditions under which grana are observed in members of the Zygnemataceae require further study in which investigators should consider the fine structure of membrane relationships as affected by the cellular environment and the physiological state of the cell.

Chloroplast Inheritance

Variability in Chloroplast Number   Plastid number is variable among species and sometimes in cells of a single filament, especially in *Sirogonium* and *Spirogyra*. In *Spirogyra* plastid number ranges from one to sixteen, with slight variations in number occurring in a species. Control mechanisms are necessary for plastid number to remain constant during filament growth and during the sexual cycle. In *Sirogonium* and *Spirogyra* these mechanisms could be (1) the constriction of the chloroplasts during cell division, a process transmitting an identical number of plastids to each daughter cell; and (2) the disorganization of the male plastids in the sexual cycle, a process transmitting only plastids from the female gamete to the first germling cell. Two questions arise concerning these mechanisms: (1) How does a variable number of plastids occur in cells of the same clone? (2) How have variable chloroplast numbers evolved in different species with the same cell dimensions?

In regard to the first question, Transeau (1951) stated that the cause of variable numbers of plastids within a single filament is unknown; however, observations on plastid number in germlings of *Sirogonium* suggest a mechanism. In many-celled germlings of *S. melanosporum*, plastid number ranges from two to nine. The basal cell has two–four plastids, the second cell three–six, the third cell four–seven, and beyond the third cell five–nine. Both short and long plastids are found within certain cells, and plastids folding back on themselves have been observed. If cell division occurs across a plastid folded back on itself, one daughter cell receives an extra plastid. This event can result in an increased plastid number if the cell with the extra plastid continues to divide. However, if plastids within a cell should fail to elongate at the same rate, cell division may eliminate the slow-growing plastid(s) from one daughter cell. If the cell which has lost a plastid continues to divide, a decrease in the plastid number per cell occurs.

Allen (1958) provided data relevant to the second question posed above.

In her study of a species complex formed from a single clonal isolation of *Spirogyra pratensis*, cultures were established with similar cell dimensions but a different plastid number. This unusual condition resulted when filaments of a large-width group and with three–four plastids per cell reverted back to a width group typical of cells with two plastids but retained the three–four plastid condition. However, from studies of germlings in three width groups, Allen concluded that the number of plastids in a germling usually depends on the cell dimensions of the germling instead of the plastid number of the parental group. Because most offspring have the same cell dimensions as the parent, the number of plastids in the offspring is generally the same as that for the parent.

MUTANTS   Chloroplast mutants have been characterized, but they have not been used extensively in genetic studies. In a preliminary study of *Z. circumcarinatum*, Gauch (1966) characterized a mutant with plastid numbers ranging from two to nine, noting that most cells contain four. Gauch observed that filaments with mutant cells conjugated with normal cells, but he did not report on zygote viability.

Pyrenoid

ORIGIN   Evidence on the origin, structure, and function of the pyrenoid has been reviewed by Czurda (1928), Bold (1951), and Granick (1961). Investigators base evidence for the origin of the pyrenoid in *Spirogyra* on light microscope observations, showing the pyrenoid to arise either *de novo* or by division of preexisting pyrenoids. Szejnman (1933) followed pyrenoids which appeared to be dividing through several cell divisions and noted that during this time, division of these pyrenoids did not occur. Szejnman thus concluded that the majority of pyrenoids arise *de novo*; in fact, in two cases *de novo* formation of a structure with the appearance of a dividing pyrenoid occurred. Szejnman further stated that of the 352 pyrenoids studied, 85 per cent formed in the morning. A more recent study on *Spirogyra* (Allen, 1958) shows that pyrenoid division occurs throughout all stages of cell division, although it is not clear whether actual divisions were observed. Thus additional evidence is required to confirm whether regular division occurs in addition to *de novo* formation.

The pyrenoids in *Zygnema* arise by division in vegetative cells. Studies of cell division in filaments from natural collections show pyrenoid division after nuclear division and immediately prior to chloroplast division (Merriman, 1906; Dohrer, 1940). Two types of pyrenoid division in *Zygnema* can be described from observations in our laboratory. If Figures 20 and 21 are compared, it will be noted that division takes place either be-

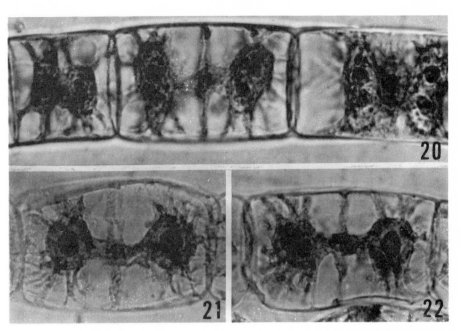

Fig. 20–22. Filaments of *Zygnema* sp. (H519). Fig. 20. Left cell in interphase of mitosis with dividing pyrenoid; middle cell in anaphase of mitosis with daughter pyrenoids, prior to plastid division; right cell prior to nuclear division showing daughter pyrenoids positioned at right angles to the filament axis. Fig. 21. Cell in anaphase of mitosis prior to pyrenoid division. Fig. 22. Cell in metaphase of mitosis with left pyrenoid divided and right pyrenoid prior to division. Note size difference between mother and daughter pyrenoids. All X 900.

fore or after nuclear division. In fact, in a single cell one pyrenoid may divide before and the other after nuclear division (Figure 22). The daughter pyrenoids, when viewed soon after division, are always smaller than the mother pyrenoid (Figure 22). If a pyrenoid divides after nuclear division, it often does so parallel to the long axis of the filament, and the chloroplast divides immediately after the pyrenoid. When the pyrenoid divides before nuclear division, it usually does so at right angles to the long axis of the filament, plastid division being delayed until the newly formed nucleus moves to the area between the separating plastids (Figure 20).

STRUCTURE   Several workers have focused their attention on the ultrastructure of pyrenoids in *Spirogyra*. Butterfass (1957a) described the pyrenoid as consisting of buckled, folded, or compressed plates between which are found lamellae pairs. Similar structure is reported for the pyrenoid of *Mougeotia* (Puiseux-Dao and Levain, 1963). The thylakoids that traverse the pyrenoid extend between the surrounding starch grains

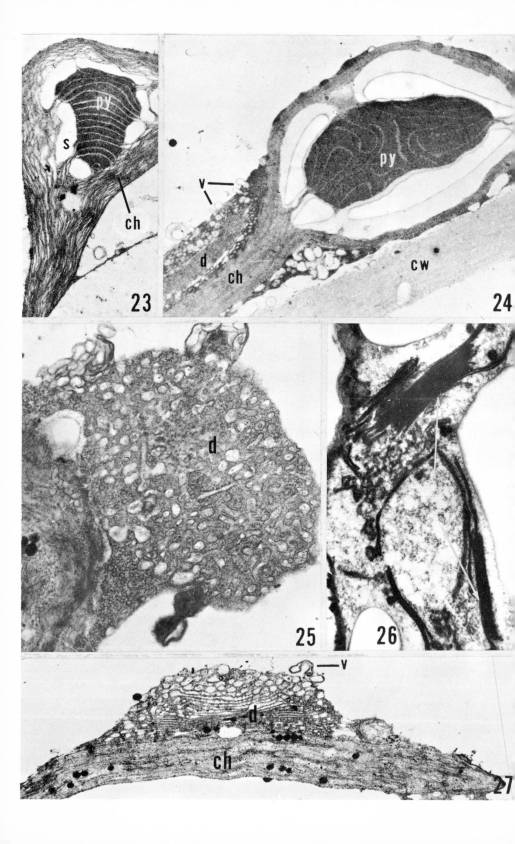

and are continuous with the lamellae of the chloroplast (Leyon, 1954; Gibbs, 1962a; Dawes, 1965).

Pyrenoids of *Sirogonium melanosporum* do not appear to differ in ultra-structure from those of *Spirogyra* or *Mougeotia*. Thylakoids of the chloroplast pass between the starch plates and are continuous with those of the pyrenoid. In transverse view, thylakoids within a pyrenoid appear arranged more or less parallel to one another (Figure 23); in longitudinal view folding is evident (Figure 24).

ASSOCIATED SUBSTANCES In *Spirogyra*, Keck and Stich (1957) found polyphosphate granules both surrounding the pyrenoids and between them, and Hunter (1961) demonstrated the enzyme acid phosphatase in the pyrenoid and zymohexase (aldolase) in association with the pyrenoids of *Spirogyra*. The presence of DNA near the pyrenoid is shown in *Chlamydomonas* (Ris and Plaut, 1962) and in *Dictyota, Padina*, and *Bryopsis* (Steffensen and Sheridan, 1965). Although investigators have attempted to identify DNA in the chloroplasts of *Spirogyra* with tritiated thymidine (Stocking and Gifford, 1959), Meyer (1966) has shown that this technique in combination with DNase and RNase reveals the label in RNA. The appearance of the pyrenoid in *Mougeotia* treated with RNase is described and illustrated by Puiseux-Dao (1962, 1964).

Karyoid

LIGHT MICROSCOPY In 1894 Palla drew attention to small granules found on the plastids of several zygnematalean species. He described them as small nuclei and referred to them as karyoids. The observance of these karyoids *in vivo* is difficult even in profile view; however, when fixed and stained with picric-aniline blue (Butterfass, 1957a) or acetocarmine (Allen, 1958), they can be seen in front view. Because of their frequent occurrence in the area of the plastid near the nucleus, their small size ($< 2\mu$), and their staining capacity with acetocarmine, karyoids may be confused with chromosomes (Allen, 1958).

FIG. 23–27. *Sirogonium melanosporum*. FIG. 23. Transverse section of pyrenoid showing parallel-appearing thylakoids, ch = chloroplast; py = pyrenoid; s = starch plate, X 17-000. Glutaraldehyde-osmium tetroxide fixation. FIG. 24. Longitudinal section of pyrenoid showing folded thylakoids along with dictyosome and vesicles; ch = chloroplast; cw = cell wall; d = dictyosome; py = pyrenoid; v = vesicles, X 24,000. Glutaraldehyde-osmium tetroxide fixation. FIG. 25. Oblique section of dictyosome showing net-like arrangement of tubules; d = dictyosome, X 29,000. Glutaraldehyde-osmium tetroxide fixation. FIG. 26. Grana (arrows) in zygospore, X 33,000. KMnO₄ fixation. FIG. 27. Transverse section of a large dictyosome (ca. 2.8 μ) on chloroplast; ch = chloroplast; d = dictyosome; v = vesicle, X 20,000. Glutaraldehyde-osmium tetroxide fixation. (Courtesy Dr. Paul G. Bartels)

ELECTRONMICROSCOPY Drawert and Mix (1962) considered the karyoid and Golgi apparatus identical in the Zygnematales. Dawes (1965) indicated that Golgi-like bodies are found on the chloroplast in *Spirogyra* in areas that occupy the karyoid position. Large dictyosomes on the plastid, especially near the nucleus, have been demonstrated in an ultrastructural study of *Mougeotia* (Puiseux-Dao and Levain, 1963). In *Sirogonium melanosporum* large dictyosomes are found on the plastids of vegetative cells (Figures 24, 25, 27) and in zygospores. On the ultrastructural level these bodies appear as stacks of large, flattened, platelike cisternae (Figures 24, 27) from which extends a net-like group of tubules (Figure 25) with associated vesicles (Figures 24, 27). This description fits that of the ultrastructure of the karyoid given by Butterfass (1957a) and that of the dictyosome presented by Mollenhauer and Morré (1966). Probably in *Sirogonium* and *Spirogyra*, the highly vacuolated condition of the cells and the small amount of cytoplasm surrounding the plastid are responsible for making these large dictyosomes appear through the light microscope as granules on the plastid.

Thus the karyoids described in early studies from light microscopy have the same structures commonly referred to as dictyosomes in electron microscopic studies. The term "karyoid," useful in its day, should be discarded in view of the current use of the terms "dictyosome" or "Golgi apparatus." Finally, it is of interest that *Spirogyra*, which has been used to study sexual reproduction in green algae, can now serve as an organism for demonstrating dictyosomes with the light microscope.

CONCLUSIONS

Experimental studies on clonal cultures of algae maintained in controlled environments have enabled phycologists to extend their knowledge of cytology, genetics, morphology, and physiology. In this regard, more attention has focused on unicellular and colonial species than on the great variety of filamentous forms. To some extent this lack of progress can be attributed to the difficulties associated with preparing axenic cultures which will grow in defined media. This may well be true for the Zygnemataceae, but in addition, the lack of identified heterothallic strains, except for species of *Zygnema*, has hampered studies requiring stages of the sexual cycle.

In this essay several suggestions have been made for specific studies on zygnematacean species. Yet, it is worth repeating that the use of newer microscopic and biochemical techniques should be helpful in understanding the mechanisms of the conjugation process, the role of the nuclear substance in the mitotic process, and the significance of the chloroplast in

genetic aspects of the sexual cycle. Experimental studies on the Zygnemataceae, as is the case with many other filamentous green algae, have hardly
begun.

Acknowledgments

I wish to acknowledge the generous assistance provided by four pre-
doctoral students, Arthur E. Dennis, Richard L. Hilton, Jr., James R.
Rosowski, and Charles V. Wells, during our investigations on the
Zygnemataceae and for assistance in compiling the literature review for
this paper. Financial support for our studies on the Zygnemataceae has
been provided by grants G-25130 and GB-2440 from the National Science
Foundation. In addition, the electron microscopic investigations were conducted in a laboratory receiving financial assistance from grant NSF GB-
3330. Lastly, I offer my sincere thanks to Dr. C. van den Hoek for his comments on the manuscript.

REFERENCES

Aleem, A. A., 1952. "Sur l'autoécologie d'une Spirogyre d'eau Saumâtre," *Compt. Rend. Acad. Sci.* (Paris), *234*, 2648–50.
———, 1961. "Effect of Salinity on the Growth and Reproduction of a Brackish Water *Spirogyra* (S. *salina* nov. sp.)," *Vie et Milieu, 12*, 497–506.
Allen, M. A., 1958. "The Biology of a Species Complex in *Spirogyra*," Ph.D. thesis, Indiana Univ. (Libr. Congr. Card No. Mic.: 58-7901), Univ. Microfilms, Ann Arbor, Mich., 240 pp.
Anderson, E. N., and E. R. Walker, 1920. "An Ecological Study of the Algae of Some Sandhill Lakes," *Trans. Amer. Microscop. Soc., 39*, 51–85.
Andrews, F. M., 1911. "Conjugation of Two Different Species of *Spirogyra*," *Bull. Torrey Bot. Club, 38*, 299.
Barr, D. J. S., and C. J. Hickman, 1967. "Chytrids and Algae II. Factors Influencing Parasitism of *Rhizophydium sphaerocarpum* on *Spirogyra*," *Can. J. Bot., 45*, 431–40.
Bary, A. de, 1858. "Untersuchungen über die Familie der Conjugaten," Leipzig, 91 pp.
Baslerová, M., and J. Dvǒrakova, 1962. *Algarum, Hepaticarum, Muscorumque in culturis collectio*, Prague: Československá Akademie věd, 59 pp.
Bennett, A. W., 1884. "Reproduction of the Zygnemaceae; a Contribution Towards the Solution of the Question—Is It of a Sexual Character?" *J. Linn. Soc. Bot., 20*, 430–39.
Biswas, K., 1936. "Association of Some of the Common Algae with Animals in Indian Waters," *Hedwigia, 76*, 114–30.
Bold, H. C., 1942. "The Cultivation of Algae," *Bot. Rev., 8*, 69–138.
———, 1951. "Cytology of algae," in *Manual of Phycology*, ed. by Smith, Waltham, Mass.: Chronica Botanica Co., pp. 203–27.
Botany School, 1966. "Culture Collection of Algae and Protozoa," Univ. of Cambridge, Cambridge, 67 pp.

Bourrelly, P., 1966. *Les algues d'eau douce*, Vol. I, Paris: N. Boubée & Cie, 511 pp.

Brandham, P. E., 1967. "Time-lapse Studies of Conjugation in *Cosmarium botrytis*. II. Pseudoconjugation and an Anisogamous Mating Behavior Involving Chemotaxis," *Can. J. Bot., 45,* 483–93.

Brown, H. B., 1908. "Algal Periodicity in Certain Ponds and Streams," *Bull. Torrey Bot. Club, 35,* 223–48.

Brunel, J., G. W. Prescott, and L. H. Tiffany, eds., 1950. *The Culturing of Algae,* Yellow Springs, Ohio: Antioch Press, 114 pp.

Butterfass, T., 1957a. "Über Grana, Karyoide und Pyrenoide von *Spirogyra*," *Protoplasma, 48,* 368–81.

————, 1957b. "Über das Vorkommen umgekehrt gewundener Chromatophoren bei *Spirogyra*," *ibid.,* 419–21.

Chamberlain, C. J., 1932. *Methods in Plant Histology*, Chicago: Univ. Chicago Press, 416 pp.

Chapman, V. J., 1964. *The Algae*, New York: Macmillan, 472 pp.

Chmielevsky, V., 1890. "Eine Notiz über das Verhalten der Chlorophyllbänder in den Zygoten der *Spirogyra*-Arten," *Bot. Zeit., 48,* 773–80.

Chu, S. P., 1942. "The Influence of the Mineral Composition of the Medium on the Growth of Planktonic Algae," *J. Ecol., 30,* 284–325.

Coleman, A. W., 1962. "Sexuality," in *Physiology and Biochemistry of Algae*, ed. by Lewin, New York: Academic Press, Inc., pp. 711–29.

Comère, J., 1913. "De l'action du milieu considerée dans ses rapports avec la distribution générale des algues d'eau douce," *Bull. Soc. Bot. France, 60,* 1–96.

Crow, C. L., 1964. "*Sirogonium sticticum*: Its Morphology, Cytology, and Sexual Cycle," M.S. Thesis, Univ. of Arizona, Tucson, 49 pp.

Czurda, V., 1922a. "Zur Frage der Nucleuslöslichkeit bei *Spirogyra*," *Arch. Protistenk., 44,* 346–74.

————, 1922b. "Über ein bisher wenig beobachtetes Gebilde und andere Erscheinungun im Kerne von *Spirogyra* (*setiformis* Kütz.)," *ibid., 45,* 163–99.

————, 1925. "Zur Kenntnis der Copulationsvorgänge bei *Spirogyra*," *ibid., 51,* 439–78.

————, 1926a. "Die Reinkultur von Conjugaten," *ibid., 53,* 215–42.

————, 1926b. "Über die Reinkultur von Conjugaten," *ibid., 54,* 355–58.

————, 1928. "Morphologie und Physiologie des Algenstärkekornes," *Beih. bot. Zentralbl., 45,* 97–270.

————, 1930. "Experimentelle Untersuchungen über die Sexualitätsverhältnisse der Zygnemalen," *ibid., 47,* 15–68.

————, 1931. "Zur Morphologie und Systematik der Zygnemalen," *ibid., 48,* 238–85.

————, 1932. "Zygnemales," part 9, in *Die Süsswasser-Flora Mitteleuropas,* ed. by Pascher, 2nd ed., Jena: Gustav Fischer, pp. 1–232.

————, 1933. "Experimentelle Analyse de Kopulationsauslösenden Bedingungen bei Mikroorganismen," *Beih. bot. Zentralbl., 51,* 711–62.

————1937. "Conjugatae," in *Handbuch der Pflanzenanatomie,* ed. by Linsbauer, Tischler, and Pascher, Vol. 6, part 2: Algen, B:b, Berlin: Gebrüder Borntraeger, pp. 1–176.

Darlington, C. D., and L. F. La Cour, 1950. *The Handling of Chromosomes*, George Allen & Unwin, 180 pp.

Dawes, C. J., 1965. "An Ultrastructure Study of *Spirogyra*," *J. Phycol., 1,* 121–27.

Decosse, J. J., and N. Aiello, 1966. "Feulgen Hydrolysis: Effects of Acid and Temperature," *J. Histochem. Soc., 14,* 601–604.

Delany, M. J., 1954. "Studies on the Life History and Ecology of *Dilta littoralis* (Womersley, 1930) (Thysanura, Machilidae)," *Trans. Roy. Entomol. Soc., London, 105,* 31–63.

Dennis, A. E., 1965. "Zygospore Formation, Germination, and the Ontogeny of the Chloroplast of *Sirogonium melanosporum* (Randhawa) Transeau," M. S. thesis, Univ. of Arizona, Tucson, 69 pp.

Dineen, C. F., 1953. "An Ecological Study of a Minnesota Pond," *Amer. Midland Nat. 50*, 349–76.

Dohrer, H., 1940. "Kernteilung und Konjugation bei *Zygnema*," *Natur und Volk, 70*, 604–609.

Doraiswami, S., 1946. "Nuclear Division in *Spirogyra*," *J. Indian Bot. Soc., 25*, 19–36.

Drawert, H., 1962. "Zur Frage der Identität von Karyoiden und Golgi-apparat bei den Conjugaten," *Naturwissenschaften, 49*, 1–3.

Dubos, R. J., 1966. "Man and his environment—scope, impact, and nature," in *Environmental Improvement*, Grad. Sch., U.S. Dept. of Agr., Washington, D.C., pp. 3–21.

Freytag, A. H., 1964. "Use of a Commercial Bleaching Agent to Improve Separation of Orchid Chromosomes," *Stain Tech., 39*, 167–69.

Fritsch, F. E., 1907. "The Sub-Aerial and Fresh-Water Algal Flora of the Tropics: A Phytogeographical and Ecological Study," *Ann. Bot., 21*, 235–75.

———, 1931. "Some Aspects of the Ecology of Fresh-Water Algae (with special reference to static waters)," *J. Ecol., 19*, 232–72.

———, 1935. *The Structure and Reproduction of the Algae*, Vol. 1, Cambridge: Cambridge Univ. Press, 791 pp.

Fritsch, F. E., and F. Rich, 1907. "Studies on the Occurrence and Reproduction of British Freshwater Algae in Nature—I. Preliminary Observations on *Spirogyra*," *Ann. Bot., 21*, 423–36.

———, 1927. "The Reproduction and Delimitation of the Genus *Zygnema*," *New Phytol. 26*, 202–208.

Gauch, H. G., Jr., 1966. "Studies on the Life Cycle and Genetics of *Zygnema*," M.S. thesis, Cornell Univ., 91 pp.

Gauthier-Lièvre, L., 1965. "Zygnémacées Africaines," *Beih. Nova Hedwigia, 20*, 1–210.

Geitler, L., 1935a. "Untersuchungen über der Kernbau von *Spirogyra* mittels Feulgens Nuklealfärbung," *Ber. deut. bot. Ges., 53*, 270–75.

———, 1935b. "Neue Untersuchungen über die Mitose von *Spirogyra*," *Arch. Protistenk., 85*, 10–19.

———, 1958. "Isogames Bewegungsverhalten unter morphologischer Anisogamie bei einer konjugaten Alge," *Biol. Zentralbl., 77*, 202–209.

Gibbs, S. P., 1962a. "The Ultrastructure of the Pyrenoids of Green Algae," *J. Ultrastructure Res., 7*, 262–72.

———, 1962b. "The Ultrastructure of the Chloroplasts of Algae," *ibid.*, 418–35.

Godward, M. B. E., 1937. "An Ecological and Taxonomic Investigation of the Littoral Algal Flora of Lake Windemere," *J. Ecol., 25*, 496–568.

———, 1942. "The Life-Cycle of *Stigeoclonium amoenum* Kütz," *New Phytol., 41*, 293–301.

———, 1947. "The Nucleolus and Nucleolar Organizers in *Spirogyra*," *Heredity, 1*, 393.

———, 1948. "The Iron Alum Acetocarmine Method for Algae," *Nature, 161*, 203.

———, 1950a. "On the Nucleolus and Nucleolar-Organizing Chromosomes of *Spirogyra*," *Ann. Bot., 14*, 39–53.

———, 1950b. "Somatic Chromosomes of Conjugales," *Nature, 165*, 653.

———, 1953. "Geitler's Nucleolar Substance in *Spirogyra*," *Ann. Bot., 17*, 403–15.

———, 1954. "The 'Diffuse' Centromere or Polycentric Chromosomes in *Spirogyra*," *ibid., 18*, 143–56.

———, 1956. "Cytotaxonomy of *Spirogyra* I. *S. submargaritata, S. subechinata* and *S. britannica*," *J. Linn. Soc. London, 55*, 532–46.

———, 1961. "Meiosis in *Spirogyra crassa*," *Heredity, 16*, 53–62.

———, ed., 1966a. *The Chromosomes of the Algae*, London: Edward Arnold Publ., 212 pp.

———, 1966b. "The Chlorophyceae," *ibid.*, pp. 1–72.

Godward, M. B. E., and E. G. Jordan, 1965. "Electron Microscopy of the Nucleolus of *Spirogyra britannica* and *Spirogyra elipsospora*," *J. Roy. Microscop. Soc., 84*, 347–60.

Godward, M. B. E., and R. E. Newnham, 1965. "Cytotaxonomy of *Spirogyra* II. *S. neglecta* (Hass.) Kütz., *S. punctulata* Jao, *S. majuscula* (Kütz.) Czurda emend., *S. ellipsospora* Transeau, *S. porticalis* (Müller) Cleve." *J. Linn. Soc. Bot., 59*, 99–110.

Granick, S., 1961. "The Chloroplasts: Inheritance, Structure, and Function," in *The Cell*, ed. by Brachet and Mirsky, Vol. 2. New York: Academic Press, pp. 489–602.

Hoshaw, R. W., 1965. "A Cultural Study of Sexuality in *Sirogonium melanosporum*," *J. Phycol., 1*, 134–38.

Hoshaw, R. W., and R. L. Hilton, 1966. "Observations on the Sexual Cycle of the Saccoderm Desmid *Spirotaenia condensata*," *J. Ariz. Acad. Sci., 4*, 88–92.

Hoshaw, R. W., and R. D. Waer, 1967. "Polycentric Chromosomes in *Sirogonium melanosporum*," *Can. J. Bot., 45*, 1169–71.

Hunter, N. W., 1961. "Demonstration of Some Enzymes in *Spirogyra* sp. by Histochemistry," *Trans. Amer. Microscop. Soc., 80*, 353–57.

Israelson, G., 1949. "On Some Attached Zygnemales and Their Significance in Classifying Streams," *Bot. Notiser 1949*, 313–58.

Johansen, D. A., 1940. *Plant Microtechnique*, New York: McGraw-Hill, 423 pp.

Jost, D. N., 1953. "Studies on the Vegetative Growth and Sexual Reproduction of *Zygnema circumcarinatum* Czurda," Ph.D. thesis, Harvard Univ., 238 pp.

Karsten, G., 1918. "Über die Tagesperiode der Kern-und Zellteilungen," *Z. Bot., 10*, 1–20.

Keck, K., and H. Stich, 1957. "The Widespread Occurrence of Polyphosphate in Lower Plants," *Ann. Bot. 21*, 611–19.

Klebs, G., 1896. *Die Bedingungen der Fortpflanzung bei einigen Algen und Pilzen*, Jena: Gustav Fischer, 543 pp.

Kniep, H., 1928. *Die Sexualität der niederen Pflanzen*, Jena: Gustav Fischer, 544 pp.

Koch, W., 1964. "Verzeichnis der Sammlung von Algenkulturen am Pflanzenphysiologischen Institut der Universität Göttingen," *Arch. Microbiol., 47*, 402–32.

Kurssanow, L., 1912. "Über Befruchtung, Reifung und Keimung bei *Zygnema*," *Flora, 104*, 65–84.

Lewin, R. A., 1959. "The Isolation of Algae," *Rev. Algol., 4*, 181–97.

Leyon, H., 1954. "The Structure of Chloroplasts—III. A Study of Pyrenoids," *Exp. Cell Res., 6*, 497–505.

Lloyd, F. E., 1924. "Conjugation in *Spirogyra*," *Trans. Roy. Can. Inst., 15 (1)*, 129–34.

———, 1926a. "Maturation and Conjugation in *Spirogyra longata*," *ibid. (2)*, 151–93.

———, 1926b. "Studies on Spirogyra. I. Additional Studies on Conjugation," *ibid. 20(5)*, 75–99.

———, 1928. "Further Observations on the Behavior of Gametes during Maturation and Conjugation in *Spirogyra*," *Protoplasma, 4*, 45–66.

Merriman, M. L., 1906. "Nuclear Division in *Zygnema*," *Bot. Gaz., 41*, 43–53.

Meyer, R. R., 1966. "Non-Specific Incorporation of H[3]-Thymidine into the Chloroplasts of *Spirogyra grevilleana*," *Biochem. Biophys. Res. Commun., 25*, 549–53.

Mollenhauer, H. H., and D. J. Morré, 1966. "Tubular Connections Between Dictyosomes and Forming Secretory Vesicles in Plant Golgi Apparatus," *J. Cell Biol. 29*, 373–76.

Myers, J., 1962. "Laboratory cultures," *Physiology and Biochemistry of Algae*, ed. by Lewin, New York: Academic Press, Inc., pp. 603–15.

Nipkow, F., 1962. "Über die Sexual-und Dauerperioden einiger Zygnemalen aus schweizeri-schen Kleingewässern," *Schweiz. Z. Hydrol., 24*, 1–43.

Oura, G., 1953. "On the Mitosis of the *Spirogyra* with Special Reference to the Nucleolar Organization and Nucleolar Organizing Chromosome," *Cytologia, 18*, 297–304.

Palla, E., 1894. "Ueber ein neues Organ der Conjugatenzelle," *Ber. deut. bot. Ges., 12*, 153–62.

Palmer, C. M., 1959. "Algae in Water Supplies," U.S. Depart. of Health, Education, and Welfare, Publ. Health Service Publ. No. 657, Washington, D.C., 88 pp.

Prasad, B. N., 1958. "Cytology and Conjugation in *Zygnema* and *Mougeotia*," *Brit. Phycol. Bull., 6*, 27–28.

Prasad, B. N., and M. B. E. Godward, 1962. "Cytological Studies in the Genus *Mougeotia*," *ibid., 2*, 111–15.

———, 1963. "On Conjugation in *Zygnema cruciatum* (Vaucher) Agardh," *Phykos, 2*, 19–21.

Prescott, G. W., 1962. *Algae of the Western Great Lakes Area, rev. ed.,* Dubuque, Iowa: Wm. C. Brown Co., 977 pp.

Pringsheim, E. G., 1946a. "The Biphasic or Soil-Water Culture Method for Growing Algae and Flagellata," *J. Ecol., 33*, 193–204.

———, 1946b. *Pure Cultures of Algae,* Cambridge: Cambrodge Univ. Press, 119 pp.

Puiseux-Dao, S., 1962. "Action de la ribonucléase sur les cellules vivantes d'un *Mougeotia* sp. (Conjugatophycées, Chlorophycées)," *J. Microscop., 1*, 473–76.

———, 1964. "Action de la ribonucléase sur des cellules vivantes de *Mougeotia* sp. (Conjugatophycées, Chlorophycées). I. Structure placé dans un milieu de culture contentant de la ribonucléase," *J. Microscop., 3*, 207–24.

Puiseux-Dao, S., and N. Levain, 1963. "Etude Cytologique d'un *Mougeotia* (Conjugato-phycées)," *J. Microscop., 2*, 461–84.

Randhawa, M. S., 1959. *Zygnemaceae,* New Delhi: Indian Council of Agricultural Research, 478 pp.

Raper, J. R., 1952. "Chemical Regulation of Sexual Processes in the Thallophytes," *Bot. Rev., 18*, 447–545.

———, 1957. "Hormones and Sexuality in Lower Plants," *Symp. Soc. Exptl. Biol. (11)*, 143–65.

Rawitscher-Kunkel, E., and L. Machlis, 1962. "The Hormonal Integration of Sexual Reproduction in *Oedogonium*," *Amer. J. Bot. 49*, 177–83.

Reichart, G., 1962. "Entwicklungsphysiologische Untersuchungen an *Spirogyra* unter besonderer Berücksichtigung der Geschlechtsbestimmung," *Protoplasma, 55*, 129–55.

———, 1963. "Versuche zur Synchronkultur von *Spirogyra*," *Ber. deut. bot. Ges., 76*, 244–47.

Rickert, F. B., 1963. "Morphological and Physiological Studies of the Genus *Spirogyra*," M. S. thesis, Univ. of Arizona, Tucson, 69 pp.

Ris, H., and W. Plaut, 1962. "Ultrastructure of DNA-Containing Areas in the Chloroplast of *Chlamydomonas*," *J. Cell Biol., 13*, 383–91.

Round, F. E., 1965. *The Biology of the Algae,* New York: St. Martins Press, 269 pp.

Saunders, H., 1931. "Conjugation in *Spirogyra*," *Ann. Bot., 45*, 233–56.

Smith, G. M., 1950. *Fresh-Water Algae of the United States,* New York: McGraw-Hill Book Co., 719 pp.

———, 1951a. "Sexuality of Algae," *The Manual of Phycology,* ed. by Smith, Waltham, Mass.: Chronica Botanica Co., pp. 229–41.

———, 1951b. "The Sexual Substances in Algae," in *Plant Growth Substances,* ed. by Skoog, Madison: Univ. of Wisconsin Press, pp. 315–28.

Sparrow, F. K., 1960. *Aquatic Phycomycetes*, 2nd rev. ed., Ann Arbor: Univ. of Michigan Press, 1187 pp.

Starr, R. C., 1954. "Heterothallism in *Cosmarium botrytis* var. *subtimidum*," *Amer. J. Bot.*, *41*, 601–607.

———, 1963. "Culture Collections of Algae," in *Culture Collections: Perspectives and Problems*, ed. by Martin, Toronto: Univ. of Toronto Press, pp. 136–39.

———, 1964. "The Culture Collection of Algae at Indiana University," *Amer. J. Bot.*, *51*, 1013–44.

Starr, R. C., and W. R. Rayburn, 1964. "Sexual Reproduction in *Mesotaenium kramstai*," *Phycologia*, *4*, 23–26.

Steffensen, D. M., and W. F. Sheridan, 1965. "Incorporation of H^3-Thymidine into Chloroplast DNA of Marine Algae," *J. Cell Biol.*, *25*, 619–26.

Stein, J. R., 1958. "A Morphologic and Genetic Study of *Gonium pectorale*,"*Amer. J. Bot.*, *45*, 664–72.

Stocking, C. R., and E. M. Gifford, Jr., 1959. "Incorporation of Thymidine into Chloroplasts of *Spirogyra*," *Biochem. Biophys. Res. Commun.*, *1*, 159–64.

Suematsu, S., 1936. "Karyological Study of *Spirogyra* by Means of Nucleal-Reaction," *Sci. Rep. Tokyo Bunrika Daigaku*, *3*, 35–40.

Symons, Fr., 1965. "Some Peculiarities Concerning the Contraction of the Gametes in *Spirogyra maxima* (Hass. Wittrock)," *Hydrobiologia*, *26*, 144–50.

Szejnman, A., 1933. "Observations Vitales sur la Formation des Pyrenoïdes chez *Spirogyra*" (in Polish, French abstract), *Acta Soc. Bot. Poloniae, 10*, 331–59.

Taylor, W. R., 1928. "The Alpine Algal Vegetation of the Mountains of British Columbia," *Proc. Acad. Nat. Sci., Phil.*, *80*, 45–114.

Thomas, D. V., 1963. "Growth and Nutrition of the Genus *Zygnema*," M. S. thesis, Univ. of Arizona, Tucson, 60 pp.

Transeau, E. N., 1916. "The Periodicity of Fresh-Water Algae," *Amer. J. Bot., 3*, 121–33.

———, 1934. "The Genera of the Zygnemataceae," *Trans. Amer. Microscop. Soc.*, *53*, 201–207.

———, 1951. *The Zygnemataceae*, Columbus: Ohio State Univ. Press, 327 pp.

Tröndle, A., 1907. "Über die Kopulation und Keimung von *Spirogyra*," *Bot. Zeit.*, *65*, 187–216.

Ueda, K., 1961. "Structure of Plant Cells with Special Reference to Lower Plants. VI. Structure of Chloroplasts in Algae," *Cytologia*, *26*, 344–58.

Waer, R. D., 1966. "A Cytological Investigation of Cell Division in the Filamentous Green Alga, *Sirogonium melanosporum* (Randhawa) Transeau," M.S. thesis, Univ. of Arizona, Tucson, 59 pp.

Weier, T. E., T. Bisalputra, and A. Harrison, 1966. "Subunits in Chloroplast Membranes of *Scenedesmus quadricauda*," *J. Ultrastructure Res.*, *15*, 38–56.

Whitford, L. A., 1960. "The Current Effect and Growth of Fresh-Water Algae," *Trans. Amer. Microscop. Soc.*, *79*, 302–309.

Whitford, L. A., and G. J. Schumacher, 1963. "Communities of Algae in North Carolina Streams and Their Seasonal Relations," *Hydrobiologia*, *22*, 133–96.

Wurtz, A. G., 1964. "Some Problems Remaining in Algae Culturing, in *Algae and Man*, ed. by Jackson, New York: Plenum Press, pp. 120–37.

Yamagishi, T., 1963. "Classification of the Zygnemataceae," *Sci. Rep. Tokyo Kyoiku Daigaku, 11*, 191–210.

X

The Approach of a Modern Algal Taxonomist

HERMAN FOREST

Department of Biology
State University College
Geneseo, New York

George Bernard Shaw was not only a great wit but a careful student of intellectual history and, when he chose to be, a keen analyst of scientific activity. In the prologue to *Back to Methuselah* (1920) he quoted Linnaeus, " 'There are just so many species as there were forms created in the beginning,' " and then he comments, ". . . though there were hundreds of Scotch gardeners, pigeon fanciers, and stock breeders then living who knew better. Linnaeus knew better before he died. In the last edition of his *System of Nature*, he began to wonder whether transmutation of species by variation might not be possible. Then came the great poet who jumped over the facts to the conclusion. Goethe said that all the shapes of creation were cousins; that there must be some common stock from which all species had sprung; that it was the environment of air that had produced the eagle, of water the seal, and of earth the mole. He could not say how this happened, but he divined that it did happen."

Almost fifty years after Shaw's comments, the scientist, the algal taxonomist, usually acts as though he believes in immutable species which have existed from the beginning of time, and there has been all too little inquiry as to what forms the environment of the air, the water, and the earth bring forth. If the environment has been neglected, so too has the other half of the modern biologist's model of reality—heredity. My focus, therefore, is on heredity and environment, not on naming, which will take care of itself in time.

My investigations as a modern taxonomist were frustrating and inconclusive, but they were instructive, and I believe that they indicate the road which must be followed if we are to be intellectually honest in the approach toward the twenty-first century. This report is confined to selected portions of my work: two genera of blue-green algae, *Nostoc* and *Anabaena*, and one species of the Oscillatoriaceae will be cited; the historical concepts of taxonomy for these algae will be reviewed; the species problem in microorganisms will be introduced as background material; and, finally, some original observations on the developmental morphology of blue-green algae will be reported. My object is to establish a few signposts, not to transport you magically to the destination.

TAXONOMIC PERSPECTIVE FROM OTHER BIOLOGICAL DISCIPLINES

Some of the oldest fossils represent blue-green algae, and among primitive organisms, their cellular organization is at least as complex as that of bacteria with which they show similarities in the fine structure of the cell membrane and other features. In gross morphology some blue-green algae resemble bacteria more than other blue-green algae. One amino acid, diaminopimelic acid, has been reported as peculiar to the two. A few bacteria contain photosynthetic lamellae. On the other hand, there are differences between the two types of organism: blue-green algae not only contain photosynthetic lamellae, but they are aerobic "Hill reactors" with oxygen output, while photosynthetic bacteria are not. They are autotrophic to a high degree with respect to growth substances (Bunt, *et al.*, 1961); they lack the appendages which enable some bacteria to be motile; and, perhaps most significantly of all, there are no bacterial parallels with the more elaborate multicellular forms of blue-green algae. Thus, while there may be points of contact between the two groups, their evolutionary divergence is extreme, and it may be unwise to extrapolate findings of bacterial genetics until similarities and differences between bacteria and blue-green algae have been delineated much more precisely.

The problem was illuminated considerably in the discussion which followed the presentation of this paper and those by G. W. Fuhs and Norma Lang. I am highly indebted to these two scientists for the ideas submitted in this note, and must admit my initial delight in discovering that the three of us had arrived at a very similar position.

First, I accept Dr. Fuh's suggestion that the sum total of chromatic material in blue-green algae be termed "nucleoid," even though there is no discrete structure, and even though apparently there are several separate structures included. The term "nucleoplasm," which I had preferred, already has a specific application to typical nuclei.

The term "thylakoid" may be applied usefully as a synonym of photosynthetic lamellae.

Although a fuller discussion of the genetic mechanism of blue-green algae must be deferred to other writings, we were in substantial agreement on two general views: That the mechanism of blue-green algae is significantly different from that known from bacteria, and that the nucleoid is polyenergidic, that is it consists of replicates of relatively small genetic linkages. The term polyploid should not be applied to blue-green algae because it assumes typical chromosomes.

Discussion resulting from the paper of R. A. Lewin further illuminated the particular area of convergence of bacteria and blue-green algae. Following the discussion, I believe that we agree that many resemblances are superficial, and that most questionable organisms can reasonably be assigned to bacteria. There remain certain cases which will baffle us, and are probably to be resolved only in terms of personal taste. One rule-of-thumb which might be applied is that if a non-green organism is otherwise morphologically indistinguishable from a blue-green algae, it should be called an alga.

The taxonomic system established for algae in the nineteenth century by Kuetzing (1849), Gomont (1892–93), and Bornet and Flahault (1886–88) remained basically unchanged and unchallenged until rather recently. However, new species were subsequently described, and a number of them may be found in the standard works of Geitler (1925, 1930–31), Elenkin (1936–49), Hollerbach, et. al. (1953), and Desikachary (1959). The concept of "type specimen," which has long been recognized in the taxonomy of higher plants, has not been applied consistently in the taxonomy of blue-green algae, and even now descriptions of new species are published without specimens being placed on permanent deposit. Among modern taxonomists of blue-green algae, Francis Drouet is unique in having accumulated a large herbarium of nineteenth and twentieth century specimens; consequently, his studies are comparable to those made by monographers of higher plants. Drouet's herbarium has made possible substantial monographic studies (Drouet and Daily, 1956; Drouet, 1962, 1963; also Fan, 1956; Cameron, 1962).

Historically, algal taxonomists have contributed little to the development of modern concepts of species. They still work with the same ideas and methods used in the nineteenth century. Morphological distinctions are still the chief criteria in distinguishing orders, families, genera, and species of blue-green algae. These criteria have been discussed by Cameron (1963). In brief, the criteria of classification of blue-green algae are:

MORPHOLOGICAL

a. Gross colony form—size, shape, color, texture.
b. Filament morphology—gelatinous sheath, arrangement within sheath, taper, constriction, branching, pseudobranching.
c. Cell morphology—size, shape, inclusion of granules or pseudovacuoles, color.
d. Shape of terminal cells; morphology of specialized cells, heterocysts and spores (akinetes).

e. Habitat ecology—Species are described as being planktonic, endophytic, edaphic, etc.

f. There are a few simple chemical tests such as the chloro-zinc-iodine stain for sheaths.

Taxonomists who study other organisms—from bacteria to mammals—have come to rely on new concepts of classification, while new techniques of study have come to be used concurrently. The methods of taxonomists now include statistical or diagrammatical analyses of multiple characters, biochemical tests, and genetic experiments. Since blue-green algae are being compared with bacteria cytologically and genetically, the contrast in their taxonomy is noteworthy. Ravin's (1963) suggestion of three categories for species classification of bacteria is a good example of modern thinking. Dr. Ralph Mattoni has provided me with a paper which is a comprehensive discussion of the problem. I feel that it is one of the classic papers of biology. (Cowan, S. T. 1962. "The Microbial Species—A macromyth?" Symp. *Soc. Gen. Microbiol.* 12: 433–455.)

Ravin applied the term *nomenspecies* to a population which shows a common group of characteristics selected for operational usefulness, such as for identification or economic value. Thus defined, *nomenspecies* would be synonymous with most legitimate species under the International Rules. Such species are limited in that, aside from the selected diagnostic characteristics, the organisms may have nothing else in common, and, by custom at least, "field" characteristics are commonly selected, whereas many characteristics are observed readily only in the laboratory.

The term *taxospecies* refers to populations having a high "coefficient of similarity" within them. Such species are best based on a number of cross-correlated characters. While the particular characteristics to be correlated are selected arbitrarily by the taxonomist, the analysis of a large number of characters by statistical methods engenders confidence that the evaluation procedure is relevant. Using the concept of *taxospecies*, it is possible to speak of various degrees of affinity even without statistical analysis.

Use of the term *genospecies* is based on the observation of genetic events in the laboratory. When genetic transfer and recombination can be demonstrated within a population it constitutes a *genospecies*.

Without accepting Ravin's ideas as being either true for bacteria or applicable to blue-green algae, the ideas can serve to emphasize that "species" is not a fixed concept, and that the method of study is closely related to the investigator's concepts. Microbial geneticists, lacking adequate morphological criteria, resort to genetic crosses and may find genospecies to be "real." While the macrobiologist can be quite oblivious to genospecies, as witness he can speak of interspecific and intergeneric crosses without feeling and contradiction in his concept of (nomen) species. The taxonomist of mosses, ferns, or seed plants bases his species primarily on gross morphology, not genetics. Similarly, blue-green algae are classified largely by their morphology, which is somewhat simpler than that of most familiar organisms.

Taxonomic perspective, aided by the identification and preservation of specimens, can avoid uncertainties which will arise from laboratory studies in which taxonomy is not the primary consideration. It is already impossible to know with reasonable certainty the identity and characteristics of several of the algae which were used in currently reported work.

Developmental Morphology in Blue-Green Algae (Nostocaceae)

In complex organisms the understanding of genetics includes a knowledge of their developmental morphology. For lower organisms this means, in particular, the morphogenesis of the sexual apparatus. For example, investigations to secure evidence of recombination in bacteria have been complemented by quests for corroboration by morphological evidence. The same investigative history might be predicted for blue-green algae. Most blue-green algae show a more elaborate morphogenesis than bacteria, and subsequent investigations may reveal even more elaborations.

Largely unknown in precise terms is the relationship of morphogenesis to the environment of blue-green algae. Yet the influence of the environment on morphogenesis is so universal among organisms that any foundation for genetics in blue-green algae must include some consideration of their ecology. Manuals frequently differentiate between species as either aquatic or terrestrial, but most actually occur in water or on soil. Algae which are calcified, or thermophilic, now appear to be ubiquitous, as Drouet concluded after studying an enormous number of preserved specimens and also some growing specimens revived from the preserved ones. Most generally, blue-green algae grow where the substrate is not too acid: a pH range of 7.2–8.2 is suitable for many. They survive or grow in a wide range of ionic concentrations; I found that only two out of forty failed to grow in unenriched sea water. An *Anabaena* culture, FOG–032 grew with only temporary retardation in a mineral solution to which .3 M NaCl had been added. Light, of course, is usually required for blue-green algae. Under laboratory conditions they have been found to grow under intensities from 50 to 300 fc. Phototropism and phototaxis have been observed. Light affects the nutrition, morphology, and developmental cycle (*Nostoc*). In the absence of light, however, some species can become heterotrophic. Moreover, several blue-greens can fix nitrogen and are able to grow on a substrate deficient in assimilable nitrogen compounds; association with bacteria provides equivalent service for others. Heterocystous species generally grow well in a medium devoid of nitrates, while other species are static, chlorotic, or slow growers.

Association with bacteria, fungi, and other microorganism is characteristic of blue-green algae, and the relationship is frequently quite tenacious. The effects of such associations may be obvious enough in lichenization, but it is quite subtle in other situations. In my study of cultures of *Anabaena*, culture MAN–036 developed only short, oval spores until repeated transfers and rapid growth apparently resulted in a reduced level of contamination, whereupon it developed as a typical *Anabaena inaequalis* (Kuetz) B. & F. with long cylindrical spores. The experience was matched with MIT–037 which eventually developed into a typical *Anabaena oscillarioides* (Kuetz.) B. & F.

Unfortunately little is known about the morphogenic effects of microbial associates. Only a single virus has been reported (Safferman and Morris, 1963, 1964; Schneider, *et. al.*, 1964), but if blue-green algae follow bacteria and actinomycetes in this respect, there must be others. There are many morphological puzzles which might be explained by a fuller understanding of contaminants. For example, two *Anabaena* cultures, UTR–040 and LBI–100, have never been observed to develop mature spores. Also, two cultures of *Nostoc*, WIS–038 and GER–013, grew well enough, but remained in one stage of development for two and one-half years; after being dried for ten months and revived, they produced other stages, whereupon one continued to produce cyclical changes, and the other lapsed mostly into its customary anabaenoid state.

It is distressing that the immense amount of observation of blue-green algae from field collections for more than a century produced so little information about their morphogenesis. An alternate source of such information, the study of cultures in the laboratory, has been probed only recently. The work of Lazaroff and Vishniac (1961,–62,–66) on the morphogenesis of *Nostoc muscorum* (Agardh) B. & F., ALL-100, established a standard of excellence and suggested directions for further work. For the first time, they followed a developmental sequence which has proved to be a model for the genus. Because of its importance in following discussions, the sequence is summarized in some detail.

Heterocystous Cycle

1. Hormogone (motile filament).
2. Cessation of movement; enlargement of intercalary cells; development of terminal ones to heterocysts.

3. Division of intercalary cells in a plane parallel to the filament axis.

4. Possible production of four cells from each intercalary cell by reduction division (no direct evidence), and the enclosure of each group of four and their immediate progeny in a common gelatinous envelope.

5. Each cell of the tetrad gives rise to a short filament capable of limited motility. "Sporogenous cycle" (a) filaments two–four cells in length can develop in darkness, but further steps in this cycle require light; (b) growth into longer filaments, which may develop terminal heterocysts; (c) formation of short fragments by formation of necridia (dead cells) and/or formation of spores (akinetes). Cells differ from undifferentiated cells by less regular shape and a denser, more refractile protoplast; (d) germination of spores to two–three-celled germlings which seem to be identical to the short motile trichomes of step 5.

6. Joining, end-to-end, of short filaments from sporogenous cycle (step d) eventually to produce heterocystous filaments. In phototrophic cultures the whole sporogenous cycle is restricted to the aseriate cells (step 4) which join to produce the elongating filament. (The elongated heterocystous filament of Lazaroff and Vishniac corresponds to the "mature" form recognized in field studies.)

7. Loosening of sheath, breaking up of filament at heterocysts to form loose heterocysts and hormogonia.

The Lazaroff cycle can be generalized to apply to other *Nostoc* species by allowing for variations, principally deletions, truncations, and/or prolongations of stages. It is also a useful guide in distinguishing the various genera which develop both spores and heterocysts. A reduced form of the cycle may be sought not only in the Nostocaceae (*Anabaena, Cylindrospermum*) but among the Rivulariaceae, which are distinguished principally by tapered filaments. The line, however, is not a sharp one.

Generalization of the Lazaroff Cycle

Truncation—Any stage can be truncated, and even omitted. In ALL-100 cultures grown in light (see the *Heterocystous cycle*) steps 4 and 5 may be omitted. The hormogones cease motility, elongate (although even step 3 can be omitted) and become kinky from cell enlargement and elongation (but not necessarily division). The cells then could be called spores, but the morphological difference from ordinary cells is a graduated one and is not always discernible. The filaments usually kink, but not always, and the color of the mass changes to a deep green if development is stopped at this stage and the culture ages. Intercalary heterocysts may develop also.

In terms of the cycle, steps 2,3,4, and 5 of the *Heterocystous cycle* have been truncated, and steps (a) and (b) of the "Sporogenous cycle" as well. Hence, heterocysts may be found in what was the old hormogone.

Subsequently, there may be a production of germlings which Lazaroff has observed to join end-to-end, or simply inplace growth resumption to form the heterocystous filaments; this constitutes step 6, which precedes the formation of hormogonia and completion of the cycle.

Variations in the Cycle of Other Nostoc *Species*

Spores have long been observed in the heterocystous stages of field collections. They have developed in the laboratory in culture of *Nostoc muscorum*, N. *ellipsosporum* (Dezmaz.) B. & F., and N. *microscopicum* (Carm.) B. & F. These observations can be reconciled with the Lazaroff cycle only by assuming that the entire cycle from the heterocystous filament to spore is truncated. Spore germlings can grow directly into heterocystous filaments again. Certain species have been illustrated in their aseriate form only, and some cultures have tended to remain in this stage, e.g., WAS–010, SHT–034, and PER–259. From the aseriate stage the rapid production of hormogones was observed; these moved independently, stopped, divided, and soon formed new aseriate packets. However, a fungal associate was visible in all cases when a *Nostoc* persisted in aseriate stage, and it has always been possible to observe the development of heterocystous filaments in these cultures. Therefore, it seems quite probable that the fungus is responsible for the amplification of the aseriate stage and for the small, tight, "punctate" colony form in the heterocystous stage. Furthermore, the punctate type of colony varies into larger, more typical colonies of *Nostoc commune*.

Although far from satisfactory, the knowledge of developmental morphology of the *Nostoc* is now sufficient to permit further studies seeking to establish its relationship with sexual phenomena.

ANABAENA

My studies of morphogenesis of *Anabaena* are not in the order of those completed for *Nostoc*. Nevertheless, these notes, which are largely from observations on FOG–032, will have relevance to subsequent discussions, and they can provide a starting line for further studies.

Anabaena develops the same three basic types of cells as *Nostoc*: vegetative cells, heterocysts, and spores. Spores are typically cylindrical with a volume which may be fifty times that of vegetative cells, but both size and shape are variable. It does not appear to be necessary for spores either to attain a certain size or to mature (develop a thick case and turn yellow) for them to germinate.

Mature spores, unmixed with vegetative filaments, have germinated after thirty-six hours under light on fresh agar surfaces. Germination varies; in some cases no septation occurs until the germling has emerged from the spore case, but in others, at least four cells can be seen within the spore walls. Heterocysts may actually be seen in emerging germlings, but other germlings develop no heterocysts until they are about sixteen cells long, when one develops in the middle. Further development of heterocysts occurs about halfway between two old heterocysts, or between the tip and a heterocyst, so that one of each eight–sixteen cells is a heterocyst. I have never observed the formation of a heterocyst at the tip of a filament, as occurs in the hormogones of *Nostoc*.

Germlings are motile as soon as they emerge, and the capacity to move is retained even by filaments several hundred cells long. Motility eventually is limited by the gelatinous matrix produced by the filaments, and possibly other factors. Yet, when filaments from stable colonies are suspended uniformly in water and spread on a new agar surface, they become motile and within twenty-four hours many of them have aggregated into their characteristic spiral masses which may become neatly domed "blobs" containing as many as 3×10^6 cells.

I have never observed successful development by an isolated spore germling and have some evidence to indicate that development usually occurs only in a group. Filaments begin to fragment only two–three days after emergence, and as early as five days after emergence enlarged cells develop. These cells suggest incipient spores, although they are generally not adjoining heterocysts. After several hours, however, division occurs, and the area soon becomes indistinguishable from the remainder of the filament. Successful spore formation has been observed first in cells adjoining heterocysts and three weeks after emergence of germlings (agar plates, continuous light).

Design for a Modern Taxonomic Study

Blue-green algae for laboratory studies are likely to be chosen from those already available in culture, preferably uncontaminated cultures. Original isolation adds materially to the effort required for studies since methods for establishing clean cultures are at best tedious and uncertain; Lewin (1959) is a good reference for such technique. Therefore, only a small number of cultures have been used for studies which I shall consider as basic. Their merits, identification, and description will be discussed here. Two means of identification are used: (a) Uniform designations for individual cultures, which are intended to identify individual isolates through any subsequent changes in nomenclature. This system, based on three letters and three numerals is explained in Appendix A. (b) Names of the algae in accordance with the International Rules of Botanical Nomenclature as far as is known.

The activity of assigning legitimate names could not be accomplished without reference to algae other than those which have been used in this study. Consequently, the discussion of the results of taxonomic studies extends beyond the scope of the report.

In addition to availability, the choice of cultures to be used in investigations is influenced greatly by knowledge of their use in previous studies. This facilitates work since at least the basic requirements for growth do not need to be learned repeatedly. Thus ALL–100 (*Nostoc muscorum* of Allison, *et al.*, 1937) which was used by Lazaroff and Vishniac (1961) was my initial choice, because the developmental cycle suggested that sexual phases might be included. Two other cultures under the name of *Nostoc muscorum*, GER–013 and WIS–038, also have been studied by Lazaroff, and these were added with the hope of finding usable genetic markers among the three cultures. All three cultures differed morphologically from each other, with only ALL–100 showing a developmental cycle. The other two remained in compact colonies consisting of heterocystous fllaments, and no distinct spores were produced. They looked more like *Anabaena* than *Nostoc*, and a study of *Anabaena* had to be undertaken to help establish their identity.

I soon chose to work with *Anabaena* because in contrast to *Nostoc*, *Anabaena* had a much simpler developmental cycle, and some cultures produced large spores continuously. Moreover, the gelatinous matrix is much less firm, thus allowing easier manipulation of filaments or spores. While it was not possible to develop a technique of fragmenting the filaments and germinating single cells, it was possible to obtain suspensions of spores and to germinate spores on agar surfaces. The characteristics strongly suggest that *Anabaena* would be a good subject for additional studies.

Ultimately, the study of *Anabaena* was conducted at three levels:

    a. A broad, taxonomic study of all available culture, herbarium specimens, and new isolations from the field, the total number being 850.

    b. A middle-level study of five cultures of *Anabaena* from the University of Indiana collection: FOG–032, MAN–036, UTR–031, UTR–032, and UTR–040. These were studied with respect to colony type, spore and filament morphology, and resistance to harmful chemicals.

c. An intensive study of a single *Anabaena* culture, FOG–032, on which the effect of a number of chemicals and radiation was studied. This culture was also used in the development of basic techniques for growing and treating *Anabaena*, and in attempts to extract nucleic acid.

The culture herein designated as FOG–032 has generally been known as Fogg's strain of *Anabaena cylindrica* Lemm. It has long been studied in respect to nitrogen fixation and other metabolic processes. (Fogg, 1942, 1953, 1956, etc.). In addition, electron microscopic studies have been made on it (Hopwood and Glauert, 1960; Wildon and Mercer, 1963a, b). Therefore, it is probably one of the most studied of all cultures. Unfortunately, the subcultures of FOG–032 at Cambridge, the University of Indiana, Prague, and Leningrad all were contaminated when examined, but a clean culture was obtained from Dr. Fogg's laboratory.

A few other cultures have received special attention. I used UTR–040 for the derivation of penicillin-resistant colonies, and Kumar derived resistance in HEC–100, which was identified as *Anabaena* but does not belong in the genus. Singh (1964) reported the achievement of resistance in *A. cycadae* Reinke and *A. dolium* Ehr., but no culture of these species is available for study.

In addition to the cultures of Nostocaceae, one taxonomically puzzling culture has been used quite frequently in laboratory studies; in this writing it is designated as KAA-100. This organism was isolated by Kratz and cleaned by Allen (Kratz and Myers, 1955). It was tentatively identified by Drouet as *Anacystis nidulans* (Richt.) D. & D., and the name has persisted, although it is obviously wrong. A footnote by Silva in Lewin (1962) altered the probable identity to *Phormidium mucicola*. Hub-Pest. & Naum. and Drouet (1963) assigned it to *Schizothrix calcicola* (Agardh) Gom.

Among blue-green algae, KAA–100 is somewhat atypical. It is thermophilic, with an optimum temperature of about $10°C$ higher that of most other blue-green algae (Kratz and Myers, 1955), as well as being very small ($1.5–2.0\ \mu$ in diameter). Although it has been considered a unicellular alga, it actually forms fragile filaments of up to $30\ \mu$ in length, disqualifying it easily from the genus *Anacystis*. Since the filaments are fragile, the alga may be grown as a homogeneous suspension in liquid cultures. Except that it is autotrophic, this blue-green alga can be handled very much as a bacterium.

What results were obtained by these approaches? In stating the results, I shall attempt to demonstrate that the athletic ability of the scientist is not less than that of Goethe, and I will leap over the data to the conclusions, tentative as they are. First, the relationship between the genera *Nostoc* and *Anabaena* was clarified. The naive notion that *Nostoc* can be distinguished by a firm sheath and a macroscopic colony form is untenable, and the field practice of labeling all free filaments as *Anabaena* is bad taxonomy. The facts of life are that the genera frequently cannot be distinguished by single observations, and that their developmental morphology must be followed.

Within the genus *Anabaena* I find four species, two aquatic, two amphibious. As far as I can tell the plants originally described as the genus *Pseudanabaena* are *Anabaena flos-aquae* (Breb.) B. & F., which has unsuspected morphological latitude. Four species suffice for the assignment of all *Nostoc* specimens, too. Finally, I almost completely agree with Drouet that the myriad of small filaments of Oscillatoriaceae which have received dozens of names are *Schizothrix calcicola* (Ag.) Gom. My reservations are frankly admitted uncertainties. These involve certain cultures of fragile filamentous algae which are usually described as unicellular. The most serious problem is KAA-100, the Kratz and Allen culture usually called *Anacystis nidulans*, but PRI-791, the Pringsheim isolate labeled *Synechococcus elongatus* Naeg. poses a similar problem.

Obviously I reveal myself as an adherent of Dr. Lumper's school of taxonomy and an opponent of Dr. Splitter's school. Possibly this prejudice is more basic than my methodology. I realized when I was a graduate student that my mind's eye was keyed quite differently from that of my major professor, Dr. Prescott—he to differences, I to similarities. I do not assert that I am right; I do assert that more heed should be paid to the final ideas of Linnaeus than his preliminary ones, and the *relationship* between myriad forms should be regarded critically. Almost every collection and culture of blue-green algae differs a little from the others, and when one becomes skilled it is possible to spot a specimen which is very much like the Fogg culture of *Anabaena*, but I doubt the wisdom of erecting species to cover minor variations which cannot be communicated by the traditional methods of keys, drawings, or terse written descriptions. Taxonomy, in my view, is an information retrieval device, and application is its test. It is, consequently, not simply new techniques of investigation which produce a modern taxonomy, but a modern attitude that the taxonomy is not fixed but must be specifically adapted to the type of information sought.

APPENDIX A

DESIGNATION OF CULTURE STRAINS

Strain designations are composed of three letters of similar symbols (without distinguishing upper from lower case) and three numerals. The letters are chosen for their mnemonic value to suggest the isolators, the place of isolation, or other similar identification. Numbers are in order of designation beginning with 100 unless a number has already been used, in which case the last three digits are suggested.

In designating new strains which have been derived from previous ones, it is suggested that the numerals rather than the letters should be changed, but such matters must be left to future judgment and arbitration. Perhaps it is not too prophetic to envisage the day when all publications will include strain designations of organisms used, when distinctive cultures and dried specimens will be deposited for future reference, and when specific journals will be selected for the publication of new names and strain designations.

Cultures Cited in the Text

ALL–100 *nostoc muscorum* (Agardh) B. & F. Cambridge 1453/12 and Univ. Indiana 486.

FOG–032 *Anabaena inaequalis* (Agardh) B. & F. Cambridge 1403/2 and Univ. Indiana 629. Widely known as Fogg's strain of *Anabaena cylindrica* Lemm.

GER–013 *Nostoc ellipsosporum* (Dezmaz) B. & F., Univ. Indiana 586. Known as Gerloff's strain of Nostoc. The culture is quite abnormal and its identification elusive. The present assignment is tentative.

HEC–100 *Nostoc* sp., perhaps *N. ellipsosporum* (Dezmaz.) B. & F. Hecker's isolate as *Cylindrosperum* sp. Also known as *Anabaena variabilis* (Kuetz.) B. & F. (see Kratz & Meyers, 1955). The culture studied was obtained from the laboratories at Westfield College, University of London. It formed only fragile filaments and was usually almost unicellular.

KAA–100 *Schizothrix calcicola* (Agardh) Gom. Determined by Drouet (1963). This is the *Anacystis nidulans* of several writings which was isolated by Kratz and cleaned by M. B. Allen. No other isolation of *Anacystis nidulans* has been located, although inquiries have been directed to the authors of several reports.

LBI–100 *Anabaena* sp.? Obtained from the mass-culture apparatus at the Biological Institute of the University of Leningrad, Oranienbaum by the courtesy of V. V. Pinnevich. The alga has produced spores neither in liquid culture (where it grows prolifically) nor on agar. Although it grew well on agar, hormogones were not produced nor were the elongated filaments motile. The vegetative cells resemble those of *A. oscillarioides* (Bory) B. & F., but there is no critical characteristic to distinguish it from a Nostoc.

MIT–037 *Anabaena oscillarioides* (Bory) B. & F., Cambridge 1403/7. Mitra's isolate, as *A. ambigua* Mitra.

MAN–036 *Anabaena inaequalis* (Kuetz) B. & F. Cambridge 1403/1 and Univ. Indiana 375. The Cambridge Catalogue does not list Manten as isolator, but gives the source as Utrecht P–36.

PER–259 *Nostoc commune* (Vauch.) Gom. The species here is taken in the extended sense to include *N. hederulae* (Menegh.) B. & F. The culture was isolated from sod-podzolic soil of a meadow near Kirov and sent by E. A. Shtina. It was identified as *Amorphonostoc punctiforme* (Kuetz.) Elenk. This is the form which has most frequently been called *N. punctiforme* (Kuetz.) Hariot.

PRI–791 *Schizothrix calcicola* (Agardh) Gom. Determined by Drouet (1963). Cambridge 1479/1 and Univ. Indiana 563.

SHT–034 *Nostoc commune* (Vauch) Gom. E. A. Shtina's 18, obtained from the Leningrad University Collection. The culture bore the notation that it was isolated by A. N. Tretiyakova from soil sent from the United States. It was identified as *Stratonostoc commune* (Vauch.) Elenk., and is quite similar to PER–259.

UTR–031 *Anabaena inaequalis* (Kuetz.) B. & F. Cambridge 1446/la and Univ. Indiana 380. Isolated at Utrecht.

UTR–032 *Anabaena inaequalis* (Kuetz.) B. & F. Cambridge 1446/lc and Univ. Indiana 381. Isolated at Utrecht.

UTR–040 *Anabaena* sp., possibly *A. inaequalis*. Cambridge 1403/4 and Univ. Indiana 377. Isolated at Utrecht.

WAS–010 *Nostoc commune* (Vauch.) B. & F. Cambridge 1453/3 and Univ. Indiana 384. Wassink's isolate.

WIS–038 *Nostoc muscorum* (Agardh) B. & F.? Univ. Indiana 1038, deposited by Lazaroff, who obtained it from the Univeristy of Wisconsin Water Chemistry Laboratory. Like GER–013, this culture remains in an anomolous anabaenoid form, but it has been observed in cyclic behavior.

REFERENCES

Allison, F. E., S. R. Hoover, and H. J. Morris. 1937 "Physiological Studies with *Nostoc muscorum*," *Bot. Gaz.*, *98*, 34–53.

Bornet, E., and C. Flahault, 1886–88. "Revision des Nostocacees Heterocystees Contenues dans les Principaux Herbiers de France," *Ann. Sci. Nat. Bot.*, *3*, 323–81; *4*, 343–73; *5*, 51–129; *7*, 177–262.

Bunt, J. S., Y. T. Tschan, and J. Gould, 1961. "Blue-Green Algae," *Nature, 192*, 1274–76.

Cameron, R. E., 1962. "Species of *Nostoc* Vaucher Occurring in the Sonoran Desert in Arizona," *Trans. Amer. Micros. Soc., 81*, 379–84.

Cameron, R. E., 1963. "Morphology of Representative Blue-Green Algae," *Ann. N.Y. Acad. Sci., 108*, 412–20.

Desikachary, T. V., 1959. "Cyanophyta," New Delhi: Indian Council of Agricultural Research.

Drouet, F., 1962. "Gomont's Ecophenes of the Blue-Green Alga, *Microcoleus vaginatus*," *Proc. Acad. Nat. Sci. Phil., 114*, 191–205.

Drouet, F. 1963. Ecophenes of *Schizothrix calcicola* (Oscillatoriaceae)," *Proc. Acad. Nat. Sci. Phil., 115*, 261–81.

Drouet, F., and W. A. Daily, 1956. "Revision of the Coccoid Myxophyceae," *Butler Univ. Studies. Bot., 12*, 1–218.

Elenkin, A. A., 1936, 1938, 1949. "Monographia algarum Cyanophycearum aquidulcium et terrestrium infinibus URSS inventarum (Sinezelenie Vodorosli SSSR)," Acad. Nauk URSS.

Fan, K. C., 1956. "Revision of *Calothrix* Agardh," *Alg. Rev. Alg. N.S., 2*, 154–78.

Fogg, G. E., 1942. "Studies on Nitrogen-Fixation by Blue-Green Algae," *Brit. Expr. Biol. 19*, 78–87.

Fogg, G. E. 1953. "Metabolism of the Algae," London: Methuen Monographs.

Fogg, G. E. 1956. "The Comparative Physiology and Biochemistry of Blue-Green Algae," Bact. Rev. *20*, 148–65.

Geitler, L., 1925. "Cyanophyceae," *Die Suesswasserflora Deutschlands, Oesterreichs und der Schweiz*, by Pascher, Heft 12, Jena.

Geitler, L. 1930–1. "Cyanophyceae," *Kryptogamen-Flora von Deutschland, Oesterreich und der Schweiz*. by L. Rabenhorst, 14, Lf. 1, 1–288 and Lf. 2., 289–464.

Gomont, M., 1892–93. "Monographia des Oscillariees (Nostocacees homocystees)," *Ann. Sci. Nat. Bot., 15*, 263–68; *16*, 91–264; and Academie de Medecine Paris, 302 pp.

Hollerbach, M. M., E. K. Kosinsky, and V. I. Poljansky, 1953. "Taxonomy of fresh water algae of the USSR," vol. 2, "Blue-green algae," Moscow: Ministry of Culture USSR.

Hopwood, D. A., and A. M. Glauert, 1960. "The Fine Structure of the Nuclear Material of a Blue-Green Alga, *Anabaena cylindrica* Lemm," *J. Biophys. and Biochem. Cyt., 8*, 813–23.

Kratz, W. A., and J. Myers, 1955. "Nutrition and Growth of Several Blue-Green Algae," *Amer. J. Bot., 42*, 282–87.

Keutzing, F. T., 1849. *Species Algarum*, Leipzig.

Lazaroff, N., 1966. "Photoinduction and Photoreversal of the Nostocacean Developmental Cycle," *J. Phycol., 2*, 7–17.

Lazaroff, N., and W. Vishniac, 1961. "The Effect of Light on the Developmental Cycle of *Nostoc muscorum*, a Filamentous Blue-Green Alga," *J. Gen. Microb., 25*, 365–74.

Lazaroff, N. and W. Vishniac, 1962. "The Participation of Filament Anastomosis in the Developmental Cycle of *Nostoc muscorum*, a Blue-Green Alga," *J. Gen. Microb., 28*, 203–210.

Lewin, R. A., 1959. "The Isolation of Algae," *Rev. Alg. N. S. 3*, 183–97.

Lewin, R. A., 1962. *Physiology and Biochemistry of Algae*, New York: Academic Press.

Ravin, A. W., 1963. "Experimental Approaches to the Study of Bacterial Phylogeny," *Amer. Nat., 97*, 307–18.

Safferman, R. S. and M. E. Morris. 1963. "Algal virus; Isolation," *Science, 140*, 679–680.

Safferman, R. S. and M. E. Morris. 1964. "Growth Characteristics of the Blue-Green Algal Virus, LPP-1," *J. Bacteriol., 88*, 771–775.

Safferman, R. S. and M. E. Morris, 1967. "Observations on the Occurrence, Distribution, and Seasonal Incidence of Blue-Green Algal Viruses," *Appl. Microbiol., 15*, 1219–22.

Schneider, I. R., T. O. Diener, and R. S. Safferman, 1964. "Blue-Green Algal Virus LPP-1; Purification and Partial Characterization," *Science, 144*, 1127–30.

Singh, R. N., 1964. "Induction of Mutation in Blue-Green Algae," Contributed papers at International Botanical Congress, Edinburgh (Joker), 472.

Wildon, D. C. and F. V. Mercer, 1963. "The Ultrastructure of the Vegetative Cell of the Blue-Green Algae," *Australian J. Biol. Sci., 16*, 585–96.

Wildon, D. C. and F. V. Mercer, 1963. "The Ultrastructure of the Heterocyst and Akinete of the Blue-Green Algae," *Arkiv. Mikrobiol., 47*, 19–31.

XI

Trends in Algal Genetics

R. H. T. MATTONI

NUS Corporation
Biological Systems Division

Studies on the genetics of algae started more than fifty years ago with the report of Pascher in 1918. The work was of historical significance to general genetics in providing the first demonstration of segregation of heritable characteristics as direct products of the meiotic division. Pascher's evidence was based on analysis of the gametes produced from zygospores obtained from crosses betweeen two unidentified species of *Chlamydomonas*. The next noteworthy work in algae genetics was carried out by Moewus (1938). Although much of this work did not stand the test of repeatability by other workers (Lewin, 1953; Gowans, 1960), Moewus' reports of recombination occurring at the two-strand stage and multiple-locus sex determination provided the stimulus which led to studies on the genetics of algae.

Contemporary research was signaled by the appearance of Lewin's paper in 1953. He succeeded in producing a series of mutant strains of *Chlamydomonas moewusii* and subsequently described their linkage relation by tetrad analysis.

In the 1950's a group of workers then at Stanford University began a program to recover morphological and biochemical mutant strains for use in studying linkage relationships and the mechanism of crossing over in greater detail. The work was initiated by Smith and Regnery (1950) using *C. reinhardi*, the dominant species for algal research today. The technique of tetrad analysis now most widely employed was originally described by Ebersold (see Levine and Ebersold, 1960). The use of algae other than *Chlamydomonas* in genetic studies has not been exploited, although Lewin (1958) suggested several marine forms which could be fruitfully investigated. Such forms might be particularly interesting for work in evolutionary genetics.

Several researchers have employed "mutant" strains of *Chlorella* for physiological studies. Although most of the character changes of the derived strains are stable (see Bendix and Allen, 1962; and Kvitko and Khropova, 1963, for exceptions), the presumptive absence of a sexual system of *Chlorella* precludes classical genetic analysis. Thus genetical interpretation of the defective strains cannot be asserted because of the well-documented occurrence of non-chromosomal genetic material in other green unicellular algae.

The material reviewed here will cover three main topics: chromosomal and non-chromosomal genetics of *Chlamydomonas* and their interactions.

For further information, the reader is referred to reviews by Levine and Ebersold (1960), Ebersold (1962), and Sager (1964).

Chromosomal Genetics

A chromosomally located mutant gene can usually be identified by showing 2:2 segregation in tetrads following a cross of the mutant marker to the wild-type strain of appropriate mating type. The operation involves mixing the two strains of opposite mating type (+ and −) in liquid, permitting the zygotes to mature under proper conditions, and isolating the four meiotic products (tetrads) by manipulation on agar plates containing appropriate nutrients (Levine and Ebersold, 1960). By further crossing the strains carrying markers of independent origin, whether of the same or different phenotype, it is possible to establish allelism and linkage relationships. At present, well over a hundred mutants have been so identified in *Chlamydomonas reinhardi*.

The most recent information on linkage indicates that the *Chlamydomonas reinhardi* map consists of fifteen linkage groups (Levine, unpublished). Although this feature is not wholly secure, it provides a curious anomaly in that the clearest analysis of the haploid chromosome number gives eight (Buffaloe, 1958; Levine and Folsome, 1959). The reasons for the discrepancy are not clear, although further effort would first be in order to unequivocally document both the number of linkage groups and chromosomes.

The early controversy concerning the time of crossing over has been clearly resolved with results that can be interpreted only by crossing over at the four-strand stage (Ebersold and Levine, 1959).

In the process of carrying out studies on the mechanisms of genetic transmission, a considerable collection of mutant strains was necessary. These strains provided useful materials for work on gene action in development. The major classes, significance, and research trends of chromosomal mutants are summarized below. Unless otherwise cited, the work involves *Chlamydomonas*.

Structural Mutants—Flagella Mutants

The study of morphogenesis of organelles is of importance to an understanding of both the mechanism of differentiation at the molecular level and the relationship of components of the genetic system in forming defined structural elements. Lewin (1953) recognized several classes of mutant strains of *C. moewusii* with impaired movement: (1) flagella lacking or encapsulated (palmella colonies), (2) abnormal flagella characterized by short length or with small swellings, and (3) grossly normal structural flagella incapable of producing directed movement (paralyzed flagella -*pf*). Warr, *et al.* (1966), showed that *C. reinhardi* mutants fall into the same classes but noted that the last class could be further subdivided. Randall, *et al.* (1964), earlier showed that one of the subclasses in which the flagella were held in the form of a "V" was structurally defective. In cross section the wild-type flagella consists of nine peripheral pairs of tubular fibers and a central pair within a bounding membrane. The *pf* mutants lack an organized central pair. Warr, *et al.* (1966), subsequently studied fourteen *pf* strains which were center-pair defective. These were genetically located at four loci, each associated with different linkage groups. Warr, *et al.*, described a partial suppression of mutant alleles at two of the loci. The suppressor was not linked to either *pf* locus. The mode of action of the suppressor was restoration of one or both of the center fibers. The expression was statistical and not complete in all individuals. Certain of the mutant strains were also shown to be leaky by producing a low proportion of individuals with normal or half-normal center fibers.

Independent of structural changes, biochemical evidence from *C. moewusii* indicates that certain *pf* mutants have both a lowered potassium uptake rate and respiration rate compared with wild type (Ronkin and Duretz, 1959). Brokaw (1960) showed that isolated flagellae have greatly lowered ATPase in a *pf* mutant.

Eyespot Mutants

Hartshorne (1953), using a single gene mutant strain lacking the eyespot, demonstrated that this organelle functions in providing phototactic information. The mutant was not completely insensitive to light, however, indicating other photoreceptive systems. Light microscope examination failed to show any evidence of eyespot structure in the mutant strain. Further study using electron microscopy would be interesting in order to describe the nature of gene action on possible ultrastructural modifications.

Genetic Control of Zygote Differentiation

The sexual cycle in the unicellular green algae usually involves formation of a zygote by union of haploid gametes. Ebersold (1967) has observed that following gametic fusions two events can occur in *C. reinhardi*. Of the fused gametes, 95 per cent differentiate to form mature zygospores. The remaining 5 per cent become functional stable diploid vegetative cells. These cells are always mating-type minus (−). The observation leads to the hypothesis that zygote formation is genetically controlled. The hypothesis would be testable by recovering a mutant capable of blocking zygote formation. Ebersold (personal communication) was able to isolate a strain which produced 90 per cent vegetative cells when mated. Subsequent analysis showed the genetic control of zygote-zygospore formation to be complex, presumably involving more than a single locus.

Further research along this line is of great significance to the study of evolutionary mechanisms. Such work particularly relates to an understanding of the origin and control of sexuality and diploidy.

Biochemical Mutants

A number of mutant strains have been isolated which are incapable of growth on a minimal mineral medium in the light. Growth of these strains on medium supplemented with specific substrates permits identification of the nature of the mutant defects in terms of biochemical pathways. Such auxotrophic strains include those requiring acetate, vitamins, and amino acids. Another group of mutants has been isolated which is resistant to various antibiotics and growth factor analogs. The latter group is primarily of interest as genetic markers.

Non-Photosynthetic Mutants

Over 200 mutants have been isolated which cannot grow in the light without an organic carbon source, usually provided as acetate. Some have been located and are found in every linkage group, thereby showing no correlation of physical location with mode of action. The majority of these acetate mutants have been isolated by Levine and his colleagues for the purpose of investigating the genetic control of photosynthesis. Each was screened and selected by its inability to fix carbon dioxide in the light. Levine (1960) gives three explanations for their inability to grow photosynthetically: (1) decreased activity or impaired synthesis of enzymes responsible for chloroplast formation; (2) decreased activity or impaired synthesis of enzymes responsible for formation of components of the electron transport system; or (3) defects in the enzymes responsible for the reductive pentose cycles. To date all classes of defects have been described.

The first class of defect has been best documented on the yellow mutant, *y–1* (Sager, 1964). Cells carrying *y–1* form only traces of chlorophyll when grown in the dark, a condition producing yellow cells. Although the chloroplast occupies the usual proportion of cell volume, it contains only a few disorganized lamellae. When placed in the light, chlorophyll synthesis is triggered and accompanied by production of a properly structured lamellar apparatus. Hudock and Levine (1964), using a similar mutant, *y–2*, showed that these morphological events were accompanied by oxygen evolution and carbon dioxide fixation by whole cells, and TPN photoreduction by isolated chloroplasts upon return to light. The *y–1* factor has an intriguing mode of transmission. It segregates only at the first meiotic division, a condition requiring close linkage to its centromere (Sager, 1955). However, it could not be mapped on any known linkage group (Sager, 1962*b*) and appears to be inducible with streptomycin, a phenomenon thus far restricted to non-chromosomal mutants (Sager and Tsubo, 1961).

Mutants have been shown to be defective because of blocking steps in the electron transport mechanism. Gorman and Levine (1966) deduced that the defect of mutant *ac–208* was its inability to synthesize plastocyanin. Evidence was derived both from the amount of plastocyanin obtained in mutant and wild type and restoration of activity in isolated chloroplast fragments when plastocyanin was added. Gorman and Levine showed that mutant *ac–206* was deficient in cytochrome 553 (cytochrome *f*). In another report (1965) they concluded that (1) electron transport across these two compounds is in series, (2) the sequence in the electron transport chain is system II– cytochrome *f*-plastocyanin–system I, and (3) a site of photosynthetic phosphorylation is on the system I side of cytochrome *f*.

Levine and Togasaki (1965) recently described the specific photosynthetic defect of the *ac–20* mutant as a lack of ribulose diphosphate carboxylase activity. The other two enzymes in the reaction chain ribose–5– phosphate to 3–phosphoglyceric acid were similar in activity to wild type.

Vitamin Mutants

Seven independent thiamine-requiring mutants of *C. reinhardi* have been described in terms of their linkage, specific requirements, and inhibition by analogs (reviewed by Ebersold, 1962).

Nakamura and Gowans (1965) reported on a series of mutants at eight non-linked loci involved in nicotinic acid metabolism in *C. eugametos*. Mutants at five loci required nicotinamide, of which one could also use the precursor quinolinic acid. The result seemingly contradicts the one-gene one-enzyme principle since there is generally only one step in the conversion of quinolinic acid to nicotinic acid. Two mutants resistant to the nicotinic acid analog 3–acetylpyridine (*apy*) were described. *Apy–1* was shown to excrete significant quantities of the normal substrate which could provide a sufficiency to insure successful competition. An alternative hypothesis would be a mutational defect in the nicotinic acid transport system which could prevent cells from accumulating the analog and might simultaneously result in the loss of nicotinic acid from the cell. A possible consequence would be de-repression of the regulatory system. No evidence was given to discriminate these possibilities.

Two mutants each in *C. reinhardi* and *C. eugametos* have been isolated which require para-aminobenzoic acid (Ebersold, *et al.*, 1962; Gowans, 1960).

Amino Acid Mutants

In spite of the relative frequency with which vitamin requiring mutants are obtained, especially nicotinamide, only three amino-acid requiring mutants have been detected in *Chlamydomonas* (Ebersold, *et al.*, 1962; Levine, unpublished). Special efforts have been implemented to isolate more, without success (Gowans, 1960). The three mutants occur in *C. reinhardi* and require arginine. The block in *arg–1* is prior to ornithine synthesis; in *arg–2* it occurs between citrulline and arginine since *arg–2* can only utilize arginine.

The reasons for the infrequency of amino acid mutants are obscure, although several hypotheses can be offered to account for the finding (Ebersold, personal communication). The most straightforward explanation would be impermeability of the cell membrane to amino acids other than arginine. Accordingly, any lesion in a synthetic pathway would produce lethality even in the presence of supplemented substrate. Preliminary evidence indicates that the cell is permeable to several amino acids. First, growth is inhibited by a variety of amino acid analogs when added separately to the growth medium. These inhibitors can be overcome by the addition of the specific L-amino acid (Nakamura, unpublished). Extension of the latter method casts doubt on another hypothesis, that certain amino acid syntheses are restricted to the chloroplast. In this case one could argue that the chloroplast envelope is impermeable. The labeling experiments indicate otherwise, although the problem of isolating pure chloroplast lysates is fraught with technical difficulties. Lastly, redundancy of the genetic factors involved in amino acid syntheses would require duplicate simultaneous mutation in order to express a lesion. Such events would occur only at the rate of the square of the spontaneous mutation frequency, which would be extraordinarily rare. A test of redundancy by inference is possible using radiation survival curves. Wetherell and Krauss (1957) investigated X-ray survival curves and concluded a considerable amount of duplication occurs in *C. eugametos*. Supporting evidence has not been found by other workers (Ebersold, 1962).

From the standpoint of comparative genetics, Kvitko and Khropova (1963) isolated three *Chlorella* "mutants" which require lysine. Kvitko, *et al.* (1966), furthermore selected a "mutant" strain of *Chlorella* which produces significant quantities of extracellular cysteine, presumably by derepression of the regulatory mechanism. Unfortunately, genetic analysis of *Chlorella* mutants is still not possible, and we therefore cannot obtain hereditary information.

NON-CHROMOSOMAL MUTANTS

The first report of a mutant showing uniparental inheritance, and hence lacking meiotic segregation, was Sager's (1954) description of the streptomycin-resistant strain *sr-2*. When wild-type cells of *C. reinhardi* are plated on agar medium containing 100 μg/ml streptomycin, two classes of resistant survivors are found. The first, *sr-1* mutants, are subsequently found to be resistant only to the 100 μg/ml level, show normal 2:2 segregation and map on linkage group IX. The *sr-2* mutants are immediately resistant to 500 μg/ml and show a non-Mendelian pattern of inheritance. Thus *sr-2* is transmitted by a mating type plus parent of all progeny, but from mating type minus to none. Sager (1960) showed that the *sr-2* mutants are stable for hundreds of generations, at different growth rates, and following extreme temperature shocks. The original finding was confirmed by Gillham and Levine (1962) and extended by them to conclusively demonstrate the earlier proposal of Sager (1960) that *sr-2* mutants are induced by the presence of streptomycin. The analysis was performed using the fluctuation test which also showed that the *sr-1* mutants arise independently of the presence of streptomycin.

Streptomycin agent can also be employed to induce other non-chromosomal factors (Sager 1962a). Gillham (1965a) showed the mutagen nitrosoguanidine induces both chromosomal (*sr-1*) and non-chromosomal (*sr-2*) mutants in addition to other non-chromosomal mutants.

Exceptions to the above uniparental pattern of inheritance are found when mating type minus *sr-2* are crossed to mating type plus wild type *(ss)*. The exceptional tetrads segregate 4 *sr-2:0 ss* progeny. Normally only *ss* colonies are expected. Gillham (1963) showed most of the clonal descendants of such tetrads later segregated *sr-2*. Thus segregation of the *sr-2* factor is post-meiotic. Known chromosomal markers, used simultaneously, segregate during meiosis.

The discovery of zygotes producing exceptional tetrads permits experimental tests of whether non-chromosomal factors can recombine. Sager and Ramanis (1965), using this technique, tested two paris of non-chromosomal factors which appeared to be linked. Gillham (1965b) presented data which indicate *sr–2* and a non-chromosomal mutant exhibiting neamine resistance (*nr–2*) are linked both in coupling and repulsion. The recombinant products of the two configurations were not strictly reciprocal.

The existence of non-chromosomal factors which carry genetic information has been unequivocally established in *Chlamydomonas*. As Sager (1960) pointed out, they share a number of characteristics with chromosomal genes: stability, mutability, maintenance of identity in heterozygotes, and segregation. Recent evidence also suggests they may be organized into linkage groups.

THE CHLOROPLAST AND THE RELATIONSHIP OF CHROMOSOMAL AND NON-CHROMOSOMAL GENETIC SYSTEMS

The chloroplast of *Chlamydomonas* is a structure of sufficient differentiation and complexity to suggest capability of virtually independent existence. It occupies more than half the cell volume. In addition to the lamellar membranes and associated chlorophyll, the chloroplast contains the eyespot, the pyrenoid, chloroplast ribosomes, and carotenoid pigments, all bounded by a double membrane envelope (Sager, 1964). Ris and Plaut (1962) were the first to identify Feulgen-positive material in the chloroplast using light microscopy, and suggested that it represents DNA. Sager and Ishida (1963) extracted DNA from isolated chloroplasts and characterized the chloroplast DNA in comparison with nuclear DNA. The chloroplast DNA represented 3 per cent of the total cellular DNA. It had a buoyant density value of 1.702 g/cm^3 (1.726 for the nuclear component) and a guanine-cytosine content of 39 per cent (62 per cent nuclear). Although it is tempting to speculate that the non-chromosomal genetic system is associated with chloroplast DNA, there is no direct supporting evidence. Inferential evidence may be found in the report of Chiang, *et al.* (1965), who found the chloroplast DNA replicated semi-conservatively (according to the Watson-Crick model) but not in synchrony with meiosis in *C. reinhardi*.

Assuming that the chloroplast DNA provides genetic information as demonstrated for non-chromosomal factors, the question of what its role may be in relation to chromosomal factors assumes importance. Sager (1964) considers three possibilities for the non-chromosomal genetic system: (1) coding for primary protein structure, (2) regulation of protein synthesis, and (3) other modes, including template-generated replication of macromolecular structures such as the chloroplast lamellae. A clear paradox lies in the abundance of nuclear genes involved in the control of photosynthesis (acetate mutants). How would they interact? Could one set provide templates and the other regulation?

Some insight into the relation of nuclear and chloroplast DNA is provided by Richards (1967) using *Euglena gracilis*. He performed hybridization experiments on DNA extracted from the two fractions and showed significant binding between the nuclear and chloroplast components. The results establish that regions of similarity exist between them. The finding suggests that some redundancy may occur in genetic information.

The trends of research on the genetics of algae are diverse, although the bulk of the effort is concentrated on a grouping of strains related to *Chlamydomonas reinhardi* and *C. eugametos*. The work is directed almost entirely to answering genetical questions on how genetic factors are transmitted and how genes act in determining structural development and biochemical pathways, particularly in electron transport during photosynthesis. A particularly exciting topic is the relationship of chromosomal and non-chromosomal genetic systems. Research into population genetics of algae are totally unreported, although this subject would be fruitful in considering adaptive changes which may be brought about by human activity.

I am deeply indebted to Dr. W. T. Ebersold for providing insight and a generous store of personal information without which this paper would not have been possible. Drs. N. Sueoka, C. S. Gowans, and N. W. Gillham critically commented upon sections of the manuscript reporting their work. Dr. R. A. Lewin kindly suggested several clarifications. Mrs. Leona Harrison aided in preparing and editing the manuscript.

Addendum: Since preparation of the manuscript, attention was called to a paper by S. I. Li, G. P. Redei, and C. S. Gowans ("A Phylogenetic Comparison of Mutation Spectra," *Molec. Gen. Genetics 1, 1967,* 77–83) which documents the comparative nutritional mutant frequency for several organisms. These data suggest a possible general phylogenetic trend. Assuming the hypothesis of differential mutant frequencies is generalized, their genetic and evolutionary basis would be extremely significant for further investigations.

REFERENCES

Bendix, S., and M. B. Allen, 1962. "Ultraviolet Induced Mutants of *Chlorella pyrenoidosa*," *Arch. Mikrobiol.*, *41*, 115–41.

Brokaw, C. J., 1960. "Decreased Adenosine Triphosphatase Activity of Flagella from a Paralyzed Mutant of *Chlamydomonas moewusii*," *Exptl. Cell Res.*, *19*, 430–32.

Buffaloe, N. D., 1958. "A Comparative Cytological Study of Four Species of *Chlamydomonas*," *Bull. Torrey Bot. Club*, *85*, 157–78.

Chiang, K. S., J. R. Kates, and N. Sueoka, 1965. "Meiotic DNA replication Mechanism of *Chlamydomonas reinhardi*," *Genetics*, *52*, 434–35. (Abstr.)

Ebersold, W. T., 1962. "Biochemical Genetics," in *Physiology and biochemistry of Algae*, pp. 731–37.

———, 1967. "Heterozygous Diploid Strains of *Chlamydomonas reinhardi*," *Science* (in press).

Ebersold, W. T., and R. P. Levine, 1959. "A Genetic Analysis of Linkage Group I of *Chlamydomonas reinhardi*," *Z. Verebr.*, *90*, 74–82.

Ebersold, W. T., R. P. Levine, E. E. Levine, and M. A. Olmsted, 1962. "Linkage Maps in *Chlamydomonas reinhardi*," *Genetics*, *47*, 531–43.

Gillham, N. W., 1963. "The Nature of Exceptions to the Pattern of Uniparental Inheritance for High Level Streptomycin Resistance in *Chlamydomonas reinhardi*," *ibid.*, *48*, 431–39.

———, 1965a. "Induction of Chromosomal and Non-Chromosomal Mutations in *Chlamydomonas reinhardi* with N-methyl-N'-nitro-N-nitrosoguanidine," *ibid.*, *52*, 520–37.

———, 1965b. "Linkage and Recombination Between Non-Chromosomal Mutations in *Chlamydomonas reinhardi*," *Proc. Natl. Acad. Sci. U.S.*, *54*, 1560–67.

Gillham, N. W., and R. P. Levine, 1962. "Studies on the Origin of Streptomycin Resistant Mutants in *Chlamydomonas reinhardi*," *Genetics*, *47*, 1463–74.

Gorman, D. S., and R. P. Levine, 1965. "Cytochrome *f* and Plastocyanin: Their Sequence in the Photosynthetic Electron Transport Chain of *Chlamydomonas reinhardi*," *Proc. Natl. Acad. Sci. U.S.*, *54*, 1665–69.

———, 1966. "Photosynthetic Electron Transport Chain of *Chlamydomonas reinhardi*. VI. Electron Transport in Mutant Strains Lacking Either Cytochrome 553 or Plastocyanin," *Plant Physiol.*, *41*, 1648–56.

Gowans, C. S., 1960. "Some Genetic Investigations on *Chlamydomonas eugametos*," *Z. Vererb.*, *91*, 63–73.

Hartshorne, J. N., 1953. The Function of the Eyespot in *Chlamydomonas*," *New Phytol.*, *52*, 292–97.

Hudock, G. A., and R. P. Levine, 1964. "Regulation of Photosynthesis in *Chlamydomonas reinhardi*," *Plant Physiol.*, *39*, 889–93.

Kvitko, K. V., and V. I. Khropova, 1963. "Ultraviolet Induced, and Spontaneous Mutations in *Chlorella vulgaris* Beijer," (in Russian, English summary) *Vest. Lenigradsk. Univ. Ser. Biol. 18 (9-2)*, 150–56.

Kvitko, K. V., I. A. Zahrov, and V. I. Khropova, 1966. "Some Principles of Investigation of Genetics and Selection of Microorganisms in Application to *Chlorella*," (in Russian) *Genetica, 2*, 148–53.

Levine, R. P., 1960. "Genetic Control of Photosynthesis in *Chlamydomonas reinhardi*," *Proc. Natl. Acad. Sci. U.S.*, *46*, 972–78.

Levine, R. P., and W. T. Ebersold, 1960. "The Genetics and Cytology of *Chlamydomonas*," *Ann. Rev. Microbiol.*, *14*, 197–216.

Levine, R. P., and C. E. Folsome, 1959. The Nuclear Cycle in *Chlamydomonas reinhardi*, *Z. Vererb., 90*, 215–22.

Levine, R. P., and R. K. Togasaki, 1965. "A Mutant Strain of *Chlamydomonas reinhardi* Lacking Ribulose Diphosphate Carboxylase Activity," *Proc. Natl. Acad. Sci. U.S., 53*, 987–90.

Lewin, R. A., 1953. "The Genetics of *Chlamydomonas moewusii* Gerloff," *J. Genet., 51*, 543–60.

———, 1958. "Genetics and Marine Algae," in *Perspectives in Marine Biology*, ed. by Buzzati-Traverso, Berkeley: Univ. of Calif. Press, pp. 547–57.

Moewus, F., 1938. "Vererbung des Geschlechts bei *Chlamydomonas eugametos* und verwandten Arten," *Biol. Zentralbl., 58*, 516–36.

Nakamura, K., and C. S. Gowans, 1965. "Genetic Control of Nicotinic Acid Metabolism in *Chlamydomonas eugametos*," *Genetics, 51*, 931–45.

Pascher, A., 1918. "Über die Kreuzung einzelliger, haploider Organismen: *Chlamydomonas*," *Ber. deut. botan. Ges., 36*, 163–68.

Randall, J., J. R. Warr, J. M. Hopkins, and A. McVittie, 1964. "A Single Gene Mutation of *Chlamydomonas reinhardi* Affecting Motility: a Genetic and Electron Microscope Study," *Nature, 203*, 912–14.

Richards, O. C., 1967. "Hybridization of *Euglena gracilis* Chloroplast and Nuclear DNA," *Proc. Natl. Acad. Sci. U.S., 57*, 156–63.

Ris, H., and W. Plaut, 1962. "Ultrastructure of DNA-Containing Areas in the Chloroplast of *Chlamydomonas*," *J. Cell Biol., 13*, 383–91.

Ronkin, R. R., and K. M. Buretz, 1959. "Sodium and Potassium in Normal and Paralyzed *Chlamydomonas*," *J. Protozool., 7*, 109–14.

Sager, R., 1954. "Mendelian and Non-Mendelian Inheritance of Streptomycin Resistance in *Chlamydomonas reinhardi*," *Proc. Natl. Acad. Sci. U.S., 40*, 356–63.

———, 1955. "Inheritance in the Green Algae *Chlamydomonas reinhardi*," *Genetics, 40*, 476–89.

———, 1960. "Genetic Systems in *Chlamydomonas*," *Science, 18*, 1459–65.

———, 1962a. "Streptomycin as a Mutagen for Non-Chromosomal Genes," *Proc. Natl. Acad. Sci. U.S., 48*, 2018–26.

———, 1962b. "A Non-Mappable Unit Factor in *Chlamydomonas*," *Genetics, 47*, 982.

———, 1964. "Studies of Cell Heredity with *Chlamydomonas*," in *Biochemistry and Physiology of Protozoa*, vol. 3, New York: Academic Press, pp. 297–318.

Sager, R., and M. R. Ishida, 1963. "Chloroplast DNA in *Chlamydomonas*," *Proc. Natl. Acad. Sci. U.S., 50*, 725–30.

Sager, R., and Z. Ramanis, 1965. "Recombination of Non-Chromosomal Genes in *Chlamydomonas*," *ibid., 53*, 1053–1961.

Sager, R., and Y. Tsubo, 1961. "Genetic Analysis of Streptomycin-Resistance and Dependence in *Chlamydomonas*," *Z. Vererb., 92*, 430–38.

Smith, G. M., and D. Regnery, 1950. "Inheritance of Sexuality in *Chlamydomonas reinhardi*," *Proc. Natl. Acad. Sci. U.S., 36*, 246–48.

Warr, J. R., A. McVittie, J. Randall, and J. M. Hopkins, 1966. "Genetic Control of Flagellar Structure in *Chlamydomonas reinhardi*," *Genet. Res. Camb., 7*, 335–51.

Wetherell, D. F., and R. N. Krauss, 1957. "X-Ray Induced Mutations in *Chlamydomonas eugametos*," *Amer. J. Bot., 44*, 609–19.

XII

Cytology of Blue-Green Algae: Light Microscopic Aspects

G. WOLFGANG FUHS

Division of Laboratories and Research
New York State Department of Health
Albany, New York

Cyanophyceae have long been recognized as unusual organisms. They share a photosynthetic metabolism with the algae while resembling bacteria in their lower degree of cellular differentiation. In recent years, the relatively close relationship between bacteria and Cyanophyceae has become more and more evident from observations on the physiology, cytochemistry, and cytomorphology of these organisms.

The absence of a nucleus is still considered the principal criterion separating bacteria and Cyanophyceae from the other members of the plant kingdom. This is reflected in the term "protocaryotes" (Chatton, 1937; Dougherty, 1957; Stanier, 1961; Stanier and van Niel, 1962; Fuhs, 1965) referring to the primitive nuclear organization of these organisms as opposed to the "eucaryotes," or organisms with "well-developed" nuclei. Other criteria shared by bacteria and Cyanophyceae are the chemical structure of the cell wall, their sensitivity toward lysozyme and penicillin, the localization of photosynthetic and respiratory functions in the cytoplasmic membrane or in organelles that are derived from the membrane in a comparatively simple fashion, and consequently, the absence of chloroplasts and mitochondria.

On the other hand there is virtually no single criterion that separates the blue-green algae from *all* other organisms, since certain pigment characteristics that separate them from the bacteria (Pringsheim, 1953, 1960) are shared by higher algae, besides the fact that apochlorotic species of Cyanophyceae do exist.

Fortunately these difficulties are of little practical importance in taxonomical work since the vast majority of Cyanophyceae are easily recognized as members of that group.

A quite relevant feature cytologically is the physical consistency of the cytoplasm which is generally referred to as viscous because no protoplasmic streaming or Brownian motion of intracellular particles is detectable.

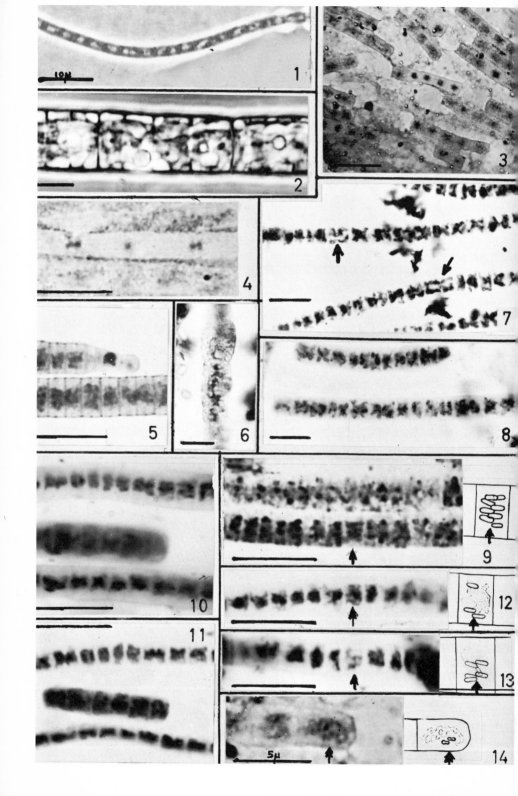

The typical cell sap vacuoles of plant cells are normally absent, and the average solids content appears to be higher than in normal plant cells. Preliminary interferometric measurements (see Figure 47 for method used) gave a cytoplasmic solids content of 21 and 24 per cent as protein in cells of *Anabaena cylindrica* and *Oscillatoria prolifica*, respectively, with nuclear areas standing out as areas of lower solids content as is the case in bacteria (Figure 1). *Oscillatoria borneti* showed an average solids content of only 12 to 16 per cent, the membranes which subdivide the cytoplasm (keritomy) standing out as denser structures (Figure 2). Thus the cytoplasm of the blue-green algae appears to be of a higher solids content than that of most plant cells which show figures between 10 and 20 per cent, but not quite as high as that of bacteria (25 to 40 per cent; Barer, 1958).

In reviewing the light microscopic cytology of the Cyanophyceae, it may be stated in advance that this field not only is still scientifically rewarding but that assistance from this side is necessary for the taxonomist, who has to distinguish between taxonomic characters and the structural changes induced by the environment, and also for the investigator of ultra-

---

The bars in all photographs except in Fig. 14 represent 10μ. FIG. 1. *Pseudanabaena catenata* in 30 per cent albumin solution, phase contrast. Bright areas represent nuclear material. FIG. 2. *Oscillatoria borneti* in 10 per cent albumin solution, phase contrast. The peripheral cytoplasm shows areas of lower density surrounded by denser partitions; the central areas show a similar pattern with smaller compartments. The large granules consist of polyphosphates. Fig. 3. *Oscillatoria amoena* (see footnote below); Feulgen's nuclear reaction (from Fuhs, 1958a). FIG. 4. *Oscillatoria amoena*, Feulgen's nuclear reaction; artificial clumping of nuclear material (from Fuhs, 1958a). FIG. 5. *Oscillatoria amoena*, neutral red staining. This figure shows the shape and cellular structure of a fully developed trichome tip consisting of a "bottle-neck" region and a nondividing, non-pigmented end cell. The stain is nonspecific. FIG. 6. *Oscillatoria borneti*, ribonuclease-pepsin-Giemsa stain; nuclear material in central area of cell. FIG. 7. *Oscillatoria prolifica*, ribonuclease-pepsin-Giemsa stain: nuclear material in certain cells separated into portions of unequal size (arrows). FIG. 8. *Oscillatoria prolifica*, ribonuclease-pepsin-Giemsa stain; nuclear material as a reticular structure of irregular shape. FIG. 9. *Oscillatoria amoena*, ribonuclease-Giemsa stain; nuclear material and some polyphosphate granules. The cell marked by the arrow is shown diagrammatically. The diagram is derived from visual analysis which in contrast to the photograph includes all optical planes. The provisional sketch was redrawn in India ink on an enlarged print of the photograph under careful analysis of the density of the silver grain. Subsequently, the silver grain was removed by chemical bleaching, and the drawing was photographically reproduced and reduced in size. The nuclear material forms rod-like elements of approximately equal size (from Fuhs, 1958a). FIG. 10. *Oscillatoria amoena*, ribonuclease-pepsin-Giemsa stain; water mount (from Fuhs, 1958a). FIG. 11. Same filaments as in Fig. 10 after dehydration and embedding in resin. Heavy shrinking has markedly reduced the clarity of the pattern (from Fuhs, 1958a). FIGS. 12 and 13. *Oscillatoria amoena*, ribonuclease-pepsin-Giemsa stain; for explanation see caption to Fig. 9 and text (from Fuhs, 1958a). FIG. 14. *Oscillatoria amoena*, Feulgen's nuclear reaction. Artificial distortion of rod-like element (dumbbell-shape). The marker in this figure represents 5μ (from Fuhs, 1958a).

structure, who needs reference techniques for the identification of certain cell inclusions.

NUCLEAR STRUCTURES

Schmitz (1879) apparently was the first to recognize the differentiation of the cell of certain Cyanophyceae into peripheral pigmented and central colorless regions which Strasburger termed *chromatoplasm* and *centroplasm* respectively (Figure 1). Schmitz also observed the basophilic character of the centroplasm. Currently available evidence shows that the chromatoplasm is characterized by the presence of the photosynthetic lamella which are quite regularly spaced and separated by layers of cytoplasmic material, which apparently have the function of a chloroplast stroma and are the site of formation and storage of the assimilation product (Fuhs, 1963). All regions that are not occupied by these compound photosynthetic or other specialized structures are *centroplasm* in Strasburger's sense. If the chromatoplasm is located in the periphery of the cells, the term *centroplasm* is quite descriptive. In many, especially the larger forms, however, the chromatoplasm may extend through almost any part of the cell. The centroplasm may assume a quite irregular branched or reticular shape and may no longer be recognizable as a compact central area.

Principal constituents of the centroplasm are the nuclear structures and the protein-synthesizing machinery, the latter represented by ribosomes. Both components accept basic dyes. In this respect the centroplasm is indistinguishable in its organization from any bacterial cytoplasm which also stains homogenous with basic dyes. The ribonucleic acid content of the centroplasm and consequently the basophilia due to this component varies with growth conditions and is highest in fast growing cells. High cytoplasmic basophilia interferes with simple nuclear staining techniques, and the problems in this respect in Cyanophyceae resemble those in bacteria.

Nevertheless, excellent presentations of the nuclear material in these forms have been given by authors such as Butschli (1890), Hegler (1901), and Guilliermond (1906, 1926), particularly with the iron hematoxylin technique, but it was not until Feulgen's nuclear reaction was successfully applied by Poljansky and Petruschewsky (1929) and Petter (1933) that the nuclear structures in Cyanophyceae were recognized as containing deoxyribonucleic acid (DNA). Studies with the Feulgen reaction have been undertaken particularly by Delaporte (1939–40), while later workers largely applied the acid-hydrolysis Giemsa technique as developed by Piekarski and Robinow (Cassel and Hutchinson, 1953).

The key word in those days was specificity of staining techniques, and it must be admitted that the Feulgen and HCl-Giemsa techniques still are unsurpassed in this respect. Techniques involving treatment in 1 N mineral acid for several minutes at 60°C are, however, far from ideal in preserving delicate structures consisting essentially of DNA. We know that DNA is the only macromolecular material contributing to the mechanical properties of these structures. DNA, however, is denatured rapidly at pH 2 and below, and it is partly degraded under the conditions of acid hydrolysis. Both effects result in a dramatic decrease in viscosity of the DNA gel. Accordingly, extended cytological structures are rounded off and appear as spheres or dumbbell-shaped elements, and narrow filaments of nuclear material are disrupted into rows of tiny beads or droplets (Figures 3, 4, and 14).

One of the effects of acid hydrolysis is to eliminate interfering cytoplasmic RNA before DNA is more seriously degraded (Vendrely and Lipardy, 1946). The same effect can be achieved by the use of enzyme, ribonuclease, without a concomitant negative effect on DNA conformation. This enzyme introduced into cytology by Boivin, et. al., (1947), has proven extremely useful in the cytology of blue-green algae (Fuhs, 1958a), especially in combination with pepsin as suggested by Peters and Wigand (1953). Pepsin treatment clears the picture, intensifies the staining effect of basic dyes, and aids in removing another type of cell inclusions, the polyphosphate granules. These elements are referred to in a later section in greater detail. At this point it is sufficient to mention that polyphosphate granules are the most strongly basophilic cell inclusions found in Cyanophyceae. Consequently, they are stained by practically any kind of basic dye, and experiments with ribonuclease and deoxyribonuclease show that their basophilia is not due to the presence of nucleic acid but caused by the (structurally similarly arranged) negative charges of the polyphosphate anion (Figures 27 and 28). The only known methods of eliminating these inclusions in cytological investigations are acid hydrolysis (which, however, negatively affects nuclear fine structure) and cultivation of the material on a medium low in phosphorus. Another possibility of staining nuclear structures in the presence of polyphosphate is with fresh solutions of the fluorescent dye, berberine sulfate (Figure 29) (old solutions no longer stain nuclear structures but are specific for polyphosphate; Krieg, 1954).

Figures 3 through 29 show the result of nuclear stains in several blue-green algae (*Oscillatoria amoena**, *O. tenuis*, *O. borneti*, and *Gloeothece* spec.). Figure 9 shows incompletely removed polyphosphate inclusions after ribonuclease-Giemsa staining. Figures 10 and 11 demonstrate the

---

*Doctor Forest informs me that the valid name for this form is *Microcoleus vaginatus*.

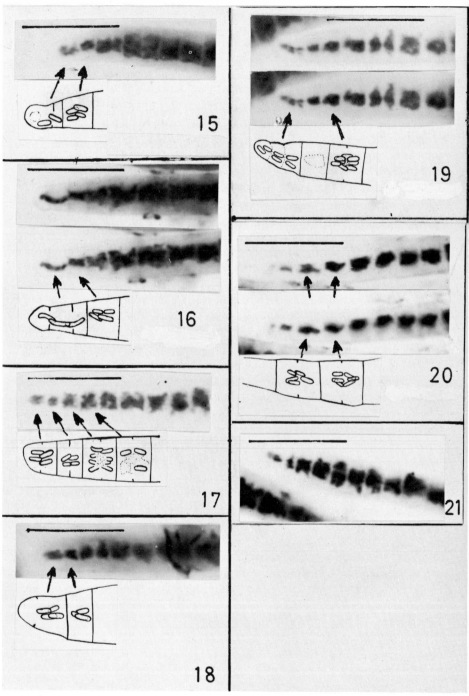

FIGS. 15–21. *Oscillatoria amoena*, ribonuclease-pepsin-Giemsa stain; reduced number of rod-like nuclear elements and patterns of nuclear division in tapered terminal regions of filaments. Figs. 16, 19, and 20 show photographs taken in different optical planes (from Fuhs, 1958a).

unfavorable effect of dehydration on structural preservation. The original water mount (Figure 10) has shrunk by one half (linear measure) due to dehydration in alcohol and embedding in resin (Figure 11).

If free from artificial distortion, the nuclear material of Cyanophyceae presents itself in the form of elongated rod- or thread-like structures which may or may not form a network or chromatic reticulum. Reports of chromatic granules could not be confirmed with modern methods (cf. Drawert, 1939–40, for *Oscillatoria borneti*; see, however, Figure 6) and may be due to the action of acid hydrolysis, incomplete removal of polyphosphate inclusions, or both. Findings with modern techniques are, however, in complete agreement with results that have been obtained by critical workers with the iron hematoxylin technique since the turn of the century.

Of the two types of nuclear organization in the larger Cyanophyceae, the reticular type will be dealt with later. We are concerned first with those forms that show an arrangement of several separated nuclear elements. Such forms were observed by several authors (e.g., Guilliermond, 1926; and Herbst, 1952), but the best earlier description is by Spearing (1937). This author found that these elements were unlike a set of chromosomes in that they were all of identical size and shape and that their number per cell was not exactly constant but varied from five to seven.

The importance of this observation became clear during the analysis of the tapered ends of the trichomes of *Oscillatoria amoena* (Fuhs, 1958a; Figure 5). *O. amoena*, upon disruption of a trichome, produces new apical cells of less than normal width. These actively dividing cells ultimately form a bottleneck-like portion, while the terminal cell is transformed into a somewhat larger, almost spherical, cell which loses pigment and apparently is no longer able to divide.

Cytological analysis of the normal cells shows a varying number (four to eight) of rod-like elements about 0.2μ wide and corresponding in length to the shortest observed cell length (Figures 9–14). Particularly clear is their appearance in the peripheral regions of the cell where they seem to separate by sliding alongside each other in opposite directions. The cells of the tapered portions of the trichome contain identical elements, but in a reduced number. The moderately wide parts contain three to six or two to four elements, with the same mode of segregation indicated (Figures 15, 17, 18, 19, 20, 21). The cells at the tip of incompleted trichome ends or next to the completed apical cell contain two elements which are distributed to different daughter cells upon division (Figures 16, 29).

Thus we observe that cells containing only one of these elements divide quite normally. Furthermore, since the tapered ends do not elongate indefinitely, but remain only a few cells long, the progeny of cells with one

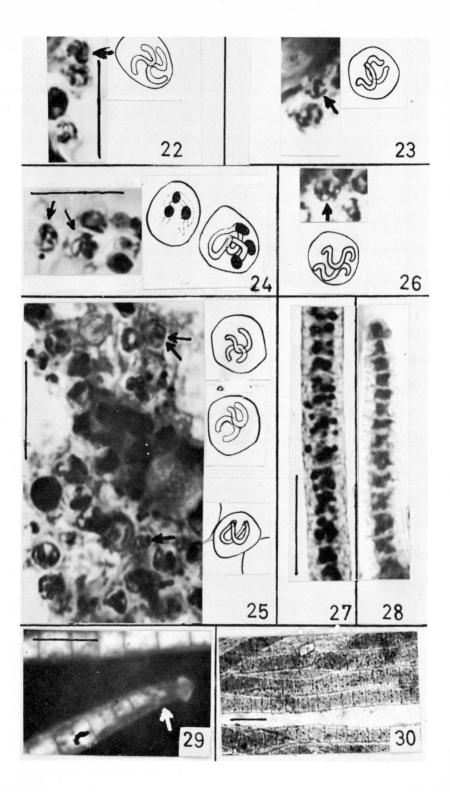

22

23

24

26

25

27

28

29

30

element must comprise "normal" cells containing four to eight elements. Thus both observations suggest that each element represents a complete genome, that the cells of normal width are polyenergidic, one energid being represented by one complete set of genetic information plus cytoplasm plus other essential components, membrane templates, etc. (Hartmann, 1953).

The formation of the tapered trichome ends could result from a complete inhibition of nuclear replication in the (new) apical cell which continues to divide until the number of chromatin elements is reduced to one, whereupon the apical cell is transformed into a resting cell. The specific signal may arise from the exposed transverse walls (which are markedly different in structure from the longitudinal walls). The degree of inhibition may decrease over a distance of several cells from the tip and result in the gradual increase of cell width from the tip. A particular and unexplained phenomenon is the controlled polyenergidy of the normal cells, i.e., the active principle regulating the number of energids per cell.

That our interpretation in terms of polyenergidy is correct has been shown in several ways. Gardner (1906) (Figure 31) described an endospore forming Cyanophycea (*Dermocarpa fucicola*) which consists of a large vesicular cell containing a giant nuclear reticulum. During endospore formation each spore receives a fragment of definite size of this reticulum. The suspicion that this reticulum might represent a polycaryon (Fuhs, 1958a) was verified by Beck (1963) with a similar alga. This alga in its fully developed state contains numerous rod-like chromatin elements. Each endospore was found to receive one of these plus a portion of the common cytoplasm. More support can be derived from X-ray experiments. Herbst (1952) described an *Oscillatoria* with several separate rod-like nuclear elements. This alga survived irradiation with 200 kr and therefore is the most X-ray resistant organism known. For comparison, Moore (1965), in experiments with the much smaller, bacteria-like blue-green alga, *Anacystis nidulans*, observed 99 per cent killing after only 120 kr. A plaus-

---

Figs. 22–26. *Gloeothece* spec., ribonuclease-pepsin-Giemsa stain; rod-like nuclear elements occurring in pairs. In Fig. 24 also polyphosphate granules. Scale marker in Fig. 22 also applies to Figs. 23 and 26 (from Fuhs, 1958a). Fig. 27. *Oscillatoria amoena*, ribonuclease-deoxyribonuclease-Giemsa stain; cytoplasmic basophilia and nuclear structures are eliminated. Polyphosphate granules stand out as deeply stained structures (from Fuhs, 1958a). Fig. 28. *Oscillatoria amoena*, treated with enzyme-free buffer solutions as control preparation; Giemsa stain. The cell showed cytoplasmic basophilia, nuclear structures, and polyphosphate granules. Cytoplasmic basophilia does not appear in the photograph due to adjusted exposure time but is indirectly reflected by the low contrast of the picture (from Fuhs, 1958a). Fig. 29. *Oscillatoria amoena*, berberine sulfate fluorescent stain. Single nuclear elements in first dividing cell of the filament (from Fuhs, 1958a). Fig. 30. *Oscillatoria amoena*, sudan black B in propylene glycol; lipid inclusions.

ible explanation would be that this small form is monoenergidic or at least less polyenergidic than the multinucleated *Oscillatoria* investigated by Herbst.

Single, rod-shaped nuclear elements were also observed in other forms (*Gloethece* sp.; Figures 22–26), but still other Cyanophyceae showed nuclear structures which were truly reticular or nearly so, so that a detailed analysis was impossible. An investigation of *Oscillatoria tenuis*, as well as *O. prolifica* (Figures 7, 8), however, disclosed that in some cells and under a favorable angle of observation the nuclear material was separated into two masses of unequal size. In the tapered terminal portions of the trichomes of *O. tenuis* the amount of chromatin per cell was reduced. These observations may indicate polyenergidy in these two species.

Ultrastructural analysis has shown that the nuclear areas in Cyanophyceae are not bounded by membranes, and that their internal structure is identical with that of bacterial nucleoids, showing the typical fibrillar pattern of histone-free DNA. This leaves ample possibility for the formation of compound nuclear structures which may contain more than one

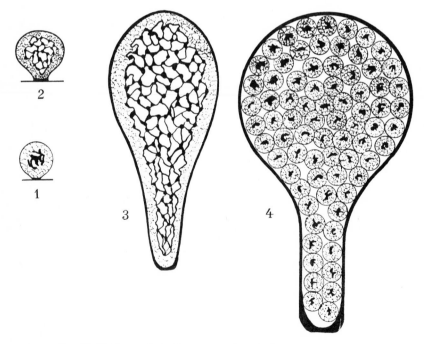

Fɪɢ. 31. Nuclear cycle in *Dermocarpa fucicola* (from Gardner, 1906).

genetic complement but are impossible to resolve with the light or electron microscopes, and thus the existence of a true nuclear reticulum in many species becomes understandable.

This is not the place to speculate in detail on the mode of replication of these elements. Certainly their analysis with particular emphasis on the possible similarity with bacterial nucleoids will prove interesting. It may be mentioned in passing that these considerations will also reflect on the question of the mechanisms of replication and division of such elements (see Fuhs, 1968, for details).

POLYPHOSPHATE GRANULES

Polyphosphates as a constituent of various microorganisms have been recognized for quite a number of years, but the coincidence of their occurrence with the presence of certain microscopically visible structures was first recognized by Wiame (1946) and further substantiated by Ebel (1952; see also reviews by Kuhl, 1960, 1962; and Harold, 1966). The principal or exclusive chemical constituent of these granules is the linear variety of inorganic phosphate polymers with an observed molecular size of up to 260 phosphate residues. The cytological equivalent are granules hitherto known as volutin, from their occurrence in *Spirillum volutans* (Meyer, 1904), or metachromatin, from their tendency to stain metachromatically with toluidine blue and a few other basic dyes.

The most characteristic property of these granules, however, is their pronounced basophilia which exceeds that of nucleic acids. After staining with basic dyes nucleic acids are decolorized at pH values around 3.5; polyphosphate granules, however, remain stained even at pH 1. Ebel and Colas (1954) proposed a cytochemical reaction specific for the high phosphate polymers. The reaction is based on the insolubility of the lead salt at pH 1. The lead salt is then converted to the sulfide (Figure 32).

Both basophilia and metachromasy of polyphosphates and nucleic acids are due to the linear array of phosphate moieties carrying negative charges, the quantitative differences reflecting the higher number of charged groups per unit length of molecule in the polyphosphates as compared with the nucleic acids. Polyphosphates interfere with almost all known staining techniques for nucleic acids, in particular for DNA, and therefore many erroneous statements as to their possible nature can be found in the literature. Polyphosphate granules even present a problem with Feulgen's nuclear reaction because they stain in a brilliant red with lencofuchsin and may interfere with the nuclear stain unless hydrolysis is intense enough for their complete removal.

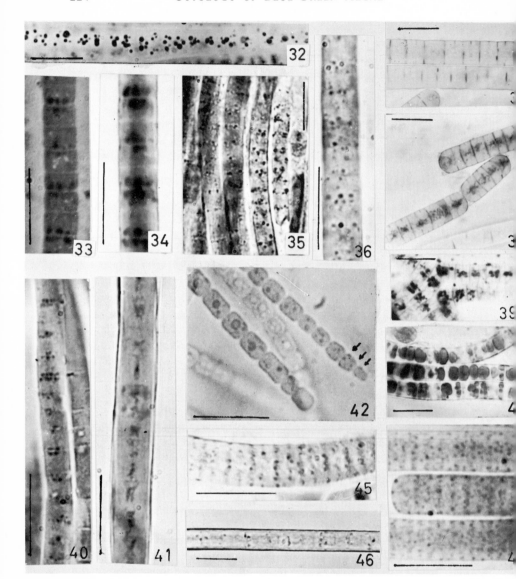

Fig. 32. *Oscillatoria amoena*, polyphosphate granules stained after Ebel and Colas (from Fuhs, 1958b). Fig. 33. *Oscillatoria amoena*, phase contrast. Cyanophycin granules stand out as dark structures (from Fuhs, 1958b). Fig. 34. *Oscillatoria amoena*, same filament as in Fig. 33, cyanophycin granules stained with acetocarmine (from Fuhs, 1958b). Fig. 35. *Oscillatoria tenuis*, acetocarmine stain, cyanophycine granules. Fig. 36. *Oscillatoria amoena*, janus green, reduced. Cyanophycin granules appear in red (from Fuhs, 1958b). Fig. 37. *Oscillatoria amoena*, janus green stain, first postvital effect (from Fuhs,1958b). Fig. 38. *Oscillatoria amoena*, janus green stain, second postvital effect (from Fuhs, 1958b).

Even greater difficulties arise with the question whether granules contain components other than polyphosphates, e.g., proteins and nucleic acids. One can agree with Harold (1966) that most, if not all, reported forms of association of granular polyphosphates with nucleic acids and proteins in homogenates are preparation artifacts, especially since a quite similar situation exists with DNA preparations. On the other hand, proof of the contrary is difficult to establish. Treatment with boiling water eliminates polyphosphate granules (Grimme, 1902) but does not easily result in the complete removal of RNA. This may indicate the absence of RNA in these granules.

Interferometric determination of the refractive index of polyphosphate granules yields variable results (for outline of method see Figure 47). Their refractive index appears to be related to the solids contents of the cell. A synthetic polyphosphate (potassium salt, Graham's salt), however, showed similar properties. Its refractive index was lowest in water (1.415); 20 per cent albumin higher in (1.44 to 1.45); and highest in a nonaqueous immersion medium (1.499). In *Oscillatoria borneti* (solids content 12 to 16 per cent), the refractive index of the polyphosphate granules was found to be 1.447 (average of five granules) and thus corresponds closely to that of the synthetic product in a 20 per cent protein solution (Figure 2). This means that the granules are at least as "solid" as pure polyphosphate would be under similar conditions. This would favor the idea that the granules are massive deposits of polyphosphate. This, of course, does not rule out that certain structures may serve as starting points of polyphosphate condensation.

For the taxonomist who works with cultures it is important to know that conventional media generally stimulate polyphosphate accumulation (Figure 32), whereas the cells of material collected in the field may be devoid of such inclusions. The ecologist may note that the cytological

---

FIG. 39. *Oscillatoria amoena*, janus green stain, third postvital effect (from Fuhs, 1958b). FIG. 40. *Oscillatoria amoena*, Baker's phospholipid stain, positive reaction in cyanophycin granules (from Fuhs, 1958b). FIG. 41. *Oscillatoria amoena*, Baker's phospholipid stain following pyridin extraction, control preparation to FIG. 40 (from Fuhs, 1958b). FIG. 42. *Anabaena cylindrica*, acetocarmin stain. Cyanophycin granules are stained in red (arrows); the large inclusions are polyphosphate granules (unstained). FIG. 43. *Oscillatoria amoena*, vacuolized filaments from old culture, acetocarmin stain. Vacuoles accept acetocarmin readily and show spatial relationships to cyanophycin granules. FIG. 44. *Oscillatoria amoena*, Nadi (indophenol blue) reaction, starting at cross-wall sites with the formation of additional deposits in other areas of the cell apparently unrelated to preformed inclusions (from Fuhs, 1958b). FIG. 45. *Oscillatoria amoena*, triphenyl tetrazolium chloride; formazan deposits appearing first at cross-wall sites; later additional deposits occur at sites apparently unrelated to preformed structures (from Fuhs, 1958b). FIG. 46. *Oscillatoria amoena*, reduction of osmium tetroxide at the sites of the cyanophycin granules.

examination of Cyanophyceae and other organisms can contribute to the knowledge of their metabolic state in that the presence of polyphosphates indicates growth limitation by factors other than phosphorus. The extraction procedure for surplus phosphates by Fitzgerald and Nelson (1966) approximately corresponds to known cytological methods of elimination of polyphosphate inclusions.

CYANOPHYCIN GRANULES

Cyanophycin granules (cianoficina, Borzi) have been observed early and were described under a variety of names. Their properties have been reviewed repeatedly and may be quoted here without an exhaustive list of references (see, e.g., Geitler, 1936; Schussnig, 1953; Fuhs, 1958b). They are usually located at the cell periphery, often in a characteristic arrangement at the cross-walls, but apparently are not an indispensable constituent of the cell, since they are absent in some forms (e.g., *Spirulina*) and in others reportedly disappear in the dark. They are variable in size, spherical or polygonal in shape, but never crystalloid. They are soluble in medium concentrated mineral acids, do not stain with basic dyes, but accept acetocarmine readily (Figures 34, 35, 42). They react positively with the Sakaguchi test for guanidine-derivatives, especially arginine (Fogg, 1951), the Altmann mitochondrial stain (Dehorne, 1920), the Harman mitochondrial stain (Fuhs, 1958b), the phospholipid test by Baker (Figures 40, 41), and occasionally with osmium tetroxide (Figure 46) (Neugnot, 1950).

Their affinity to janus green is particularly interesting in that it is a reaction restricted to living cells. It is obtained with extremely dilute solutions (1:100,000) only and is of transient nature because the dye has a toxic effect. In its postvital effects, the dye acts as any other basic dye would, i.e., the cyanophycin granules are decolorized, and membrane sites (Figure 37), the nuclear material (Figure 38), and the polyphosphate granules (Figure 39) become stained, in that order. These postvital effects have been considered as vital staining by some authors, which has caused much confusion in the literature. It has been indicated that janus green is taken up and reduced intracellularly and remains in that form unless reoxidized at the sites of respiratory activity (Cooperstein and Lazarow, 1953). If Cyanophyceae after vital staining with janus green are stored for several hours in the dark under a slide sealed with paraffin, the color of the stained cyanophycin granules changes from greenish blue to the red color of the reduced derivative, diethyl safranin (Figure 36). This is in accordance with the proposed mechanism.

While the reactive sites of janus green, acetocarmine, and the Baker phospholipid test are identical with the cyanophycin granules as seen in bright field and phase contrast microscopy of living cells (compare Figures 33 and 34), the sites of tetrazolium reduction and the indophenol test are not as well defined. The first deposits of formazan and the indophenol blue appear at the membranes, including the sites where the cyanophycin granules are located, but very soon more deposits are formed which do not show any relation to preformed cell constituents (Figures 44, 45). Osmium tetroxide, however, appears to react specifically with the cyanophycin granules (Figure 46).

The functions of the cyanophycin granules are not clear. Among various speculations the idea of some mitochondrial function is the most appealing (Dehorne, 1920; Fuhs, 1958a). Evidence mentioned in the introduction points towards the cytoplasmic membrane and its invaginations (photosynthetic lamella) as the site of respiratory activity in Cyanophyceae. Light microscopic evidence suggests similarities between cyanophycin granules and bacterial plasmalemmasomes (mesosomes), but available electron microscopic evidence so far does not support this idea. Unfortunately, light microscopic methods of identification of these structures are not suitable for electron microscopic identification.

VACUOLES

The occurrence of vacuoles has been reported frequently, particularly in cells from ageing cultures and certain specialized structures; the hairs of Rivulariacea indicating decreased viability and impending inability to divide (Guilliermond, 1926; von Zastrow, 1953), for example. Many earlier reports on vacuoles in cells supposedly vitally stained with neutral red or methylene blue may have described artifacts produced by the action of the dye (Spearing, 1961). In an old and partly bleached culture of *Oscillatoria amoena* vacuoles were observed which were readily stained with acetocarmine and in their arrangement resembled hypertrophic cyanophycin granules (Figure 43), but similar vacuoles observed in other forms did not accept the dye. Their nature is not clear.

GAS VACUOLES

The gas vacuoles (Klebahn, 1895, 1922, 1925; Strodtmann 1895; Canabaeus, 1929; for more literature see Fogg, 1941) of Cyanophyceae are cell inclusions the occurrence of which is dependent on certain metabolic processes, although their exact mechanism of formation is not known. Gas vacuoles occur also in bacteria (Wille, 1902; Kolkwitz, 1928; Houwink, 1956).

Gas vacuoles disappear upon mechanical compression of the algae presumably due to dissolution of the gas and form again during decompression in their original location and in their original shape, indicating that they are not just gas bubbles distributed at random (Pringsheim, 1966). They disappear also upon exposure of the cells to lipid solvents or other agents affecting lipid-containing membranes; thus, a membranous boundary seems to exist. These techniques are helpful in the light microscopic identification. A recent description of gas vacuoles in a newly isolated species (*Oscillatoria agardhii* var. *suspensa,* Pringsheim, 1965) may serve as a reminder that light microscopic examination and identification, at least in certain instances, can present problems.

Gas vacuoles similar to polyphosphate granules do not absorb visible light, and therefore are poor amplitude objects. They are excellent phase objects, however, because the refractive index of polyphosphate is much higher, and that of gas vacuoles much lower, than that of the cytoplasm. By the same token, under conditions of poor resolution (low aperture of illumination and observation) the gas vacuoles are characterized by diffraction fringes (in this form they are depicted in the literature). At the highest available apertures, the complete disappearance of these fringes renders the gas vacuoles almost invisible.

The phase contrast image of these vacuoles can be quite confusing since the difference in optical path may exceed one quarter of one wavelength. This results in "false reversal" wich means that a structure of lower refractive index, which in the positive phase contrast system would normally appear darker than the background, appears brighter instead. Since polyphosphate granules, if present, may produce the same phenomenon (but in the opposite sense), the resulting image will be highly ambiguous and impossible to analyze.

The interference microscope of Jamin and Lebedeff (Piller, 1962) allows the measurement of phase differences up to and exceeding one wavelength. A quantitative study using this instrument has recently been undertaken in our laboratory. The results will be published in greater detail elsewhere. In a first qualitative approach with *Oscillatoria prolifica*, however, observation of the sequence of interference colors (see Gahm, 1963) produced by the cytoplasm (profile C-C in Figure 47), the background (0-0) and the profile containing a gas vacuole (G-G) revealed that the average refractive index along the profile G-G was lower than that along the profile 0-0 (and much lower than that of the profile C-C). This means that the vacuole must contain a material the refractive index of

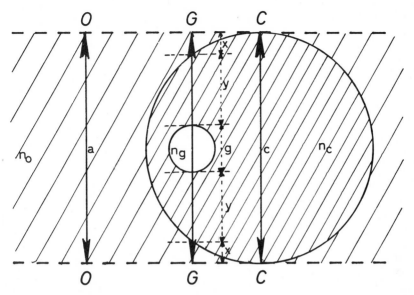

FIG. 47. Diagrammatic representation of cross-sectioned *Oscillatoria* cell containing a gas vacuole. The optical path length along each profile equals the product of thickness and refractive index or the sum of these products: for profile O-O: $d_o = a \cdot n_o$; for profile C-C: $d_c = c \cdot n_c$; for profile G-G: $d_g = 2 (x \cdot n_o + y \cdot n_c) + g \cdot n_g$. The refractive index of the embedding medium (n_o) is known. Path differences $d_c - d_o$ and $d_g - d_o$ are determined interferometrically, and thicknesses of the cylindrical or spherical structures involved by measuring the widths with a precision ocular micrometer. The location of the cell inclusion which determines x and y is obtained in the same manner. From the results, the values of n_c and n_g are obtained by calculation.

which is significantly below that of the embedding medium, water. This identifies the vacuole as a structure which contains a gas. If the gas vacuole consists of substructures in the form of gas-filled vesicles (Bowen and Jensen, 1965; Jost and Matile, 1966), the actual refractive index could be expected to be somewhat above that of a pure gas.

LIPID INCLUSIONS

The suspected presence of poly-β-hydroxybutyrate in the blue-green algae is reflected in occasional positive results twith lipid stains such as sudan black B. The granules are usually quite small and irregularly distributed throughout the cell (Figure 30). No detailed account of their occurrence in relation to certain environmental conditions can be given at the present time.

Conclusions

Upon closer examination, the cell structure of the Cyanophyceae reveals a multitude of structures and modes of response to environmental conditions. The latter point is reason for everyone concerned with the taxonomy, ecology, and ultrastructure of these forms to acquire some basic knowledge of their light microscopic cytology.

As to continued research efforts, the study of the structures of proto-caryotic cells on a comparative basis appears particularly promising and should, and undoubtedly will, receive increased attention by workers in this field.

Acknowledgments

Figures 3, 4, and 9 through 29 are reproduced with the permission of Springer-Verlag, Berlin-Heidelberg-New York as the publisher of "*Archiv für Mikrobiologie.*" Figures 32 through 34, 26 through 31, 41, 44, and 45 are from "*Österreichische Botanische Zeitschrift*" and are reproduced with the permission of Springer-Verlag, Vienna.

REFERENCES

Barer, R., 1958. "Concentration and Mass Measurement in Microbiology," *J. Appl. Bact., 21*, 146–59.

Beck, S., 1963. "Licht-und elektronmikroskopische Untersuchungen an einer sporenbil-denden Cyanophycee aus dem Formenkreis von *Pleurocapsa fuliginosa* Hauck, *Flora, 153*, 194–216.

Boivin, A., Tulasne, R., Vendrely, R., and Minck, R., 1947. "Le noyau des bactéries. Cytologie et cytochimie des bactéries normales et des bactéries traitées par la pénicilline," *Arch. Sci. physiol., 1*, 307.

Bowen, C. C., and Jensen, T. E., 1965. "Blue-Green Algae. Fine Structure of the Gas Vacuoles," *Science, 147*, 1460–62.

Bütschli, O., 1890. *Über den Bau der Bakterien und verwandter Organismen*, Leipzig.

Canabaeus, L., 1929. "Über die Heterocysten und Gasvakuolen der Blaualgen and ihre Beziehungen zueinander unter besonderer Berücksichtigung der Gattung *Anabaena*," *Pflanzenforschung (Kolkwitz)*, 13, Jena.

Cassel, W. A., and Hutchinson, W. G., 1953. "Nuclear Studies on the Smaller Myxophyceae," *Exp. Cell Res., 6*, 134–50.

Chatton, E., 1937. *Titres et Travaux Scientifiques*, Sète: Sottano.

Cooperstein, S. J., and Lazarow, A., 1953. "Studies on the Mechanism of Janus Green B Staining of Mitochondria III. Reduction of Janus Green B by Isolated Enzyme Syst-tems," *Exp. Cell Res., 5*, 82.

Dehorne, A., 1920. "Contribution a l'étude comparée de l'appareil nucléaire des Infusoires, des Euglènes et des Cyanophycées," *Arch. Zool. exp. et gén., 60*, 47–176.

Delaporte, B. "Recherches cytologiques sur les Bactéries et les Cyanophycées," *Rev. gén. Bot.*, *51*, 615–43 (1939); *52*, 40–48, 75–96, 112–60 (1940).

Dougherty, E. C., 1957. "Neologisms Needed for Structures of Primitive Organisms I." *J. Protozool.*, *4*; suppl., p. 14.

Drawert H., 1949. "Zellmorphologische und zellphysiologische Studien an Cyanophyceen, I. Literaturübersicht und Versuche mit *Oscillatoria borneti* Zukal," *Planta, 37*, 161–209.

Ebel, J. P., 1952. "Recherches sur les polyphosphates contenus dans les diverses cellules vivantes," *Bull. Soc. Chim. biol.*, *24*, 321–29, 330–34, 491–97, 498–505.

Ebel, J. P., and Colas, J., 1954. "Etude cytochimique des corpuscules métachromatiques des levures et des divers microorganismes," *Rapp. et Comm. VIII Int. Cgr. Bot. Paris, Sect. 21*, 36–37.

Fitzgerald, G. P., and Nelson, T. C., 1966. "Extractive and Enzymatic Analysis for Limiting or Surplus Phosphorus in Algae," *J. Phycol.*, *1*, 32–37.

Fogg, G. E., 1946. "The Gas-Vacuoles of the Myxophyceae (Cyanophyceae)," *Biol. Revs.*, *16*, 205–17.

Fuhs, G. W., 1958a. "Bau, Verhalton und Bedeutung der kernaquivalenten Strukturen von *Oscillatoria amoena* (Kutz) Gom." *Arch. Mikrobiol.*, *28*, 270–302.

_____, 1958b. "Über die Natur der Granula im Cytoplasma von *Oscillatoria amoena* (Kütz) Gom." *Osterr. bot. Zeitschr.*, *104*, 531–51.

_____, 1963. "Cytochemisch-elektronenmikroskopische Lokalisierung der Ribonuklein säure und des Assimilats in Cyanophyceen," *Protoplasma, 56*, 178–87.

_____, 1965. "Fine Structure and Replication of Bacterial Nucleoids," *Bact. Revs.*, *29*, 277–93.

_____, "Nuclear Structures in Protocaryotic Organisms (Bacteria and Cyanophyceae)," in *Protoplasmatologia, Handbuch der Protoplasmaforschung,* Part V,4 Vienna: Springer (late 1968), in press.

Gahm, J., 1963. "The Interference Color Chart According to Michel-Levy," *Zeiss Werkzeitschrift No. 48.*

Gardner, N. L., 1906. "Cytological Studies in Cyanophyceae," U. Calif. Publ., *Botany, 2*, 237–96.

Geitler, L., 1936. "Schizophyzeen," in *Handbuch der Pflanzenanatomie* (Linsbauer) II/VI/ IB, Berlin: Borntraeger.

Grimme, A., 1902. "Die wichtigsten Methoden der Bakterienfarbung in ihrer Wirkung auf die Membran, den Protoplasten und die Einschlusse der Bakterienzelle," *Zbl. Bakt. I. Orig.*, *32*, 1–16, 81–90, 161–80, 241–55, 321–27.

Guilliermond, A., 1906. "Contribution a l'étude des Cyanophycées," *Rev. gén. Bot., 18*, 392–408, 447–65.

_____, 1926. "Nouvelles recherches sur la structure des Cyanophycées," *ibid., 38*, 129–45, 177–90.

Harold, F. M., 1966. "Inorganic Polyphosphates in Biology: Structure, Metabolism, and Function," *Bact. Revs., 30*, 772–94.

Hartmann, M., 1953. *Allgemeine Biologie*, 4th ed., Stuttgart: Fischer.

Hegler, R., 1901. "Untersuchungen über die Organisation der Phycochromaceenzellen," *Jb. wiss. Bot., 36*, 229.

Herbst, F., 1952. "Strahlenbiologische und cytologische Untersuchungen an Blaualgen," Diss. phil. Fak. U. Köln.

Houwink, A. L., 1956. "Flagella, Gas Vacuoles and Cell-Wall Structure in *Halobacterium halobium*; an Electron Microscope Study," *J. Gen. Microbiol., 15*, 146–50.

Jost, M., and Matile, P., 1966. "Zur Charakterisierung der Gasvacuolen der Blaualge *Oscillatoria rubescens*," *Arch. Mikrobiol., 53*, 50–58.

Klebahn, H., 1895. "Gasvakuolen, ein Bestandteil der Zellen der Wasserblüte bildenden Phycochromaceen," *Flora, 80*, 241.

———, 1922. "Neue Untersuchungen über Gasvakuolen," *Jb. wiss., Bot., 61*, 535–89.

———, 1925. "Weitere Untersuchungen über die Gasvakuolen," *Ber. dtsch. bot. Ges., 43*, 143–59.

Kolkwitz, R., 1928. "Über Gasvakuolen bei Bakterien," *ibid., 46*, 29–34.

Krieg, A., 1954. "Nachweis von Kernäquivalenten in Zyanophyzeen," *Exper., 10*, 204–205.

Kuhl, A., 1960. "Die Biologie der condensierten anorganischen Phosphate," *Erg. Biol., 23*, 144–86.

———, 1962. "Inorganic Phosphorus Uptake and Metabolism," in *Biochemistry and Physiology of Algae*, R. A. Lewin, ed., 211–29.

Meyer, A., 1904. "Orientierende Untersuchungen über Verbreitung, Morphologie and Chemie des Volutins," *Bot. Ztg., 62*, 113–56.

Moore, R. B., 1966. "Survival Studies on the Blue-Green Algae, *Anacystis nidulans,*" Ph.D. thesis, U. Texas, Austin.

Neugnot, D., 1950. "Contribution a l'etude cytochimique des cyanophycées par application des techniques de mise en évidence de l'appareil nucleaire chez les Bactéries," *Compt. rend. Acad. Sci. Paris, 230*, 1311.

Peters, M. D., and Wigand, R., 1953. "Enzymatisch-elektronenoptische Analyse der Nucleinsäureverteilung, dargestellt an *Escherichia coli* als Modell," *Z. Naturf.*, 8b, 180–92.

Petter, H. F. M., 1933. "La reaction nucléale de Feulgen chez quelques vegetaux inferieurs," *Compt. rend. Acad. Sci. Paris, 197*, 88.

Piller, H., 1962. "Durchlicht-Interferenzmikroskopie nach dem Jamin-Lebedeff-Prinzip," *Zeiss-Mittelungen, 2*, 309–34.

Poljansky, G., and Petruschewsky, G., 1929. "Zur Frage uber die Struktur der Cyanophyceenzelle," *Arch. Protistenk, 67*, 11–45.

Pringsheim, E. G., 1953. "Die Stellung der grünen Bakterien im System der Organismen," *Arch. Mikrobiol., 19*, 353–64.

———, 1960. "Der grüne Farbstoff der Chlorobakterien, eine Berichtigung," *ibid., 36*, 98.

———, 1965. "*Oscillatoria agardhii* var. *suspensa* nov. var., Kleine Mitteilungen über Flagellaten und Algen," *ibid., 50*, 401–13.

———, 1966. "The nature of pseudovacuoles in Cyanophyceae," *Nature, 210*, 549–50.

Schmitz, F., 1879. "Untersuchungen über die Zellkerne der Thallophyten," *Sitzber. niederrh. Ges. Nat. Heilk.*, Bonn, 345.

Schussnig, B., 1953. *Handbuch der Protophytenkunde I*, Jena: Fischer.

Spearing, J. K., 1937. "Cytological Studies on the Myxophyceae," *Arch. Protistenk., 89*, 209–78.

———, 1961. "Studies on the Cyanophycean Cell I—Vital Staining, a Study in the Production of Artifacts," *La Cellule, 61*, 243–91.

Stanier, R. Y., 1961. "La place des bactéries dans le monde vivant," *An. Inst. Pasteur, 101*, 297–312.

Stanier, R. Y., and van Niel, C. B., 1962. "The Concept of a Bacterium," *Arch. Mikrobiol., 42*, 17–35.

Strodtmann, S., 1895. "Die Ursache des Schwebevermögens bei den Cyanophyceen," *Biol. Zbl., 15*.

Vendrely, R., and Lipardy, J., 1946. "Acides nucléiques et noyaux bactériéns," *Compt. rend. Acad. Sci. Paris, 223*, 342–44.

Wiame, J. M., 1947. "Etude d'une substance polyphosphorée, basophile et métachromatique chez les levures," *Biochim. Biophys. Acta, 1*, 234–55.

Wille, N., 1902. "Über Gasvakuolen bei einer Bakterie," *Biol. Zbl., 22*, 700.

von Zastrow, E. M., 1953. "Über die Organisation der Cyanophyceenzelle," *Arch. Mikrobiol., 19*, 174–205.

XIII

Ultrastructure of the Blue-Green Algae

NORMA J. LANG

Department of Botany
University of California
Davis, California

The unique position of the Cyanophyta is becoming an established certainty as information from more detailed investigations into their substructure and biochemical processes is accumulated. Each morphological study strongly supports the great structural similarity between the blue-greens and bacteria, while physiological and biochemical research continues to draw close comparisons between blue-green and green algae and even higher plants. It thus appears clear that the blue-greens have retained a structural simplicity upon which physiological complexity has been built.

One might well ask why cannot the reverse be true. Why cannot the structural simplicity have been derived through sequential reduction during time concomitant with the retention of an ancestral physiological complexity? That this is most probably not the case is suggested by the recent discoveries of Barghoorn and Tyler (1965) and others of fossil remains of blue-green-like cells and filaments in strata some two billion years of age when the only other extant organisms were equally simply structured bacteria. Even the most avid paleobotanists would not wish to state that any higher plant forms were coexisting at such an early period in earth's history.

Let us then assume the early origin of a photosynthetic system and the later origin of organisms similar to modern blue-greens as derivatives of those earliest cell-forming processes. Here it is of interest to note that chlorophyll a and bacteriochlorophyll molecules are but slightly different, the chlorophyll a molecule being somewhat more complex and possibly derived from bacteriochlorophyll.

Echlin and Morris (1965) have comprehensively reviewed the evidence for similarities between the only known prokaryotes, the bacteria, and blue-green algae, and I shall allude to these only briefly during this discussion. Rather than attempting to draw comparisons, I shall emphasize those features most characteristic of that level of organization which we identify as a blue-green alga.

Yet there are other reasons why a discussion of these algae is significant to the central theme of these meetings. Man and his environment are in-

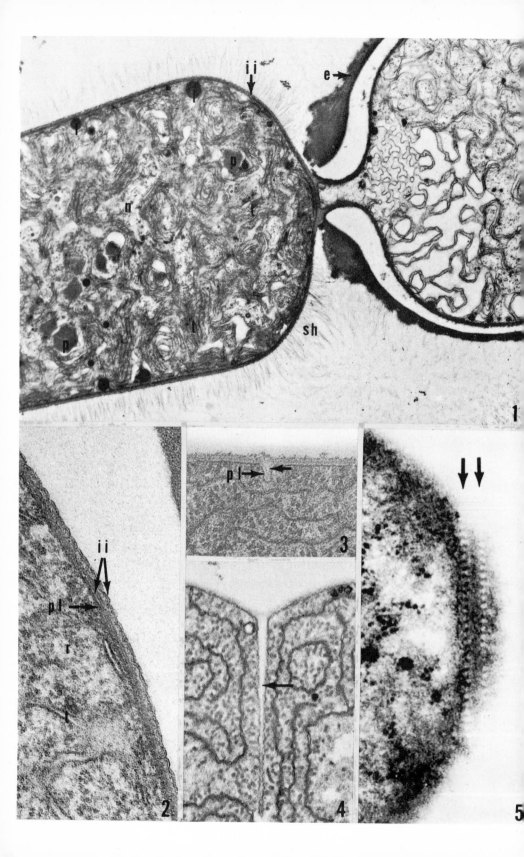

extricably associated; the blue-greens are an inevitable feature of virtually all habitats, and many others not as *yet* utilized for housing developments or freeways. We shall hear about the medical effects of direct contact between man and other animals and various toxic blue-greens. The noxious blooms of *Microcystis* and *Aphanizomenon* are of increasingly common occurrence in surface waters impounded for recreational and industrial uses and human consumption. Blue-greens of various species are able to inhabit environments whose extremes are tolerated only by a like number of bacterial species. One of the best examples of this environmental tolerance is offered by the observations of Shields and Drouet (1962). They found natural populations of *Microcoleus vaginatus* 0.6 miles from ground zero within three months after a twenty-kiloton tower test, and they considered these algae to be survivors of the atomic blast. One could continue to list the unusual habitats in which these algae thrive, especially those within the bodies of other plants and animals, but such a listing would serve only to recall these familiar facts to you.

Rather, I wish to inform you of perhaps some less familiar facts about the blue-green algal cell's external and internal features discovered in the last few years through the application of the electron microscopic technique. This research tool has been of great value in allowing us to see the intricacy of structure in cells whose very size is limiting for more than gross observation by other means. And as these structural features of normal vegetative cells are illustrated, the accompanying flexibility of structure in different forms and in different stages of development will be emphasized.

FIG. 1. Longitudinal section of part of a vegetative cell (to left) and heterocyst (to right) of *Anabaena cylindrica*. The fine fibrils comprising the sheath (sh) are oriented perpendicular to the cell surface and appear to arise from the outermost layer of the inner investment (ii) in this osmium tetroxide fixation. Cellular components shown are photosynthetic thylakoids (t), nucleoplasmic regions (n), polyphosphate granules (p), and probable lipid droplets (l). Note the thickened envelope (e) around the heterocyst and the very apparent difference in arrangement of the heterocyst thylakoids as compared with the vegetative cell. × 27,000. Fig. 2. Higher magnification of the inner investment(ii) or cell wall in *Anabaena azollae*, in this case of a developing heterocyst. The inner investment (ii) is composed of at least four layers with different staining characteristics external to the plasmalemma (pl). Ribosomes (r) and portions of the photosynthetic thylakoids (t) appear beneath the plasmalemma (pl). × 80,000. FIG. 3. Early stage in cell division in *Anabaena* sp. in which invagination of the plasmalemma (pl) and some additional layers (arrow) of the inner investment initiate the iris-diaphragm-like ingrowth. × 42,000. FIG. 4. More advanced stage in cell division in *Anabaena* sp. where the newly forming cross wall (arrow) is approximately one-third completed. × 30,000. FIG. 5. Rows of pores (arrows) in the longitudinal wall occur on either side of the junction with a cross wall in *Symploca muscorum*. Micrograph courtesy of Pankratz and Bowen, 1963. *Am. J. Bot., 50*, 387–99. × 85,000.

SHEATH

Virtually all free-living blue-green algal cells and filaments are surrounded by a sheath of mucilaginous character. The sheath may be quite variable in thickness and in submicroscopic aspect; this latter condition could well be species specific or could reflect erroneous conclusions based on fixation artifacts. Electron micrographs have shown distinct fibrils embedded in an amorphous matrix, the fibrils being oriented parallel to the cell surface, perpendicular to it or arranged in a random pattern. In *Scytonema* (Singh, 1954) and *Tolypothrix* (Ventrakaramen and Mehtra, 1962), the fibrils were said to be of cellulose, although Metzner (1955) found no conclusive evidence of cellulose in the blue-green algae. Jost's (1965) application of the nonchemical freeze-etching technique to trichomes of *Oscillatoria* clearly demonstrated a fibrillar substructure in the sheath layer, each fibril being about 30 A in diameter. An electron micrograph of *Anabaena cylindrica* after osmium tetroxide fixation shows these fine fibrils which here are oriented perpendicular to the cell surface (Figure 1).

CELL WALL

Between the sheath and the plasmalemma is a complex series of four layers with different staining characteristics (Figure 2). These layers comprise the cell wall proper, or the inner investment using another terminology. One of the most recent studies (Höcht, Martin, and Kandler, 1965) on the chemical composition of the walls of a variety of blue-greens has reported that the major wall components were mureins composed of muramic acid, glucosamine, glutamic acid, diaminopimelic acid, and alanine, much as in the Gram negative bacteria. A number of sugars such as galactosamine, glucose, xylose, and mannose were also noted. The electron transparent 100 A thick layer immediately next to the plasmalemma is considered by Jost (1965) to be the mucopolymer layer. This layer was designated the L I layer by Jost (1965) and the inner layer or I layer by Pankratz and Bowen (1963). The freeze-etching technique has revealed that the mucopolymer layer has a densely globular substructure on the longitudinal walls and it is somewhat less globular on the transverse walls.

During cell division in a filament such as *Oscillatoria* there is some uncertainty as to how many of the longitudinal wall layers participate in cross-wall formation. It is clear that the mucopolymer layer L I and probably also L II do participate in the iris-diaphragm ingrowth (Figures 3, 4). In the case of simpler forms such as *Anacystis,* cell division is by simple constriction and severance (Figure 7). Several authors have suggested that cytoplasmic connections in the form of plasmodesmata occur between adjacent cells in the filamentous forms. However, none of the published electron micrographs purporting to indicate such structures have been very convincing.

One other feature which is especially clear in *Symploca muscorum* (Pankratz and Bowen, 1963) is the presence of pores in the longitudinal wall adjacent to its junction with a cross wall (Figure 5). The possibility that mucilage secretion takes place through such pores is an attractive idea, especially as a part of the movement mechanism.

PLASMALEMMA

The blue-green algal protoplast is completely encompassed by a single 70–80 A thick membrane, the plasmalemma (Figure 3). Functionally, this plasmalemma does not appear to differ from the osmo-regulatory membranes in other plant and animal cells; however, the possibility that respiratory enzymes may be located in this membrane, as in the case of some bacteria, cannot be disregarded. Echlin (1964) has suggested that a membranous intrusion of the plasmalemma, which he called a lamellasome, may be the counterpart of the bacterial mesosome both in structure and in function. Firm experimental evidence is lacking on this point, although a number of laboratories are working on the identification of the respiratory sites in the blue-greens.

PHOTOSYNTHETIC MEMBRANES

As seen with the light microscope, the internal structure of a blue-green alga has been typified as being composed of a peripheral pigmented area, the chromatoplasm, and a non-pigmented central area, the centroplasm. Further, with the light microscope one can detect large granular inclusions of cyanophycin and refractive pseudovacuoles, especially in planktonic forms. That the concept of chromatoplasm and centroplasm is no longer tenable for most of the blue-greens has been demonstrated dramatically by electron microscope studies.

An ultrathin section of an *Anabaena* cell, for example, immediately reveals a wealth of unsuspected detail (Figure 6). The so-called chromatoplasm can be resolved as a system of single flattened sacs, or thylakoids, which may be predominantly in a peripheral position parallel to the plasmalemma but which may also pass through the central area and be continuous with other thylakoids on the opposite side of the cell. Each thyla-

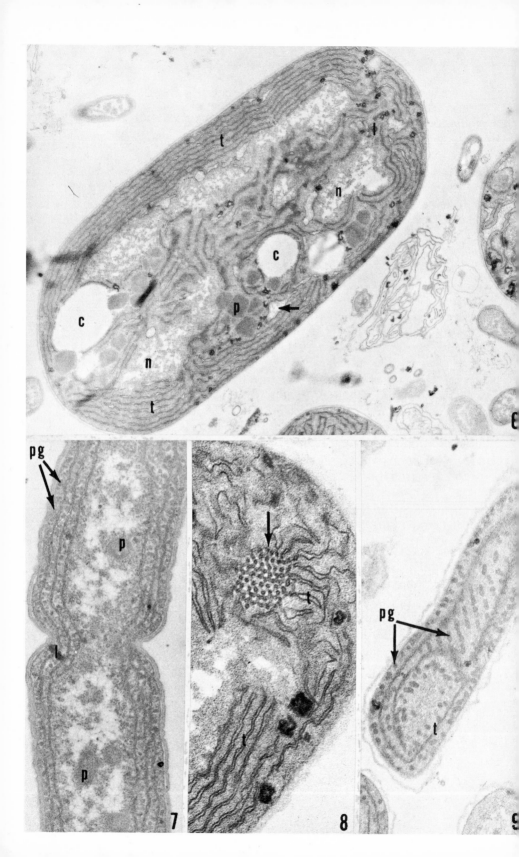

koid is composed of a single membrane enclosing an intrathylakoidal space. The thylakoid membranes are the sites of the photosynthetic chlorophyll a, as demonstrated in the fractionation work by Shatkin (1960), and the chemical similarity of these thylakoids and those of *Chlorella* and higher green plants has recently been presented (Schmitz, 1967). As is the case with chlorophyll-bearing membranes in higher plants, the blue-green algal photosynthetic membrane has a globular substructure (Fuhs, 1966).

Thylakoids may connect to the plasmalemma (Schnepf, 1964), and the origin of thylakoids by invagination of this membrane has been suggested by both Pankratz and Bowen (1963) and Jost (1965), the latter in the case of young hormogonia of *Oscillatoria rubescens*.

The elegant work by Gantt and Conti (1966) on the attachment of phycobilin pigment granules to the thylakoids in the red alga *Porphyridium* mentioned the discovery of similar phycobilin granules attached to the thylakoids in an unidentified marine *Oscillatoria*-like organism, although no micrographs were shown. Their proof of the phycobilin nature of these 350 A granules attached to the thylakoids in *Porphyridium* appears to be well founded, and since it is simply a matter of achieving the proper fixation schedule, we may expect to see additional evidence for the site of the phycobilins in a great variety of blue-green cells shortly. The natural and environmentally-induced variations in true pigmentation in these algae, disregarding coloration in the sheaths, suggest a number of interesting investigations into structure-function relationships in the photosynthetic process.

FIG. 6. Longitudinal section of a mature *Anabaena* sp. vegetative cell in which most of the subcellular structure common to blue-green algae is evident. The photosynthetic thylakoids (t) are predominantly peripheral but may also extend into the central region. Occasional inflation of the thylakoids may be seen (arrow). In addition to the nucleoplasmic regions (n), polyphosphate granules (p), lipid droplets (l), and cyanophycin granules (c) are indicated. In this fixation the material forming the cyanophycin granules is leached out during preparation. Micrograph from Lang and Rae, 1967. *Protoplasma, 64*, 67–74. × 11,000. FIG. 7. The two to four photosynthetic thylakoids of *Anacystis nidulans* are totally peripheral, and the DNA-containing nucleoplasm is distinct from the pigment-bearing thylakoids. Simple cell division by constriction or fission severs the cell into two equal-sized daughter cells, but the means by which genetic equivalence is maintained in the absence of a mitotic process is unknown. Other cellular inclusions are polyphosphate granules (p), lipid droplets (l) and polyglucoside granules (pg). × 36,000. FIG. 8. An aged cell of *Anabaena* sp. in which the photosynthetic thylakoids (t) have formed into a lattice configuration (arrow) resembling the prolamellar body of higher plant chloroplasts. Micrograph from Lang and Rae, 1967. *Protoplasma, 64*, 67–74. × 48,000. FIG. 9. Polyglucoside granules (pg) in *Anacystis nidulans* are associated with the photosynthetic thylakoids (t) but are not attached to them. In the upper portion of this cell an oblique section through a row of the polyglucoside granules indicates a helical deposition pattern whose physiological basis is unknown. The granules can be completely degraded by treatment with diastase. × 41,000.

The thylakoids in the blue-greens, as in the photosynthetic bacteria, display a number of morphological forms depending on the organism in question, the age and physiological state of the cell, and the type of cell being observed. A few examples will suffice to demonstrate the plasticity of the thylakoidal system. One of the simplest thylakoidal systems is present in *Anacystis nidulans*, where the thylakoids are flat, parallel to the plasmalemma, and peripheral in the cell (Figure 7). It is not unusual to view thylakoids whose apposed membranes have separated, giving the appearance of intrathylakoidal vacuolation (Figure 6). Such swollen thylakoids are particularly evident in aging cells (Madsen, 1966) and at the polar regions in heterocysts (Lang, 1965). Further, in cultures of *Anabaena* some five to six months after transfer, thylakoid lattice configurations (Figure 8) resembling somewhat the prolamellar body of higher plant chloroplasts have been discovered (Lang and Rae, 1967).

GRANULAR INCLUSIONS

Another cellular component intimately associated with the photosynthetic thylakoids is the polyglucoside storage product in the form of discrete submicroscopic granules and rod-like forms. These granules occur between thylakoids and are apparently not attached to them, unlike the attached phycobilin granules (Gantt and Conti, 1966). A particular helical pattern in which the polyglucoside is deposited (Figure 9) was recently discovered in *Anacystis nidulans* (Lang, unpublished), although the physiological basis for such a pattern is obscure. The polyglucoside nature of these granules has been enzymatically demonstrated through diastase degradation (Fuhs, 1963; Giesy, 1964).

Scattered amongst the thylakoids are very electron-dense globules termed β-granules by Pankratz and Bowen (1963). Although the chemical nature of these dense globules is uncertain, they may represent lipoidal (Figures 1, 6) material since their fixation image is much like the lipid-containing osmiophilic globules in higher plant chloroplasts. Although these dense globules are variable in size, they can be distinguished easily from two other types of granules in the cells, polyhedral bodies and cyanophycin granules, which are larger and morphologically distinctive (Figure 6).

The polyhedral bodies are large polygonal shaped bodies found most commonly in association with the nucleoplasmic regions of the cells. As their name suggests, these bodies are polygonal in outline, and they have a medium electron density. With certain combinations of fixatives and post-stains a faint substructure becomes apparent in the polyhedral bodies, and Costerton (1960), as cited by Echlin and Morris (1965), considered them to be protein bodies. The light microscope studies of Talpasayi (1963) indicated the abundance of polyphosphate deposits in blue-green cells, and the polyhedral bodies may be the electron microscopic counterpart of such substances.

The well-known cyanophycin granules are frequently found to have a patterned substructure which has been called crystalline, in that internal striations are present. Again we are uncertain as to the chemical composition of these bodies, although Fogg (1951) found a positive reaction to the Sakaguchi test for proteins containing arginine. These structured granules, as they have been called (Pankratz and Bowen, 1963), were initially thought to be the sites of respiratory activity and therefore mitochondrial equivalents (Drews and Niklowitz, 1956); but this work has not been substantiated in more recent studies. In many preparations, the material forming the cyanophycin granules is leached out leaving only an empty space or a granular residue (Figure 6). Typical ribosomes and polyribosomes are scattered throughout the cell and in largest numbers near the nucleoplasm.

NUCLEOPLASM

The nucleoplasm is formed by an anastomosing network of very thin fibrils. Again the type of fixation is important in the form of these DNA-containing fibrils, and in most cases one sees only coalesced groups of fibrils (Figures 6, 7). The fact that this area does contain DNA has been demonstrated by the Feulgen technique and autoradiography of incorporated radioactive thymidine (Leak, 1965). There is no spindle apparatus during cell division, and the mechanism by which genetic equivalence is maintained in daughter cells is unknown. De and Ghosh (1965) have recently shown the absence of histones in the blue-green nucleoplasm, and it is possible that the DNA of these cells may be in the form of a single long strand as noted in bacterial cells. This would still not suggest the replication mechanism at division.

OTHER FEATURES

Gas vacuoles or pseudovacuoles (Figure 10) may also be visualized with the electron microscope as groups of cylindrical, membrane-bound bodies (Bowen and Jensen, 1965). The freeze-etch work of Jost (1965) has demonstrated their reality, and Jost and Matile (1966) discovered that the gas vacuole membranes are composed of β-carotene, 4-keto-β-carotene, and

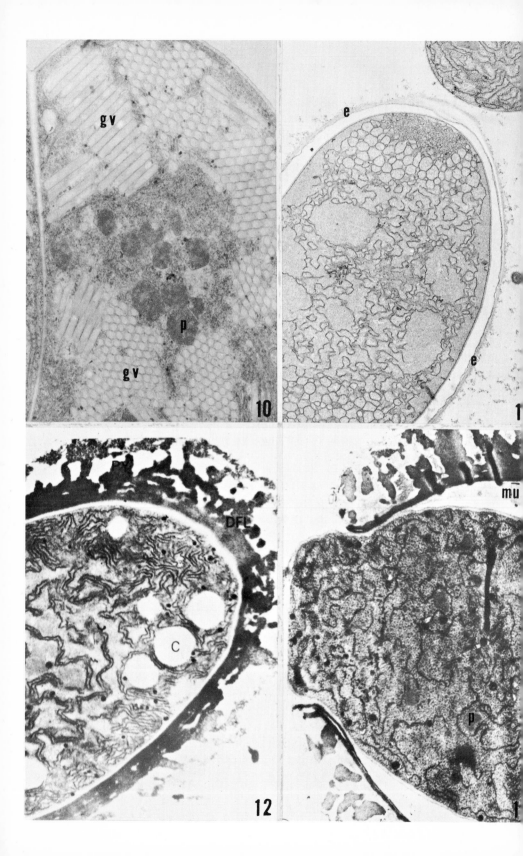

probably a fatty acid. The gaseous content has not been identified. The presence of a DNA-virus in cells of *Plectonema boryanum* has now been established by Schneider, Diener, and Safferman (1964).

We thus have a concept of the blue-green cell which goes far beyond the older idea of centroplasm and chromatoplasm and granular inclusions. These simple cells contain a multiplicity of structure, and much future work will be required to ascertain the chemical composition and physiological significance of these structures and their relationship to environmental change and developmental stages.

The previous discussion has been primarily concerned with the aspect of vegetative cells, but information is also beginning to accumulate on the two distinctive spore-types in this group, the heterocyst and akinete. The functional significance of heterocysts present in most members of the suborder Nostochineae has been debated for a considerable period (Fritsch, 1951). Wolk (1965) has presented evidence that in *Anabaena cylindrica* the akinete is the spore-type specialized for surviving periods of phosphate deficiency and the heterocyst for surviving periods of nitrogen deficiency. He was able to induce germination of 3 to 10 per cent by media manipulation, and it is evident that this cell is certainly not degenerate as one might assume by observing its clear, homogeneous aspect with the light microscope.

When a heterocyst differentiates from a vegetative cell, the initial changes involve an increase in cell size and the deposition of additional envelope layers outside the cell wall (Lang, 1965). During this early period

---

FIG. 10. Gas vacuoles (gv) or pseudovacuoles in *Nostoc* sp. appear as groups of cylindrical membrane-bound bodies in longisection and tightly-packed polygonal bodies in cross-section. Large polygonal granules of polyphosphate (p) show some areas of different electron density with this fixation. Micrograph courtesy of David L. Brown, Dept. of Botany, Univ. of California, Davis, Calif. × 23,000. FIG. 11. Longitudinal section of a developing heterocyst in *Anabaena azollae* in which the changes in the orientation of photosynthetic thylakoids may be compared to an adjacent vegetative cell (upper right). The thylakoids become packed into a lattice-like or honeycomb configuration at the heterocyst poles. The absence of the usual storage granules is apparent as is the presence of the heterocyst envelope layers (e) formed external to the plasmalemma. Micrograph from Lang, 1965. *J. Phycol.*, *1*, 127–34. × 9,600. FIG. 12. Maturing akinete of *Cylindrospermum* sp. in which the spiny envelope is formed by the deposition of dense fibrillar layers (DFL) external to the plasmalemma. Characteristic of this spore is the accumulation of quantities of cyanophycin storage granules (c). The photosynthetic thylakoids are more contorted in the akinetes than in the vegetative cells of this organism. Micrograph courtesy of Marcia Madsen Miller. × 16,600. FIG. 13. Germinating akinete of *Cylindrospermum* sp. in which the germling filament has undergone cell division prior to exit through a terminal pore (to the left). The germling cytoplasm is characterized by the absence of cyanophycin granules, the presence of polyphosphate granules (p), and a less well-developed thylakoid system. The germling filament appears to be pushed from the akinete envelope by a mucilage material (mu) secreted between it and the envelope. Micrograph courtesy of Marcia Madsen Miller. × 11,600.

the cytoplasm is little different from that in a neighboring, nondifferentiating cell. However, as envelope deposition continues, there is a reduction in the number and size of the polyglucoside granules and the polyphosphate polyhedral bodies, and the photosynthetic thylakoids begin to contract and seemingly move toward the polar regions where they assume a lattice-like configuration (Figure 11). A discussion of this sequence in *Anabaena azollae* within *Azolla* leaves has been published (Lang, 1965); however, Grilli (1964) in the same organism has shown stages interpreted as contraction of the protoplast and reformation of the heterocyst internal to the original wall, essentially a reverse sequence. Now that conditions whereby formation and germination can be induced are known, it should be possible to follow these developments under controlled culture conditions.

The course of akinete formation and germination has been followed in *Cylindrospermum* by Madsen (1966). Many of the initial stages are quite similar to those enumerated for the heterocyst of *Anabaena azollae*, in that the differentiating cell enlarges during progressive deposition of several envelope layers (Figure 12). In the case of *Cylindrospermum* the mature akinete envelope is characterized by its thick, spiny form. During differentiation the quantity of polyglucoside granules decreases while cyanophycin granules increase in both size and number. The thylakoids also contort and become arranged into groups of two's and three's. Germination of these akinetes occurred in at least two different ways. The young germling was seen to exit either through a terminal opening opposite the heterocyst (Figure 13), or dissolution of the entire akinete envelope permitted its release. Divisions within the germling could occur either before or during or after release from the envelope. In the case of exit through a terminal opening, the secretion of mucilage between the germling and the envelope appeared to aid in pushing the germling free. The character of the cytoplasm in young germlings was quite different in that dense quantities of polyglucoside had reformed, lipid deposits were abundant, and cyanophycin granules were usually absent. It was suggested (Madsen, 1966) that some *de novo* thylakoid formation occurred by the coalescence of vesicles.

This brief, though multifaceted, discussion of the substructural features of the cyanophycean cell has imparted the basic premises and ideas currently held about this group. The prokaryotes are distinguished by the absence of discrete nuclei, chloroplasts, mitochondria, dictyosomes, and endoplasmic reticulum. Yet, the complexity of architecture in young cells, aging cells, and differentiating cells is only now beginning to be realized. The future investigations into the influences of environmental modifications on ultrastructure, necessarily based therefore on changes in physiological processes, will be of great significance in understanding this so-called primitive group of plants.

REFERENCES

Barghoorn, E. S., and S. A. Tyler, 1965. "Microorganisms from the Gunflint Chert," *Science, 147*, 563–77.

Bowen, C. C., and T. E. Jensen, 1965. "Blue-Green Algae: Fine Structure of the Gas Vacuoles," *ibid.*, 1460–62.

De, D. N., and S. N. Ghosh, 1965. "Cytochemical Evidence for the Apparent Absence of Histone in the Cells of Cyanophyceae," *J. Histochem. Cytochem., 13*, 298.

Drews, G., and W. Niklowitz, 1956. "Beiträge zur Cytologie der Blaualgen. II. Zentroplasma und granuläre Einschlüsse von *Phormidium uncinatum*," *Arch. Mikrobiol., 24*, 147–62.

Echlin, P., 1964. "Intra-Cytoplasmic Membranous Inclusions in the Blue-Green Alga *Anacystis nidulans*," *ibid., 49*, 267–74.

Echlin, P., and I. Morris, 1965. "The Relationship Between Blue-Green Algae and Bacteria," *Biol. Rev., 40*, 143–87.

Fogg, G. E., 1951. "Growth and Heterocyst Production in *Anabaena cylindrica* Lewin. III. The Cytology of Heterocysts," *Ann. Bot. Lond., N.S., 15*, 23–36.

Fritsch, F. E., 1951. "The Heterocyst: a Botanical Enigma," *Proc. Linn. Soc. Lond., 162*, 194–211.

Fuhs, G. W., 1963. "Cytochemisch-elektronenmikroskopische Lokalisierung der Ribonukleinsäure und des Assimilats in Cyanophyceen," *Protoplasma, 56*, 178–87.

———, 1966. "Spherical Subunits in Photosynthetic Membranes of two Cyanophyceae and the Bacterium *Rhodospirillum rubrum*," *Arch. Mikrobiol., 54*, 253–65.

Gantt, E., and S. F. Conti, 1966. "Granules Associated with the Chloroplast Lamellae of *Porphyridium cruentum*," *J. Cell Biol., 29*, 423–34.

Giesy, R. M., 1964. "A Light and Electron Microscopic Study of Inter-Lamellar Polyglucoside Bodies in *Oscillatoria chalybea*," *Am. J. Bot., 51*, 388–96.

Grilli, M., 1964. "Infrastrutture di *Anabaena azollae* vivente nelle foglioline di *Azolla caroliniana*," *Ann. Microbiol. Enzimol., 14*, 69–90.

Höcht, H., H. H. Martin, and O. Kandler, 1965. "Zur Kenntnis der chemischen Zusammensetzung der Zellwand der Blaualgen," *Z. Pflanzenphysiol., 53*, 39–57.

Jost, M., 1965. "Die Ultrastruktur von *Oscillatoria rubescens* D.C.," *Arch. Mikrobiol., 50*, 211–45.

Jost, M., and P. Matile, 1966. "Zur Charakterisierung der Gasvacuolen der Blaualge *Oscillatoria rubescens*," *ibid., 53*, 50–58.

Lang, N. J., 1965. "Electron Microscopic Study of Heterocyst Development in *Anabaena azollae* Strasburger," *J. Phycol., 1*, 127–34.

Lang, N. J., and P. M. M. Rae, 1967. "Structures in a Blue-Green Alga Resembling Prolamellar Bodies," *Protoplasma, 64*, 67–74.

Leak, L. V., 1965. "Electron Microscopic Autoradiography Incorporation of H^3-Thymidine in a Blue-Green Alga, *Anabaena* sp.," *J. Ultrastruct. Res., 12*, 135–46.

Madsen, M. J., 1966. "Electron Microscopy of the Blue-Green Algae, *Cylindrospermum* and *Gloeotrichia*," M.A. thesis, University of California, Davis.

Metzner, I., 1955. "Zur Chemie und zum submikroskopischen Aufbau der Zellwände, Scheiden und Gallerten von Cyanophyceen," *Arch. Mikrobiol., 22*, 45–77.

Pankratz, H. S., and C. C. Bowen, 1963. "Cytology of Blue-Green Algae. I. The Cells of *Symploca muscorum*," *Am. J. Bot., 50*, 387–99.

Schmitz, R., 1967. "Über die Zusammensetzung der pigmenthaltigen Strukturen aus Prokaryonten. I. Untersuchungen an Thylakoiden von *Oscillatoria chalybea* Kütz," *Arch. Mikrobiol., 56*, 225–37.

Schneider, I. R., T. O. Diener, and R. S. Safferman, 1964. "Blue-Green Algal Virus LPP-1: Purification and Partial Characterization," *Science, 144*, 1127–30.

Schnepf, E., 1964. "Zur Feinstruktur von *Geosiphon pyriforme*. Ein Versuch zur Deutung cytoplasmatischer Membranen und Kompartimente," *Arch Mikrobiol., 49*, 112–31.

Shatkin, A. J., 1960. "A Chlorophyll-Containing Cell Fraction from the Blue-Green Alga, *Anabaena variabilis," J. Biophys. Biochem. Cytol., 7,* 583–85.

Shields, L. M., and F. Drouet, 1962. "Distribution of Terrestrial Algae within the Nevada Test Site," *Am. J. Bot., 49*, 547–54.

Singh, R. N., 1954. "Electron Microscopy of Sheath of the Blue-Green Alga *Scytonema pseudogyanense," Proc. European Cong. Electron Micros.*, Ghent, Belgium.

Talpasayi, E. R. S., 1963. "Polyphosphate Containing Particles of Blue-Green Algae," *Cytologia, 28*, 76–80.

Ventrakaramen, G. S., and S. G. Mehtra, 1962. "Submicroscopic Structure of the Mucilage of the Blue-Green Alga *Tolypothrix tenuis," Rev. Algol., 6,* 92–94.

Wolk, C. P., 1965. "Heterocyst Germination under Defined Conditions," *Nature, 205*, 201–202.

XIV

Main Trends in Experimental Work with Algal Cultures in the U.S.S.R.

B. V. GROMOV

Biological Institute
University of Leningrad
Leningrad, U.S.S.R.

In the U.S.S.R. significant attention is now being directed toward various problems concerned with the cultivation of algae. This interest has been aroused by the need to find new sources of food and fodder material, particularly in the field of industrial photosynthesis. Work with algae is also seen as a means of determining the maximal possible productivity of biosynthesis in living organisms, the natural limits of this productivity, and possible genetical and other methods to overcome these limits.

Experiments with algal cultures were initiated in our country near the end of the last century. The Russian scientist Famintzin (1871) was the first to cultivate algae in the laboratory in an artificial mineral medium.

At the beginning of this century Artari (1903, 1904, 1906, 1913) published several fundamental works on the experimental examination of algae in cultural conditions. He considered the pure culture method as the main way for studying algology, including the problems of classification. Artari's publications have not become less important; in fact, his arguments in favour of work with pure cultures are still timely.

During the 'twenties at Moscow University, Uspenskiy (1963) conducted cultural examinations of algae obtained from the waters near Moscow. Uspenskiy tried to determine the dependence of algal morphology and physiology on their ecology. His experiments showed that a concentration of ferrous salts in the environmental solution was of a great importance for algal distribution and ecology, and he later worked out the compositions of several nutrient media for laboratory cultivation of algae.

Subsequent investigations of algal cultures were performed by Gusseva (1935, 1940), Aleev and Mudrretzova-Viss (1936), Cherassimov (1937), and others, but work with algal cultures did not begin on a large scale until the end of World War II. Examinations of algae in laboratory cultures gradually developed as the main trend in our algology. In addition, the cultures of unicellular algae were widely used as a model for different experiments connected with the solution of some general plant physiology problems, especially for the work in photosynthesis. These numerous publications and reports require separate consideration by adequate specialists and will not be cited here.

Special field work was organized at many laboratories to obtain initial material for the algal cultures, and material was collected from different geographic and ecological environments. Special methods for isolating unicellular algae in their natural habitats were worked out (Schavelson, 1964; Goriunova and Ovsiannicova, 1962). For this purpose Goriunova and Ovsiannicova used special microcuvettes on the surfaces of slides or obtained growth of algal colonies in the solid medium enclosed in Pasteur pipettes.

Some scientists are working with unialgal cultures contaminated with different heterotrophic microorganisms. Sometimes such experiments give interesting data, but it is always desirable and often necessary to deal with pure cultures. The problem of bacteriological purification of algae, therefore, attracts the attention of many algologists. Unicellular green algae can usually be purified by routine bacteriological techniques, especially when solid organic media, on which bacterial growth is readily visible, are used (Goriunova, 1950; Gromov, 1965). Gajewskaja (1946) used treatment of material with iodine or rivanole solutions alternated with sterile medium washing. This method has often been successful even when applied to blue-green algae. Vinogradov and Boijchenko (1942) used the treatment with iodine and bromine for the purification of diatoms. Ultraviolet light has also been used for the purification of blue-green algae (Goriunova and Ovsiannikova, 1962; Rubenchik, Bershova, and Knizhnik, 1965; Gussev, Telitchenko, and Fedorov, 1964). In motile species a pure culture sometimes can be obtained by isolating single threads crawling away from the inoculate on the agar surface (Goriunova, 1948, 1950). Pure cultures of *Mastigocladus laminosus* were obtained by Goriunova, Odoevskaja, and Gerasimenko (1956) in the media containing *Vaccinium vitis ideae* berry juice, which contains some bactericide compounds. In purifying blue-green algae Gussev, Telitchenko, and Fedorov (1964) filtered material through an appropriate glass filter. By means of such filtration, threads and spores were obtained free from the slime which contains many bacterial cells. The material was then treated with ultraviolet light or other bactericidal agents.

The widespread development of work with algal cultures resulted in the organization of culture collections. Different methods of culture storage were considered. In our collection at the Biological Institute we have about 400 cultures representing different systematical groups of algae (Gromov, 1965a). More than one hundred strains of green, primarily protococcus, algae have been collected in the laboratory of photosynthesis at the Moscow Plant Physiology Institute of the Academy of Science. (Vladimirova and Ignatievskaja, 1966). Zhdannikova, *et al.* (1964), showed that protococcus algae retained viability for more than one year when stored in darkness at low temperatures (3-4 °C) on the surface of agar slants or in moist sand. The optimum temperature for the growth of thermophilic *Chlorella* strains was not changed after the storage of cultures at room temperature (Truhin, 1966). According to our experience with a relatively large collection it is necessary to transfer the algae to fresh medium every two to three months, at least with the most tender forms (Gromov, 1965a).

Many of our scientists are studying the laboratory conditions of protococcus and blue-green algae, especially nitrogen-fixing ones. Interest in blue-green algae in particular has grown recently because some peculiar patterns of this group have been made clear. A collection of unialgal cultures of blue-green algae obtained from regions with different climatic conditions has been created at the Kirov Institute of Agriculture (Perminova, 1964; Tretiakova, 1965, 1966). *Nostoc muscogum* strains of different origin showed morphological differences, different growth rates, and different nitrogen-fixing capacities. The *Tolypothrix tennuis* strains did not show such a variability (Tretiakova, 1965, 1966). Sirenko and Bogdanova (1965) cultivated in various media several unialgal strains of blue-green algae obtained from different ecological conditions. The growth of some species, especially that of *Anabaena variabilis*, was stimulated in the presence of auxin or vitamin P.

Nitrogen-fixing algae were isolated from the soil, plankton, and the surface layer of rice fields in Middle Asia (Kuchkarova, *et al.*, 1965, Voropaeva, 1966) and from the waters and the bottom of the Karakum Canal (Kogan, 1966). Two strains have been described by Kogan as new species: *Anabaena karakumica* and *Anabaenopsis intermedia.*

Several workers have studied pure cultures of blue-green algae including *Oscillatoria splendida* (Goriunova, 1950), *Anabaena variabilis*, *Nodularia spumigena*, *Lyngbya cryptovaginata*, *Amorphonostoc punctiforme*, *Phormidium uncinatum* (Telitchenko and Gussev, 1964), *Lyngbia aestuarii* (Goriunova and Rzhanova, 1964), *Anabaena hassallii* (Rubenchik, *et al.*, 1965), *Phormidium uncinatum* (Rzhanova and Goriunova, 1965), and others. The growth patterns of blue-green algae cultivated in different conditions have also been investigated. Fedorov (1962) observed a regular degradation of the determined cell number in the course of *Anabaena variabilis* and *Amorphonostoc punctiforme* growth. Triphenyl-tetrazolium chloride was used for the determination of dead and viable cells (Ivanova and Michailovskaia, 1962; Gussev and Fedorov, 1962; Fedorov, 1962). Fedorov (1962) believed that during the multiplication of blue-green algae the determinated part of daughter cells die.

Gussev (1962, Shaposhnicov and Gussev, 1964) observed the harmful influence of oxygen on the growth of *Anabaena variabilis* and *Amorphonostoc punctiforme* even if in usual atmospheric concentrations. This statement was disputed by data obtained in the laboratory of Pinevitch at our institute (Kovachova, 1966). In the light, acetate, glucose, and ethanole stimulated the growth of *Anabaena variabilis*, although in the darkness this algae did not grow (Gussev, 1962, 1964). Gussev (1966) considered the physiological properties of blue-green algae (growth in organic media, nitrogen fixation) as characters related to the systematical position of the organisms.

Pigment system variations caused by the diverse conditions of nitrogen and carbon nutrition, light intensity, and its spectrum composition were different in different species (Gussev and Vasilkova, 1965; Ievner, Gussev, and Shestakov, 1965; Gussev, 1966.) Deviation from the classical form of chromatic adaptation were observed under conditions of different light intensity and in the presence of available organic compounds. On the basis of his own observations and literature, Gussev (1966) stated that the presence of C-phycocianin and C-phycoeritrin in the pigment system is characteristic of the determinate species and is to be considered in connection with the systematic position of the organisms.

Much investigation has been made of the organic compounds released by growing blue-green algae. According to an earlier observation by Nikitinskij (1930), during the growth of *Stigeoclonium tenue* about 0.17 mg of carbon was detected in the soluble organic compounds per one gram of dry algae. In the organic compounds released by *Oscillatoria splendida* Goriunova (1950) discovered aldehydes, volatile acids, citric, oxalic, tartaric, and succinic acids. Free amino acids and polypeptides were determined by Goriunova and Rzhanova (1964) in the compounds released by *Lyngbya aestuarii*, and they considered the release of organic compounds by the algae belonging to the Hormogoniales as a consequence of their mode of reproduction when a part of the threads were destroyed during the hormogone liberation.

In certain cases it was possible to observe a depression of the growth of bacteria and other organisms in the cultures of blue-green algae. Goriunova (1950) noted the depression of bacteria by *Oscillatoria splendida*, and Gussev and Telitchenko (1962, 1964) observed the toxic action of the growing cultures of *Anabaena variabilis* on *Escherichia coli, Daphnia,* and carps. Other algae investigated were *Nodularia spumigena, Lyngbya cryptovaginata,* and *Amorphonostoc punctiforme. Phormidium uncinatum* did not possess such a toxic effect.

The influence of heterotrophic organisms on the growth of blue-green algae remains almost obscure. When dealing with a pure culture of *Anabaena hassallii,* the casual agent of water blooms in Kiev environments,

Rubenchik, *et al.* (1965), found that twenty-eight strains of Streptomyces and three bacterial strains from 838 examined cultures produced a harmful effect on the growth of the alga in solid media. In a liquid medium this effect was less obvious. Some bacteria and Streptomyces strains stimulated growth of *Anabaena hassallii*.

Ukrainian bacteriologists initiated the study of viruses of blue-green algae in our country. They isolated a virus of *Microcystis pulverea* which caused a lysis of this alga (Goriushyn and Chaplinskaya, 1966; Rubenchik, *et al.*, 1966).

Blue-green algae are considered as prospective forms for large-scale cultivation. According to Rzhanova and Goriunova (1965) *Phormidium uncinatum* from the point of view of its amino acid composition is of value as a protein source. These authors emphasize that blue-green algae are relatively rich in basic amino acids, lysine, and ornithine.

Recently Stoletov, *et al.* (1965), began studying the mutation process in *Anacystis nidulans*.

Special scientific attention has been given to the investigation of protococcus algae, initially that of *Chlorella* and *Scenedesmus*, which are easily cultivated from the practical point of view. The physiological diversity of systematically related forms has been examined for *Chlorella* and *Scenedesmus* species in laboratory collections by strains obtained from different sources. Vladimirova, Semenenko, and Nichiporovich (1962) observed that in *Chlorella* strains there exists a wide variability of temperature limits for growth, stability to prolonged intensive cultivation, and sensitivity to high salt concentrations and saturation light intensity. Goriunova and Ovsiannikova (1962) reported that obligate autotrophic *Chlorella* strains can be obtained from pure flowing water, myxotrophic and heterotrophic strains being characteristic for soil and waste waters. Truhin (1963, 1966), when working with *Chlorella* strains originated from different geographical areas, observed the increase in the number of relatively thermophilic strains in southern forms.

The possibility of a physiological approach to the classification of unicellular algae is under investigation. In our laboratory Avilov (1963, 1965) and Gromov and Skrupskaya (1965) examined the physiological patterns of eighty-six *Chlorella* strains. Among others we tested such characteristics as availability of different carbon and nitrogen sources in the conditions of darkness, starch hydrolysis, methylene blue reduction, and pigmentation in different media. Groups of correlative characteristics have been established, and in accordance with them, strains have been subdivided into seven groups (Gromov, Avilov, and Skrupskaya, 1965). Material was regarded from the point of view of phonetic classification (Gromov and Avilov, 1965). The use of computers for the *Chlorella* classification based on

Adansonian postulates gave interesting results which did not contradict the routine scheme. Adansonian principles appear to be useful not only in bacterial and Streptomycetes classification, but also in the classification of some algal groups. The reasonability of *Chlorella* groups established by us was confirmed by Andreeva (1967) who examined the same collection of strains from the viewpoint of classical algology.

In some experiments an attempt was made to use the nucleotide composition of DNA as a criterion for subdivision of strains, a method which has a wide application in the Streptomycetes and bacterial classification. It was established that the DNA base composition was variable in algae and especially in green algae (Serenkov, 1962; Serenkov and Vladychenskaja, 1962; Serenkov and Pachomova, 1959, 1960; Pachomova and Serenkov, 1962, 1963). Pachomova and Serenkov (1962, 1963) did not find any significant change in the nucleotide DNA composition of *Scenedesmus* cultivated under different conditions and in different parts of algae growth curve. Pinevitch and Nikiforova (1964) found that all cultures of *Chlorella*, *Scenedesmus*, and *Ankistrodesmus* examined belong to a well-determined general coccoid type. The real distinction was observed in the DNA composition of different genera, but not in the DNA composition of different *Scenedesmus* and *Ankistrodesmus* species. In contrast, *Chlorella* species showed clear differences in DNA composition (*C. vulgaris*, *C. pyrenoidosa*, and *C. ellipsoidea* were examined). Pinevitch and Nikiforova consider this genus to be heterochemotypic, a possibility which is a reflection on its complex composition, including unrelated forms.

The pigment system composition of twenty species of *Chlorella*, *Scenedesmus*, and *Ankistrodesmus* was examined at our institute in Pinevich's laboratory (Varasova, Vasiljeva, and Pinevich, 1965). The total pigment level in all species examined during growth in mineral media changed in similar limits, the quantity of green pigments being less variable than that of yellow pigments. The pigment system of *Chlorella* cells remained stable during a prolonged period of dark exposure.

The nutritional requirements of different protococcus algae during heterotrophic or myxotrophic growth were examined by several scientists. Artari (1903) found that different carbohydrates, alcohols, and organic acids are readily available for many unicellular green algae. According to Avilov (1963, 1965), who examined different *Chlorella* strains, the most part grew well in the presence of glucose and galactose, but only some strains show good growth on fructose, mannose, arabinose, and acetate.

Mineeva (1962) examined the utilization of organic compounds by *Chlorella vulgaris* and *Scenedesmus obliquus* under different growth conditions. She found that the cell material contained about $\frac{1}{3}$ organic compounds assimilated in darkness, $\frac{2}{3}$ being used for energy needs. Heterotrophic growth was possible in the more narrow pH limits than autotrophic growth. Light of low intensity had a strong effect on the uptake of glucose by *Chlorella* and *Scenedesmus*, but this effect was not connected with photosynthetic assimilation. Mineeva observed utilization of organic compounds by *Chlorella* even in conditions of light saturation of photosynthesis.

During heterotrophic growth *Scenedesmus* cells contained less protein and DNA than cells grown in the light (Pachomova, 1964).

The possible effect of biostimulators on algal growth also attracts the attention of investigators. It was found that gibberellin improved the multiplication of *Pediastrum boryanum* (Goriachev, 1963), *Scenedesmus*, *Ankistrodesmus* (Ermolajeva and Fedorova, 1964), and *Chlorella* (Pinevich, Versilin, and Vasilyeva, 1961). In all cases the cell size was not changed. Maleine acid hydrozide stimulated *Chlorella* growth (Pinevich and Versilin, 1961).

Goriunova and Nasonova (1955) reported a seasonal fluctuation of growth intensity of protococcus algae; this observation, however, was not confirmed by others authors (Shaposhnikov, *et al.*, 1964; Vladimirova and Ignatievskaja, 1966). According to Feokistova (1965), seasonal changes in the growth of protococcus algae might be revealed or not, depending on the conditions of cultivation.

Work with synchronous *Chlorella* cultures was initiated by Spectorov and Linkova (1962, 1963). They found that optimal temperatures for cell growth and development were different (Spectorova, 1965, 1967). Consumption of $C^{14}O_2$ by cells in the different stages of cell development in synchronized *Chlorella* cultures was examined by Shkolnik, *et al.* (1965). Synchronized cultures of *Scenedesmus obliquus* were obtained by Markarova and Baslavskaya (1965) and of *Scenedesmus quadricauda* by Baslavskaya and Bamburova (1966). Changes in photosynthetic activity and chemical composition of cells during growth and development were registered.

Several publications were dedicated to examining the nitrogen nutrition of protococcus algae. It was confirmed that ammonium is preferably assimilated by algae in comparison with nitrate (Pinevich, Versilin, and Maslov, 1961; Tomova, Evstigneyeva, and Kretovich, 1964). Not ammonium salts but urea was recommended for laboratory cultivation of algae because of the physiological acidity of ammonium salts. Nitrates were recommended as a source of nitrogen for large-scale outdoor cultures where hard bacterial contamination took place (Pinevich, Versilin, and Maslov, 1961).

The biochemical composition of protococcus algae was intensively investigated. Diverse amino acids were determinated in the proteins of

Chlorella and *Scenedesmus* (Pachomova, 1964; Sisakian, *et al.*, 1962). The amino acid composition of algal cells grown autotrophically or heterotrophically was somewhat different (Pachomova, 1964). In our institute, Bers (1965) undertook the separation of the total acid-soluble protein extract by means of paper electrophoresis, DEAE sephadecs chromatography, and disc electrophoresis in polyacrylamide gel (Bers, *et al.*, 1966). No significant changes in fractions caused by different growth conditions were observed.

The lability of *Chlorella* metabolism attracts the attention of numerous physiologists. It was shown that the total nitrogen level in cells depends on the nitrogen source (Baslavskaya and Feofarova, 1959; Pinevich, Versilin, and Maslov, 1961; Iaaska, 1964; Tomova, *et al.*, 1964). The total nitrogen content was higher in conditions favorable for rapid growth (Vladimirova and Kuznetsov, 1964), but sharp changes in the biochemical composition of *Chlorella vulgaris* were observed under conditions deficient in essential nutrient elements; these changes were specific for the given element. An increase in the carbohydrate fraction was observed in all examinations of the *C. vulgaris* strain (Gitelzon, Sadikova, Borodkina, and Bazanova, 1966). Especially radical changes in metabolism are characteristic of nitrogen deficiency. The increase of carbohydrate and lipid synthesis took place during nitrogen starvation, but the correlation between carbohydrate and lipid synthesis rates varied depending on the strain and growth conditions (Iaaska, 1964; Klyachko-Gurvich, 1964, 1966; Klyachko-Gurvich and Zhukova, 1966; Kuznetsov, 1966). According to Iaaska (1964), *Chlorella vulgaris*, *Chlorococcum botryoides*, and *Oocystis* sp. accumulate lipids when grown in a nitrogen-deficient medium; *Scenedesmus quadricauda* showed an insignificant change in carbohydrates and lipid content. *Chlorella vulgaris* strain "K" in the absence of available nitrogen accumulated starch; *Chlorella pyrenoidosa* strain "84" accumulated lipids and its oleic acid content grew especially (Klyachko-Gurvich and Zhukova, 1966). The accumulation and content of mineral compounds in the cells were also affected by nitrogen deficiency (Kuznetsov, 1966). The chlorophyll content of algal cells and their photosynthetic capacity decreased during prolonged exposure to the nitrogen-free medium, but the cells remained viable a long time (Baslavskaya, Kulikova, and Kurkova, 1966).

The examination of the lipid composition of *Chlorella* was initiated at our institute by Maslov (1966).

The phosphate metabolism in *Scenedesmus quadricauda* and *S. obliquus* has been investigated by Baslavskaya and co-workers (Baslavskaya and Weber, 1959; Baslavskaya and Bystrova, 1964; Weber, 1959; Baslavskaya, Kulikova, Markarova, and Savchenko, 1966). Phosphate accumulation was greater in the light than in the dark. The majority of intracellular phosphorus was observed in the acid-soluble fractions, especially in the polyphosphates. Vagabov and Serenkov (1963) reported an increase of a nonacid-soluble polyphosphate fraction in the *Scenedesmus obliquus* cells during the growth of the culture. Polyphosphate metabolism in algal cells has been investigated at our institute by Nekrasova (1966).

Recently, there has been much investigation of the organic compounds excreted by protococcus algae into the medium. About 5–10 per cent of organic matter accumulated by *Chlorella* was discovered in the culture medium, sometimes even 30 per cent (Pimenova and Maksimova, 1966). Algae excreted three to five times more organic matter during a lag period of growth and in the beginning of a lag phase than during exponential growth or during a stationary phase (Maksimova, Toropova, and Pimenova, 1965; Pimenova and Maksimova, 1966). The excretion of organic matter into the medium increased under unfavorable growth conditions (Tauts, 1964; Pimenova and Maksimova, 1966). Carbohydrates, acetic, formic, glicolic, pyruvic, α-ketoglutaric, and glioxilic acids were discovered in the culture medium of *Chlorella*, but nitrogenous organic compounds were not detected. The composition of organic matter excreted by different *Chlorella* strains was somewhat different. As the authors cited above believe, the excretion of organic compounds does not depend on the decay of dead cells but is determined by the peculiar type of reproduction of protococcus algae by means of autospores.

The effect of changes in temperature conditions on the growth and metabolism of protococcus algae is under investigation. The differences in free amino acid levels and composition depending on the temperature were detected in *Chlorella* (Zalensky, *et al.*, 1965; Glagoleva, *et al.*, 1965), and the same is true concerning the nucleotide content (Nechayeva, 1964). The temperatures optimal for growth and photosynthesis were found to be different, as were the temperatures optimal for different strains (Daletzkaya and Chiulanovskaya, 1964). It was observed in several strains obtained from diverse geographical conditions that the light intensities optimal for growth depended on the temperature (Truhin, 1963; Smirnov, 1966; Vladimirova, Semenenko, Zhukova, and Kovanova, 1966).

The resistance to high temperature of different strains of *Chlorella* and *Scenedesmus* was variable (Vladimirova, Semenenko, and Nichiporovich, 1962; Truhin, 1963, 1966). Truhin (1966) considered as thermophilic strains those which remained viable after a ten-day incubation at 40–41°C in light. The action of high temperature on the *Chlorella* cells was investigated by Godnev and Liachnovich (1964, 1966). Truhin (1966) pointed out that cells grown at a higher temperature are more resistant to heating, and he also observed an increase of the temperature optimum in some strains. Adaptation of *Chlorella pyrenoidosa* to higher temperature, revealed in the increase of optimum temperature for photosynthesis, was observed by Daletzkaya and Chiulanovskaya (1964). In some instances the inhibitory effect of a high temperature was strengthened by high light intensity. In *Chlorella* strain "K" temperature above maximal inhibited cell division at first, giant cells being formed under such conditions (Vladimirova, Semenenko, Zhukova, and Kovanova, 1966). Gusseva (1940) found protococcus algae to be more resistant to the inhibitory action of copper than blue-green algae and diatoms. Examination of our *Chlorella* strain collection showed that strains differed significantly in their resistance to low pH value (Gromov, Avilov, and Skrupskaya, 1965). Varasova, *et al.* (1965), observed rapid pigment degradation in *Chlorella pyrenoidosa* suspended in a medium of pH 3, but colorless cells gradually restored their pigments. In this case the selection of acid-fast cells did not take place. The ability of *Chlorella* to reparation after the action of extreme pH values was also investigated by Antonijan (1966b).

The resistance of *Chlorella* to ultraviolet radiation has been investigated by Zaharov and Tugarinov (1964) and Anikeeva and her co-worker (1964). Dose effect curves were found to be S shaped. DL_{50} for *Chlorella vulgaris* was 14.5 kr (Zaharov and Tugarinov, 1964), but the sensitivity of different strains differed markedly (Anikeeva, *et al.*, 1964). After-effects of ultraviolet treatment on the number of autospores in mother cells and growth dynamics has been detected in several generations.

The growth of *Chlorella vulgaris* was stimulated by irradiation if doses were 0.5–1 kr, the higher doses being inhibitory (Gileva, *et al.*, 1965). A lethal effect was registered if doses were 25 kr or above.

Morphological and physiological variabilities of some algae have been investigated in laboratory cultures. In the 'twenties Uspenskiy (1963) undertook extensive work in Spirogyra, examining the variability of its morphological characteristics. Later, working with blue-green algae and *Euglena gracilis*, Poljansky (1938, 1948) tried to establish the degree of stability of morphological characteristics. He wanted to establish a value for classifying these species. The high-speed development of methods and ideas in microbial genetics after the war allowed the research on algal variability to be based on a more scientific foundation. *Chlorella* became a principal object in genetics experiments.

At our institute, Kvitko (1961) initiated an investigation of the mutation process in *Chlorella vulgaris* strain "B." A number of pigment mutants was obtained, and the mutants devoid of violoxanthine were light sensitive (Varasova and Kvitko, 1962). The mutagenic activity of ultraviolet light, X-rays, ethylenimine, nitrosomethyl urea (Kvitko, Zaharov, and Khropova, 1966), and incorporated C^{14} (Pluciennik, 1965) were later investigated. The mutation rate-dose dependence was S-shaped for ultraviolet and incorporated C^{14}, and nearly linear for X-rays and ethylenimine (Zaharov and Tugarinov, 1964; Khropova, Kvitko, and Zaharov, 1964). Tugarinov and Kuznetsov (1966) found that the number of pigment mutations after X-ray treatment increased in the presence of streptomycin, concentrations of which were without mutagenic activity. Relative specificity was observed in the frequency of diverse classes of pigment mutants caused by different mutagens (Khropova, et al., 1964). Ensuing classes of mutants besides pigment were described: aucsotrophic (Zaharov and Fridljanskaya, 1963; Kvitko and Khropova, 1963), mutants with rough colonies, mutants excreting a brown pigment into the medium, slow growing mutants (Khropova, et al., 1964), mutants containing more cystein (Kvitko, et al., 1966), and streptomycin-resistant and streptomycin-dependent (Tugarinov, 1965). The adaptive nature of streptomycin-resistant mutants obtained in the medium with streptomycin was demonstrated by (Tugarinov (1965). Spontaneous and induced mutants resistant to the inhibitory amino acid concentrations were also obtained (Kvitko, et al., 1966). Spontaneous mutants resistant to alanine appeared with the frequency of 6×10^{-7} per mitosis (Kvitko, et al., 1966).

The process of mutation in several strains of Chlorella vulgaris and C. ellipsoidea has been investigated by Anikeeva, Vaulina, and Shevchenko, (1964) at the Moscow Institute of Biophysics.

The pigment and morphological mutants and those with dwarfish or spotted colonies have also been described. The character and frequency of spontaneous mutation differed in different strains, as did a spectrum of induced and spontaneous mutants. In these strains the mutation rate-ultra-violet-dose curve was S shaped and linear when X-rays were used similarly to the data obtained with the strain "B." The character of X-ray effect on strains examined shows that Chlorella cells are haploid.

The effect of mitotic drugs—colchicine, chlortetracycline, and tripaflavine—on the cells of several algae was investigated by Gerasimenko (1965). The sensitivity of different algae varied. In some forms, including Chlorella and Scenedesmus, mitotic drugs provoked morphological divergence and an increase in cell size and number of nuclei. These changes were reversible; Gerasimenko failed to obtain stable polyploid forms.

Problems of large-scale cultivation of algae under natural or artificial light were considered in numerous publications. The highest harvests obtained thus far from the laboratory Chlorella cultures correspond to 100–150 g/m² per day of dry weight, the efficiency of photosynthesis being 10–12 per cent (Gitelson, Lisovskiy, and Terskov, 1966; Semenenko, Vladimirova, Soglin, Tauts, Philipovskiy, Klyachko-Gurvich, Kuznetsov, Kovanova, and Raijkov, 1966). According to Gitelson, Lisovskiy, and Terskov (1966), the algal culture will not replace higher plants as a source of nutritional material, being less practical from an economical point of view. Large-scale cultures of algae are deemed a possible means of producing biostimulators (Nichiporovich, 1961). For instance, Pinevitch, Khazanskaya, and Afanasyeva (1966) observed the stimulation of yeast growth and fermentative activity in the presence of a small quantity of *Chlorella*. Cultivated algae serve as food for the invertebrates which are used for fish nutrition at the fish breeding plants (Gajewskaja, 1953, 1956). Algal culture is considered a useful means of producing labeled compounds (Nichiporovich, 1961). Karpov (1963) worked out a method for the C^{14} amino acid production by *Chlorella* cultures.

The culture of algae is also seen as a possible component of closed ecological systems (Gitelson, Lisovskiy and Terskov, 1966 and other). Vinberg and co-workers (1966) successfully elaborated methods of waste water regeneration in ponds where microbiological processes of organic matter mineralization are associated with the utilization of formed mineral compounds and CO_2 by unicellular algae.

In the fifties, methods of algal mass cultivation were developed by Gajewskaja (1952, 1953, 1954, 1955, 1956) and Smirnov (1955). Gajewskaja cultivated algae in the laboratory and in the open air. Since 1957, the large-scale cultivation of protococcus algae in the open air has been employed at our institute (Chesnokov, *et al.*, 1960, 1961). Pinevich and co-workers (1964) constructed the most profitable type of standard installations for the mass cultivation of algae in the open air. They worked out a suitable nutrient solution (Pinevich, Versilin, and Maslov, 1961) and selected strains of algae (Pinevich and Versilin, 1961, 1963). Large-scale cultures of protococcus algae give optimal harvests about 10–20 g/m^2 dry weight per day in the Leningrad climate. The cultivation of algae in the open air was realized at Viliams Institute near Moscow (Rusina, 1961), in Middle Asia near Tashkent (Troiskaia, 1960; Muzafarov, *et al.*, 1961), and in Tadjikistan (Machmadbekov and Haitova, 1965). Strains from collections or local strains of *Chlorella, Scenedesmus*, and *Ankistrodesmus* were used for large-scale cultures in the open air.

The selection of productive forms is recognized as an important way for improving the effectiveness of the culture, and different methods of strain selection and evaluation have already been discussed (Vladimirova and Semenenko, 1962; Vaulina and Anikeeva, 1964, 1965; Schavelson and Potechina, 1965). Determination of the productivity of different strains, especially strains of *Chlorella* under different conditions of temperature and light intensity, showed that the experimental value of different forms depends on the given experimental conditions; determination of the proper correlation between light intensity and temperature for the strain used was found to be of a great importance (Vladimirova, Ignatievskaiya, and Raiykov, 1966).

The methods for evaluating the utility of different forms for intensive laboratory cultivation were developed at the Institute of Plant Physiology, Academy of Science, U.S.S.R., by Vladimirova, Semenenko, and Nichiporovich (1962) and Vladimirova and Semenenko (1962). A comparison of productivity in *Chlorella* strains obtained from different geographical points showed that the northern strains were more productive in the conditions of moderate temperature and comparatively low light intensity, but southern strains were better in the conditions of higher temperature and light intensity (Truhin, 1966). High temperature strains were more productive under the conditions of intensive laboratory cultivation (Truhin, 1966; Vladimirova, Semenenko, Zhukova, and Kovanova, 1966). Different strains of *Chlorella* and *Scenedesmus* were used for intensive laboratory cultivation, and Truhin (1966) tested some representatives of other genera and observed a good growth of *Chlorococcum* strains.

One important aspect of the possibility of algae utilization in the ecological system is the creation of normal conditions for human life during prolonged space flights (Nichiporovich, 1961; Nichiporovich, Semenenko, and Vladimirova, 1962). The development of the study of algal culture utilization in the air regeneration system was based on previous experience obtained by Chesnokov and Pinevich and co-workers (Chesnokov, Pinevich, Versilin, and Stepanova, 1960, 1961; Chesnokov, 1962; Pinevich and Versilin, 1961; Pinevich, Versilin and Maslov, 1961; Pinevich and Versilin, 1963) and by Nichiporovich, Semenenko, and Vladimiriva (1961, 1962). Construction of a fermenter for the intensive cultivation of *Chlorella* has been worked out by Kovrov and Bogdanov (1964a,b,c). At a light intensity of 80–90 kilolux the maximum obtained harvests were about 40 g/l or 100 g/m² of dry weight per day. The growth of high-yielding *Chlorella* strains under intensive continuous culture has been investigated by Semenenko, Vladimirova, Soglin, Tauts, Phillipovskiy, Klyachko-Gurvich, Kuznetsov, Kovanova, and Raijkov (1966). Stable high yields of about 140–150 g/m² dry weight per day were obtained during a long period of time (forty days) in the installations described by the authors. Tamiya's medium was usually used as a basic mineral solution for the intensive cultivation of *Chlorella*. It was found that the concentration of this medium might be increased several times, since in the more concentrated media the flotation of cells was less expressed (Godnev and Liachnovich, 1964). Kuznetsov and Vladimirova (1964) found that growth in Tamiya's medium was limited by the concentration of iron which had to be increased. The absorption of main elements from the medium by *Chlorella* cells was calculated by determining the changes in the composition of the medium in growing cultures (Kuznetsov and Vladimirova, 1965). For the continuous cultivation of *Chlorella* with the return of solution Kuznetsov and Semenenko (1966) proposed a balanced medium. Reparation of the medium was achieved by

the addition to the exhaust medium of a solution containing mineral compounds in quantities characteristic for the *Chlorella* cells. The optimal
concentration of CO_2 in the gas mixture was examined, too (Semenenko,
Vladimirova, Soglin, and Popova, 1966).

The first attempts to support the respiration of men and animals by gas-
exchange system based on the *Chlorella* photosynthesis were undertaken by
Meleshko and co-workers. They carried out the wide examination of
Chlorella cultures as a possible part of the ecological system (Meleshko,
1964; Korotaev, Kustov, Meleshko, Poddubnaja, and Shepelev, 1964;
Galkina, 1964; Ivanov and Aleksandrova, 1964; Lebedeva, Meleshko, and
Shakhova, 1965; Meleshko and Krasotchenko, 1965). In the course of experiments with the photosynthetic closed installations of high productivity, it was found that one liter of CO_2 was assimilated for the creation of
1 gram of dry weight algae during intensive cultivation of *Chlorella* in the
nitrate medium, 1.24 liter of O_2 being liberated simultaneously. In one
gram of algae 452 mg C, 79 mg N, 17.4 mg P, 16 mg K, 11.2 mg S, 5.7 mg
Mg, and 0.3 mg Fe was accumulated (Lebedeva, Meleshko, and Shakhova,
1965; Meleshko, Lebedeva and Galkina, 1966; Shepelev, 1966). The accumulation of toxic compounds—carbon dioxide, oxides of nitrogen, and
hydrocarbons—has also been detected in the gas (Korotaev, Kustov,
Meleshko, Poddubnaja, and Shepelev, 1964). The photosynthetic coefficient of Chlorella in the nitrate medium was between 0.75–0.81, with an
average of 0.79. In the medium with urea, the photosynthetic coefficient
increased to 1.0. If the medium for algae was obtained by the mineralization of human waste, the coefficient was 0.82. Thus, the photosynthetic coefficient of *Chlorella* in the nitrate medium corresponded to the human respiratory coefficient under conditions of normal nutrition. From this viewpoint, algae are more suitable than higher plants which have a photosynthetic coefficient near 1.0 (Shepelev, 1966).

The accumulation of biologically active organic compounds in the medium in dense suspension became an important factor for the cultivation of
algae. In her intensive culture of *Chlorella*, Galkina (1964) observed the
accumulation of compounds which stimulated growth at the beginning
but had an inhibitory action in the culture with higher density.

Smirnov (1963, 1964) carried out a mathematical analysis of the *Chlorella* growth parameters important for the development of an automatic
culture control. The questions of automatic control of *Chlorella* cultivation
were considered by Gitelzon and co-workers (Gitelzon, Terskov, Batov,
Baklanov, and Kovrov, 1964). These authors developed a scheme for the
automatic search of optimal growth conditions. Under conditions of artificially created high cell density, Meleshko (1964) obtained the highest
productivity of *Chlorella* culture, 8–10 liter of oxygen per hour from one
liter of suspension.

The possibility of animal and human waste regeneration in the laboratory cultures of protococcus algae has been demonstrated (Baranov, Glazacheva and Ian, 1964; Baranov, Ian, Odinsova and Glazacheva, 1964; Rerberg and Vorobieva, 1964ab; Rerberg, Vorobieva, Kuzmina and Barkhatova, 1965; Rerberg, Kuzmina, and Barkhatova, 1964; Rerberg and Kuzmina, 1964).

Data obtained in our country and abroad show a practical acceptability and high effectivity of the culture of unicellular algae as an element of the ecological system in space vehicles. The possibility exists to reduce the weight of algal suspension to several kilograms for one person (Shepelev, 1966).

It is interesting to note that after a twenty-four-hour flight in the second space ship *Chlorella pyrenoidosa* remained viable, and no significant irreversible changes could be observed in major physiological processes such as photosynthesis, growth, or reproduction (Semenenko and Vladimirova, 1962).

Examination of the interrelations of algae and other microorganisms is essential to the understanding of algal ecology. Now this problem has a special significance in connection with the practical application of algal cultures. Practical utilization of cultivated algae is impossible without the development of algal pathology.

Microorganisms contaminating algal cultures in the open air near Leningrad were examined by us (Gromov, 1965b); cultures in the Moscow district were examined by Pimenova, Maksimova, and Balizkaya (1962) and Maksimova (1966). The quantity of bacteria in the cultures of protococcus algae was very high. In some instances the weight of bacteria reached 60 per cent of the algal biomass. The systematical position of contaminating bacteria in the cultures in the open air and laboratory cultures are variable; gram negative rods, especially belonging to *Pseudomonas*, *Flavobacterium*, *Achromobacter*, and *Agrobacterium*, predominated (Maksimova, 1966; Lewina, 1961; Vladimirova, 1961; Gromov, 1965b; Gromov and Skrupskaya, 1965). *Caulobacter* (Zavarsina, 1961; Gromov, 1964) and *Hyphomicrobium vulgare* (Zavarsin, 1960; Gromov, 1965b) were detected as usual contaminants. Observations showed that the intensity of bacterial growth in algal cultures depends on the growth conditions and organisms. Diverse bacteria, including the coli-typhoid group, introduced into the culture of protococcus algae grew there much better than in the control mineral solution; therefore, organic compounds excreted by algae were available to these bacteria (Vladimirova and Basitova, 1961; Telitchenko, Davydova, and Fedorov, 1962; Fedorov, Kuschner, and Telitchenko, 1962; Maksimova, 1966). An active bacterial multiplication usually took place only in the first stages of cultivation. When the density of algal cells in the culture became high, many bacterial forms died partially or completely (Vladimirova, 1961; Lewina, 1961; Vladimirova and Basitova, 1961; Gromov and Skrupskaya, 1965; Maksimova, 1966). It was shown that protococcus algae exerted inhibitory action on the phages of the coli-typhoid bacterial group. If in high concentrations, the T_1 and T_2 phages of *Escherichia coli* were inactivated in the growing cultures of *Chlorella vulgaris* and *Scenedesmus quadricauda* (Davydova, Pospelova, and Telitchenko, 1962; Telitchenko and Fedorov, 1962; Sadovskaya and Telitchenko, 1966).

The cause of bacterial death in algae cultures has not yet been elucidated. Maksimova (Maksimova and Lastochkina, 1964; Maksimova, 1966) failed to find bactericidal activity of the filtrates from the algal cultures where bacteria died. Some authors considered the pH changes in the medium during algal growth to be important (Fedorov, Kuschner and Telitchenko, 1962) or the increase of redox potential characteristic for the rapidly growing algal cultures where intensive photosynthesis takes place (Maksimova and Fedenko, 1965; Maksimova, 1966). The last suggestion has been well argued by various authors.

We observed depression of bacterial growth in the cultures of some *Chlorella* strains cultivated in the organic glucose medium, and the effect was connected with the pH fall (Gromov and Maslennikova, 1965). In this case the accumulation of organic acids took place during the glucose oxidation by algae.

In the conditions of mineral media contaminating bacteria usually have not had a significant influence on the growth of algae (Vladimirova, 1961; Vladimirova and Basitova, 1961; Gromov, 1965; Maksimova, 1966). The stimulatory action of contaminating bacteria on the growth of algae was not observed, but sometimes contaminating microorganisms had an inhibitory action on the growth of algae or even caused its death (Maksimova, 1966; Leonova and Antonenko, 1966). Maksimova (1966) observed a decrease in the growth of *Chlorella vulgaris* culture slightly contaminated by *Pseudomonas pyocyaneum*. We found that numerous soil bacteria, streptomycetes, and fungi had antagonistic action on *Chlorella* growth under conditions of solid medium (Gromov and Kameshkova, 1964). These microorganisms, however, cannot be considered as usual contaminants in algal cultures.

The specific microorganisms adapted at the expense of algae have, of course, significance for algae cultivation. Zavarsina (Zavarsina and Protsenko, 1958; Zavarsina, 1961, 1964) observed lysis of *Chlorella pyrenoidosa* cells in laboratory cultures, and the biological nature of the process has been demonstrated. A similar lytic agent was later obtained from the mass culture of *Chlorella vulgaris* in the open air in our laboratory (Mamkaeva, 1966). Our agent differed in the *Chlorella* strains which it attacked. According to Zavarsina, a lytic agent was similar to the bacterial viruses. Virus particles were discovered too by electron micrographs. The particles designated as chlorellophages consisted of a polyhedral head and a short tail with threads on its end (Tikhonenko and Zavarsina, 1966). The active lysis of *Chlorella* cells was possible only in the presence of bacteria, although bacteria growing in the infected cultures themselves had no harmful effect on *Chlorella* growth (Zavarsina, 1964). Zavarsina believes that contaminating bacteria take part in the chlorellophage transfer, activate it, and complete the destruction of the cell.

Two strains of endoparasites belonging to the genus *Amoeboaphelidium* were obtained by us from mass cultures of *Chlorella* and *Scenedesmus* (Gromov and Mamkaeva, 1966a,b). The active motile amoeba represents the free living stage of the parasite. This amoeba penetrates into the algal cell and forms a slowly growing protoplasmatic body. The mature body subdivides into amoebas which leave the destroyed cell. One strain attacks only some *Chlorella* strains; another becomes a parasite in the cells of different protococcus algae.

The brackish water forms *Dunaliella salina* and *Asteromonas gracilis* are considered as a perspective from the practical point of view. *Dunaliella* can be used as a good source of carotene (Drokova, 1960) and vitamins (Drokova, 1960; Massjuk, 1961) or can serve as a first-step food material in the nutrition chain for valuable fishes (Massjuk, 1965a,b). Methods for the bacteriological purification of brackish water algae were worked out by Alyoshina (1961). The optimum temperature for the growth of *D. salina* (Yurkova, 1965) and limits of mineral salts concentrations (Milko, 1962; Massjuk, 1965a,b) were detected. *D. salina* could withstand sharp changes in the concentration of mineral salt, concentration optimal for the growth and carotene accumulation being different (Massjuk, 1965).

The biochemical composition of *D. salina* was investigated by Serenkov and Pachomova (1961, 1962), Pachomova (1964), and Vagabov and Serenkov (1963). The conditions needed for maximal carotene accumulation were detected by Drokova (1960) and Milko (1963a,b).

The optimal composition of nutrient solution for *Asteromonas gracilis* was found by Voskresensky and Yurina (1965) and Yurina (1966), temperature limits for the growth by Voskresensky and Yurina (1965), and optimal light intensity by Yurina (1966). The biochemical composition of *A. gracilis* was investigated by Yurina and Pachomova (1966). Large-scale cultivation of *A. gracilis* was performed by Voskresensky and Yurina (1965). Harvests of about 7.5 g/m² of dry weight material per day were obtained from the 150–300 liter ponds. These harvests are comparable with the harvests obtained from *Chlorella* cultures.

Some experimental works have also been made with the cultures of *Pediastrum* (Goriachev, 1947, 1960, 1961, 1963), *Euglena* (Zaar and Kasinova, 1963), *Chlamydomonas* (Pimenova and Kondratieva, 1965; Gorbunova, 1966), diatoms (Goriunova, 1954; Levshina, 1965), and dinoflagellates (Akinina, 1966).

The review given above is not exhaustive, but it shows that the cultures of algae in our country have become an important object in experimental biology. It seems obvious that in a short time cultivated algae will have an effective application for human life.

REFERENCES

Ahinina, D. K., 1966. "Dependence of photosynthesis of *Prorocentrum micans* and *Gymnodinium kowalewskii* on solar radiation intensity," *Physiologia rasteniy*, *13*, *2*; 226–30.

Aleev, B. S., and Mudretzova-Viss, C. A., 1936. "The influence of the concentration of nitrogenous compounds on the multiplication of *Pediastrum boryanum* (Turp) Menegh," *Microbiologia*, *5*, *4*, 464–86.

Alyoshina, E. S., 1961. "Obtaining bacteriologically pure cultures of green flagellant halophilic algae," *Vestnic* Moscovskogo Univ., ser. biol. No. 4, Moscow Univ., 62–66.

Andreyeva, V. M., 1967. "On some problems of the taxonomy of the genus *Chlorella*, *Botanicheskiy J.*, *52*, *1*, 82–86.

Anikeeva, I. D., Vaulina, E. N., and Shevchenko, V. A., 1964. "Influence of U.V.-rays on *Chlorella*," *Radiobiologiya*, *4*, *6*, 883–92.

Antonijan, A. A., 199a. "Action of the nutrient solution osmotic strength on the growth and biochemical composition of *Chlorella pyrenoidosa*," tezisy Konf., "Mechanismy biologicheskih processov," Univ. Leningrad, Leningrad, 5.

———, 1966b. "Action of extreme pH value on the growth and biochemical composition of *Chlorella pyrenoidosa*," 6.

Artari, A. P., 1903. *K voprosu o vlijanii sredy na formu i rasvitie vodorosleiy* [On the problem of the environment's action on algal morphology and development], Moscow.

———, 1904. "Metod chistyh culturi i ego nauchnoe znachenie" [Pure culture method and it's scientific significance], *Nauchnoe slovo*, Moscow.

———, 1906. "Der Einfluss der Konzentrationen der Nahrlosungen auf die Entwicklung einiger gruner Algen," *Jahrb. f. Wiss. Bot. Bd. 43*, H. 2.

———, 1913. "Zur Physiologie des Chlamydomonaden," *ibid.*, H. 4.

Avilov, I. A., 1963. "Utilization of different carbon sources by algae of the genus *Chlorella* in the dark," *Vestnik*, Leningrad. Univ. No. 15, ser. biol., 3, 62–69.

———, 1965a. "Ulilization of some carbohydrates by the algae of genus *Chlorella*," Trudy Peterhofskogo Biol. Inst., No. 19, Univ. Leningrad, Leningrad, 131–36.

———, 1965b. "Adsortpion of methylene blue by *Chlorella* cells," *ibid.*, 137–44.

Baranov, S. A., Ian, N. A., Odinsova, M. A., and Glazacheva, I. V., 1964. "On the cultivation of microalgae enrichment cultures with the excretions of man and animals," in *Upravliaemoe cultivirovanie microvodorosleiy* [Directed cultivation of microalgae], Nauka, Moscow, 86–97.

Baranov, S. A., Glasacheva, I. V., and Ian, N. A., 1964. "On the continuous cultivation of microalgae with the excretions of man and animals," *ibid.*, 98–109.

Baslavskaya, S. S., and Bamburova, L. S., 1966. "On the assimilative activity and composition of *Scenedesmus quadricauds* cells of various ages," *Vestnik* Moscovskogo Univ., ser. biol., No. 5, Moscow Univ., Moscow, 27–34.

Baslavskaya, S. S., and Bystrova, E. I., 1964. "The effect of light upon phosphorus exchange in protococcus algae," Doklady Ac. Nauk U.S.S.R., *155,5,* 1220–23.

Baslavskaya, S. S., and Feofarova, N. B., 1959. "Some data on the growth composition of *Scenedesmus quadricauda* (Turp) Breb. under conditions of ammonium and nitrate nutrition, Nauchnye doklady vischeiy schkoly, biol. nauky, *1,* 147–52.

Baslavskaya, S. S., Kulikova, R. F., and Kurkova, E. B., 1966. "The action of nitrogen deficiency and nitrogen feeding on the photosynthesis, chlorophyll content, and growth of the culture of protococcus algae," *Bull.* Mosc. obschestva ispytateleiy prirody, otd. biol., **71, 2,** 107–17.

Baslavskaya, S. S., Kulikova, R. F., Markarova, E. N., and Savchenko, R. V., 1966. "A study of phosphorus metabolism in Protococcales," Nauchnye doklady vyscheiy schkoly, biol. nauky, *2,* 144–48.

Baslavskaya, S. S., and Weber, H., 1959. "The effect of light on transformation of phosphates in plants," Doklady Ac. Nauk, U.S.S.R., *124, 1,* 227–30.

Bers, E. P., 1965. "Studies of proteins in protococcus algae *Chlorella pyrenoidosa,*" *Vestnik* Leningrad. Univ., No. 9, ser. biol., *2,* 157–60.

Bers, E. P., Pinevitch, V. V., and Reznik, K. P., 1966. "Investigation of proteins of protococcus algae," *ibid.*, No. 21, *4,* 47–51.

Cherassimov, P. A., 1937. "On the influence of copper sulphate on algae of the group Protococcales," *Microbiologia, 6, 1,* 35–46.

Chesnokov, V. A., 1962. "On some physiological aspects of increasing productivity of unicellular algae," *Vestnik* Leningrad. Univ., No. 9, ser. biol., *2,* 113–22.

Chesnokov, V. A., Pinevitch, V. V., and Versilin, N. N., 1961. "Some results of large-scale cultivation of algae," in *Pervichnaia produksia moreiy i vnutrennich vod* [Primary production in seas and inland waters], Minsk, 333–38.

Chesnokov, V. A., Pinevitch, V. V., Versilin, N. N., and Stepanova, A. M., 1960. "Some results of large-scale culture of algae," *Vestnik* Leningrad. Univ., No. 9, ser. biol., *2,* 29–36.

Daletzkaya, I. A., and Chiulanovskaya, M. V., 1964. The effect of temperature on growth and photosynthesis in *Chlorella,*" *Botanicheskiy J., 49,* 8, 1147–59.

Davydova, N. V., Pospelova, V. V., and Telitchenko, M. M., 1962. "Interrelation between algae and microorganisms," Rep. III. *Bull.* exp. biol. med., *11,* 84–87.

Drokova, I. G., 1960. "Investigation of algae for β-carotin content," *Ukrainskiy bot. J., 17,* 2, 39–42.

Ermolajeva, L. M., and Fedorov, V. G., 1964. "On the action of gibberellin on algal development," Nauchnye doklady vyscheiy schkoly, biol. nauk, *1,* 133–35.

Famintzin, A., 1871. "Die anorganische Salze als ausgereichnetes Hülfsmittel zum Studium der Entwicklung niederer chlorophyllhaltiger Organismen," *Bull.* Acad. Sci. St. Petersburg, Bd. *17,* S. 31.

Fedorov, V. D., 1962. "On the regularity underlying the death of cells in multiplying cultures of blue-green algae *Anabaena variabilis* and *Amorphonostoc punctiforme,*" Doklady Ac. Nauk U.S.S.R., *144, 6,* 1380–83.

Fedorov, V. D., Kuschner, S. G., and Telitchenko, M. M., 1962. "Interrelation between algae and microorganisms," Rep. 1. Nauchnye doklady vyscheiy schkoly, biol. nauky, *2,* 160–64.

Feoktistova, O. I., 1965. "A study of the seasonal periodicity of *Chlorella* development as dependent on cultivation conditions," *Physiologia rasteniy, 12,5,* 888–93.

Gajewskaja, N. S., 1946. "A new method of rapidly obtaining bacteria-free cultures of algae," *Bull.* Mosc. obschestva ispytateleiy prirody, nov. ser., otd. biol. *51,2,* 13–19.

————, 1952. "On the cultivation of protococcus algae with fluorescent lamps," *ibid.*, *57,4*, 35–42.

————, 1953. "Large-scale cultivation of protococcus algae for fish-breeding," Trudy Vsesoiusnogo gidrobiol. obschestva, *5*, 72–108.

————, 1954. "A new protoccoccus alga for the large-scale cultivation of *Lagerheimia ciliata* (Lagerh) Chodat," *Bull.* Mosc. obschestva ispytateleiy prirody, nov. ser., otd. biol., *59,1*, 83–84.

————, 1955. "Mass cultivation of protococcus algae with fluorescent lamps submerged in the culture," *ibid., 60,2*, 91–98.

————, 1956. "The problem of unicellular algae utilization," *Priroda, 4*, 3–51.

Galkina, T. B., 1964. "Repeated usage of nutrient media for the cultivation of *Chlorella*," in *Problemy kosmicheskoiy biologii,* Vol. 3, Ac. Nauk U.S.S.R., Moscow, 428–31.

Gerasimenko, L. M., 1965. "Morphological and cytological changes in some algae produced by Colchycine, Chlortetracycline, and Tripaflavine," *Microbiologia, 34,5*, 851–57.

Gileva, E. A., Timofeeva, N. A., and Timofeev-Resovsky, N. V., 1965. "Influence of Co[60] irradiation on the growth of *Chlorella* cultures," *Radiobiologia, 5,5*, 732–34.

Gitelzon, I. I., Lisovskiy, G. M., and Terskov, I. A., 1966. "On the perspectivity of micro-algae culture compared to higher plants," in *Upravliaemyiy biosynthez*, Nauka, Moscow, 68–75.

Gitelzon, I. I., Sadikova, G. I., Borodkina, L. N., and Bazanova, M. I., 1966. "Changes of growth rate and chemical composition of microalga *Chlorella* caused by limitation of biosynthesis by biogenes," *ibid.,* 110–16.

Gitelzon, I. I., Terskov, I. A., Kovrov, B. G., Viojtovich, Ia. V., and Sadikova, G. I., 1964. "Nitrogen nutrition of *Chlorella* under conditions of continuous cultivation," in *Upravliaemoe cultivirovanie microvodorosleiy*, Nauka, Moscow, 47–55.

Gitelzon, I. I., Terskov, I. A., Baklanov, O. G., and Kovrov, B. G., 1964. "Automation of the cultivation of unicellular for a closed biological system," in *Problemy kosmicheskoiy biologii* Vol. 3, Ac. Sci. U.S.S.R., Moscow, 472–76.

Glagoleva, T. A., Mamushina, N. S., and Zalensky, O. V., 1965. "After-effect of temperature on the character of C[14] metabolism in *Chlorella pyrenoidosa* Chick," *Botanicheskiy J., 50,4*, 461–72.

Godnev, T. N., and Liachnovich, Ia. P., 1964. "Influence of changes in concentration of Tamiya medium on the growth of *Chlorella,*" in *Physiologicheskie osobennosty kultiviruemych rasteniiy* [Physiological patterns of cultivated plants], Nauka i technika, Minsk, 10–14.

————, 1966. "After-effect of thermoimpulse on the pigment formation in *Chlorella* suspension," in *Upravliaemyiy biosynthez*, Nauka, Moscow, 175–78.

Gorbunova, N. P., 1966. "On the synsoospores in algae and experimental receiving of them in *Chlamydomonas girus* Pasch," *Botanicheskiy J., 51,3*, 382–88.

Goriachev, P. P., 1947. "The influence of the composition of the nutrient solution on *Pediastrum boryanum* (Turp) Menegh," *Microbiologia, 16,1*, 75–83.

————, 1960. "Variations of the cell and coenobium shape in *Pediastrum tetras* (Ehr) Ralfs," *Botanicheskiy J., 45,5*, 732–34.

————, 1961. "The range of variation of the cell and coenobium shape of *Pediastrum polydens* and *P. kawraiskyi,*" *ibid., 46,7*, 998–1001.

————, 1963. "The effect of gibberellin upon the cells and coenobia of *Pediastrum boryanum* (Turp) Menegh," *Microbiologia, 32,2*, 296–98.

Goriunova, S. V., 1948. "Bacteriological purification of algal cultures by means of combined media," *ibid., 17,4*, 243–47.

————, 1950. *Chimicheskiiy sostav i prijiznennye vydelenia sineselenoiy vodorosli "Oscillatoria splendida Grew"* [Chemical composition of the blue-green algae

Oscillatoria splendida Grew and material excreted by it in the course of growth], Ac. Sci. U.S.S.R., Moscow.

————, 1954. "Compounds excreted by living cells of *Synedra* sp.," Trudy inst. microbiologii, No. 3, Ac. Sci. U.S.S.R., Moscow, 194–200.

Goriunova, S. V., and Nasonova, M. V., 1955. "The seasonal periodicity of growth and development in unicellular green algae," *Microbiologia, 24,2*, 193–98.

Goriunova, S. V., Odoevskaja, N. S., and Gerasimenko, L. M., 1965. "A method for purification of blue-green algae from contaminating bacteria," *ibid., 34,6*, 1077–79.

Goriunova, S. V., and Ovsiannikova, M. N., 1962. "On the methods of isolating active *Chlorella* strains from nature," *ibid., 31*, 3, 520–25.

Goriunova, S. V., and Rzhanova, G. N., 1964. "Vital excretion of nitrogen-containing substances in *Lyngbya aestuarii* and their physiological role," in *Biologia sinezelenych vodorosleiy* [Biology of the Cyanophyta], Moscow Univ., Moscow, 111–18.

Goriushyn, V. A., and Chaplinskaya, S. M., 1966. "Existance of viruses of blue-green algae," *Microbiol. J.*, Kiev, *2*, 94–97.

Gromov, B. V., 1964. "Bacteria of *Caulobacter* genus accompanying algae in cultures," *Microbiologia, 33,2*, 298–305.

————, 1965a. "Collection of algal cultures in the Biological Institute of Leningrad University," Trudy Peterhofskogo Biol. Inst., No. 19, Univ. Leningrad, Leningrad, 125–30.

————, 1965b. "Contaminating microorganisms in installations for the large-scale cultivation of protococcus algae in the open air," *ibid.*, 149–54.

Gromov, B. V., and Avilov, I. A., 1965. "Phenetical classification of the algae genus *Chlorella*," *Vestnik* Leningrad. Univ., No. 9, ser. biol., *2*, 118–23.

Gromov, B. V., Avilov, I. A., and Skrupskaya, V. A., 1965. "On the physiological criteria for the classification of algae genus *Chlorella*," *ibid.*, No. 21, *4*, 112–23.

Gromov, B. V., and Kameshkova, N. N., 1964. "Isolation of microorganisms antagonistic to the alga *Chlorella* from the soil," Nauchnye doklady vyscheiy schkoly, biol. nauky, *1*, 171–74.

Gromov, B. V., and Maslennikova, V. G., 1965. "Formation of organic acids from glucose in *Chlorella* cultures," Trudy Peterhofskogo Biol. Inst., No. 19, Univ. Leningrad, Leningrad, 145–49.

Gromov, B. V., and Mamkaeva, K. A., 1966a. "Endoparasites of the protococcus algae," Abstr. IX Intern. Congr. Microbiol., Moscow, 341.

————, 1966b. "Endoparasites of the protococus algae," *Microbiologia, 35,6*, 1073–79.

Gromov, B. V., and Skrupskaya, V. A., 1965. "Examination of the bacteria accompanying *Chlorella pyrenoidosa* in laboratory cultures," Trudy Peterhofskogo Biol. Inst., No. 19, Univ. Leningrad, Leningrad, 155–61.

Gussev, M. V., 1962a. On the problem of obtaining maximal harvests from the laboratory cultures of blue-green alga *Anabaena variabilis*," *Bull.* Mosc. obschestva ispytateleiy prirody, otd. biol., *67,3*, 150.

————, 1962b. "The effect of dilute oxygen on the development of blue-green algae," Doklady Ac. Nauk U.S.S.R., *147,4*, 947–50.

————, 1966. "Comparative physiology of the blue-green algae," *Uspexhi microbiologii* [Advances in microbiology] *3*, 74–103.

Gussev, M. V., and Fedorov, V. D., 1962. "A triphenyl-tetrazolium chloride study of the condition of morphologically differentiated cells in developing cultures of blue-green algae," *Microbiologia, 31,3*, 478–81.

Gussev, M. V., and Telitchenko, M. M., 1962. "Interrelations between blue-green algae, bacteria, and crustacean," *Bull*, Mosc. obschestva ispytateleiy prirody, nov. ser., otd. biol., *67,6*, 134–35.

Gussev, M. V., Telitchenko, M. M., and Fedorov, V. D., 1964. "Principles of isolation, purification, and cultivation of the blue-green algae," in *Biologia sinezelenych vodorosleiy* [Biology of the Cyanophyta], Moscow Univ., Moscow, 55–65.

Gussev, M. V., and Vasilkova, E. I., 1965. "Change in composition and pigment content of blue-green algae in the presence of additional carbon and nitrogen sources," *Microbiologia, 34,3*, 477–82.

Gusseva, K. A., 1935. "The conditions of mass development and the physiology of nutrition of *Synura*," *ibid., 4,1*, 24–44.

———, 1940. "The action of copper on algae, *ibid., 9,5*, 480–89.

Jaaska, V., 1964a. "Effect of nitrogen nutrition conditions on the chemical composition of some green algae," ENSV Teaduste Akad. toimetised. Biol. seer., *13,1*, 33–39.

———, 1964b. "Effect of different nitrogen sources on the chemical composition of the green algae *Scenedesmus quadricauda* and *Chlorococcum botryoides*," *ibid., 13,2*, 123–25.

Jevner, V. D., Gussev, M. V., and Shestakov, S. V., 1965. "Change in composition and content of pigments of blue-green algae as a function of spectral composition of light and of the degree of illumination," *Microbiologia, 34,2*, 209–15.

Ivanov, E. A., and Aleksandrova, I. V., 1964. "Analysis of two methods for the evaluation of *Chlorella* photosynthesis intensity," *Problemy kosmicheskoy biologii*, Vol. 3, Ac. Sci. U.S.S.R., Moscow, 415–27.

Ivanova, G. M., and Mikhailovskaia, T. A., 1962. Determination of dead and living cells in the blue-green algae cultures by means of triphenyl-tetrazolium chloride," *Bull.* Mosc. obschestva ispytateley prirody, nov. ser., otd. biol., *67,3*, 151.

Karpov, V. L., 1963. "A preparative isolation C^{14}-amino acids by ion-exchange and paper chromotography," *Vestnik* Leningrad. Univ., No. 9 ser. biol., *2*, 108–14.

Khropova, V. I., Kvitko, K. V., and Zakharov, I. A., 1964. "A comparative study of the mutagenic action of different types of radiation and ethyleneimine on the alga *Chlorella*," in *Issledovania po genetike*, No. 2, Univ. Leningrad, Leningrad, 69–76.

Klyachko-Gurvich, G. L., 1964. "Directed biosynthesis of carbohydrates in *Chlorella*," *Physiologia rasteniy, 11,6*, 978–87.

———, 1966. "On the directed synthesis of proteins, carbohydrates, and lipids by *Chlorella*," in *Upravliaemyiy biosynthez*, Nauka, Moscow, 116–21.

Klyachko-Gurvich, G. L., and Zhukova, T. A., 1966. "Changes in the biosynthesis of fatty acids due to nitrogen deficiency in *Chlorella pyrenoidosa*," *Physiologia rasteniy, 13,1*, 15–24.

Kogan, Sh.I., 1966. "Nitrogen fixing blue-green algae from the soil and waters of Southern Turkmenistan," *Isvestia* Ac. Nauk Turkm. S.S.R., ser. biol., No. 3, Ashkhabad, 15–23.

Korotaev, M. M., Kustov, V. V., Meleshko, G. I., Poddubnaia, L. T., and Shepelev, E. Ia., 1964. "Toxic gaseous compounds excreted by *Chlorella*," in *Problemy kosmicheskoy biologii*, Vol. 3, Ac, Sci. U.S.S.R., Moscow, 204–209.

Kovachova, N. G., 1966. "Cultivation of *Anabaena variabilis* in the oxygen atmosphere," Tezisy Konf. *Mechanismy biologicheskih processov* Univ. Leningrad, Leningrad, 13.

Kovrov, B. G., and Budanov, A. S., 1964a. "Tubular barbatageless fermenter for the cultivation of *Chlorella*," in *Upravliaemoe cultivirovanie microvodorosleiy*, Nauka, Moscow, 5–7.

———, 1964b. "Small laboratory fermenter for the intensive cultivation of *Chlorella* in the directed conditions," *ibid.,* 8–11.

———, 1964c. "Construction of laboratory fermenters for the intensive cultivation of *Chlorella*," *ibid.,* 12–23.

Kuchkarova, M. A., Maksudov, T. U., Hodjaeva, and Voropaeva, O. G., 1965. "Isolation and selection of nitrogen fixing blue-green algae from the rice fields of Middle Asia," in *Materialy Zakavkazskoiy konf. po sporovym rasten*, Ac. Sci. Azerb. S.S.R., Baku 55–57.

Kuznetsov, E. D., 1966. "Some features of mineral nutrition during nitrogen deficiency," *Physiologia rasteniy, 13,1*, 25–28.

Kuznetsov, E. D., and Semenenko, V. E., 1966. "Balanced media and the prospects of the usage for the stabilization of unicellular algae mineral nutrition conditions during prolonged intensive cultivation," in *Upravliaemyiy biosynthez*, Nauka, Moscow, 105–10.

Kuznetsov, E. D., and Vladimirova, M. G., 1964. "Iron as a factor restricting the growth of *Chlorella* in the Tamiya nutrition solution," *Physiologia rasteniy, 11,4*, 615–19.

————, 1965. "Variation of the mineral composition of the nutrient medium of growing *Chlorella*," *ibid., 12,1*, 33–38.

Kvitko, K. V., 1961. "Receiving *Chlorella* cultures from single cells," in *Issledovania po genetike*, No. 1, Univ. Leningrad, Leningrad, 50–53.

Kvitko, K. V., and Khropova, V. I., 1963. "Ultra-violet induced and spontaneous mutants of *Chlorella vulgaris* Beijer," *Vestnik* Leningrad. Univ., No. 9, ser. biol., *2*, 150–56.

Kvitko, K. V., Zaharov, I. A., and Khropova, V. I., 1966. "Some principles of investigation of genetics and selection of microorganisms in application to *Chlorella*," *Genetica, 2*, 148–53.

Lebedeva, E. V., Meleshko, G. E., and Shakhova, A. N., 1965. "Consumption of mineral elements by *Chlorella* cells during intensive cultivation," in *Problemy kosmicheskoiy biologii*, Vol. 4, Ac. Sci. U.S.S.R., Moscow, 687–93.

Leonova, L. I., and Antonenko, S. V., 1966. "On the interrelations of *Chlorella* and accompanying microorganisms in the course of prolonged combined cultivation," in *Upravliaemyiy biosynthez*, Nauka, Moscow, 169–75.

Levshina, N. A., 1965. "The influence of CO_2 on the development of diatoms," *Bull.* Mosc. obschestva ispytateleiy prirody, nov. ser., otd. biol., *70,2*, 139–40.

Lewina, R. I., 1961. "Antagonism between planktonic algae and microorganisms in biological ponds," in *Ochistka stochnych vod v biologicheskih prudah* [Waste water regeneration in biological ponds], Minsk, 136–47.

————, 1964. "Antagonism between protococcal algae and the coli-typhoid group of microorganisms," *Microbiologia, 33,5*, 887–93.

Machmadbekov, S., and Haitova, L. T., 1965. "Productivity of *Chlorella* and the perspectives of its utilization for different purposes," in *Physiologia rasteniy—selskomu chosiaiystvu* [Plant physiology for agriculture], Ac. Sci. Tajik. S.S.R., Duchanbe, 55–65.

Maksimova, I. V., 1966. "Interrelations of algae with bacteria and other microorganisms in mixed cultures," Trudy Moscovskogo obschestva ispytateleiy prirody, *24*, 160–83.

Maksimova, I. V., and Fedenko, E. P., 1965. The effect of the oxidation-reduction potential on bacterial development in algal cultures," *Microbiologia, 34,2*, 344–49.

Maksimova, I. V., and Lastochkina, K. D., 1964. "The cause of death of bacteria in the culture of growing algae," Rep. 1. *Vestink* Moscovskogo Univ., ser. biol., No. 3, Moscow Univ., Moscow, 40–47.

Maksimova, I. V., Toropova, E. G., and Pimenova, M. N., 1965. "Release of organic compounds by green algae grown in mineral media," *Microbiologia, 34,3*, 483–90.

Mamkaeva, K. A., 1966. "Studies of lysis in cultures of *Chlorella*," *ibid., 35,5*, 853–59.

Markarova, E. N., and Baslavaskaya, S. S., 1965. "On the growth and photosynthesis of the cells of *Scenedesmus obliquus* (Turp) Kutz. in synchronous culture," *Botanicheskiy J., 50,11*, 1568–70.

Maslov, Y. I., 1966. "On fractionation of lipids," *Vestnik* Leningrad Univ. No. 21, ser. biol., *4*, 102–109.

Massjuk, N. P., 1961. "On the effect of gibberellic acid on alga *Dunaliella salina* Teod," *Ukrainskiy Bot. J., 18,5*, 62–64.

———, 1965a. Effect of Na, Mg, Cl, and SO₄ ions on the growth, reproduction, and carotene formation of *Dunaliella salina* Teod," *ibid., 22,5*, 3–11.

———, 1965b. "Carbonates and bicarbonates as stimulators of growth and carotene accumulation in *Dunaliella salina* Teod," *ibid., 6*, 18–22.

Meleshko, G. I., 1964. "On the increasing of *Chlorella* culture photosynthetic productivity in fermenters for biological air regeneration," *Problemy kosmicheskoiy biologii*, Vol. 3, Ac. Sci. U.S.S.R., Moscow, 410–14.

Meleshko, G. I., and Krasotchenko, L. M., 1965. "Carbon nutrition conditions in the intensive culture of *Chlorella*," *ibid.*, Vol. 4, 676–82.

Meleshko, G. I., Lebedeva, E. K., and Galkina, T. B., 1966. "On the balance of macroelements in the intensive culture of *Chlorella*," in *Upravliaemyiy biosynthez*, Nauka, Moscow, 122–27.

Milko, E. S., 1962. Studies of the necessities of the two species of the algae *Dunaliella* in mineral and organic components of the surroundings," *Vestnik* Moscovskogo Univ., ser. biol., No. 1, Moscow Univ., Moscow, 18–24.

———, 1963. "The effect of various factors of the surroundings upon pigment formation in the *Dunaliella salina* alga," *Microbiologia, 32,2*, 299–308.

———, 1963. "The effect of illumination and temperature on pigment formation in *Dunaliella salina*," *ibid. 4*, 590–97.

Mineeva, L. A., 1962a. "The effect of pH upon autotrophic and heterotropic nutrition of *Chlorella vulgaris* and *Scenedesmus obliquus*," *ibid., 31,2*, 233–40.

———, 1962b. "The effect of light intensity upon autotrophic and heterotrophic nutrition of *Chlorella vulgaris* and *Scenedesmus obliquus*, *ibid., 3*, 411–16.

Muzafarov, A. M., Milogradova, E. I., Skriabina, T. A., and Khudaberdyeva, R., 1961. "Experience of *Chlorella* cultivation in Uzbekistan," *Uzbekskiy biol. J.*, No. 3, Ac. Sci. Uzb. S.S.R., Tashkent, 16–21.

Nechaeva, E. P., 1964. "Differences in the nucleotide composition of plants induced by various external conditions," *Physiologia rasteniy, 11,4*, 689–94.

Nekrasova, E. A., 1966. "Accumulation of inorganic condensed phosphates by *Chlorella* under different conditions of mineral nutrition," Tezisy Konf. *Mechanismy biologicheskih processov*, Univ. Leningrad, Leningrad, 17.

Nikiporovich, A. A., 1961. *O proizvodstvennoiy kulture odnokletochnych vodorosleiy* [On the industrial culture of unicellular algae], Znanie, Moscow.

Nikiporovich, A. A., Semenenko, V. E., Vladimirova, M. G., and Spectorov, K. S., 1962. Some principles of intensification of photosynehetic productivity of unicellular algae," *Isvestia* Ac. Sci. U.S.S.R., ser. biol., *2*, 163–72.

Nikitinskij, Ia. Ia., 1930. "*Stigeoclonium tenue* Kg.: Morphology, physiology, ecology," Trudy Inst. soorujeniy, Vol. 4, Moscow.

Pachomova, M. V., 1964. "The biochemical investigation of some algae species," *Bull.* Mosc. obschestva ispytateleiy prirody, nov. ser., otd. biol., *69,3*, 110–26.

———, 1966. "Acid-soluble nucleotides and their derivates dynamics in continuous *Chlorella* culture as affected by cell-division rate," in *Upravliaemyiy biosynthez*, Nauka, Moscow, 178–84.

Pachomova, M. V., and Serenkov, G. P., 1962a. "The influence of light and darkness on the chemical composition of the green alga *Scenedesmus quadricauda*," *Vestnik* Moscovskogo Univ., ser. biol., No. 4, Moscow Univ., Moscow, 44–48.

———, 1962b. "A study of the nucleotide composition of RNA in the green alga *Dunaliella salina*," Doklady Ac. Nauk U.S.S.R., *144,6*, 1390–93.

———, 1963. "The influence of light and darkness on the chemical composition of green alga *Scenedesmus quadricauda*," Biochimia, *28,5*, 808–15.

Perminova, G. N., 1964. "Growth of some soil Cyanophyta on nitrogen-deficient media," *Botanicheskiy J. 49,9*, 1302–304.

Pimenova, M. N., and Kondratieva, T. F., 1965. "A contribution to the use of acetate by *Chlamydomonas globosa*," *Microbiologia, 34,2*, 230–35.

Pimenova, M. N., and Maksimova, I. V., 1966. "Assimilation of organic matter in autotrophic cultures of algae," Trudy Moscovckogo obschestva ispytateleiy prirody, *24*, 131–41.

Pimenova, M. N., Maksimova, I. V., and Balizkaya, R. M., 1962. A contribution to the composition of concomitant microflora in mass cultivation of algae in open reservoirs, *Microbiologia, 31,2*, 332–38.

Pinevich, V. V., Khazanskaya, L. N., and Afanasyeva, O. V., 1966. "Influence of *Chlorella* on fermentative activity and reproduction of baker's yeast," *Vestnik* Leningrad. Univ., No. 21, ser. biol., *4*, 64–70.

Pinevich, V. V., and Nikiforova, L. F., 1964. "Nucleotide composition of DNA and RNA of protococcus algae," *ibid.*, No. 15, *3*, 97–104.

Pinevich, V. V., and Versilin, N. N., 1961a. "Unicellular algae cultures for industrial purposes," in *Kormovye belky i biostimuliatory dlia zhyvotnovodstva* [Fodder proteins and biostimulators for cattle-breeding], Ac. Sci. U.S.S.R., Moscow, 96–102.

———, 1961. "The effect of maleic acid hydrazide on certain protococcal algae," Doklady Ac. Nauk U.S.S.R. *137,5*, 1230–32.

———, 1963. "Mass culturing of unicellular algae in the open air," *Vestnik* Leningrad. Univ., No. 15, ser. biol., *3*, 75–97.

Pinevich, V. V., Versilin, N. N., and Maslov, Y. I., 1961. "Effect of different forms of nitrogen on the growth and accumulation of biomass by *Chlorella pyrenoidosa*," *ibid.*, No. 9, *2*, 16–25.

Pinevich, V. V., Versilin, N. N., and Stepanov, S. I., 1964. "A standard installation for mass culture of unicellular algae," *Physiologia rasteniy, 11,6*, 1084–89.

Pinevich, V. V., Versilin, N. N., and Vasilyeva, V. E., 1961. "Action of gibberellic acid on protococcus algae," Nauchnye doklady vyscheiy schkoly, biol. nauky, *3*, 151–55.

Pluciennik, Henryk, 1965. "The mutation process of *Chlorella* induced by incorporation of radioactive carbon dioxide," *Genetica, 5*, 19–25.

Poljansky, V. S., 1938. "Notes sur la morphologie due genre *Calothrix* (Ag.) V. Poljansk. sensu lat. *Calothrix parva* Ercegovic (?) dans les conditions de culture," Trudy Bot. Inst. Ac. Sci. U.S.S.R., ser. II, *4*, 41–58.

———, 1948. "Experimental examination of *Euglena gracilis* Klebs variability in the cultural conditions," Uchenye zapisky Leningr. ped. inst. im. Gerzena, Vol. 70, Leningrad, 153–70.

Rerberg, M. S., and Kuzmina, R. I., 1964. "On the prolonged stepped cultivation of protococcus algae and associated bacteria with the excretion of man," in *Upravliaemoe cultivirovanie microvodorosleiy*, Nauka, Moscow, 119–23.

Rerberg, M. S., Kuzmina, R. I., and Barkhatova, I. M., 1964. "Regeneration of the excretion of man by means of an algae-bacterial community," *ibid.*, 131–35.

Rerberg, M. S., and Vorobieva, T. I., 1964a. "Comparison of the growth of protococcus algae in the mineral media and organic medium "B," *ibid.*, 110–18.

———, 1964b. "On the cultivation of protococcus algae with human excretion under sterile and unsterile conditions," *ibid.*, 124–30.

Rerberg, M. S., Vorobieva, T. I., Kuzmina, R. I., and Barkhatova, I. M., 1965. "Regeneration of human excretion by means of a naturally developing algae-bacterial community," in *Problemy kosmicheskoiy biologii*, Ac. Sci. U.S.S.R., Moscow, 598–604.

Rubenchik, L. I., Bershova, O. I., and Knizhnik, Sh. P., 1965. "On the interrelation of *Anabaena* with bacteria and actynomycetes," in *Ecologia i physiologia sinezelenych vodorosleiy* [Ecology and physiology of Cyanophyceae], Nauka, Moscow, 223–26.

Rubenchik, L. I., Bershova, O. I., Novicov, N. S., and Koptyeva, Zh. P., 1966. "Lysis of blue-green alga *Microcystis pulverea*," *Microbiol. J.* Kiev, *2*, 88–91.

Rusina, O. N., 1961. "Some problems of the large-scale cultivation of algea," in *Pervichnaia producsia moreiy i vnutrennich vod* [Primary production in seas and inland waters], Minsk, 339–41.

Rzhanova, G. N., and Goriunova, S. V., 1965. "Amino acid composition of the blue-green algae *Phormidiun uncinatum* (Ag) Gom.," *Microbiologia, 34,2*, 268–72.

Sadovskaya, S. P., and Telitchenko, M. M., 1966. "The effect of *Chlorella vulgaris* and *Scenedesmus obliquus* on the viability of *Escherichia coli* bacteriophages," *Bull. exper. biol. med.*, *6*, 71–74.

Semenenko, V. E., and Vladimirova, M. G., 1962. "Effect of cosmic flight conditions in the sputnik space ship on the viability of *Chlorella*," in *Problemy kosmicheskioy biologii*, Vol. 1, Ac. Sci. U.S.S.R., Moscow, 190–203.

Semenenko, V. E., Vladimirova, M. G., and Nikiporovich, A. A., 1962. "Some principles of the intensification of unicellular algae culture photosynthetic productivity," *ibid.*, Vol. 2, 326–39.

Semenenko, V. E., Vladimirova, M. G., Soglin, L. N., and Popova, M. A., 1966. "Dependence of the *Chlorella* growth, productivity, and photosynthetic intensity from CO_2 concentration in the gas mixture and ventilation coefficient of the culture," in *Upravliaemyiy biosynthez*, Nauka, Moscow, 128–36.

Semenenko, V. E., Vladimirova, M. G., Soglin, L. N., Tauts, M. I., Phillipovskiy, Iu. N., Klyachko-Gurvich, G. L., Kuznetsov, E. D., Kovanova, E. S., and Raijkov, N. I., 1966. "Prolonged continuous directed cultivation of algae and physiological and chemical characteristics of the productivity and efficiency of light energy utilization by *Chlorella*," *ibid.*, 75–86.

Serenkov, G. P., 1962. "Nucleic acids and evolution of algae," *Isvestia* Ac. Sci. U.S.S.R., ser. biol., *6* 857–68.

Serenkov, G. P., and Pachomova, M. V., 1959. "Nucleotide composition of deoxyribonucleic and ribonucleic acids of some algae and higher plants," Nauchnye doklady vyscheiy schkoly, biol. nauky, *4*, 156–61.

——, 1960. "Studies of the nitrous compounds of algae," *Vestink* Moscovskogo Univ., ser. biol., No. 6, Moscow Univ., Moscow, 15–24.

——, 1961. "The study of the chemical composition of the green alga *Dunaliella salina* Teod," *ibid.*, No. 3, 22–26.

Serenkov, G. P., and Vladychenskaya, N. S., 1962. "Study of nucleic acids in some alagal species," Nauchnye doklady vyscheiy schkoly, biol. nauky, *2*, 147–51.

Shaposhnikov, V. N., and Gussev, M. V., 1964. "The role of oxygen in the vital activity of some blue-green algae," in *Biologia sinezelenych vodorosleiy* [Biology of the Cyanophyta], Moscow Univ., Moscow, 119–40.

Shaposhnikov, V. N., Pimenova, M. N., Maksimova, I. V., Zhdannikova, E. N., and Ramenskaya, A. A., 1964. "On seasonal periodicity in the development of green algae under laboratory conditions," *Microbiologia, 33,2*, 221–23.

Schavelson, R. A., 1964. "The experience of collecting unicellular green algae (Chlorophyta) under field conditions," *Botanicheskiy J. 47,11*, 1654–55.

Schavelson, R. A., and Potechina, N. A., 1965. "A method of primary selection of productive *Chlorella* strains," *Genetica, 5*, 65–67.

Shevchenko, V. A., 1965. "X-ray influence on survival and mutagenic process in *Chlorella*," *Radiobiologia, 5,2*, 253–59.

Shepelev, E. Ia., 1966. "Life support system in the space vehicles based on the biological turnover of elements," in *Kosmicheskaia biologia i medisina*, Nauka, Moscow, 330–62.

Shkolnik, R. Ya., Doman, N. G., Spektorov, K. S., and Linkova, E. A., 1965. "Intermediate photosynthesis products of a synchronous culture of *Chlorella pyrenoidosa* at different development stages," Doklady Ac. Nauk. U.S.S.R., *161,5*, 1231–34.

Shtina, E. A., 1964. "On the role of algae in nitrogen accumulation in the soil," *Agrochimia, 4*, 77–83.

Sirenko, L. A., 1965. "Effect of various factors on the fat-soluble pigment complex of blue-green algae," *Ukrainskiy Bot. J., 22,6*, 23–29.

Sirenko, L. A., and Bogdanova, T. L., 1965. "On methods of laboratory cultivation of blue-green algae," in *Ecologia i physiologia sinezelenych vodorosleiy* [Ecology and physiology of Cyanophyceae], Nauka, Moscow, 195–201.

Sisakian, N. M., Bezinger, E. N., and Shaposhnikova, M. G., 1962. "Amino acid composition of *Chlorella*," in *Problemy kosmicheskoiy biologii*, Ac. Sci. U.S.S.R., Moscow, Vol. 1, 371–76.

Sisakian, N. M., Parin, V. V., Chernigovskiy, V. N., and Iazdovskiy, V. I., 1962. "Some problems of the examination and development of space, *ibid.*, 5–16.

Smirnov, I. V., 1963. "Theoretical basis for the principle of algal cultivation," *Biophysica, 8,1*, 90–100.

———, 1964. "Mathematical analysis of the process of *Chlorella* cultivation in biological asymmetrical fermenters," in *Problemy kosmicheskoiy biologii*, Vol. 3, Ac. Sci. U.S.S.R., Moscow, 432–48.

———, 1966. "A study of temperature conditions optimal for a thermophilous strain of *Chlorella*," Doklady Ac. Nauk U.S.S.R., *167,6*, 1405–408.

Smirnov, N. N. 1955. "The influence of different nutritional conditions on the develoment of fodder protococcus algae," Trudy Mosc. technol. inst. rybn. prom. i choziaiystva, No. 7, Moscow, 102–32.

Spektorov, K. S., and Linkova, E. A., 1962. "A new simplified method of synchronized *Chlorella* culture," Doklady Ac. Nauk U.S.S.R., *147,4*, 967–69.

———, 1963. "Effect of light intensity and temperature on the growth and development of a synchronous cultures of *Chlorella pyrenoidosa*," *Physiologia rasteniy, 10,6*, 667–72.

Spektorova, L. V., 1965. "Biological parameters of the development cycle of a synchronous culture of a thermophylic *Chlorella pyrenoidosa* strain," *ibid., 12,1*, 27–32.

———, 1967. "Destermination of the potential productivity of *Chlorella* by means of the synchronized culture method," *Botanicheskiy J., 52,1*, 73–81.

Stoletov, V. D., Ievner, V. D., Garibian, D. V., and Shestakow, S. V., 1965. "Induction of pigment mutants in *Anacystis nidulans* by nitrosomethyl urea," *Genetica,6*:61–66.

Tauts, M. I., 1964. "Study of the effect of the products of life activity of *Chlorella* on its growth under conditions of intense culture," *Physiologia rasteniy, 11,2*, 247–56.

Telitchenko, M. M., Davydova, N. V., and Fedorov, V. D., 1962. "Interrelation between algae and microorganisms," Rep II. Nauchnye doklady vyscheiy schkoly, biol. nauky, 4, 157–63.

Telitchenko, M. M., and Fedorov, V. D., 1962. "On the problem of the interrelation between algae and bacteria in waters," *Bull.* Mosc. obschestva ispytateleiy prirody, otd. biol., *47,3*, 148–49.

Telitchenko, M. M., and Gussev, M. V., 1964. "The interrelations between some blue-green algae and bacteria, crustacea, and fishes," in *Biologia sinezelenych vodorosleiy* [Biology of the Cyanophyta], Moscow Univ., Moscow, 99–109.

Tikhonenko, A. S., and Zavarsina, N. B., 1966. "Morphology of the *Chlorella pyrenoidosa* lytic agent," *Microbiologia, 35,5*, 850–952.

Tomova, N. G., Evstigneyeva, Z. G., and Kretovich, W. L., 1964. "Assimilation of nitrate and ammonium nitrogen by *Chlorella pyrenoidosa*," *Physiologia rasteniy, 11,6*, 988–97.

Tretiakova, A. N., 1965. "A comparative study of nitrogen-fixing blue-green algae isolated from various soils of the U.S.S.R.," *Microbiologia, 34,3*, 491–96.

——, 1966. "Characteristic morphological features of the strains of some Cyanophyta isolated from different soils of the U.S.S.R.," *Botanicheskiy J., 51*, 1489–93.

Troiskaia, E. N., 1960. "On the cultivation of Middle Asian *Chlorella* strain in the cement reservoirs," in *Voprosy biologii i kraevoiy medisiny* [Some problems of biology and local medicine], Tashkent 22–26.

Truhin, N. V., 1963a. "Light optimum for the growth of *Chlorella pyrenoidosa* as affected by temperature," Doklady Ac. Nauk U.S.S.R., *149, 6*, 1450–52.

——, 1963b. "Comparative evaluation of occurrence in reservoirs of thermophil strains of *Chlorella* and *Scenedesmus*," *Microbiologia, 32,3*, 513–19.

——, 1966. "Productivity of thermophilic isolates of *Chlorella*, isolated from water bodies in different geographical zones," in *Rastitelnost volzhskich vodochranilisch* [Flora of the Volga storage lakes], Ac. Sci. U.S.S.R., Moscow, 78–92.

——, 1966b. "Influence of temperature of cultivation upon the level of the temperature optimum of *Chlorella pyrenoidosa*," *ibid.*, 93–103.

——, 1966c. "Growth productivity of different protococal algae in mass cultures," in *Produkirovanie i krugovorot organicheskogo veschestva vo vnutrennich vodoemach* [Production and circulation of organic matter in inland basins], Nauka, Moscow, 216–21.

Tugarinov, V. V., 1965. "Receiving of streptomycin-resistant and streptomycin-dependant strains in *Chlorella vulgaris*," *Vestnik* Leningrad. Univ., No. 9, ser. biol., *2*, 136–42.

Tugarinov, V. V., and Kuznetsov, V. V., 1966. "The combined effect produced by X-rays and streptomycin on mutability of *Chlorella*," Doklady Ac. Nauk U.S.S.R., 166, *3*, 722–25.

Uspenskiy, E. E., 1963. *Physico-chimicheskie uslovia sredy kak osnova microbiologicheskich processov* [Physico-chemical conditions of the medium as a basis for microbiological processes], Ac. Sci. U.S.S.R., Moscow.

Vagabov, V. M., and Serenkov, G. P., 1963. "The study of polyphosphates in two species of green algae," *Vestnik* Moscovskogo Univ., ser. biol., Moscow Univ., Moscow, 38–47.

Varasova, N. N., Vasilyeva, V. E., and Pinevich, V. V., 1965. "Photosynthetically active pigments of Chlorophyceae and the influence of different growing conditions upon them," *Vestnik* Leningrad. Univ. No. 15, ser. biol., *3*, 97–104.

Varasova, N. N., and Kvitko, K. V., 1962. "The pigment system of *Chlorella vulgaris* mutants," *ibid.*, 119–23.

Vaulina, E. N., and Anikeeva, I.D., 1964. "Estimation of the productivity of *Chlorella* strains in liquid culture," *Biophysica, 9,3*, 393–94.

——, 1965. "Productivity evaluation of *Chlorella* strains," *Genetica, 5*, 176–77.

Vinberg, G. G., Ostapenia, P. V., Sivko, T. N., and Lewina, R. I., 1966. *Biologicheskie prudy v practike ochistky stochnych vod* [Biological ponds in the practice of waste water regeneration], Belarus, Minsk.

Vinogradov, A. P., and Bojchenko, E. A., 1943. "Decay of kaolin by diatoms," Doklady Ac. Nauk U.S.S.R., *37,4*, 158–62.

Vladimirova, M. G., 1961. "The dynamics of development of bacterial microflora in *Chlorella* cultures," *Microbiologia, 30,3*, 421–45.

Vladimirova, M. G., and Basitova, L. V., 1961. "Development of *Chlorella pyrenoidosa* and of bacteria of the Pseudomonas group upon joint cultivation," *ibid., 30,4*, 593–600.

Vladimirova, M. G., and Ignatievskaja, M. A., 1966. "Study of the effect of *Chlorella* cultures on their producivity," *ibid., 35,3*, 538–43.

Vladimirova, M. G., Ignatievskaja, M. A., and Raijkov, N. I., 1966. "Productivity of strains of unicellular algae in the conditions of intensive laboratory or pilot plant cultivation," in *Upravliaemyiy biosynthez,* Nauka, Moscow, 86–93.

Vladimirova, M. G., and Kuznetsov, E. D., 1964. "Dynamics of variation of the nitrogen and phosphorus content in the medium under various conditions of intense cultivation of *Chlorella*," *Physiologia rasteniy, 11,5*, 827–37.

Vladimirova, M. G., and Semenenko, V. E., 1962. *Intensivnaia kultura odnokletochnych vodorosleiy* [Intensive culture of unicellular algae], Ac. Sci. U.S.S.R., Moscow.

Vladimirova, M. G., Semenenko, V. E., and Nikiporovich, A. A., 1962. "Comparative examiination of the productivity of different unicellular algae," in *Problemy kosmicheskoiy biologii*, Vol. 2, Ac. Sci. U.S.S.R., Moscow, 314–25.

Vladimirova, M. G., Semenenko, V. E., Zhukova, T. S., and Kovanova, E. S., 1966. "Comparative examination of growth and photosynthetic productivity of the mesophylic and thermophylic strains of *Chlorella* as affected by light intensity and temperature," in *Upravliaemyiy biosynthez,* Nauka, Moscow.

Voropaeva, O. G., 1966. "On nitrogen fixation in some species of blue-green algae isolated from the rice fields of Middle Asia," *Usbekskiy biol. J., No. 1*, Tashkent, 52–55.

Voskresensky, K. A., and Yurina, E. V., 1965. "*Asteromonas gracilis* Artari as a culture for mass growing," *Vestnik* Moscovskogo Univ., ser. biol., No. 2, Moscow Univ., Moscow, 29–35.

Zaar, E. L., and Kasinova, G. V., 1963. "The effect of certain physical and chemical agents on the re-synthesis of chlorophyll in the apochloritic cells of *Euglena gracilis* Klebs," *Botanicheskiy J., 48,6*, 896–98.

Zaharov, I. A., and Fridljanskaya, I. I., 1963. "Isolation of auxotrophic mutants of *Chlorella* by replica plating technique," *Vestnik* Leningrad. Univ., No. 9, ser. biol., *2*, 159–61.

Zaharov, I. A., and Tugarinov, V. V., 1964. "Radiosensitivity of *Chlorella vulgaris*," *Radiobiologia, 4,1*, 92–95.

Zalenskiy, O. V., Glagolyeva, T. A., and Mamushina, N. S., 1965. "The effect of temperature on the free amino acid content of *Chlorella pyrenoidosa*," *Physiologia rasteniy, 12,6*, 1081–83.

Zavarsin, G. A., 1960. "The life-cycle and nuclear changes in *Hyphomicrobium vulgare* Stutz et Hartleb," *Microbiologia, 29,1*, 38–42.

Zavarsina, N. B., 1961. "The lytic agent in cultures of *Chlorella pyrenoidosa*, Doklady Ac. Nauk U.S.S.R., *137,2*, 435–37.

———, 1964. "Lysis of *Chlorella* cultures in the absence of bacteria," *Microbiologia, 33,4*, 561–64.

Zavarsina, N. B., and Protsenko, A. E., 1958. "On the lysis of *Chlorella pyrenoidosa* cultures," Doklady Ac. Nauk U.S.S.R., *122,5*, 936–39.

Zhdannikova, E. N., Pimenova, M. N., Maksimova, I. V., and Balizkaya, R. M., 1964. "Preservation of algae collections," *Vestnik* Moscovskogo Univ. ser. biol., No. 1, Moscow Univ., Moscow, 45–49.

Yurina, E. V., 1966. "The experience in cultivating of the galobiontic algae: *Asteromonas gracilis* Artari and *Dunaliella salina* Teod," *ibid.*, No. 6, 76–83.

Yurina, E. V., and Pachomova, M. V., 1966. "The influence of sources of nigrogen nutrition on the growth of the green alga *Asteromonas gracilis* Artari and its biochemical composition," *ibid.*, No. 5, 35–38.

Yurkova, G. N., 1965. "Effect of the temperature factor on *Dunaliella salina* Teod," *Ukrainskiy Bot. J.*, *22*,*6*, 51–57.

XV

Medical Aspects of Phycology

MORTON SCHWIMMER, M.D.
and DAVID SCHWIMMER, M.D.

New York Medical College
Metropolitan Medical Center
New York, New York

ALGAL TOXICITY IN ANIMALS—MORTON SCHWIMMER, M.D.

We are interested in the association between algae and human disease. Inasmuch as animal experimentation is one of the prime ways of determining the effect of various substances on man, it is essential that we recognize algal toxicity in animal life so as to better understand the disease potential of algae in relation to humans.

Algae Isolated from Normal Animal Alimentary Tract

Since 1836, when Valentin first reported the isolation of algae in normal animal alimentary tract (*Hygrocrocis intestinalis* in the intestine of a cockroach), forty-seven separate isolations of algae in normal animal alimentary tracts have been achieved. Hosts included myriapods, toads, guinea pigs, pigs, goats, sheep, horses, hens, deer, boar, agouti, rats, viscacha, mice, frogs, ducks, euphasids, penguins, and various water birds. The predominant algae groups were blue-greens, greens, and diatoms. Algae have been found in every part of the digestive system.

Animal Intoxications Caused by Algae (Table I)

Since Francis' report in 1878, over sixty-five separate episodes of freshwater algal toxicity in animals have been reported in the literature. However, there are undoubtedly many small outbreaks of authentic algal poisoning which remain unreported because they are small or because there is a tendency on the part of both veterinarian and farmer to attribute peculiar animal losses to causes more widely known and better understood than toxic algal poisoning.

279

TABLE I. ANIMAL INTOXICATIONS FROM ALGAL BLOOMS

1878. Lake Alexandrina, Murray River estuary, Adelaide, Australia (Francis, 1878). Algae: *Nodularia spumigera*. Victims: sheep, horses, dogs, pigs, cattle. Manifestations of toxicity: "Acts poisonously, rapidly causes death; symptoms—stupor and unconsciousness, falling and remaining quiet, as if asleep, unless touched, when convulsions come on, with head and neck drawn back by rigid spasm, which subsides before death."

1882. Lakes Sakatah and Tetonka, Waterville, Minn., U.S.A. (Porter, 1887; Stalker, 1887; Arthur, 1887). Algae: *Rivularia fluitans* (*Gloeotrichia pisum*). 2 horses, 2 hogs, over 30 cattle. Animals which had been permitted to drink "were suddenly stricken down in great agony, and died, some of them not even getting back to their yards, six hundred feet distant."

1883. Lake Gorman, Cordova and Lakes Sakatah and Tetonka, Waterville, Minn., U.S.A. (Porter, 1887; Arthur, 1887; Stalker, 1887). Algae: *Gloeotrichia pisum*. 2 calves, 5 cows, horses. "The victims have been observed from the time of drinking the water thick with algae, till their death, which usually occurs in from twenty minutes to an hour and a half, in but two or three instances. The cattle did not appear to suffer pain, but lay down as if enervated and soon expired."

1900. Lake near Fergus Falls, Minn., U.S.A. (Nelson, 1903). Algae: *Aphanizomenon flos-aquae*. Cattle. "... several cattle in a pasture adjoining the shore of the lake had died, apparently from poisoning."

1911. Lake Ann, Howard Lake, Minn., U.S.A. (Fitch, Bishop, Boyd, Gortner, Rogers, and Tilden, 1934). Algae: "Waterbloom." Cattle. Death.

1914–44. Northeastern Free State, and Southeastern Transvaal, Union of South Africa (Steyn, 1945; Stephens, 1948). Algae: "Algae." Thousands of stock, mainly sheep and cattle. Death.

1914. Winnipeg Lake, Albion, Minn., U.S.A. (Cotton, 1914). Algae: *Anabaena*. Cattle. Weakness, nausea, severe thirst, "... another of the herd ... staggered, wilted down, and was dead before the owner could reach the spot."

1917–18. Fort Saskatchewan, Alberta, Canada (Gillam, 1925). Algae: Blue-green. Several hogs. Death.

1917–18. Lougheed, Alberta, Canada (Gillam, 1925). Algae: Blue-green. Hogs. "... hurried respiration, a staggering gait, and rigors, immediately followed by death ... These symptoms ... closely resemble those of anthrax."

1917–18. Lake Saskatoon, Alberta, Canada (Gillam, 1925). Algae: Blue-green. Horses, cattle, hogs, poultry, wild birds. As at Lougheed, Alberta.

1918. Oaks Lake, Windom, Minn., U.S.A. (Fitch, Bishop, Boyd, Gortner, Rogers and Tilden, 1934). Algae: *Coelosphaerium kuetzingianum*; *Anabaena flos-aquae*. 1 sheep, 17 hogs, 50 chickens. Death.

1924. Fraser Lake, Ontario, Canada (Howard and Berry, 1933). Algae: *Anabaena*. 20 cattle and other animals. "When animals drank in proximity to this material, they apparently were poisoned."

1925. Big Stone Lake, Wilmot, S. D., U.S.A. (WILMOT ENTERPRISE, 1925). Algae: Blue-green. 4 cows, 128 hogs, 54 chickens, 19 turkeys, 14 geese. "Stricken suddenly ... all died in short time .... The 4 cows were seen walking down to the water and about 2 hours later were found dead."

1925. Southern Mich., U.S.A. (Woodcock, 1927). Algae: "Algae." Stock. "Poisoning."

1927. Wakkerstroon District, Union of South Africa (Steyn, 1945). Algae:

Blue-green. Horses, cattle, sheep, mules, hares, water birds. Animals found dead.

1928. Lake Vesijarvi, Finland (Hindersson, 1933). Algae: *Anabaena Lemmermanni.* 40 animals. Livestock suddenly became ill after drinking algae-contaminated water, developing labored breathing, rapid pulse, occasional diarrhea, extreme weakness, falling, and death.

1930. Lake Ann, Howard Lake, Minn., U.S.A. (Fitch, Bishop, Boyd, Gortner, Rogers, and Tilden, 1934). Algae: *Microcystis flos-aquae; Microcystis aeruginosa.* 9 cattle. "At 1:30 P.M., in good condition; at 3:00 P.M., some animals were lying down apparently sick and in a short time these were dead."

1930–33. Lake Lac qui Parle, Milan, Minn., U.S.A. (Fitch, Bishop, Boyd, Gortner, Rogers, and Tilden, 1934). Algae: *Microcystis flos-aquae; Anabaena flos-aquae; Aphanizomenon flos-aquae;* and unidentified blue-green. 45 turkeys, 4 ducks, 2 geese, cows, pigs, horses. Died within a few minutes after drinking from lake covered with a thick scum of algae.

1931–33. East Okoboji and Storm Lakes, Iowa, U.S.A. (Prescott, 1933, 1938, 1939). Algae: *Aphanizomenon flos-aquae.* "Many thousands of fish." Death.

1933. Hall Lake, Fairmont, Minn., U.S.A. (Fitch, Bishop, Boyd, Gortner, Rogers, and Tilden, 1934). Algae: *Microcystis flos-aquae* and other bluegreens. 13 sheep, 8 lambs, a number of chickens. Died in convulsions within a few minutes after drinking from the lake; others were found dead within hours after drinking.

1933. McGuire Lake, Grand Rapids, Minn., U.S.A. (Fitch, Bishop, Boyd, Gortner, Rogers, and Tilden, 1934). Algae: *Microcystis* and *Anabaena.* 3 cattle. Died shortly after drinking from the lake.

1938. Finncastle Lakes, Alberta, Canada (McLeod and Bondar, 1952). Algae: "Algae". Waterfowl, shore birds. Death.

1938–40,49. Netley Marsh, Lake Winnipeg, Manitoba, Canada (McLeod and Bondar, 1952). Algae: "Algae". Waterfowl. Death.

1939. Fort Collins, Col., U.S.A. (Deem and Thorpe, 1939; Durrell and Deem, 1939). Algae: *Anabaena flos-aquae.* 4 Pekin ducks, snakes, salamanders, carp, wild birds, horses, calf, herons. Found dead on shore. Horse lethargic, developed subnormal temperature. Two herons showed partial paralysis; seemed alert, held head erect, but couldn't walk or stand; recovered completely in several days.

1940–42. Lake Ymsen, Mariestad, Skaraborg, Sweden, (Berlin, 1948). Algae: *Anabaena.* Fish, mergansers, divers, cats. High fish mortality. Mergansers and divers died in large numbers, landing on ice, during autumn migration; birds lay out on ice, crawled around, unable to lift, flapped weakly with stiff, outstretched wings, and lay with widely opened beaks. Many froze to the ice.

1940–43. Vaaldam, Transvaal, Union of South Africa (Steyn, 1944; 1945; Stephens, 1948; Luow, 1950). Algae: *Microcystis toxica* and *Microcystis flos-aquae.* Sheep, cattle, dogs, fish. "If large quantities of the algae are consumed, animals ... are found dead near the water, dying from acute general paralysis or with strychnine-like convulsions. If smaller quantities of the contaminated water are taken, affected animals usually show (a) constipation (hard feces being covered with blood); (b) drop in milk yield; (c) general weakness; (d) signs of burning (photosensitization) of skin by sun. In protracted cases jaundice resulted.

1942. Wakkerstroon District, Union of South Africa (Steyn, 1943, 1944). Algae: *Microcystis flos-aquae.* Cattle, horses, sheep, mules, hares, water birds.

TABLE I. (Continued)

1943. Missouri River, Havre, Mont., U.S.A. (Quin, 1943). Algae: "Vasser-bloom". Range sheep. "Most of the sheep died within a few hours after drinking river water."

1944-45. East Okoboji, Lower Gar, and Center Lakes, Iowa, U.S.A. (Rose, 1953). Algae: *Anabaena flos-aquae*. 37 hogs, 4 sheep, 2 cattle, 3 horses, several dogs, cats, squirrels, chickens, turkeys, songbirds. Found dead.

1944. Laguna Bedetti, Santa Tome, Province of Santa Fe, Republic of Argentina (Mullor, 1945; Mullor and Wachs, 1948). Algae: *Anabaena venenosa*. 1,000 Indian Runner ducks. Found dead or dying.

1945. Lake Alexandrina, Australia, (Olson, 1952). Algae: *Microcystis flos-aquae* and *Nodularia spumigera*. Sheep and cattle. Died after drinking lake water.

1945. Lake Dauphin, Manitoba, Canada (McLeod and Bonder, 1952). Algae: "Waterbloom". Horse, several calves, 2 pigs, cat. Progressive muscular weakness, paralysis, and death.

1945. Bermuda (Prescott, 1948). Algae: *Aphanizomenon flos-aquae*. Cattle. Died after drinking from pools in which the plants had formed a dense bloom.

1945-50. Whitewater Lake, Manitoba, Canada (McLeod and Bondar, 1952; Olson). Algae: "Algae". Waterfowl, shore birds, ducks. Found dead.

1946. Upper Des Lacs Lake, N. D., U.S.A. (Brandenburg and Shigley, 1947). Algae: "Waterbloom". Over 20 cattle, a number of deer. Nervous symptoms developed 15-20 minutes after drinking; death occurred in 4 hours. Three or four cattle showed severe photosensitization manifested by blistering of the skin of *all* white-haired areas, with extensive skin sloughing.

1946. Yahara River below Lake Kegonsa, Wisc., U.S.A. (K. M. Mackenthum, E. F. Herman and A. F. Bartsch, 1948). Algae: *Aphanizomenon flos-aquae*. Thousands of fish, mainly carp. "The fish, crowded close to shore, were breathing at the surface and showed marked distress before expiring."

1948. Sturgeon Lake, Ontario, Canada (Barnum, Henderson and Stewart, 1950; Stewart, Barnum and Henderson, 1950; MacKinnon, 1950). Algae: Blue-green. Cattle. Cattle from five neighboring farms were found dead. One cow was seen to die 20 minutes after drinking from the lake. Others remained stuporous 4-5 days, with head and neck extended or retracted; some of these cows recovered with treatment.

1948. Storm Lake, Iowa, U.S.A. (Rose, 1953; Prescott, 1948). Algae: Blue-green. A few dogs, "hundreds of thousands" of fish. Found dead.

1948. Round Lake, Minn., U.S.A. (Olson, 1951; Scott, 1952). Algae: *Polycystis aeruginosa*. 5 horses, 2 dogs, pheasants, heron, snipe. Horses died suddenly; one dog dead in two hours, one exceedingly ill but recovered. Other animals found dead.

1948. Fox Lake, Minn., U.S.A. (Olson, 1951; 1952). Algae: *Anabaena Lemmermanni*. 79 hogs, 2 horses, many ducks, chickens, cats, dogs and wild animals. Many found dead; others seen to be weak and paralyzed.

1949. Sturgeon Lake, Ontario, Canada (Barnum, Henderson and Stewart, 1950; Stewart, Barnum and Henderson, 1950; MacKinnon, 1950). Algae: *Microcystis incerta*, *Microcystis flos-aquae*, *Microcystis aeruginosa*, *Anabaena torulosa*, and *Anabaena* sp. 16 cows. Muscular twitching, weakness, sunken and glassy eyes. Nine died in 4-6 hours; 3 recovered after treatment. The toxic substance appeared to act rapidly, the time between ingestion of water and death being less than one hour in several cases.

1950. Duck Lake, Alberta, Canada (O'Donoghue and Wilton, 1951). Algae: Blue-green. 2 cows. Two hours after drinking from lake, cow was unable to rise; breathing rapid, pulse thin and weak; dead by the third hour. The other cow walked eight to ten yards before falling; recovered.

1950. Baptiste Lake, Alberta, Canada (O'Donoghue and Wilton, 1951). Algae: Microcystis. 2 horses, 6 pigs, 30 chickens, 2 turkeys, 3 dogs. "Horses: sudden purgation, with marked weakness; went down, rolled and struggled, legs held out stiffly. Slimy discharge from nostrils, choking. Poultry: partial paralysis, unsteady gait or inability to walk. Pigs: one hour after feeding had spasms, thrashing of legs, circling, foaming discharge from the mouth, squealing as if in pain; all dead in 20 minutes. Dogs: yelping, pain, convulsions, rapid death."

1951. Lake Dauphin, Manitoba, Canada (McLeod and Bondar, 1952). Algae: Aphanizomenon flos-aquae, Anabaena flos-aquae, and Microcystis aeruginosa. 1 horse, 9 spaniel dogs. Muscular weakness, paralysis and death. (The horse also showed profuse sweating.) All ten dead within the hour.

1951. Tel Joseph and Beth Hashita Ponds, Israel (Shelubsky Shile, 1951). Algae: Microcystis aeruginosa and Microcystis sp. Fish. Many fish found dead.

1952. Storm Lake, Iowa, U.S.A. (Rose, 1953; Firkins, 1953). Algae: Anabaena flos-aquae. 5000-7000 Franklin's gulls, 560 ducks, 400 coots, 200 pheasants, 50 fox squirrels, 18 muskrats, 15 dogs, 4 cats, 2 hogs, 2 hawks, 1 skunk, 1 mink, "numerous" songbirds. "If ingested dose is large, animal will exhibit peracute prostration and convulsions followed by death. Those mildly affected show restlessness, weakness, deep breathing and rigid paralysis. Two gulls were presented in a semi-conscious state; one showed symptoms of poisoning and had suffered mechanical injury also. It died very soon. The other gull, when teased about the head with a stick, would grab the stick in its mouth and could be suspended in this manner, indicating tonic spasm and not paresis. Gull recovered, was freed three days later; after four or five attempts to take flight, it was able to take off.

1952-53. Lake Semekhovichi, Zhabchitskii District, Pinsk Province, USSR (Vinberg, 1954). Algae: Microcystis aeruginosa and other blue-greens. Horses, livestock, ducks, geese, cats, dogs, waterfowl. Horses and livestock drank with great reluctance; all others died immediately after drinking the water.

1956-58. Stock pond, Waco, Tex., U.S.A. (Davidson, 1959). Algae: Nostoc rivulare. Numerous fish, frogs, chickens, ducks, turkey and cattle. "Wild and domestic animals that drank water containing a heavy accumulation of this alga became ill or died." "Numerous dead fish and frogs were observed along the waterline near the heaviest bloom, others floated on the surface and appeared to be intoxicated. Chickens, ducks, turkey and cattle died within a few hours or became acutely ill (restlessness, repeated swallowing, blinking of the eyes, and convulsions).

1959. Echo Lake, Regina, Saskatchewan, Canada (Dillenberg, 1959; Dillenberg and Dehnel, 1960; Gorham, 1960). Algae: Microcystis sp., Anabaena sp., and Coelosphaerium sp. A number of dogs, geese and many large fish. "Dogs died after swimming in the lake ... or were sick after lapping up water from the lake. Many large fish were found dead along the lake shore." Dogs became visibly uncomfortable shortly after leaving the water, lied down, starting retching and convulsive movements and soon showed foam at the mouth and

TABLE I. (Continued)

then had diarrhea. They were, within half to one hour, unable to rise and would not respond to fondling, or profferred water or food. Death followed after a short period of labored breathing, interrupted by convulsions. Geese swam for 5–10 minutes, then hurriedly came ashore and died within a few minutes under craning of their necks.

1959. Kindersley Lake, Saskatchewan, Canada, (Dillenberg, 1959; Dillenberg and Dehnel, 1960). Algae: Blue-green. 2 horses. "Died after drinking algal scum."

1959. Souris River Dam, Weyburn, Saskatchewan, Canada (Dillenberg, 1959; Dillenberg and Dehnel, 1960; Senior, 1960). Algae: *Anabaena* and *Aphanizomenon*. 3 cows. "Died after drinking algal scum."

1959. Lost Mountain Lake, Regina, Saskatchewan, Canada (Dillenberg, 1959; Dillenberg and Dehnel, 1960). Algae: Algal scum. 4 dogs. Death.

1959. Balgonie, Saskatchewan, Canada (Dillenberg, 1959; Dillenberg and Dehnel, 1960). Algae: *Aphanizomenon flos-aquae*. 1 Newfoundland dog. Died after drinking water from a blooming farm dug-out.

1959. Govan, Long Lake, Saskatchewan, Canada (Dillenberg, 1959; Dillenberg and Dehnel, 1960). Algae: *Microcystis* and *Anabaena*. 3 cows. "... a farmer reported two cows had died 12–16 hours after the lake had bloomed and herd had watered at the beach. They were found lying on their sides, breathing hard and already moribund. They had froth around the nozzles and were quite blue-nosed. A third cow was found to be sick 10 hours later but made a remarkably quick recovery; 10 days later this cow showed a peculiar sloughing of the skin around the nostrils and large scabs on its udder."

1959. Buffalo Pound Lake, Moose Jaw, Saskatchewan, Canada (Dillenberg, 1959; Dillenberg and Dehnel, 1960). Algae: *Microcystis* and *Anabaena*. 3 cows, 6 dogs. Found dead after heavy scum had formed on the south shore of the lake.

1959. Johnston Lake, Saskatchewan, Canada (Dillenberg, 1959; Dillenberg and Dehnel, 1960; Gorham, 1960). Algae: *Microcystis* and *Anabaena*. Over 3,000 wild ducks. "... mass-killing of wild ducks; 50 birds found alive and transported to a nearby slough recovered."

1959. Saskatchewan, Canada (Senior, 1960). Algae: *Microcystis aeruginosa*, *Microcystis flos-aquae*, and *Anabaena flos-aquae*. Approx. 30 dogs. "... dogs were seen swimming in the lake or slaking their thirst at the water's edge. Within 15–30 minutes discomfort was noted followed by nausea, persistent vomiting, evidence of abdominal pain and occasionally, convulsions. Invariably, death occurred in one to two hours. Some recovered following a violent bout of vomiting and diarrhea."

1960. Algae: "Toxic algal types". Cows. "... sudden onset and rapid death."

1960. Algae: "Toxic algal types." Cattle, horses. "... rapid death."

1960–61. Saskatchewan, Canada, (Dillenberg, 1962). Algae: *Microcystis*, *Anabaena*, and *Aphanizomenon*. Livestock. "... widespread loss."

The genera of blue-green algae incriminated have been *Nodularia, Rivularia, Aphanizomenon, Oscillaria, Anabaena, Microcystis, Coelosphaerium*, and *Nostoc*.

The outbreaks of toxicity have been in many different parts of the world, in such diverse locales as Australia, U.S.A., Germany, Union of

South Africa, Canada, Hungary, Finland, Sweden, Argentina, Bermuda, Israel, and Russia. Among the victims were livestock (including sheep, cattle, hogs, chickens, and ducks), domestic animals (horses, dogs, and cats), shore birds, land birds, and wildlife.

Gastrointestinal: The most common clinical manifestations have been those involving the gastrointestinal tract. Most often mentioned have been vomiting, diarrhea, and thirst. A composite picture of the post-mortem findings in the gastrointestinal tract ranges from simple inflammations to petechiae and gross hemorrhage. Necrosis and atrophy have also been described, as have various kinds of ascites.

Hepatic: The chief clinical manifestations have been jaundice and photosensitivity of the skin. Hepato-splenomegaly has been prominent on autopsy, with varying degrees of congestion and necrosis. Ascites, occasionally frankly bloody, has also been noted.

Neuromuscular: Some of the neuromuscular symptoms have been rather severe and dramatic. Outstanding have been spasms, twitching, and convulsions; weakness, incoordination, and paralysis; and lethargy verging into stupor and death. Post-mortem findings have paradoxically been reported to show only congestion of the cerebro-spinal blood vessels and meninges.

Respiratory: Animals exposed to toxic algae have manifested striking respiratory symptoms, including mild to severe dyspnea and cyanosis. Choking has often been present, with wheezing or even frank foamy discharges from the nostrils.

Pathological examinations have shown hyperemia, pleural effusions, and pulmonary edema.

Cardiovascular: The circulatory manifestations in contrast to the neuromuscular ones have been less prominent clinically than on autopsy. Weak and rapid pulse have been described. Post-mortem examinations have indicated striking damage, the heart often being flaccid and dilated. Hemorrhages and pericardial effusions have also been prominent.

To corroborate the role of algae as causative agents in the etiology of animal intoxications, diverse experiments have been performed with the algal blooms collected from areas of toxic incidents. There are no fewer than fifty such scientific studies reported in the literature to date, encompassing over 500 individual experiments, utilizing literally thousands of test animals. Not only were the investigators able to reproduce similar clinical manifestations and post-mortem findings, but also, because they were able to give selective dosages both orally and parenterally, more extensive system disorders could be induced.

The genera of blue-green algae tested were *Nodularia, Microcystis, Anabaena, Nostoc, Lyngbya, Aphanizomenon, Coelosphaerium*, and *Gloeotrichia*. Test animals included sheep, cattle, pigs, cats, rabbits, guinea pigs, mice, rats, chickens, ducks, pigeons, fish, frogs, and the cladoceran *Daphnia*.

Gastrointestinal symptoms included anorexia, extreme salivation, abnormal swallowing motions, abdominal distention, and disturbance of intestinal motility. As in the spontaneous toxic episodes, there was evidence of varying degrees of inflammation or hemorrhagic congestion in the whole tract, as well as serous and bloody ascites.

Hepatic damage following administration of suspected algae was indicated by anorexia, weight loss, jaundice, and ascites. Far more striking were the post-mortem findings which varied from minor to extreme damage, depending upon the size of the administered dose. In the acute cases the liver was markedly congested, dark, and either brittle or flabby; on microscopic examination, hepatic cells were swollen and cytoplasm granular and vacuolated with evident albuminous degeneration. In other animals, hepatic damage could be followed through successive stages of acute parenchymatous, hydropic, and fatty degeneration, to centrolobular necrosis. In animals receiving repeated dosages, and surviving a number of months, the *livers* and *spleens* showed characteristic gross and microscopic findings of cirrhosis.

Toxic Manifestations Following Experimental Administration of Naturally Occurring Toxic Freshwater Algae. (Table II)

The experimental administration of toxic algae produced the complete gamut of *neuromuscular disturbances*, from minor restlessness through spasms, convulsions, paralysis, coma, and death. Post-mortem findings were limited to muscular hyperemia and congestion of the dura mater.

The *respiratory disorders* induced in the experiments included chiefly, dyspnea, tachypnea, sneezing, coughing, salivation, wheezing, cyanosis, and death. Pathological lesions included pulmonary edema, petechial, and gross hemorrhages, in the parenchyma and alveoli, and serous or serosanguineous pleural effusions.

The *cardiovascular manifestations* could be better observed in the experimental animals than in the natural toxic incidents. Clinical findings included pallor and vasospasm of ears, tails, and conjunctivae. There were also tachycardia, variable strength of pulse, arrhythmias, fall in blood pressure, and death.

As in the natural incidents, autopsies showed the *hearts* flaccid and dilated, especially on the right side. There were also petechial and generalized hemorrhages as well as pericardial effusions.

TABLE II. EXPERIMENTS WITH FRESHWATER ALGAL BLOOMS
FROM AREAS OF TOXIC INCIDENTS

1879. Francis (Australia). **Algae:** *Nodularia spumigera.* **Animals:** Sheep. **Procedure:** Feeding fresh lakewater algal suspension. **Results:** Death in 15 hours.
1886. Arthur Stalker (U.S.A.). **Algae:** *Gloeotrichia pisum.* Horse, calf. Feeding fresh lakewater algal suspension on successive days, two weeks after spontaneous toxic episode. No adverse effects.
1925. Wilmot Enterprise (U.S.A.). **Algae:** Blue-green. Potato bugs. Application of green lake scum to potato plants. Death of potato plant and bugs.
1933. Hindersson (Finland). **Algae:** *Anabaena* and *Aphanizomenon.* Heifer. Feeding fresh lakewater algal suspension. Restlessness, tachypnea, tachycardia, weak pulse, asthenia, collapse, and coma within 15 minutes. No gross changes on autopsy.
1933. Prescott (U.S.A.). **Algae:** *Apahanizomenon flos-aquae.* Various species of fish. Immersion in tank containing varying amounts of decaying algae. Distress, disorientation and incoordination within one hour. Death in 1½–6 hours without evidence of oxygen want.
1934–35. Fitch, Bishop, Boyd, Gortner, Rogers, and Tilden (U.S.A.). **Algae:** *Coelosphaerium kuetzingianum* and *Anabaena flos-aquae.* Dog. Feeding fresh lakewater algal suspension. Death.
_____. **Algae:** *Microcystis flos-aquae* and *Microcystis aeruginosa.* Rabbits, guinea pigs, cattle. Feeding fresh lakewater algal suspension. No ill-effects.
_____. _____. Cattle. Feeding algae stored under varying temperature conditions. No ill-effects observed with variations in temperature or periods of storage.
_____. **Algae:** *Microcystis flos-aquae.* Rabbits, guinea pigs, pigeons. Feeding of fresh lakewater algal suspension. Immediate restlessness, urination, defecation, sneezing, dyspnea, salivation, foamy tears, muscular spasms and sudden death.
_____. _____. Rabbits, guinea pigs, pigeons. Intraperitoneal injection of fresh lakewater algal suspension. Symptoms similar to those with oral feeding, with death in few minutes to hours.
_____. **Algae:** *Microcystis flos-aquae, Anabaena flos-aquae,* and *Aphanizomenon flos-aquae.* Guinea pigs. Intraperitoneal injection of fresh lakewater algal suspension. Findings similar to those above.
1939. Deem and Thorpe (U.S.A.). **Algae:** *Anabaena flos-aquae.* Chickens, rabbit, guinea pigs. Intraperitoneal injection of lakewater algal suspensions (some fresh, some boiled, some refrigerated as much as three weeks) stored under varying temperature conditions. 2–5 cc killed animals within 5–38 minutes.
_____. _____. Guinea pig. Intraperitoneal injection of 5 cc algal suspensions passed through Seitz bacterial filter. Death within 22 minutes: this tended to exclude bacteria as source of toxin.
_____. _____. Rabbit. Intraperitoneal injection of 10 cc suspension collected 3 days after spontaneous toxic episode. Death in 90 minutes. With time, material started to decompose and became less toxic.
_____. _____. Rabbits, sheep. Feeding of lakewater algal suspension taken from same area 3 days later and subjected to heat, storage at room temperature or refrigeration. No toxicity.

TABLE II. (Continued)

———. ———. Guinea pigs. Intraperitoneal injections of suspensions together with botulinus antitoxins. Death in 15 minutes: toxic principle was not thought to be one of the toxins of *Clostridium botulinum*.

1942. Mason and Wheeler (U.S.A.). **Algae:** *Microcystis aeruginosa.* Mice, cats. Subcutaneous and intraperitoneal injection of lethal doses of partially purified extracts. After latent period, pallor, hypotension, tachycardia, hypothermia, hyperglycemia; terminal hemodilution and death in respiratory failure.

1942. Wheeler, Lackey and Schott (U.S.A.). **Algae:** *Microcystis aeruginosa.* Mice, guinea pigs, rabbit. Subcutaneous or intraperitoneal injections of fresh lakewater algal suspensions. In mice injected intraperitoneally or subcutaneously, death occurred when dosage exceeded 0.25 ml; seldom in less than 16 or more than 36 hours. Two ml given intraperitoneally in guinea pigs resulted in death in 24 hours. Rabbit showed no ill effects.

———. ———. Guinea pigs, mice. Feeding of fresh lakewater algal suspensions. Only slightly toxic; nearly always survived.

———. ———. Mice. Subcutaneous injections of fresh lakewater algal filtrates. No effect, even though injected water contained large numbers of bacteria.

———. ———. Mice, guinea pigs. Subcutaneous and intraperitoneal injections of algal concentrates subjected to prolonged refrigeration. In mice death occurred in 40–90 minutes. Minimal lethal dose was only 0.025 ml. Guinea pigs survived for more than 4 hours.

———. ———. Mice. Subcutaneous injections of algal concentrates subjected to prolonged refrigeration, dehydration resuspension. In 30 minutes: periods of apathy alternating with restlessness and exaggerated response to stimuli: ears and tails became chalky white, eyes light pink; death followed rapid superficial respirations. Post mortem: no bleeding on cutting through the skin or abdominal wall; heart ventricle found contracted, colorless, beating slowly; auricles were dilated, beat twice or more for each ventricular beat, or quite disassociated from ventricles; liver enormously dilated, dark; intestines were contracted; visceral circulation no more in evidence than peripheral, except that engorged liver bled profusely when incised.

———. ———. ———. Injection of algal material treated by pasteurization, filtration and autoclaving. Uniform death time made hypothesis of a bacterial toxin appear unlikely.

———. ———. ———. Subcutaneous injection of algal filtrates subjected to various types of water purification procedures in regular use in water treatment plants. Alum coagulation-treated algae killed mice within 40 minutes. Alum coagulation and chlorination-treated algae killed mice within same time. Algal filtrates adsorbed on carbon were less toxic.

1943–45. Steyn (Union of South Africa). **Algae:** *Microcystis toxica.* Rabbits, cattle. Drenched or dosed with water contaminated with fresh algae. Showed hard, tough livers months, or even more than a year, afterwards.

1943–45. Steyn; 1948. Stephens (Union of South Africa). **Algae:** *Microcystis toxica.* Cattle, sheep. Controlled feeding of fresh living algae. Acute: convulsions, paralysis, death within hours. Semi-acute: jaundice, photosensitivity, diarrhea, constipation with bloody slime, weight loss, death in several weeks. Chronic: sick for weeks or months, emaciation, poor appetite, skin lesions. Post mortem findings in acute cases: lungs usually full of blood;

liver enlarged, dark red or black in color, very brittle, sometimes even flabby, with thick, sticky, blackish blood flowing from the cut surface whence liver cells easily scraped like pulp; spleen enlarged; coagulated or uncoagulated blood may be present in the abdominal cavity; stomach mucous membrane may show bloody patches; intestines, especially the large intestines, may contain congealed blood with presence of bloody patches on the mucous membrane. Post mortem findings in chronic cases: yellowish or bloody liquid usually found in the pericardial sac and thoracic and abdominal cavities. Liver either yellow and soft or brittle, or brownish yellow and hard.

1945. Mullor (Argentina). **Algae:** *Anabaena venenosa*. Duck, chickens. Feeding and subcutaneous injection of fresh lagoon algal concentrate. Restlessness, excitability, tachycardia, arrhythmia, increased heart rate and blood pressure, tremors, hyperlachrymation, ataxia, paralysis, convulsions and death within 15–120 minutes. Post mortem findings: **gross:** visceral and muscular hyperemia, hemorrhages, particularly in the abdomen; sanguinous infiltration in liver and intestine; heart in diastole, dilated 3–4 times normal volume; red cells only slightly altered; intestinal mucosa partially desquamated and hemorrhagic.

———. ———. Ducks, guinea pigs, dogs, chickens. Feeding and parenteal administration of dried lagoon algae to warm blooded animals. Those injected died within 10–20 minutes with symptoms as above. Those fed showed no adverse effects.

———. ———. Frogs, fish. Immersion in, and injection of, resuspended dried lagoon algae. Those injected died within 5–12 minutes with symptoms as above. Simple immersion caused no toxicity.

1946. Ashworth and Mason (U.S.A.). **Algae:** *Microcystis aeruginosa*. Rats. Intraperitoneal injections of algal extract to animals sacrificed at set intervals to determine progressive pathological changes. There was generalized cellular damage with particularly severe injury to liver parenchyma. Hepatic injury can be followed through successive stages of acute parenchymatous, hydropic and fatty degeneration, to necrosis in the centers of the lobule. Dead liver cells disintegrate rapidly by cytolysis and fragmentation of cytoplasm into the circulating blood. There is marked engorgement of the centers of the lobules. Dead liver cells are removed at 24–48 hours; regeneration is in progress at 3–5 days, and there is complete restoration of liver lobules within 30 days after administration of the extract. Acute parenchymatous and hydropic degeneration, and focal necrosis as well as hyperemia are observed in the heart and kidneys. Small hemorrhages and occasionally edema occur in the lungs.

1947. Brandenburg and Shigley (U.S.A.). **Algae:** "Waterbloom". Hens. Feeding and intraperitoneal injections of lakewater algal specimens obtained two weeks after death of livestock. Restlessness; blinking of the eyes; repeated swallowing with upward jerking of head; clonic spasms; frequent defecation; death in 10–90 minutes.

1948. Mackenthum, Herman and Bartsch (U.S.A.). **Algae:** *Aphanizomenon flosaquae*. Perch, crappies. Immersion in toxic river water algae sample. All dead in 30 hours.

———. ———. Perch, crappies, suckers. Immersion in toxic river water algae sample obtained one week later, 14 miles downstream. Loss of equilibrium by third day; deaths commencing on fifth day. All dead by eighth day.

1949. Stewart, Barnum and Henderson (Canada). **Algae:** *Microcystis aerugi-*

TABLE II. (Continued)

nosa, Microcystis flos-aquae, Microcystis incerta, Anabaena torulosa, Anabaena sp., *Nostoc* sps., and *Lyngbya* sps. Cow. Administration by stomach tube of measured amount of fresh algae-water mixture. Defecation, muscular twitchings, accelerated respiration followed by diminution with dyspnoea, eyes dull and cloudy, staggering within 15 minutes, collapse, and death within 25 minutes. Post Mortem: gross: blood in vessels dark and fluid; petechial hemorrhages in epicardium, endocardium and lungs; liver swollen, mottled with pale yellowish irregular areas; **microscopic:** recent hemorrhage into lung alveoli and bronchi; heart showed myocardial hemorrhages and interstitial edema separating fibers and bundles; early degenerative changes in myocardium and Purkinje's fibers; liver cells swollen with cytoplasm granular and vacuolated; in the kidney every glomerular space and many of the tubules contained albuminous fluid.

————. ————. Pigeons, rats, mice, guinea pigs and rabbits. Administration as drinking water of unmeasured amounts of fresh algae-water mixture. Pigeons showed muscular spasms, pupils initially markedly constricted then later dilated; death in 24 hours. Post mortem: showed tissue congestion and degeneration. Rats listless. Other animals appeared unaffected.

————. ————. Rats. Administration as drinking water of unmeasured amounts of fresh algae-water mixture given to animals previously deprived of water for two days. Two out of three died within 24 hours.

————. ————. Guinea pigs, rabbits, mice. Oral administration of measured amounts of fresh algal water mixture. Guinea pigs unaffected; of 5 rabbits, 3 died in 10 minutes exhibiting symptoms of forelimb stiffness, prostration, terminal gasping respirations. Microscopic examination revealed albuminous degeneration in the renal tubular epithelium and in the liver cells.

————. ————. Rabbits, pigeons, guinea pigs, mice. Intravenous and intraperitoneal injections of bacterial-free algae-water filtrates. Rabbits: paralysis, respiratory distress and death in 10 minutes; albuminous degeneration in kidney and liver. Pigeons: muscular spasm; death in 15 minutes. Tissues showed congestion and degeneration. Guinea pigs unaffected. Mice: restlessness, urination, defecation, stiffness, tremors, terminal clonic spasms, deep breathing and death in 8–10 minutes.

————. ————. Mice. Intraperitoneal injections of unfiltered water scum mixture. Same toxicity as filtrate above.

————. **Algae:** *Anabaena Microcystis.* Mice. Intraperitoneal injections of unfiltered algae water mixture collected from same site 10 days later. Only half as toxic as the original sample.

————. ————. ————. Intraperitoneal injections of sterile algal filtrate collected from same site 10 days later. Nontoxic even when concentrated 30 times.

————. **Algae:** Unidentified algae. Mice. Intraperitoneal injections of algae-water mixture collected from same site 2 months after the initial sample. Nontoxic even when concentrated 10 times.

1950. Shelubsky [Shilo] (Israel). **Algae:** *Microcystis aeruginosa.* Mice, rats, frogs, carp. Subcutaneous and intraperitoneal injections of living lake algae. Mice died in 10 minutes–2 hours; rats, 4–5 hours; carp, 36–96 hours; frogs—death time unstated.

_____. **Algae:** *Microcystis* sp. Mice, rats, frogs, carp. Subcutaneous and intraperitoneal injections of living lake algae. Same as above.

_____. **Algae:** *Microcystis aeruginosa.* Mice. Intraperitoneal injections of algal suspensions, extracts, and purified fractions. Death within 2 hours.

_____. **Algae:** *Microcystis.* Mice. Intraperitoneal injections of alkali treated aqueous extract of dried algae boiled, stored in ice box, or at room temperature for varying time periods. Extract at 100°C was nontoxic. That at room temperature or in ice box, of variable toxicity depending on period of storage.

_____. _____. _____. Intraperitoneal injections of ashes of algal toxin. Nontoxic.

_____. _____. _____. Intraperitoneal injection of algal toxin treated by human blood, rich in esterase. Retained toxicity, signifying the absence of esters in the toxin.

_____. _____. Rabbits. Intravenous injection of algal suspensions and aqueous extracts to determine whether the algal toxin was either an antigen or hapten. Elicited a formation of precipitin.

1950. Luow and Smit (Union of South Africa). **Algae:** *Microcystis toxica.* Rabbits. Dosing with extract from fluorescent filtrate of fresh algae. Restlessness, dyspnea, progressive paralysis, coma and death in 4 hours after oral administration and within 30 minutes after injection. Chronic cases: listlessness, cachexia, ascites and cirrhosis. Post mortem: ascites, tumor splenis, kidney hyperemia, liver necrosis and hemorrhages.

_____. _____. Rats, rabbits. Oral and subcutaneous administration of alkaloid nitrate derivative of algal filtrate. Signs of uneasiness; recovered completely.

_____. _____. Rabbit. Dosing with phosphotungstate derivative of algal filtrate. Died soon with typical symptoms and post-mortem appearances of algal poisoning.

_____. _____. Rats. Intraperitoneal injection of hydrochloride derivative of algal filtrate. Same as above.

_____. _____. Rabbits. Dosing with watery filtrate from fresh algae. Nontoxic.

_____. _____. _____. Oral administration of freshly preserved 1-month, 15-month, and 42-month-old algae. Typical symptoms of algae poisoning followed by death within 3–4 hours.

_____. _____. Rat. Intraperitoneal injections of alcohol extract of preserved algae. As above.

_____. _____. _____. Intraperitoneal injection of chloroform extract of preserved algae. Died with typical symptoms a few hours after injection.

_____. _____. _____. Intraperitoneal injection of alcohol percolate fractioned by ether precipitation. Death.

_____. _____. _____. Intraperitoneal injection of filtrate from previous fractions evaporated. Death.

_____. _____. _____. Intraperitoneal injection of alkaloid hydrochloride from the pictrate. Killed animal within an hour with typical symptoms and post-mortem appearance of algae poisoning.

1951. Olson (U.S.A.). **Algae:** *Polycystis seruginosa* (*Microcystis*). Mice. Laboratory testing of fresh lake water algae. Typical toxic symptoms of algae poisoning.

_____. **Algae:** *Anabaena Lemmermanni* and *Polycystis aeruginosa* (*Microcystis*

TABLE II. (Continued)

aeruginosa). Mice, rabbits, chickens, hamsters, guinea pigs. Oral and intraperitoneal administration of crude unpurified lake water algae material. Paralysis and death usually in 5–20 minutes.

————. ————. Mice. Intraperitoneal injection of crude unpurified lake water algae material collected at same site 9 days later. Death in 5 hours.

1951. O'Donoghue and Wilton (Canada). **Algae:** *Microcystis* sp. Rabbits, guinea pigs, heifer, pig, chickens. Fresh algal suspension given as water supply or by stomach tube. Pig dead in 25 minutes. Post mortem: inflammation of stomach and intestinal mucous membrane; early degeneration of liver with granular cytoplasm; splenic hemorrhages with hemosiderin deposits. Kidneys showed marked cloudy swelling and slight hemorrhage.

————. ————. Rabbits, guinea pigs. Intraperitoneal and intravenous injection of bacteria-free fresh algal filtrate. Guinea pigs unaffected; both rabbits sick; one recovered, the other died in 45 minutes. Post mortem: liver dark, mottled; gall bladder distended; microscopical findings of early degenerative changes in liver and kidney; hemosiderin deposits in the latter.

————. ————. Guinea pigs, rabbits, chickens. Intraperitoneal injection of bacteria-free algal filtrate, stood at room temperature for 10 days. No effect.

1952. McLeod and Bondar (Canada). **Algae:** *Aphanizomenon flos-aquae, Anabaena flos-aquae,* and *Microcystis aeruginosa.* Rats, mice. Oral and intraperitoneal administration of 0.5–2 ml unpreserved fresh lake water algae. Loss of equilibrium, progressive paralysis, clonic muscular spasms, impaired respiration, cyanosis, and death within 20 hours.

————. ————. Oral and intraperitoneal administration of filtrate of fresh lake water algae. No effect.

————. ————. ————. Oral and intraperitoneal administration of filtered fresh lake water algal residue, resuspended in distilled water. Same symptoms as in first test, with death in 12–50 hours for all except one.

————. ————. Mice. Oral and intraperitoneal administration of filtered fresh lake water algal residue, frozen for 24 hours, then thawed and resuspended. Dead in 20–50 hours; follows characteristic signs of algal poisoning.

————. ————. ————. Oral and intraperitoneal administration of material obtained by passage of fresh sand-ground lake water algae through plain and Seitz filters. Half developed diarrhea but survived; remainder died within 24–65 hours.

————. ————. ————. Intraperitoneal administration of heat dried, (3 days at 37° C) resuspended fresh lake water algae. Both sickened; one survived, and the other died in 12 hours.

1953. Rose (U.S.A.) **Algae:** *Anabaena flos-aquae.* Rabbit. Oral pipette administration of 2 cc fresh lake water algae. Abdominal convulsions and loss of hind legs control within 30 minutes; flaccid paralysis at 75 minutes; dead at 100 minutes.

1953. Firkins, Jones in Rose (U.S.A.). **Algae:** *Anabaena flos-aquae.* Chickens, guinea pigs, rabbits, mice. Force-feeding and voluntary feeding of fresh lake water algae collected in same area 4 years later. Death in all cases.

————. ————. ————. Oral and intraperitoneal administration of bacteria-free filtrates of lake water algae. All died; some in 2–3 minutes; others within 24–28 hours.

————. ————. ————. Neutralization tests of bacteria-free algal filtrates with
botulinus antitoxins A, B, and C. All negative.

————. ————. ————. Force-feeding and voluntary feeding of lake water
algae stored 6 weeks. Death in all cases.

————. ————. ————. Inoculation of bacteria-free filtrates of lake water algae
stored 6 weeks. Sudden death.

1953. Beardmore and Port in Rose (U.S.A.). **Algae:** *Anabaena flos-aquae.*
Guinea pigs, mouse. Intraperitoneal injection of bacteria-free filtrates of lake
water algae. Typical symptoms of toxicity leading to death of mouse in four
minutes and of guinea pigs in 12 minutes.

————. ————. Mouse. Intraperitoneal injection of bacteria-free filtrate of lake
water algae stored one year. Did not succumb.

1953. Biester in Rose (U.S.A.). **Algae:** *Anabaena flos-aquae.* Laboratory animals. Intraperitoneal injection of crude lake water algal material. Killed
upon injection.

————. ————. ————. Intraperitoneal injection of refined lake water algal
material. Killed upon injection.

1953. Grant and Hughes (Canada). **Algae:** *Microcystis aeruginosa, Coelosphaerium naegelianum, Anabaena* sp., *Gloeotrichia echinulata,* and *Lyngbya
birgei.* Mice. Intraperitoneal injection of fresh lake-water algae collected
from a lake when there was no "true bloom," and subjected to incubation for
varying time periods. No lethal effects were obtained with freshly collected
material. After incubation at 27° C for 18 hours all died——one within 5
minutes after exhibiting muscle spasms and convulsions; the remainder died
within 12 hours.

————. ————. ————. Intraperitoneal injection of fresh algae, stored for a
long time under refrigeration, then subjected to incubation for varying time
periods. Material incubated at 27° C for 18 hours caused death of one out of
10; incubation at 27° C for 24 hours caused death of 6 out of 10.

————. ————. ————. Intraperitoneal injection of fresh algae collected from a
lake covered by algal scum, subjected to incubation for varying time periods.
Material injected after 4½ hours incubation killed one out of 10; after 12
hours, one out of 10 died; after 18 hours 2 out of 10 died after mild paralysis.

————. ————. ————. Intraperitoneal injection of fresh algae collected from a
lake covered by algal scum, stored under refrigeration, then subjected to incubation for varying time periods. Material injected after 6 hours incubation
killed 2 out of 10; after 13 hours incubation, 4 out of 10 died; after 26½ hours,
6 out of 10 died.

1955. McIvor and Grant.(Canada). **Algae:** *Microcystis aeruginosa, Coelosphaerium naegelianum, Anabaena* sp., *Aphanizomenon flos-aquae, Gloectrichia
echinulata,* and *Lyngbya birgei.* Mice. Intraperitoneal injection of freeze-
dried algae before incubation. 0.25 ml of 2.5% suspension caused 40% mortality in 24 hours; 0.50 ml resulted in 100% mortality in 24 hours.

————. ————. ————. Intraperitoneal injection of freeze-dried algae after incubation 19 hours at 35° C. 0.25 ml of 1.25% suspension caused 100% mortality in 24 hours: half-strength suspension resulted in 40% mortality in 24 hours.

————. ————. ————. Intraperitoneal injection of 0.25 ml suspension of mechanically disintegrated algal cells. No mortality.

————. ————. ————. Intraperitoneal injection of 0.50 ml suspension of mechanically disintegrated algal cells. No mortality with double strength.

TABLE II. (Continued)

————. ————. ————. Intraperitoneal injection of 0.25 ml of algal suspension incubated 19 hours at 35°C. No mortality.

————. ————. ————. Intraperitoneal injection of 0.50 ml of algal suspension incubated 19 hours at 35°C. 40% mortality.

————. ————. ————. Intraperitoneal injection of 0.25 ml of algal suspension incubated 19 hours, then mechanically disintegrated. 60% mortality.

————. ————. ————. Intraperitoneal injection of 0.50 ml of algal suspension incubated 19 hours, then mechanically disintegrated. 100% mortality.

————. ————. ————. Intraperitoneal injection of 0.50 ml of algal suspension that was incubated, mechanically disintegrated and passed through a bacterial filter. No mortality.

————. ————. ————. Intraperitoneal injection of 0.50 ml of algal suspension that was mechanically disintegrated, filtered, evaporated, and reconstituted in water. No mortality.

————. ————. ————. Intraperitoneal injection of 0.5 ml of algal suspension that was mechanically disintegrated, filtered, evaporated, reconstituted in water, and incubated 19 hours at 35°C. 100% mortality.

————. ————. ————. Intraperitoneal injection of 0.25 ml of algal suspension incubated 19 hours at 35°C and pH 9, then restored to pH 7. 80% mortality.

————. ————. ————. Intraperitoneal injection of 0.50 ml filtrate of algal suspension incubated 19 hours at 35°C and pH 9, restored to pH 7, diluted, centrifuged, and filtered. No mortality.

————. ————. ————. Intraperitoneal injection of 0.25 ml of suspension of residue of preceding test, incubated 72 hours at 35°C. 100% mortality.

————. ————. ————. Intraperitoneal injection of 0.25 ml of algal suspension incubated 19 hours at 35°C and pH 5, restored to pH 7. No mortality.

————. ————. ————. Intraperitoneal injection of 0.50 ml filtrate of algal suspension incubated 19 hours at 35°C at pH 5, restored to pH 7, and filtered. No mortality.

————. ————. ————. Intraperitoneal injection of 0.25 ml suspension of residue of preceding test, resuspended, and incubated 72 hours at 35°C. 100% mortality.

————. ————. ————. Intraperitoneal injection of algal suspension subjected to chloroform extraction, then dissolved in water. No toxicity.

————. ————. ————. Intraperitoneal injection of algal suspension subjected to chloroform extraction, then dissolved in peanut oil. No toxicity.

————. ————. ————. Intraperitoneal injection of algal suspension subjected to 95% ethanol extraction, then dissolved in water. No toxicity.

————. ————. ————. Intraperitoneal injection of algal suspension subjected to 95% ethanol extraction, then dissolved in peanut oil. No toxicity.

————. ————. ————. Intraperitoneal injection of algal residue moistened with formaldehyde incubated and extracted with 95% alcohol. No toxicity.

1959. Davidson (U.S.A.). **Algae:** *Nostoc rivulare.* Mice. Intraperitoneal injection of fresh algal suspension. Restlessness, repeated swallowing, blinking of eyes, convulsions, death within 2 hours.

————. ————. ————. Oral administration of non-bacteria-free crude extract of preserved algae. Hair ruffled, nervousness.

————. ————. ————. Intraperitoneal injection of non-bacteria-free crude extract of preserved algae. 30 minute latent period, restlessness, jerky body motions, anorexia, visual impairment, stiffening of limbs, abdominal swelling, convulsions, prostration, tachypnoea, death. Of 3 test animals, 2 eviscerated at 24 hours. One death at 6 hours, the other 2 within 48 hours.

————. ————. ————. Subcutaneous injection of non-bacteria-free crude extract of preserved algae. All developed tumors on shoulders at three months and died within nine months.

————. ————. ————. Intermittent local application to shaved area of non-bacteria-free crude extract of preserved algae. Heavy scales at 24 hours: scales shed at 96 hours. Hair grew again within several weeks.

————. ————. ————. Oral administration of bacteria-free aqueous extract of preserved algae. No symptoms.

————. ————. ————. Intraperitoneal injection of bacteria-free aqueous extract of preserved algae. 2 out of 3 developed nervousness. Left eye of one injected with sublethal dose showed signs of atrophy within 2 weeks and complete degeneration at end of 3rd week. Large tumors on shoulders and backs within 3 months: death within 9 months.

————. ————. ————. Subcutaneous injection of bacteria-free aqueous extract of preserved algae. Hair ruffled, nervousness.

————. ————. ————. Intermittent local application to shaved area of bacteria-free aqueous extract of preserved algae. No symptoms.

————. ————. ————. Oral administration of bacteria-free aqueous filtrate of preserved algae. No symptoms.

————. ————. ————. Intraperitoneal injection of bacteria-free aqueous filtrate of preserved algae. 3 with shoulder tumors at 6 months.

————. ————. ————. Subcutaneous injection of bacteria-free aqueous filtrate of preserved algae. Hair ruffled, nervousness.

————. ————. ————. Intermittent local application to shaven skin of bacteria-free aqueous filtrate of preserved algae. No symptoms.

————. ————. ————. Intraperitoneal injection of unautoclaved crude algal extract. Sublethal doses produced characteristic transitory symptoms of algal poisoning. Within 6 months tumors appeared on the shoulder and abdominal regions. MLD was 0.933 mg of algae per g. body weight. MLD or greater doses killed mice in 15–60 hours, depending on strength.

————. ————. ————. Intraperitoneal injection of autoclaved crude algal extract. No effect—implying that the toxic factor is unstable when autoclaved.

————. ————. ————. Intraperitoneal injection of saline suspension of living bacterial associates of algae. Symptomless—suggesting that living bacterial associates had no toxic properties.

————. ————. ————. Intraperitoneal injection of saline suspension of dead bacterial associates of algae. Symptomless—suggesting that dead bacterial associates also have no toxic properties.

————. ————. ————. Intraperitoneal injection of crude algal extract containing living bacterial associates. Typical symptoms of algae poisoning, with death of all animals within 19 hours.

————. ————. ————. Intraperitoneal injection of crude algal extract containing dead bacterial associates. Typical symptoms of algae poisoning, with death of all animals within 8 hours.

————. ————. ————. Intraperitoneal injection of lethal dose of crude algal extract to determine effect on body temperature. Within 10 hours after injection, body temperature dropped from 98.8 to 76°F.

TABLE II. (Continued)

————. ————. ————. Intraperitoneal injection of lethal dose of crude algal extract to determine effect on rate of heartbeat. As measured by electrocardiograph, heart rate was reduced 180 beats per minute.

————. ————. ————. Intraperitoneal injection of lethal dose of crude algal extract to determine effect on respiration rate. Respiratory rate increased by 60 per minute.

————. ————. ————. Intraperitoneal injection of lethal dose of crude algal extract to determine effect on blood sugar level. Decrease of blood sugar of 19 mg/100 ml blood in 10 hours.

————. ————. ————. Intraperitoneal injection of lethal dose of crude algal extract to determine effect on blood coagulation time. Blood coagulation time was reduced from 5 minutes to 3 minutes.

————. ————. ————. Intraperitoneal injection of lethal dose of crude algal extract to determine effect on red blood cell count. At the end of 6 hours the count was reduced by 2,500,000 red blood cells/cm of blood.

1959. Dillenberg; 1960. Dillenberg and Dehnel; Senior (Canada). **Algae:** *Microcystis* sp., *Anabaena* sp., and *Coelosphaerium*. Mice. Oral administration of fresh lake water algal scum. No ill-effects.

————. ————. ————. Intraperitoneal injection of fresh lake water algal scum. Immediate visible discomfort, agitation, convulsive twitchings of legs, high jumps; within 20 minutes they crouched, fell on their sides, nose and tail bluish gray in color, and died, legs outstretched within 60–90 minutes; liver dark red, congested on post mortem; peritoneal serosa inflamed; anal region moist with a sticky slime.

————. **Algae:** *Aphanizomenon flos-aquae*. Mice. Intraperitoneal injection of farm dug-out algal scum. Lethal within 8 hours.

————. **Algae:** *Anabaena* and *Aphanizomenon flos-aquae*. Mice. Intraperitoneal injection of fresh algal scum from river dam site. Piloerection, crouched position, refusal of food and water. Half died in 10–14 hours. On autopsy, the livers were congested. Surviving mice attained apparent full health within 36 hours.

————. **Algae:** *Microcystis* and *Anabaena*. Mice. Intraperitoneal injection of undiluted fresh algal scum from lake serving as municipal water supply. All died within 10 hours, manifesting typical signs of algal toxicity. Livers were markedly congested.

————. ————. ————. Intraperitoneal injection of the clear, bluish-violet-colored water beneath the algal scum on lake serving as municipal water supply. Same toxic picture as above.

————. ————. ————. Intraperitoneal injection of alcohol extract of algal scum on lake serving as municipal water supply. Lethal to test animals.

————. ————. ————. Intraperitoneal injection of aqueous extract of algal scum on lake serving as municipal water supply. Equally as lethal as the preceding.

————. ————. ————. Intraperitoneal injection of raw untreated lake water. Listless for a day.

————. ————. ————. Intraperitoneal injection of finished clear-well product of lake water. Showed no sickening effect.

————. **Algae:** *Anabaena* and *Aphanizomenon*. Intraperitoneal injection of fresh algal scum collected at Souris River dam, the initial stage of municipal drinking water supply distribution. Death occurred within 8 hours.

_____. _____. *Daphnia* (water fleas). Immersion in fresh algal scum collected at Souris River dam. Immobility within 30 minutes.

_____. _____. Mice. Intraperitoneal injection of fresh algal scum collected in Weyburn City water plant after passage through 5-mile pipeline from the Souris River dam. Toxicity manifested after 18 hours.

_____. _____. *Daphnia* (water fleas). Immersion in fresh algal scum collected in Weyburn City water plant after 5-mile pipeline passage from Souris River dam. Immobilized after 52 hours.

_____. _____. Mice. Intraperitoneal injection of finished clear-well drinking water, still showing some algal cells. No toxicity.

_____. _____. *Daphnia*. Immersion in finished clear-well drinking water, still showing some algal cells. No toxicity.

_____. **Algae:** *Microcystis*. Mice. Intraperitoneal injection of lakewater specimen obtained 3 days after lake had "bloomed" and mass killing of wild ducks occurred. No toxic manifestations

_____. _____. *Daphnia* (water fleas). Immersion in lakewater specimen obtained 3 days after lake had "bloomed" and mass killing of wild ducks occurred. Not immobilized.

_____. _____. Mice. Intraperitoneal injection of algal scum collected from mud holes adjoining lake shore, 5 days after lake "bloomed" and mass killing of wild ducks occurred. Typical findings of algal poisoning with death in 5 hours.

_____. _____. *Daphnia* (water fleas). Immersion in algal scum collected from mud holes adjoining lake shore, 5 days after lake "bloomed" and mass killing of wild ducks occurred. Died within 2 hours.

1960. Olson (U.S.A.). **Algae:** *Anabaena circinalis, Anabaena flos-aquae, Anabaena Lemmermanni, Anabaena spiroides, Aphanizomenon flos-aquae, Coelosphaerium naegelianum, Lyngbya birgei, Microcystis aeruginosa, Microcystis incerta,* and *Trichodesmium lacustre.* Mice. Intraperitoneal injections of 25 specimens of toxic blooms collected in Minnesota in 1948. All but 2 were definitely toxic.

_____. _____. _____. Intraperitoneal injection of 17 specimens of toxic blooms collected in Minnesota in 1949. All were toxic.

_____. _____. _____. Intraperitoneal injection of 18 specimens of toxic blooms collected in Minnesota in 1950. Only half were poisonous.

1960. Gorham (Canada). **Algae:** *Anabaena flos-aquae* (3 blooms). Mice. Intraperitoneal injection of lyophilized cells in doses ranging from 40–640 mg/kg body weight. All 3 blooms produced "slow-deaths."

_____. **Algae:** *Aphanizomenon flos-aquae* (1 bloom). Mice. Intraperitoneal injection of lyophilized cells in doses ranging from 40–640 mg/kg body weight. Produced "slow-death."

_____. **Algae:** *Microcystis aeruginosa* (6 blooms). Mice. Intraperitoneal injection of lyophilized cells in doses ranging from 40–640 mg/kg body weight. Half produced "fast-deaths"; half produced "slow-deaths."

_____. **Algae:** *Lyngbya birgei* (1 bloom). Mice. Intraperitoneal injection of lyophilized cells in doses ranging from 40–640 mg/kg body weight. Produced "slow-death."

1961. Gorham, Anet, Bishop, Hammer, Harris, Hughes, Konst, Machen, McBride, McKercher, McLachlan, Simpson, Wright and Zehnder (Canada). **Algae:** *Anabaena flos-aquae* (8 blooms). Mice. Intraperitoneal injection of lyophilized cells in doses ranging from 40–640 mg/kg body weight. 5 blooms produced

TABLE II. (Continued)

"very fast deaths" (1–10 minutes); 3 produced no deaths or "slow-deaths" (4–48 hours).

———. **Algae:** *Aphanizomenon flos-aquae* (1 bloom). Mice. Intraperitoneal injection of lyophilized cells in doses ranging from 40–6 40 mg/kg body weight. Produced no death or "slow-death" (4–48 hours).

———. **Algae:** *Lyngbya bergei* (1 bloom). Mice. Intraperitoneal injection of lyophilized cells in doses ranging from 40–640 mg/kg body weight. Produced no death or "slow-death" (4–48 hours).

———. **Algae:** *Microcystis aeruginosa* (10 blooms). Mice. Intraperitoneal injection of lyophilized cells in doses ranging from 40–640 mg/kg body weight. 7 blooms produced "fast-deaths" (1–2 hours); 3 produced no deaths or "slow-deaths" (4–48 hours).

———. **Algae:** *Aphanizomenon plus Microcystis* (4 blooms). Mice. Intraperitoneal injection of lyophilized cells in doses ranging from 40–640 mg/kg body weight. All produced "fast-deaths" in 1–2 hours.

———. **Algae:** *Anabaena flos-aquae* (5 blooms). Mice. Lyophilized cells that were proven toxic when administered intraperitoneally, were given orally. Toxic by oral route as well as intraperitoneally.

———. **Algae:** *Anabaena flos-aquae*. Mice. Intraperitoneal injection of lyophilized cells in doses ranging from 40–640 mg/kg body weight were performed for comparative purposes in the laboratory of Dr. L. D. Jones in South Dakota. Findings were identical.

———. ———. Intraperitoneal injection of lyophilized cells in doses ranging from 40–640 mg/kg body weight were performed for comparative purposes in the laboratory of Dr. T. Olson in Minnesota. Findings were identical.

Microscopically there were noted acute parenchymatous and hydropic degeneration, and focal necrosis.

Similar microscopic changes were noted in the *kidney*, with evidence also of moderate nephrosis and albuminous degeneration.

Toxic Manifestations Following Experimental Administration of Cultured Algae. (Table III)

Having observed apparent toxicity of naturally occurring algal blooms, on both spontaneous and experimental administration, there remained only the development of unialgal cultures to study more intensively their true toxic potential. Since 1935, over thirty separate investigators have conducted such studies and ninety-five distinct toxicity studies have been performed on laboratory cultured algae. The algae tested have included greens as well as blue-greens, *Chlorella* and *Scenedesmus* among the former, and *Prototheca, Anabaena, Oscillatoria, Coelosphaerium, Microcystis,* and *Aphanizomenon* among the others.

TABLE III. EXPERIMENTS WITH TOXIC UNIALGAL CULTURES
Part 1. Mass Cultures Developed Primarily as Water-Denying Agents
Procedure: intraperitoneal injection unless otherwise stated.
Animal subjects: Mice, unless otherwise stated.

1951. Olson (U.S.A.). Algae: *Microcystis aeruginosa*. Unialgal culture suspension. Low toxicity varying greatly from one harvest to the next.

1955. McIvor and Grant (Canada). Algae: *Anabaena cylindrica*. Old unialgal culture. 60% mortality.

_____. _____. Double dose of above specimen. 100% mortality.

_____. _____. Old unialgal culture incubated 27 hours. 20% mortality.

_____. _____. Old unialgal culture incubated 48 hours. 60% mortality.

_____. _____. Old unialgal culture incubated 190 hours. No mortality.

1958. Chaput and Grant (Canada). Algae: *Anabaena variables*. Measured amounts of unincubated algal culture slurry. No toxicity.

_____. _____. Measured amounts of algal culture slurry incubated at 37°C. Toxic only after 18–24 hours incubation, at dosages greater than 200 mg/kg.

_____. Algae: *Anabaena sp*. Measured amounts of unincubated algal culture slurry. No toxicity.

_____. _____. Measured amounts of algal culture slurry incubated at 37°C. Toxic only after 18–24 hours incubation, at dosages greater than 200 mg/kg.

_____. Algae: *Anabaena cylindrica*. 120 mg/kg unincubated 23-day-old unialgal culture slurry. No mortality in 24 hours.

_____. _____. 120 mg/kg 23-day-old unialgal culture slurry incubated 17 hours. 60% mortality in 24 hours.

_____. _____. 120 mg/kg 23-day-old unialgal culture slurry incubated 24 hours. 100% mortality in 24 hours.

_____. _____. 120 mg/kg 23-day-old unialgal culture slurry incubated 41 hours. 100% mortality in 24 hours.

_____. _____. 120 mg/kg 23-day-old unialgal culture slurry incubated 48 hours. 100% mortality in 24 hours.

_____. Algae: *Anabaena catenula*. 150 mg/kg Unincubated 23-day-old unialgal culture slurry. No mortality in 24 hours.

_____. _____. 150 mg/kg 23-day-old unialgal culture slurry incubated 24 hours. 100% mortality in 24 hours.

_____. _____. 150 mg/kg 23-day-old unialgal culture slurry incubated 31 hours. 100% mortality in 24 hours.

_____. Algae: *Anacystis montana*. 18 mg/kg unincubated unialgal culture slurry. No deaths.

_____. _____. 36 mg/kg unincubated unialgal culture slurry. No deaths.

_____. _____. 72 mg/kg unincubated unialgal culture slurry. No deaths.

_____. _____. 18 mg/kg unialgal culture slurry incubated 24 hours at 37°C. None died.

_____. _____. 36 mg/kg unialgal culture slurry incubated 24 hours at 37°C. 4 out of 5 died.

_____. _____. 72 mg/kg unialgal culture slurry incubated 24 hours at 37°C. All 5 died.

_____. Algae: *Microcystis aeruginosa*. 23 mg/kg unincubated unialgal culture slurry. No deaths.

_____. _____. 42 mg/kg unincubated unialgal culture slurry. No deaths.

_____. _____. 78 mg/kg unincubated unialgal culture slurry. No deaths.

TABLE III. (Continued)

————. ————. 24 mg/kg unialgal culture slurry incubated 24 hours at 37°C. 1 out of 3 died.

————. ————. 42 mg/kg unialgal culture slurry incubated 24 hours at 37°C. 1 out of 3 died.

————. ————. 84 mg/kg unialgal culture slurry incubated 24 hours at 37°C. 2 out of 3 died.

1957. Thomson, Laing and Grant (Canada). **Algae:** *Nostoc* sp. 3-day culture of bacterial contaminant "1" associated with blue-green unialgal culture. No deaths.

————. **Algae:** *Nostoc ellipsosporum.* 3-day culture of bacterial contaminant "2." No deaths.

————. ————. 3-day culture of bacterial contaminant "3." 2 out of 5 died.

————. **Algae:** *Anacystis montana.* 3-day culture of bacterial contaminant "4." All 5 died.

————. ————. 3-day culture of bacterial contaminant "5." All 5 died.

————. **Algae:** *Microcystis aeruginosa.* 3-day culture of bacterial contaminant "6." All 5 died.

————. ————. 3-day culture of bacterial contaminant "7." All 5 died.

————. ————. 3-day culture of bacterial contaminant "8." All 5 died.

————. ————. Doses as high as 480 mg/kg of unialgal culture specimen freed completely of bacteria. Nontoxic.

1958. Thomson (Canada). **Algae:** *Anacystis montana.* 30 mg/kg unincubated bacteria-contaminated unialgal culture. No mortality.

————. ————. 30 mg/kg bacteria-contaminated unialgal culture incubated 16 hours. 40% mortality.

————. ————. 120 mg/kg unincubated bacteria-contaminated unialgal culture. 20% mortality.

————. ————. 120 mg/kg bacteria-contaminated unialgal culture incubated 16 hours. 80% mortality.

————. ————. 480 mg/kg unincubated bacteria-contaminated unialgal culture. 100% mortality.

————. ————. 480 mg/kg bacteria-contaminated unialgal culture incubated 16 hours. 100% mortality.

————. ————. 30 mg/kg unincubated bacteria-free unialgal culture. No mortality.

————. ————. 30 mg/kg bacteria-free unialgal culture incubated 16 hours. No mortality.

————. ————. 120 mg/kg unincubated bacteria-free unialgal culture. No mortality.

————. ————. 120 mg/kg mice bacteria-free unialgal culture incubated 16 hours. No mortality.

————. ————. 480 mg/kg unincubated bacteria-free unialgal culture. No mortality.

————. ————. 480 mg/kg bacteria-free unialgal culture incubated 16 hours. No mortality.

————. ————. 30 mg/kg unincubated bacterial contaminant of unialgal culture. 40% mortality.

————. ————. 30 mg/kg bacterial contaminant of unialgal culture incubated 16 hours. 60% mortality.

_____. _____. 120 mg/kg unincubated bacterial contaminant of unialgal culture. 80% mortality.

_____. _____. 120 mg/kg bacterial contaminant of unialgal culture incubated 16 hours. 90% mortality.

_____. _____. 480 mg/kg unincubated bacterial contaminant of unialgal culture. 100% mortality.

_____. _____. 480 mg/kg bacterial contaminant of unialgal culture incubated 16 hours. 100% mortality.

_____. _____. A series of sublethal doses of bacterial contaminant, then challenged with the bacteria and later with contaminated algae. 70% recovered from lethal doses of the bacterial toxin. Immunity of approximately the same order protected the animals against lethal doses of the original toxic algae.

_____. Algae: 25 samples of algae collected from local ponds and cultured in the laboratory. Toxic bacterial species isolated from the algal cultures. Effect was that of a "slow acting" neurotoxin: partial paralysis of the hind legs and spasmodic movements, with death in not less than 4 hours.

1955, 1956, 1958. Hughes, Gorham and Zehnder (Canada). Algae: *Microcystis aeruginosa* (*Anacystis cyanea*). 550 mg/kg freshly harvested cells from 40-day culture. All sickened and died without convulsion in 24–52 hours.

_____. _____. 550 mg/kg freshly harvested cells from 40-day culture, after incubation for 11 or 23 hours. Pallor and convulsions followed by death of all mice in 30–60 minutes.

_____. _____. 7 mg/kg of filtrate of harvested cells from 40-day culture. Nontoxic.

_____. _____. 40 mg/kg unincubated 3-day culture "A" cells stored 15 hours at 5°C. Maximal survival time 24–48 hours. Slow death symptoms.

_____. _____. 80 mg/kg of material, as above. Maximal survival time 24–48 hours. Slow death symptoms.

_____. _____. 160 mg/kg of material, as above. Maximal survival time 24–48 hours. Slow death symptoms.

_____. _____. 320 mg/kg of material, as above. Maximal survival time 24–48 hours. Slow death symptoms. LD 100.

_____. _____. 480 mg/kg of material, as above. Maximal survival time 24–48 hours. Slow death symptoms.

_____. _____. 40 mg/kg 3-day culture "A" cells incubated 15 hrs. Maximal survival time 2.3 hrs. Fast death symptoms.

_____. _____. 80 mg/kg of material, as above. Maximal survival time 2.3 hrs. Fast death symptoms. LD 100.

_____. _____. 160 mg/kg of material, as above. Maximal survival time 2.3 hrs. Fast death symptoms.

_____. _____. 320 mg/kg of material, as above. Maximal survival time 2.3 hrs. Fast death symptoms.

_____. _____. 480 mg/kg of material, as above. Maximal survival time 2.3 hrs. Fast death symptoms.

_____. _____. 40 mg/kg unincubated 3-day culture "B" cells, stored 15 hours at 5°C. Maximal survival time 3.3 hrs. Fast deaths.

_____. _____. 80 mg/kg of material, as above. Maximal survival time 3.3 hrs. Fast deaths.

_____. _____. 160 mg/kg of material, as above. Maximal survival time 3.3 hrs. Fast deaths.

TABLE III. (Continued)

———. ———. 320 mg/kg of material, as above. Maximal survival time 3.3 hrs. Slow death symptoms.

———. ———. 480 mg/kg of material, as above. Maximal survival time 3.3 hrs. Fast deaths. LD 100.

———. ———. 40 mg/kg 3-day culture "A" cells incubated 15 hrs. Maximal survival time 2.4 hrs. Fast deaths.

———. ———. 80 mg/kg of material, as above. Maximal survival time 2.4 hrs. Fast deaths.

———. ———. 160 mg/kg of material, as above. Maximal survival time 2.4 hrs. Fast deaths. LD 100.

———. ———. 320 mg/kg of material, as above. Maximal survival time 2.4 hrs. Fast deaths.

———. ———. 480 mg/kg of material, as above. Maximal survival time 2.4 hrs. Fast deaths.

———. ———. 240 mg/kg extract of culture filtrate "A." Nontoxic.

———. ———. 160 mg/kg extract of culture filtrate "B." Produced fast deaths.

———. Algae: *Microcystis aeruginosa* NRC–1. 20 mg/kg of freshly harvested laboratory cultured cells. Slow death symptoms.

———. ———. 40 mg/kg of material, as above. Slow-death symptoms.

———. ———. 80 mg/kg of material, as above. Slow-death symptoms.

———. ———. 160 mg/kg of material, as above. Some slow deaths. 50% mortality. Remainder slow death symptoms.

———. ———. 320 mg/kg of material, as above. Fast deaths. 75% mortality.

———. ———. 20 mg/kg of freshly harvested laboratory cultured cells subjected to incubation 21 hours. Fast deaths.

———. ———. 40 mg/kg of material, as above. Fast deaths.

———. ———. 80 mg/kg of material, as above. Fast deaths. LD 100.

———. ———. 160 mg/kg of material, as above. Fast deaths.

———. ———. 320 mg/kg of material, as above. Fast deaths.

———. ———. 20 mg/kg of freshly harvested laboratory cultured cells subjected to freezing. Fast deaths.

———. ———. 40 mg/kg of material, as above. Fast deaths.

———. ———. 80 mg/kg of material, as above. Fast deaths. LD 100.

———. ———. 160 mg/kg of material, as above. Fast deaths.

———. ———. 320 mg/kg of material, as above. Fast deaths.

———. ———. 20 mg/kg of freshly harvested cultured cells, first incubated and then treated by freezing. Fast deaths.

———. ———. 40 mg/kg of material, as above. Fast deaths.

———. ———. 80 mg/kg of material, as above. Fast deaths. LD 100.

———. ———. 160 mg/kg of material, as above. Fast deaths.

———. ———. 320 mg/kg of material, as above. Fast deaths.

———. ———. 20 mg/kg of freshly harvested cultured cells first treated by freezing and then incubated. Fast deaths.

———. ———. 40 mg/kg of material, as above. Fast deaths.

———. ———. 80 mg/kg of material, as above. Fast deaths. LD 100.

———. ———. 160 mg/kg of material, as above. Fast deaths.

———. ———. 320 mg/kg of material, as above. Fast deaths.

———. ———. Culture solution. Nontoxic.

————. ————. Culture filtrate. Nontoxic.

————. ————. 20 mg/kg control cells. No deaths.

————. ————. 40 mg/kg control cells. No deaths.

————. ————. 80 mg/kg control cells. No deaths.

————. ————. 160 mg/kg control cells. No deaths. Slow-death symptoms.

————. ————. 320 mg/kg control cells. No deaths. Slow-death symptoms.

————. ————. 20 mg/kg of cells incubated 18 hours. Fast deaths.

————. ————. 40 mg/kg of material, as above. Fast deaths.

————. ————. 80 mg/kg of material, as above. Fast deaths.

————. ————. 160 mg/kg of material, as above. Fast deaths. LD 100.

————. ————. 320 mg/kg of material, as above. Fast deaths.

————. ————. 20 mg/kg of 75% disintegrated cells. Fast deaths.

————. ————. 40 mg/kg of material, as above. Fast deaths.

————. ————. 80 mg/kg of material, as above. Fast deaths.

————. ————. 160 mg/kg of material, as above. Fast deaths. LD 100.

————. ————. 320 mg/kg of material, as above. Fast deaths.

————. ————. 20 mg/kg of cells first incubated and then disintegrated. Fast deaths.

————. ————. 40 mg/kg of material, as above. Fast deaths.

————. ————. 80 mg/kg of material, as above. Fast deaths.

————. ————. 160 mg/kg of material, as above. Fast deaths. LD 100.

————. ————. 320 mg/kg of material, as above. Fast deaths.

————. ————. 20 mg/kg of cells first disintegrated and then incubated. Fast deaths.

————. ————. 40 mg/kg of material, as above. Fast deaths.

————. ————. 80 mg/kg of material, as above. Fast deaths.

————. ————. 160 mg/kg of material, as above. Fast deaths. LD 100.

————. ————. 320 mg/kg of material, as above. Fast deaths.

————. ————. Extracts of completely lysed, 20–31-day-old cultures. Produced fast deaths.

————. ————. Daily samples taken for growth and toxicity determinations to find out at what developmental stage the cells of an actively growing culture would reach maximum toxicity and also the degree of toxicity. LD 100 of the cells reached a minimum on the 4th and 5th days: thereafter it increased as the culture began to foam until, by the 14th day, most of the toxin had disappeared.

————. ————. Another culture, where daily samples were taken as above; cell counts were also made and extracts of the culture filtrate were prepared and tested for toxicity. LD 100 of the cells did not change during the first 5 days. It decreased on the 6th day and remained at the same level on the 7th or final day. The cell count increased steadily during the first 5 days and lowered on the last 2 days, indicative of lysis.

————. ————. Fast death factor was detected in the culture filtrate on and after the 3rd day, indicating that leakage and/or lysis was occurring even in the early stages of growth.

1959. Bishop, Anet and Gorham (Canada). Algae: *Microcystis aeruginosa* NRC–1. To bioassay toxin to test efficacy of alcohol extraction from freeze-dried unialgal culture. 80–85% toxin removal by alcohol extraction.

————. ————. To bioassay dialyzate of alcohol extract. 50% of total toxicity recovered in 4 days; 80% after 8 days.

————. ————. To bioassay toxin to test efficacy of sodium salt extraction

TABLE III. (Continued)

procedure compared to alcohol extraction. Same symptoms of toxicity as those injected with aqueous suspensions of lyophilized cells prior to extraction.

_____. _____. Distillates of algal toxin to determine volatility. Nontoxic.

_____. _____. For bioassay to determine behavior of algal toxin toward basic ion-exchange resins. Showed complete recovery of toxin.

_____. _____. To determine behavior of algal toxin toward acidic ion-exchange resins. No recovery of toxin.

_____. _____. To test solubility properties for solvents miscible in water and to test solubility properties for solvents immiscible in water. The toxin was found to be soluble in methanol, ethanol, n-butanol and, as its sodium salt, in water. It was insoluble in ether, petroleum ether, benzene, chloroform, carbon tetrachloride, ethyl acetate, carbon disulphide, and, as the free-acid, in water. Low solubility of the toxin was observed in acetone and 2-butanone.

_____. _____. To test for toxin stability towards different solvents and towards aqueous solutions at various pH levels. Toxin was stable towards all solvents tested except 2-butanone in which 95% of the toxicity was lost after 5 days. It was stable in all buffers up to and including that at pH 10. It was destroyed at higher pH levels. No loss after 3 or 8 hours, 25–50% loss after 24 hours, and 75–100% loss after 50 hours.

_____. _____. For bioassay in countercurrent distribution studies. The solubility properties of the 2 components, (A) [sodium salt of toxin] and (B) [free-acid form of toxin], could be reversed by acidification or neutralization. The countercurrent distribution was therefore separating only the salt form (component A) from the free-acid form (component B) of the toxin, both of which were extracted from the algae cells by 95% ethanol. Components A and B each had the same LD_{100} (2–3 mg/kg) as the material in the dialyzate from procedure (b) showing that no purification of the toxin was being obtained by countercurrent distribution.

_____. _____. Toxin eluted after paper chromatography was performed to determine a typical chromatogram. Toxin was found in the area from R_f 0.39 to R_f 0.70 and included the fastest moving yellow band.

_____. _____. For bioassay of eluted sections of chromatograms in attempt to separate the toxin from its pigments. Toxin was contained in an area extending from R_f 0.63 to R_f 0.87 and was completely separated from the yellow pigments.

_____. _____. For bioassay to determine behavior of proteolytic enzymes, pepsin, papain, trypsin, chymotrypsin, carboxypeptidase, polidase, and takadiastase. None of the enzymes caused any loss of toxicity.

_____. _____. For bioassay of toxin subjected to partial acid hydrolysis. Hydrolysis caused a loss of 50% of toxicity in 24 hours, 75% in 48 hours, and 100% in 70 hours.

_____. _____. For bioassay of eluates of the toxin subjected to paper electrophoresis. At pH values of 2.2 to 5.0 acetic acid.

_____. _____. For bioassay of eluates of peptides separated from the algae by paper electrophoresis. Of 5 peptides in the algae, only peptide #2 was toxic.

_____. _____. For bioassay of the toxic peptide #2 to determine LD_{50}. Analysis of the resulting probit curve gave $LD_{50} = 0.593–0116$ ml for a 15-g mouse. On a weight basis this gave $LD_{50} = 0.466–0.013$ mg/kg body weight.

1960. Gorham (Canada). **Algae:** *Anabaena.* 20–640 mg/kg of disintegrated, lyophilized culture cells. No deaths.

_____. _____. 80–120 mg/kg fresh culture cells. No deaths.

_____. **Algae:** *Aphanizomenon.* 20–640 mg/kg of disintegrated, lyophilized culture cells. Produced slow deaths.

_____. **Algae:** *Coelosphaerium.* 20–640 mg/kg of disintegrated, lyophilized culture cells. Produced slow deaths.

_____. **Algae:** *Gloeotrichia.* 20–640 mg/kg of disintegrated, lyophilized culture cells. No deaths.

_____. **Algae:** *Microcystis.* 20–1280 mg/kg of disintegrated, lyophilized culture cells. Of 19 cultures, 8 produced fast deaths, 6 slow deaths, and 5 no toxicity.

_____. **Algae:** *Anacystis.* 20–1280 mg/kg of disintegrated, lyophilized culture cells. Of 11 cultures, 6 produced slow deaths and 5 no toxicity.

_____. **Algae:** *Nodularia.* 20–640 mg/kg of disintegrated, lyophilized culture cells. No deaths.

_____. **Algae:** *Scenedesmus.* 80–120 mg/kg fresh culture cells. No deaths.

_____. **Algae:** *Chlorella.* 20–640 mg/kg of disintegrated, lyophilized culture cells.

_____. 80–120 mg/kg fresh culture cells.

1960. Harris and Gorham (Canada). **Algae:** *Microcystis aeruginosa* NRC–1. Algae grown under different temperature conditions. Best yields of algae occurred at 28–32.5°C, but maximum production of fast death factor occurred at 25°C.

1960. Simpson and Gorham; Gorham (Canada). **Algae:** *Microcystis aeruginosa* NRC–1. Unialgal cultures treated with ultraviolet radiation, and with a variety of antiseptics, antibiotics and bacteriostatic agents given singly, in combination, or in succession (in order to decrease or eliminate bacteria). In a lysed culture, the algae-rich fraction contained fast death factor and the bacteria-rich fraction contained only slow death factor.

_____. _____. Bacterial contaminants of unialgal cultures. Produced a pronounced inflammation of the intestinal and peritoneal lining.

_____. _____. Double strength bacterial contaminants of unialgal cultures. No effect.

_____. _____. Incubated bacterial contaminants of unialgal cultures. A different type of fast death was observed.

1960. Konst, McKercher, Gorham, Robertson, and Howe; Gorham (Canada). **Algae:** *Microcystis aeruginosa.* NRC–1. Oral administration of lyophilized unialgal culture cells to fasted animals. Mice, guinea pigs, rabbits, chicken, sheep, calves. The largest animals survived 9 to 18 hours. Convulsions frequently observed. Autopsy findings of hyperemia of liver, indicative of congestion and hemorrhage, was the most characteristic symptom.

_____. _____. Oral administration of lyophilized unialgal culture cells to fasted waterfowl. Domestic duck. Nontoxic.

1961. Gorham, Anet, Bishop, Hammer, Harris, Hughes, Konst, Machin, McBride, McKercher, McLachlan, Simpson, Wright, and Zehnder (Canada). **Algae:** *Microcystis aeruginosa* NRC–1. Lyophilized cells of samples sent to Steyn in South Africa. Laboratory animals. Toxic effects were undistinguishable from that observed previously with *Microcystis toxica* in the Transvaal.

_____. _____. **Algae:** *Anabaena flos-aquae* (7 strains). Lyophilized cells and culture filtrates in doses ranging from 40 to 640 mg/kg body weight. 5 strains

TABLE III. (Continued)

produced very fast deaths (1–10 min.); 2 strains produced no deaths or slow deaths (4–48 hrs).

———. ———. Algae: *Microcystis aeruginosa* (19 strains). In doses ranging from 40 to 640 mg/kg body weight. 8 strains produced fast deaths (1–2 hrs); 11 strains produced no deaths or slow deaths (4–48 hrs.).

TABLE III. EXPERIMENTS WITH TOXIC UNIALGAL CULTURES
Part 2. Algae Cultured as Food Source

1949. Fisher and Burlew (U.S.A.). Algae: *Chlorella pyrenoidosa*. Fed a diet containing 35% dried algae. Animals: Rats. Weight increase first two weeks was half that of control group on regular diet; the remaining three weeks, rate of weight increase was only 1/3 as great as control group. One algae-fed rat died during tests.

1951. Henry [in Geoghegan] (England) [in Burlew]. Algae: *Chlorella vulgaris*. Fed a diet containing 17% freeze-dried algae. On the basis of protein efficiency, algae were slightly superior to dried brewer's yeast but inferior to dried skim milk.

1952. Combs (U.S.A.). Algae: *Chlorella pyrenoidosa*. Chicks. Including 5% dried algae. Impacted beak condition.

———. ———. Including 5% dried algae. Chicks. Impacted beak condition.

———. ———. Including 10% dried algae. Chicks. The resultant growth-depressing action was thought to be due to the hygroscopic nature of the algae causing impacted beaks.

———. ———. Including 20% dried algae. Chicks. Developed impacted beaks and beak deformities.

1957. Fink and Herold (Germany). Algae: *Scenedesmus obliquus*. Feeding experiments with dried algae. Rats. No toxic effect.

1958. Fink and Herold (Germany). Algae: *Scenedesmus obliquus*. With fresh autumn unialgal culture for 90 days. Rats. Diet poorly taken; animals showed steady weight loss, roughness of the fur, scabs at the snout, tail, and limbs. Three of the 6 animals died: on histologic examination showed hepatic necrosis; life span of animals with liver injury was 68 days.

———. ———. With dried autumn unialgal culture for 120 days. Rats. Good nutritional value.

———. ———. After 90 days of feeding of fresh algae, surviving rats were fed with the previously tested dried algal material. The animals once again gained weight, comparable to initial dry-algal feeding study. Roughness of the fur, and scabs at the snout, tail, and limbs disappeared after continued feeding with dried algae.

———. ———. Feeding experiments with fresh spring unialgal culture for 120 days. Rats. Did not eat more than in fall. Weight losses were greater and fatalities occurred earlier. All 6 died; 3 had liver damage; average duration of life of animals with liver damage was 36 days.

———. ———. Feeding experiments with dried algal material of same quantities as in experiment with fresh algae, to rule out possibility that weight loss could be due to relatively small intake of food. Compared with earlier dried-algal feeding experiments, a smaller but steady weight gain within same period was observed, showing that small amounts of food cannot be responsible

for the great losses of weight and for the fatalities in the animals fed with
diets of fresh algal substance.

1958. Hayami and Shino (Japan). **Algae:** *Chlorella.* Control diet of 14% casein
for 35 days. Rats. Some animals died within 2 to 3 weeks. Good weight increase, rate of nitrogen retention and absorption.

_____. _____. Containing 19% decolorized algae for 35 days. Rats. Fair
weight increase, rate of nitrogen retention and absorption.

_____. _____. Containing 25% ordinary dry algae for 35 days. Rats. Some
animals died within 2 to 3 weeks. Poor weight increase, rate of nitrogen retention and absorption.

1961. Cook and Lau (U.S.A.). **Algae:** *Chlorella Scenedesmus.* Fed sewage-
grown algae in cooked and dried form. Rats. Lowering of protein efficiency
ratio.

1962. Bowman, Middlebrook and McDaniel (U.S.A.). Mice. **Algae:** *Chlorella
pyrenoidosa.* Dried algae for 15 days. Weight loss.

_____. _____. **Algae:** *Anacystis nidulans.* Dried algae for 15 days. Weight
loss.

1963. Sunde and Madiedo (U.S.A.). **Algae:** Algae. Dried algae. Hens. Laid
eggs with darker egg yolks.

1956. The Administration Agency for Science and Technics (Japan). **Algae:**
Chlorella. Fed dessicated, powdered undecolorized, uncooked algae. Provoked diarrhea.

1960. Arakawa, Tsurumi, Murakami, Hoshino and Nagashimu (Japan). **Algae:**
Chlorella. Basic feed mixed with 50% powdered algae. 60% (12 out of 20)
developed diarrhea and died following weight loss. Remainder showed marked
weight loss.

_____. _____. **Algae:** *Chlorella.* Double rations of above feed for three-week
period. 10% mortality. All showed weight loss as compared to controls.

_____. _____. Basic feed mixed with 20% powdered algae for 25 days. 8 out of
22 mice developed diarrhea and died following weight loss. The remainder
weighed less than controls.

_____. _____. Basic feed mixed with 10% powdered algae for 54 days. No
deaths.

1960. Arakawa, Tsurumi, Murakami, Muto, Hoshino and Yagi (Japan). **Algae:**
Chlorella. Natural, undecolorized algae-supplemented feed mixture for a year.
Initial diarrhea; decreased egg-laying; eggs weighed less; eggs are bluish
when seen through light; when boiled, they are yellower than normal; hens'
beaks, legs, and feathers became yellowish.

The animals tested were a monkey, kittens, guinea pigs, rabbits,
chickens, sheep, calves, and mice. Modes of administration included introduction into rectum and colon, oral feeding, and intraperitoneal injection. In practically all respects, the clinical and autopsy findings paralleled those seen on administration of naturally occurring toxic blooms.

Of added particular interest are some reports on green algae, generally
thought to be nontoxic and widely considered as potential large-scale food
sources. Herold and Fink (1958), in Germany, fed *Scenedesmus* to mice,
and the animals developed hepatic necrosis. In Japan, Arakawa and his

colleagues (1960) observed diarrhea, weight loss, and decreased egg-laying in hens fed either decolorized or undecolorized *Chlorella*. When they fed *Chlorella* to mice, many developed diarrhea and died.

Lubitz, working with the General Dynamics Electric Boat Division and the aerospace Biochemical Laboratory (1962), fed 92 per cent *Chlorella* to rats with resultant histopathologic abnormalities in the pancreas, salivary glands, kidney, and lens of the eye.

Fish Intoxications Due to Algae

Fish, like land animals and birds, have also been victims of algal poisoning. As might be expected, fish deaths have been reported only when occurring *en masse*. They have been noted in all types of water—fresh, brackish, and marine. It is frustrating to note that fish kills are routinely attributed to botulism; to changes in water temperature; to oxygen lack from blocking of gills by sand or from blanketing of the water surface by algae; to detonation of underwater mines; and to contamination of the water by insecticides and industrial pollutants. The role of algal toxins has been generally more unknown than ignored.

Among the first reports of freshwater incidents are those by Cohn in 1883, and Kafka in 1892; in both cases the implicated organism was *Anabaena*. Strodtmann in 1898 mentioned only "waterbloom." Somewhat more informative are the 1913 episode reported by Seydel in Germany, and the 1914 one by Naday in Hungary. Naday attributed the fish deaths to either direct algal poisoning or anoxia from the thick waterbloom blanket. Prescott, after the Iowa incidents, suggested that bacterial action upon disintegrating algae might use up oxygen and further contribute to the anoxia of fish and small aquatic animals. Similar ideas were expressed by Mackenthun, *et al.*, concerning thousands of dyspneic and dying carp exposed to *Aphanizomenon*. Impressive numbers of freshwater fish deaths have also been documented by Berlin, Steyn, Shilo, Braginskii, Davidson, Kim, Mikhailov, and Teplyi in such diverse locales as Iowa, Texas, Saskatchewan, Israel, Russia, Germany, and South Africa. (See Table IV.)

As expected, experimental studies were made to elucidate the mechanisms of algal noxiousness, mostly with algae taken directly from the areas of fish kills. In evaluating these experiments, it is important to remember that, perforce, they were not optimally timed, since they were undertaken only *after* fish deaths, probably *after* peaks of algal toxicity.

Prescott in 1933 placed several species of fish into tanks containing varying amounts of decaying *Aphanizomenon*. Within an hour there occurred

TABLE IV. FISH INTOXICATIONS DUE TO ALGAE—FRESHWATER
Part 1. Fish Kills Associated with Toxic Algae

1880. Lake near Zirke, Posen, west-central Poland, near the Wartha River (Cohn, 1883) in Lampert 1899. Algae: *Anabaena circinalis*. Victims: fish. Manifestations of Toxicity: death.

1892. Komarov pond, Austro-Hungary (Kafka, 1892). Algae: *Anabaena* and *Oscillaria*. Fish. Death.

1898. North German Lakes (Strodtmann, 1898). Algae: *Waterbloom*. Fish. Death.

1913. Kleinsee, near Pinnow, Germany (Seydel, 1913). Algae: *Oscillaria*, *Anabaena*, and *Bolycystis*. Carp, pike, perch, catfish, bream, chub, roach. Death.

1914. Lakes in Hungary (Naday, 1914). Algae: *Anabaena circinalis* and *Clathrocystis circinalis*. Fish. Death.

1931–1933. East Okoboji and Storm Lakes, Iowa, U.S.A. (Prescott, 1933, 1939, 1950). Algae: *Aphanizomenon flos-aquae*. Hundreds of thousands of fish: perch, crappie, sunfish, minnows and blue-gills. Death.

1940–1942. Lake Ymsen, Mariestad, Skaraborg, Sweden (Berlin, 1948). Algae: *Anabaena*. Fish. Death.

1940–1943. Vaaldam, Transvaal, Union of South Africa (Steyn, 194). Algae: *Microcystis toxica* and *Microcystis flos-aquae*. Fish. Death.

1946. Yahara River, below Lake Kegonsa, Wisconsin, U.S.A. (Mackenthum, Herman, and Bartsch, 1948). Algae: *Aphanizomenon flos-aquae*. Thousands of fish, mainly carp; also northern pike, yellow pike, perch, black crappies, blue-gills, suckers, black bullheads, buffalo, hog suckers, and eels. The fish, crowded close to shore, were breathing at the surface and showed marked distress before expiring.

1948. Storm Lake, Iowa, U.S.A. (Rose, 194 ; Prescott 19). Algae: "*blue-green algae*." Hundreds of thousands of fish. Death.

1951. Tel Joseph and Beth Hashita Ponds, Israel (Shilo [Shelubsky], 1951). Algae: *Microcystis aeruginosa* and *Microcystis* sp. Carp, other fish. Untoward effect on the fish population and occasionally with heavy mortality.

1955. Ukraine, USSR (Braginskii, 1955). Algae: *Microcystis* and *Aphanizomenon flos-aquae*. Fish. Harmful.

1956–1958. Stock pond, Waco, Texas, U.S.A. (Davidson, 195). Algae: *Nostoc rivulare*. Fish. Death.

1956–1959. Damchik sector of the Astrakhan Nature Reserve, central and eastern parts of the Volga delta, and Volga River upstream between Astrakhan and Saratov, and in the Akhtuba River, USSR (Kun, 1960; Astrakhova, Kun, and Teplyi, 1960; Kun, Teplyi and Astrakhova, 1961; Mikhailov and Teplyi, 1961). Algae: *Microcystis aeruginosa*. Carp (sazan), catfish, sheat fish, roach, bream. Restlessness, increased activity, turning frequently on side, laboured respirations, death.

1959. Echo Lake, Regina, Saskatchewan, Canada (Dillenberg and Dehnel, 1959; Forham, 1960). Algae: *Microcystis* sp., *Anabaena* sp., and *Coelosphaerium* sp. Fish. Death.

Part 2. Experiments With Toxic Algae From Areas of Fish Kills

1933. Prescott (U.S.A.). Algae: *Aphanizomenon flos-aquae*. Subject: Various species of fish. Procedure: Placing of fish in tank containing varying amounts

TABLE IV. (Continued)

of decaying algae. **Results**: Distress, disorientation and incoordination within the hour. Death in $1\frac{1}{2}$ to 6 hours without evidence of oxygen want.

1945. Mullor (Argentina). **Algae**: *Anabaena venenosa*. Frogs, fish. Immersion in, and injection of, resuspended dried lagoon algae on cold-blooded animals. Those injected died within 5 to 12 minutes with typical symptoms. Simple immersion caused no toxicity.

1948. Mackenthum, Herman and Bartsch (U.S.A.). **Algae**: *Aphanizomenon flos-aquae*. Perch, crappies. Immersion in toxic river water algae sample. All dead in 30 hours.

———. **Algae**: *Aphanizomenon flos-aquae*. Perch, crappies, suckers. Immersion in toxic river water algae sample obtained one week later, 14 miles downstream. Loss of equilibrium by third day, deaths commencing on fifth day. All dead by eighth day.

1950. Shelubsky [Shilo] (Israel). **Algae**: *Microcystis aeruginosa*. Frogs, carp. Living lake algae injected subcutaneously and intraperitoneally. Carp died in 36 to 96 hours; frogs, death time unstated.

———. **Algae**: *Microcystis* sp. Frogs, carp. Living lake algae injected subcutaneously and intraperitoneally. Same as above.

1955. Braginskii (USSR). **Algae**: *Microcystis*. Daphnia, Cyclops, other crustaceans. Immersion in concentrated algae pond water preparations. Instant death of zooplankton.

———. **Algae**: *Microcystis*. Daphnia, Cyclops, other crustaceans. Immersion in diluted filtrates. Death also occurred rapidly: in dilution of 1 : 2 and 1 : 4 some crustaceans were dead in 10–15 minutes and all were dead in 30–60 minutes. [The oxygen content of the medium was sufficiently high.]

———. **Algae**: *Aphanizomenon flos-aquae*. Daphnia, Cyclops, other crustaceans. Immersion in concentrated algae pond water preparations. The crustaceans showed distress symptoms in 15–30 minutes. Complete death followed in a few hours.

———. **Algae**: *Aphanizomenon flos-aquae*. Daphnia, Cyclops, other crustaceans. Immersion in diluted preparations. No harmful effects.

1961. Kun, Teplyi, and Astakhova (USSR). **Algae**: *Aphanizomenon flos-aquae*, *Microcystis aeruginosa*, and *Anabaena flos-aquae*. Healthy carp imported from the Ural River. Intraperitoneal injection of sterile 1-week-old infusion of algae obtained from water in the Stalingrad water reservoir. Restless, displayed increased activity; then alternately overactive and sluggish; progressed to erratic behavior, frequently turning on the side, laboured respirations, convulsions and death. On the 3rd day after intraperitoneal injections, inflamed patches appeared on the skin, hemorrhage occurred in the skin and the anal mucosa became inflamed. Dissection revealed heavy hemorrhage in the parenchymatous tissue of the kidneys, petechial hemorrhage in the parenchyma of the liver and the mucosa and the anterior part of the intestine. The liver, kidneys, heart, and spleen were flabby and pale-colored. The walls of the intestines were withered, sheathing pale, and the gastric cavity bloated with gases. The tissues of the gonads were inflamed and hemorrhages had occurred in the diencephalon and mesencephalon. The gills were dark brown, but no destruction of tissue was discovered in macroscopic examinations.

———. **Algae**: *Microcystis aeruginosa*, *Aphanizomenon flos-aquae*, and *Anabaena flos-aquae*. Healthy carp imported from the Ural River. Intraperitoneal injection of sterile 1-week-old infusion of algae from the Kutum River. Same symptoms as above. The pathological changes were similar to those in the first group, but the damage to the internal organs was greater. For example, copious fat deposits were found under the outer membranes of the heart, the kidney capsule, and in the tissue of the liver. Infarct of the myocardium was observed, and also petechial hemorrhage in the mucosa of the intermediate part of the intestine and the tissue of the gonads; isolated patches of dead tissue were found in the gills and a hemorrhage had occurred in every gill arch. The pathological changes in the organs and tissues described above are usual in poisoning. Beyond doubt, the disease and death of carp in the first two groups were caused by heavy poisoning resulting from the intraperitoneally introduced infusion of blue-green algae.

_____. Algae: *Aphanizomenon flos-aquae*, *Microcystis aeruginosa*, and *Anabaena flos-aquae*. Carp. Oral feeding a non-sterile infusion of algae from the Stalingrad water reservoir. Death was delayed several days longer than above. Same symptoms as above. The lesion of the skin was less marked and appeared somewhat later, on the sixth day. The examination revealed a slight inflammation of skin patches, ulceration of the base of the pectoral fin, and inflammation of the anal and caudal fins. A general depigmentation of the skin, a softening of isolated patches of the skin, and an inflammation of the mucosa of the anus occured by the time of death in both carp. Dissection revealed the same pathological changes as in the organs of the fish of groups I and II. The cause of death of these fish was therefore the same as that of the fish of groups I and II.

_____. Algae: *Microcystis aeruginosa* and *Aphanizomenon flos-aquae*. Carp. Intraperitoneal injection of live ground up algal suspension to determine whether the fish deaths were caused by toxic products of protein decomposition or the toxin from blue-green algae. For the first day the fish behaved normally. On the second day their activity decreased and the coordination of movements was impaired. One fish died at the end of the second day. The second died at the beginning of the third day. Before death, hemorrhages, skin inflammation processes and a general depigmentation was observed. Gills acquired a brown shade. Dissection revealed petechial hemorrhages in the liver, kidneys, and spleen. Moreover, a fatty degeneration had occurred in the liver, an ulceration in the mucuous membrane of the intestine, a fatty deposition in the pericardial sac, as well as inflammation processes in the diencephalon. All these symptoms attest to an acute poisoning of the organism that was caused by toxins from blue-green algae.

_____. Algae: *Microcystis aeruginosa*, *Aphanizomenon flos-aquae*, and *Anabaena flos-aquae*. Carp. Control group given physiological solution in the same dosages as used with suspension and infusion. Dissection revealed no organic pathology.

_____. Algae: *Microcystis aeruginosa*, *Aphanizomenon*, and *Anabaena*. Carp. Immersion in water containing 100 times normal concentration of algae. At first there were no pathological skin changes and the behaviour was normal. On the second day all fish became hyperactive and a depigmentation of the skin took place. One carp suffered impaired coordination, lying on its side from time to time. It died on the third day. Dissection revealed a marked hyperemia of the parenchymatous organs and brain sinuses, hemorrhages in the diencephalon and the thymus, as well as petechial ulcerations of the mucosa of the interior part of the intestine. On the eighth day the activity of the fish

TABLE IV. (Continued)

became normal, but the depigmentation and skin hemorrhages increased somewhat. On the eleventh day part of the skin inflammation disappeared and depigmentation decreased. Towards the end of the experiment the condition of
the fish improved further, depigmentation almost disappeared and a rapid heal-
ing of the lesions and inflamed patches of skin began. An analysis of blood on
the eighth and eleventh days showed that a mass destruction of the nuclei of
erythrocytes, which occurs in intoxication, took place in the first period of
time that the fish spent in the infusion, whereas at the end of the experiment
no destruction of blood cells could be discovered and numerous young cells
were observed. This attests to a normalization of hematogenic processes in
the organism. External examination and dissection showed that depigmentation of the skin disappeared almost entirely. Liver, kidneys, and spleen were
moderately plethoric. Only residual traces of petechial hemorrhages remained
in the mucosa of the anterior part of the intestine. A slight hyperemia was observed in the brain.

————. Algae: *Microcystis aeruginosa, Aphanizomenon,* and *Anabaena. Daphnia.* Immersion in algal water mixture with variation in aeration and light.
Such prolonged survival and even recovery of the fish in a medium containing
algae suggested that the toxins of algae in the water either changed their
properties or disappeared entirely as a result of a depressed state of the algae,
which remained without sunlight for a long time. In order to obtain a definite
answer to this question, we carried out an experiment with *daphnia,* which were
kept in two jars in water taken from an aquarium and containing algae. One of
the jars remained in the same room with the aquaria and was aerated, and the
other was put in good light and was not aerated. A third jar containing *daphnia*
in ordinary river water without algae was also put in good light. *Daphnia* in
the jar in good light and containing blue-green algae died at the beginning of
the third day, whereas in the other two jars they lived to the end of the experiment. A microscopic examination of the morphology of *Microcystis aeruginosa*
colonies in this experiment revealed a diminution of the colonies in volume and
formation of spores in the absence of light. In the jar in which *daphnia* had
died, most colonies began to assume normal size and form, and vacuoles appeared inside the colonies, which without light vanished completely. We therefore consider that the improved condition of carp towards the end of the experiment was a result of the cessation of the effect of toxins of blue green algae.

Part 3. Experiments With Toxic Unialgal Cultures

1954. Ryther (U.S.A.). Algae: *Chlorella vulgaris.* Subject: *Daphnia magna*
(Cladoceran). Procedure: Feeding growing algae to determine filtering rate.
Results: The filtering rate appears to be determined by the concentration of
the algae in the water.
————. ————. ————. Feeding senescent algae to determine filtering rate.
Filtering rate was much lower at any concentration than that of animals feeding
upon corresponding concentration of log-phase algae.
————. ————. ————. Feeding of filtered pond water conditioned with a suspension of 0.5 million non-dividing *Chlorella* for 48 hours, then subjected to
refiltration and addition of senescent algae. A further inhibition of the filtering rate was produced, suggesting that Chlorellin released into water from
senescent algae had demonstrable effect.

————. ————. ————. Feeding senescent algae of varying concentrations after 12 hours of exposure. None showed signs of having fed during test period.

————. Algae: *Navicula pelliculosa* and *Scenedesmus quadricauda.* Feeding experiments similar to those described above were performed both with rapidly growing and senescent cells of both species at various concentrations. Results were similar to that with *Chlorella.* If the observed depression of the filtering rate resulted from the inhibitory product of the algae, chlorellin, then it must follow that both *Navicula* and *Scenedesmus* produce substances of a similar nature which also act as inhibitors upon the feeding process of the cladoceran.

————. Algae: *Chlorella.* Feeding of log-phase algae to test long term effect of the age of alga upon the growth, reproduction and survival. The animals which were fed log-phase *Chlorella* grew rapidly throughout the 13 day experiment and by the 12th day had reached a high rate of reproduction. No animals died in the group.

————. ————. ————. Feeding of senescent *Chlorella* to test long term effect of the age of *Chlorella* upon the growth, reproduction and survival. Those fed senescent algae grew slowly with no evidence of ecdysis during test. No young were produced nor were eggs observed. Animals were completely unpigmented in contrast to the reddish-brown color of the *Daphnia* which were fed growing *Chlorella*, and were relatively inactive, mostly resting on the bottom. They began to die on 10th day: all dead by 13th day.

distress, disorientation, and incoordination; in one and one-half to six hours, death took place without evidence of oxygen want. Prescott suspected that hydroxylamine from decaying algae might have been the toxic factor. Mullor achieved no toxicity on immersing frogs and fish in a tank containing lagoon *Anabaena*, but injection of such an *Anabaena* suspension caused death in five to twelve minutes with neuromuscular disturbances. Mackenthun also noted neurological symptoms in fish immersed in *Aphanizomenon* suspensions. Death occurred within thirty hours with relatively fresh algal specimens, but only between the fifth and eighth days if algae were obtained a week later. Shilo injected live *Microcystis* from a lake subcutaneously and intraperitoneally into frogs and carp, with death occurring in thirty-six to ninety-six hours. Braginskii used *Daphnia*, *Cyclops*, and other zooplanktonic crustaceans as subjects in immersion experiments. Concentrated pond water preparations of *Microcystis* caused "instant" death, while dilute filtrates took ten to sixty minutes to kill, the time lengthening with dilution. With *Aphanizomenon*, concentrated preparations produced distress in fifteen to thirty minutes and death in a few hours. Very dilute specimens had no untoward effect.

A careful study of carp disease (also some catfish, bream, and roach) in the Volga delta was reported in 1961 by Kun, Teplyi, and Astakhova. In one experiment, healthy carp imported from the Ural River were injected intraperitoneally with a one-week old "sterile" infusion of *Aphanizom-*

enon, Microcystis, and *Anabaena* from either the Stalingrad water reservoir or the Kutum River. Initially the fish in both groups became restless, then alternately sluggish and overactive on about the fourth and fifth days. Erratic behavior, frequent turning, labored respiration, convulsions, and death occurred on the fifth and sixth days. On the third day, inflammation and hemorrhage appeared in the skin and the anal mucosa. Autopsy of the carp given Stalingrad algae revealed gross hemorrhage in the renal parenchyma, diencephalon, and mesencephalon, but only petechiae in the liver and upper gut. The intestinal walls were contracted, the mucosa pale, the stomach dilated, and the gonads inflamed. The gills were dark brown (congested) but seemed undamaged. Post-mortem findings in the carp given Kutum River algae were similar but more severe. There were marked fat deposits in the pericardium, renal capsule, and liver, myocardial infarction, hemorrhages in the gonads and gill arches, and patchy necrosis in the gills. The authors felt these were "beyond doubt . . . caused by heavy poisoning resulting from the intraperitoneally introduced infusion of blue-green algae." When carp were *fed* the same (but unsterile). Stalingrad reservoir algal infusion death occurred after seven and one-half to ten days, with no symptoms until the day of death. Similar results with feeding of a mixture of live *Microcystis* and *Aphanizomenon* tended to exclude protein decomposition as a cause of pathological changes.

Kun and his colleagues also immersed carp in water containing 100 times normal concentration of the three algae. One carp died on the third day with findings similar to those in the previous experiments. The other carp developed progressive behavior disturbances, depigmentation, inflammation, and hemorrhages during the first eight to eleven days, then began to recover, with a disappearance of these manifestations.

Ryther demonstrated that inhibition of feeding of *Daphnia* came chiefly from ingestion of algal substances, and only a small part from toxins diffused into the surrounding water. The minimum inhibition was produced by actively growing algae, the maximum by senescent nondividing ones. Ryther considered the noxious material to be identical with the antibiotic *chlorellin.*

Fish kills comparable to those in freshwater have been reported in brackish waters. Such moderately saline waters abound especially in swampy areas, in coastal regions and estuaries, and in locales with dikes and canals. Prominently implicated in those fish deaths has been the flagellate *Prymnesium parvum.* The chief reported effects have been upon the nervous and respiratory systems, with equilibrial disturbances followed by breathing difficulties (see Table V).

TABLE V. FISH INTOXICATIONS DUE TO ALGAE—BRACKISH WATER
Part I. Fish Kills Associated with Toxic Algae

1917. **Locale and Author**: Rostock Harbour, on the Baltic coast of Germany
(Lindemann, 1917). **Algae Involved**: *Heterocapsa triquetra* (dinoflagellate) and
Glenodinium foliaceum (dinoflagellate). **Victims**: Fish. **Manifestation of
Toxicity**: Death.

1920. Workumer Niewland Polder, a diked marsh in the Netherlands (Liebert and
Deerns, 1920). **Algae**: *Prymnesium parvum* (flagellate) [Chrysomonadine Van
Workum]. Roach, reed roach, whitebait, bream, pike, tench, carp, and eel.
Equilibrium disturbances, heavy breathing, death within 30 minutes. The
gills quickly became bloodless.

1922. Kurisches Haff and Stettiner Haff, two Baltic lagoons (Sjostedt, 1922).
Algae: "blue-greens." Fish. Death.

1933. Selsø Sø, a lake in the Lesser Belt of Denmark (Otterstrom and Steemann
Nielsen, 1939). **Algae**: *Prymnesium parvum* (flagellate). Fish. Death.

1938. Ketting Nor, a creek in the Lesser Belt of Denmark (Otterstrom and
Steemann Nielsen, 1939; Sproton, 1946). **Algae**: *Prymnesium parvum* (flagellate). Pike, perch, roach, rudd, bream, tench, carp, and eel. Dead fish were
observed floating in large quantities.

1939. Selsø Sø, Danish lake (Otterstrom and Steemann Nielsen, 1939; Sproton,
1946). **Algae**: *Prymnesium parvum* (flagellate). Pike, perch, roach, rudd,
bream, tench, carp, and eel. Dead fish were observed all over the lake. Many
eel went out of the water onto the shore; many were found half-dead at the
edge of the water.

1939. Bruges Zeebrugge Canal, Belgium (Wolosyznska and Conrad, 193; Koch,
193). **Algae**: *Pyrodinium phoneus* (dinoflagellate). Mussels.

1941. Zuiderzee, Holland (Kristensen, 1941). **Algae**: *Aphanizomenon flos-aquae*
(blue-green). Fish, frogs, newts. Death.

1945–46. Breeding ponds in the Valley of Bet Sheon and Bet Hoarava, Palestine
(Reich and Aschner, 1947). **Algae**: *Prymnesium parvum* (flagellate). Carp.
Deviated from usual behaviour, many appeared sluggish then tried to leap out
of the water. Later became listless and died by the thousands. The gills
appeared reddish-violet in color due to accumulation of blood from the veins.

1956–57. Lagoa Rodrigo de Freitas and Bay of Guanabara, Brazil (de Oliveira,
do Nascimento, Krau, and Miranda, 195). **Algae**: *Glenodinium trichoideum*
(dinoflagellate) and *Anabaena sproides* (blue-green). Fish. Large numbers
were killed rapidly. Death.

2. Experiments With Toxic Algae From Areas of Fish Kills

Reference: 1920 Liebert and Deerns (Holland). **Algae Tested**: *Prymnesium
parvum*. **Procedure**: Placed in poisoned water. **Subject**: Roach, whitebait.
Results: Showed equilibrium disturbances within 9 minutes after having been
put in the water. They turned over and soon would float around immobile,
with bellies up and the tail lower than the head. Shortly after immersion they
started breathing rapidly.

———, ———, Immersed in water from which the flagellates had been filtered.
Roach, whitebait. No toxicity.

———, ———, Immersed in water heated to 90°C. Roach, whitebait. No toxicity.

TABLE V. (Continued)

————, ————, Immersed in water heated to 60°C for 10 minutes. Roach, white-bait. No toxicity.

————, ————, Immersed in water heated to 52°C. Roach, whitebait. Though flagellates were killed and the poison weakened, equilibrium disturbance after 4 hours.

————, ————, Immersed in water heated to 42°C for 10 minutes. Roach, white-bait. The flagellates were killed (as evidenced nacroscopically) but the poison was not destroyed.

————, ————, Immersed in mixture of flagellated filtration residue and city water. Roach, whitebait. Toxic.

————, ————, Flagellates were inactivated by light reduction. Roach, whitebait. Water harmless (since the light encouraged the growth of bacteria and was thought to inactivate the algae, this was thought to be a means of ruling out bacteria as the source of the toxin.)

————. ————. Flagellates were spread over the gills. Roach, whitebait. Fish died.

————. ————. Flagellates were spread over the gills, then fish returned to normal water within 10 minutes. Roach, whitebait. Recovered.

————. ————. Injection of flagellates into fish spinal cord. Roach, whitebait Non-poisonous (apparently the poisoning is the result of a hemolytic process).

1938. Otterstrom and Steemann-Nielsen (Denmark). Algae: *Prymnesium parvum.* Fish from elsewhere were put into net bags and lowered into slow-moving contaminated dam water for seven hours. Eel. When taken from the water they were on the point of dying.

————. ————. Put into net bags and lowered into fast moving contaminated dam water. Eel. After 80 minutes, 2 out of 3 had died.

1938–1939. Otterstrom and Steemann-Nielsen (Denmark). ————. Exposed in laboratory to water containing large numbers of the phytoflagellate. Fish. Died with typical symptoms in the course of a few minutes.

————. ————. Exposed in laboratory to water containing flagellates that had been killed by heat or water from which flagellates had been eliminated by centrifugation. Fish. The toxic principle remained in the supernatant water while the sediment with the bodies of the flagellates had no toxic effect.

1939. ————. Fish were put into a net bag and lowered into the surface water of lake. Eel. After 4 hours they were feeble, but not dead.

————. ————. Immersion in tap water with 6% sodium chloride. Perch, pope, roach. Unhurt after 22 hours.

————. ————. Immersed in Ketting Lake flagellate water, 2 days old. Perch, roach, pope. Died in about 1 hour.

————. ————. Immersed in Ketting Lake flagellate water, 4 days old, 30 minutes; then removed to tap water. Perch, pope. Perch died after 55 minutes. Pope alive after 2 hours but perished in the night.

————. ————. Immersed in Ketting Lake flagellate water, 4 days old. Perch, pope. Died after 1 hour, 45 minutes.

————. ————. Immersed in Ketting Lake flagellate water, 6 days old. Perch. Died after 2 hours.

————. ————. Immersed in Ketting Lake flagellate water, centrifuged 30 minutes. Perch. Died in 2½ hours.

————. ————. Immersed in Ketting Lake flagellate water, 10 days old, boiled for 20 minutes, then cooled. Perch. Alive after 6 hours, seemed feeble.

———. ———. Immersed in tap water through which the distillate from the boiling flagellate water had been led; cooled. Perch. Unhurt after 6 hours.

———. ———. Immersed in Ketting Lake flagellate water, 12 days after the water was taken from Ketting Lake. Perch. Died after 4 hours and 12 minutes. Flagellate water grown less poisonous.

———. ———. Immersed in pure culture of the flagellate with about 400 individuals per cubic mm. Perch. Unhurt after several days.

———. ———. Immersion in 2 liters Selsø Lake flagellate water. Perch. Died after 2 hours.

———. ———. Immersion in tap water with 2% sodium chloride. Perch. Unhurt after 2 hours.

———. ———. Immersed in 21% of flagellate water, 13°C. Perch. Died in 2–3 hours.

———. ———. Immersed in flagellate water filtered through asbestos filter, 13°C. Perch. Unhurt after 33 hours.

———. ———. Immersion in flagellate water filtered through asbestos filter, without airing. Perch. Unhurt after 4½ hours.

———. ———. Immersion in 100% flagellate water. Perch. Died in 2–3 hours.

———. ———. Immersion in 25% flagellate water. Perch. Died in 2–3 hours.

———. ———. Immersion in 3% flagellate water. Perch. Died in 6 hours.

———. ———. Immersion in 1% flagellate water. Perch. Lived at least 7 hours.

———. ———. Immersion in 0.1% flagellate water. Perch. Alive after 20 hours.

———. ———. Immersion in flagellate water. Roach. Died after 2 hours.

———. ———. Immersion in 100% flagellate water. Perch. Died in 3–4 hours.

———. ———. Immersion in 25% flagellate water. Perch. Died in 3–4 hours, 15 minutes.

———. ———. Immersion in 16% flagellate water. Perch. Died after 4 hours.

———. ———. Immersion in 8% flagellate water. Perch. Died in 3–8 hours.

———. ———. Immersion in flagellate water centrifuged 20 minutes. Perch. Died after 3 hours, 19 minutes.

———. ———. Immersion in centrifuged sediment suspended in tap water with 4% sodium chloride. Perch. Alive after 24 hours.

———. ———. Immersion in flagellate water heated to 42°C and then cooled down to 16°C. Perch. Died in 2–4 hours.

———. ———. Immersion in flagellate water also heated to 42°C and then cooled down to 16°C. Perch. Died after 2 hours and 22 minutes.

———. ———. Immersion in flagellate water heated to 11°C. Perch. Died after 2 hours and 52 minutes.

———. ———. Immersion in Selsø Sø flagellate water heated to 11°C. Perch. Died in 3–4 hours.

———. ———. Immersion in Selsø Sø flagellate water heated to 60°C and then cooled down to 16°C. Perch. Died in 3–4 hours.

———. ———. Immersion in Selsø Sø flagellate water heated to 80°C and then cooled down to 16°C. Perch. Died in 3–4 hours.

———. ———. Immersion in Selsø Sø flagellate water heated to 100°C and then cooled down to 16°C. Perch. Alive after 7 hours.

———. ———. Immersion in flagellate water 1 hour; then removal to tap water. Perch. Died after 4 hours.

———. ———. Immersion in flagellate water (fetched the day before). Perch. Died after 2 hours.

———. ———. Immersion in tap water with 4% sodium chloride. Perch. Unhurt.

TABLE V. (Continued)

————. ————. Immersion in flagellate water 10 minutes; then tap water. Perch. Died in 25–30 hours.

————. ————. Immersion in flagellate water 20 minutes; then tap water. Perch. One died in 1½ hours; the other seemed unhurt after 45 hours.

————. ————. Immersion in flagellate water 30 minutes; then tap water. Perch. One died after 4½ hours; the other alive after 10 hours.

————. ————. Immersion in flagellate water 40 minutes; then tap water. Perch. One died after 8 hours; the other alive after 10 hours.

————. ————. Immersion in flagellate water 50 minutes; then tap water. Perch. One died after 4½ hours; the other alive after 10½ hours.

————. ————. Immersion in flagellate water 60 minutes; then tap water. Perch. One died after 2 hours; the other alive after 7 hours.

————. ————. Immersion in flagellate water all the time. Perch. Died after 4 hours.

————. ————. Immersion in flagellate water. Perch. Died after 3 hours, 21 minutes.

————. ————. Immersion in flagellate water in which has been suspended ground charcoal, filtered through ordinary filter paper. Perch. Unhurt after 76 hours.

————. ————. Immersion in flagellate water. Perch, pope. Died after 4–5 hours.

————. ————. Immersion in flagellate water to which had been added ground charcoal, and then filtered through ordinary filter paper. Perch, pope. Died in less than 7 hours.

————. ————. Immersion in flagellate water. *Dreissensia*. All died.

————. ————. Immersion in tap water. *Dreissensia*. All remained alive.

————. ————. Immersion in flagellate water; after 3 days the concentration of salt was halved by adding tap water. *Dreissensia*. All died within 96 hours.

————. ————. Immersion in tap water with 4% sodium chloride; after 3 days, halving of salt concentration. *Dreissensia*. All alive on the fifth day.

————. ————. Immersion in flagellate water heated to 8°C. Perch. Died in 3–4 hours.

————. ————. Immersion in flagellate water boiled for about 5 minutes; then cooled to 17°C. Perch. Alive after 5 days.

————. ————. Immersion in tap water. Suspended asbestos filter with sediment from flagellate water sprinkled on the gills of the fish. Perch. Alive after 48 hours; perished in the night.

————. ————. Immersion in tap water. Pure, suspended asbestos sprinkled on the gills of the fish. Perch. Unhurt after 6½ hours.

————. ————. Immersion in flagellate water. Perch. Died in 3–3½ hours.

————. ————. Immersion in 500cc tap water in which was suspended sediment from 600cc of flagellate water, together with upper layer of asbestos filter. Perch, pope. Died in 1½–3 hours.

————. ————. Immersion in flagellate water, filtered through Seitz asbestos filter without previous centrifugalization. Perch. Unhurt after 6½ hours.

————. ————. Immersion in tap water with suspended asbestos. Pope. Alive after 48 hours.

————. ————. Corresponding experiment, carried out in a vessel. Pope. Alive after 48 hours.

————. ————. Immersion in flagellate water, centrifugalized for 15 minutes, then filtered through asbestos filter. Perch, pope. Alive after 48 hours.

————. ————. Immersion in flagellate water treated with charcoal and then centrifugalized. Perch. One was alive after 48 hours; the other was alive after 24 hours but perished thereafter.

1947. Reich and Aschner (Palestine). **Algae:** *Prymnesium parvum.* Exposed fish to pond water containing high numbers of flagellates. *Gambusia affinis.* Died in 2–4 hours. (There is good reason to believe that bacteria are responsible for the rapid loss of toxicity.)

————. ————. Fish were placed in untreated contaminated pond water, and contaminated pond water treated 18 hours earlier with ammonium sulfate. Carp. Half an hour after transfer the carp in the untreated pond showed typical symptoms of the disease, dying in 2 hours. The carp in the treated pond remained normal.

————. ————. A week later the above experiment was repeated without any further addition of ammonium sulfate. Carp. The result was exactly the same; carp in the untreated pond died, the others remained healthy.

————. ————. Ammonium sulfate subsequently added to the pond containing the *Prymnesium.* Carp. Fish introduced into this pond 12 hours thereafter remained healthy.

————. ————. Four storage ponds were filled with brackish water from the Jordan River. Phytoflagellate were added to each pond. The 1st and 3rd ponds were treated with ammonium sulfate: 2nd and 4th ponds remained untreated. Carp.

————. ————. A week later cages containing fish were introduced into the 3rd and 4th basins. Carp. In the fourth basin, which was untreated, the fish died after 3 hours. In the 3rd basin, which had been treated with ammonium sulfate, the carp remained normal.

————. ————. On the same day, small glass jars were filled with water from each of the four ponds and stocked with *Gambusia.* Carp. After an hour and a quarter, the fish were normal in the jars which contained the ammonium sulfate while those in the other two had died.

————. ————. *Gambusia* were immersed in water taken from a pond which at the time of the experiment was devoid of fish but contained 390,000 *Prymnesium* per ml. Carp. Fish killed in 30 minutes.

————. ————. *Gambusia* were immersed directly into this pond in wire cages. Carp. Dead after two hours.

————. ————. After application of ammonium sulfate test samples were taken every two hours. Carp. The water gradually lost its toxicity. After 18 hours, carp and *Gambusia* placed into the water remained perfectly healthy.

————. ————. As a control, water had been taken from this pond immediately before the application of the salt. Carp. This water retained its toxicity for 5 days.

————. ————. Fish were immersed in untreated saline water containing the phytoflagellate and in water treated with ammonium sulfate. *Gambusia,* Carp. Treatment with ammonium sulfate sufficed for immediate destruction of the *Prymnesium* and the cessation of disease.

3. Experiments With Toxic Unialgal Cultures

1953. Shilo [Shelubsky] and Aschner (Israel) **Algae:** *Prymnesium parvum.* Immersion of test animals in culture fluid, observing the relationship between

TABLE V. (Continued)

toxin concentration and equilibrium-loss time. *Gambusia* minnows. Relationship between minimal lethal concentration and equilibrium-loss time was constant in all toxin solutions. Equilibrium-loss time decreased as amount of toxin increased above 1 T.U., and approached a constant (15–30 min.) at 5 T.U./20 ml or more. Above 2 T.U./20 ml, the plot of reciprocal toxicity against the equilibrium-loss time deviates only slightly from a straight line. Loss of equilibrium sense was always followed by death of *Gambusia*. Minimal lethal concentration and minimal concentration causing the loss of the equilibrium sense are therefore identical.

―――. ―――. Immersion of test animals in culture fluid, observing the relationship between toxin concentration and tail-curvature time. Tadpoles. Similar to that of equilibrium-loss time in *Gambusia* minnows to toxin concentration; tadpole requires more toxin for a visible response, the minimum effective dose being 2.2 T.U./20 ml. As toxin dose increased, curvature-time decreased at a decreasing rate and became constant above 50 T.U./20 ml at a value near 8 min. Curvature-times of 15–30 min. were satisfactory for assay. Curvature response was always followed by death of tadpole.

―――. ―――. Bioassay of cell-free toxin solution after centrifugation. *Gambusia* minnows and tadpoles. The cell-free fluid was as toxic as the original cell suspension.

―――. ―――. Bioassay of cell-free toxin solution after centrifugation and refrigeration up to 4 weeks. *Gambusia* minnows and tadpoles. No loss of potency with storage.

―――. ―――. Bioassay of non-toxic pond water subjected to different lighting conditions (diffuse daylight, fluorescent light and laboratory interior), to check influence of light on cell density and toxicity of cultures. *Gambusia* minnows. Light greatly augmented cell density and toxin production within 24–72 hours.

―――. ―――. Bioassay of culture fluids to determine relationship between algal population density and toxicity. ―――. When the population density of laboratory cultures was increased by growth-promoting supplements to numbers in excess of 5×10^{0} flagellates/ml, an inverse relationship between cell count and toxicity was sometimes observed.

―――. ―――. Bioassay of culture fluid to determine effect of saline dilution on toxicity of dense algal cultures. ―――. Dilution of such dense cultures with sea water or pond water rapidly re-established the normal-toxicity:count ratio.

―――. ―――. Bioassay to determine effect on culture supernatant. ―――. At 97° and 80°, toxicity of culture supernatant fluid declined rapidly; at 62° the decline was relatively slow. Thermal inactivation became progressively slower as the concentration of the toxin fell. At room temperature and at 4° there was no detectable loss of toxicity for at least 7 days, provided that bacterial growth did not occur and oxidation was prevented.

―――. ―――. Bioassay to determine idem diffusibility. Solutions of toxin in cellophane tubing showed no significant fall in titre when suspended in frequent renewed distilled water or in isotonic sodium chloride solution (0.16°/0) for 12–24 hrs. at 4°.

―――. ―――. Bioassay to determine effect of pH value of culture fluid on toxicity. ―――. Toxicity was independent of pH value within the range 7.5–9.0. The toxicity decreased rapidly at pH values below 7.5, and was zero at pH 6.0. At moderate acidities, the inactivating effect of hydrogen ion was almost completely reversible for at least several days, though variation of pH value might also be affecting susceptibility of test animal.

_____. _____. Bioassay to determine effect of oxidizing agents on toxic solution. _____. Toxicity declined when oxygen was bubbled through a solution of toxin; air produced the same result, though somewhat more slowly. Potassium permanganate or sodium hypochloride added to culture supernatant fluid immediately destroyed toxicity.

_____. _____. Bioassay to determine effect of adsorbents on toxic material in culture supernatant fluid. _____. At room temperature, the toxicity of 50 ml containing 2.5 T.U. was completely removed within 5 min by 2–5 g of kaolin, Norit A (acid washed), activated charcoal, or calcium sulphate; Decalso, calcium carbonate, kieselguhr, fuller's earth and activated alumina removed little or no toxin. Highly toxic cultures were rapidly detoxified by stirring with pond-bottom soils.

_____. _____. Bioassay of algal toxin subjected to the action of microorganisms. _____. Washed suspensions of *Proteus vulgaris* and of *Bacillus subtilis* decreased the potency of prymnesium toxic culture supernatant fluid by at least 50% in 1 hour, whereas *Bacterium coli* was almost without effect.

1954. Reich and Kahn (Israel). **Algae:** *Prymnesium parvum*. Bacteria-free cultures were tested for toxicity. Fish. Had no poisonous effect on fish, or only slightly so.

1958. Reich and Rotberg (Israel). _____. Bioassay to investigate influence on toxin formation of variation in the salt content of culture medium. *Gambusia*. The formation of toxin seemed to decrease with increasing salt concentration.

_____. _____. Bioassay to investigate influence on toxin formation of calcium. _____. The cultures in calcium poor sea water were less toxic than those in sea water with a normal calcium content.

_____. _____. Bioassay to investigate influence on toxin formation of addition of phosphates. _____. No effect.

_____. _____. Bioassay to determine effect on culture toxin of addition of fish. _____. Reduces toxicity of cultures.

1958 Yariv (Israel). _____. Tested biological activity of culture supernatants. Erythrocytes from bovine and other animal species. Hemolysis.

1960 Shilo and Rosenberg. _____. Tested biological activity of culture supernatants on normal and tumor cells. Normal and tumor cells. Lysis.

1961 Yariv and Hestrin (Israel). **Algae:** *Prymnesium parvum*. Standard assay system. Bovine erythrocytes. Percentage of hemolysis was determined colorimetrically. The decrease of optical density was closely proportional to the percentage of hemolysis.

_____. _____. Test of hemolytic activity. Paper chromatography. Any hemoglobin released by hemolysis was moved by the current and formed a dark spot in the region above the hemolysis.

_____. _____. Measurement of ichthyotoxic activity. *Gambusia* minnows. Ichthyotoxicity was measured on the basis of the ability of prymnesin to enhance the susceptibility of fish to the lethal action of streptomycin.

_____. _____. Determination of effect of prymnesin on susceptibility of fish to poisoning by $CaCl_2$, streptomycin, SO_4, $CaSo_4$, $MgCl_2$. *Gambusia* minnows. Cofactors all had practically the same LD 100 values when measured in absence of prymnesin on prymnesin-pretreated minnows as when measured in the presence of prymnesin. ... the survival times of fish in the cofactor + prymnesin systems probably depended on the time required for the action of

TABLE V. (Continued)

cofactor on the prymnesin-sensitized fish, rather than on the time during which the sensitization by prymnesin was accomplished.

————. ————. Determination of effect of standing at room temperature on LD 100 value of prymnesin. *Gambusia* minnows. The LD 100 value of prymnesin in the standard assay system was doubled when a solution of prymnesin (20 units/ml) was held for 6 hrs at room temperature at about pH 10 before the test was carried out. The solution, thus partially inactivated, was rapidly restored to its original titre by subsequent incubation at pH 4–0.

————. ————. Determination of effect of dialysis through cellophane. *Gambusia* minnows. When toxic samples were dialysed through cellophane (72 hr; 6°; pH 4–0), the separated dialysate and dialysand had no lethal effect on fish, but were again toxic when pooled.

1962 Reich and Parnas (Israel). **Algae:** *Prymnesium parvum*. Effect of illumination on ichthyotoxin production determined by incubation of culture while being subjected to alternate 12-hour periods of light and darkness for 3 weeks. *Gambusia*. Ichthyotoxic activity diminishes gradually upon exposure to light. With onset of darkness the ichthyotoxic activity rises once more, reaching a maximum after 7½ hours and remaining at this high level for the duration of the dark period.

————. **Algae:** *Prymnesium parvum*. Cultures maintained under constant illumination for 3 weeks after which time half were kept darkened for another 8 hours. *Gambusia*. Findings prove once more the dependence of ichthyotoxic activity on the absence of light.

1962 Parnas, Reich, and Bergmann (Israel). **Algae:** *Prymnesium parvum*. Determination of effect of light on the extracellular as well as on the purified intracellular toxin. *Gambusia*. ... the influence of various regions of the spectrum on the extracellular toxin was studied. ... The data indicate that inactivation also occurs in the absence of cells. The upper limit for inactivation by visible light is 510 mu. Identical results were obtained with purified intracellular toxin.

————. ————. Determination of influence of chlorophyll and carotene on ichthyotoxic activity. *Gambusia*. Inactivation occurs also in the absence of these pigments.

————. ————. Determination of changes in absorption spectrum of purified intracellular toxin during photochemical inactivation. *Gambusia*. Under ultraviolet irradiation, the general pattern of the absorption spectrum is retained but its intensity is diminished, a fact that suggests a drop in the concentration of the absorbing material. On the other hand, there is no change in the absorption spectrum of the dark control.

————. ————. Determination of influence of oxygen and glutathione on the inactivation process. *Gambusia*. Since *Prymnesium* cells liberate oxygen in visible light, the rapid photo-inactivation in plain cultures may be due to the high concentration of oxygen. To test this hypothesis, the photochemical process was compared in atmospheres of either pure O_2 or pure N_2. In both instances, inactivation occurred at the same rate. Likewise, the addition of 1% glutathione had no effect on the velocity of the photochemical process.

1963 Parnas, Reich, and Bergmann (Israel). **Algae:** *Prymnesium parvum* (phytoflagellate). Studies on effect of toxin on neural transmission. Frog. (1) Toxin produces slowly progressing neuromuscular block without affecting the response of the muscle to direct stimulation; (2) Polysynaptic spinal reflexes are

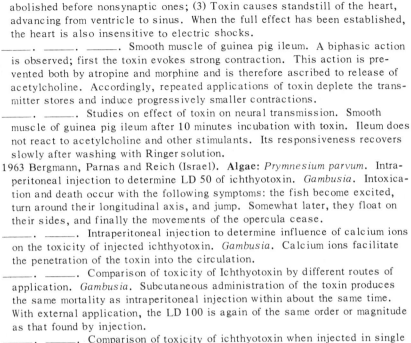

abolished before nonsynaptic ones; (3) Toxin causes standstill of the heart, advancing from ventricle to sinus. When the full effect has been established, the heart is also insensitive to electric shocks.

———. ———. ———. Smooth muscle of guinea pig ileum. A biphasic action is observed; first the toxin evokes strong contraction. This action is prevented both by atropine and morphine and is therefore ascribed to release of acetylcholine. Accordingly, repeated applications of toxin deplete the transmitter stores and induce progressively smaller contractions.

———. ———. Studies on effect of toxin on neural transmission. Smooth muscle of guinea pig ileum after 10 minutes incubation with toxin. Ileum does not react to acetylcholine and other stimulants. Its responsiveness recovers slowly after washing with Ringer solution.

1963 Bergmann, Parnas and Reich (Israel). Algae: *Prymnesium parvum*. Intraperitoneal injection to determine LD 50 of ichthyotoxin. *Gambusia*. Intoxication and death occur with the following symptoms: the fish become excited, turn around their longitudinal axis, and jump. Somewhat later, they float on their sides, and finally the movements of the opercula cease.

———. ———. Intraperitoneal injection to determine influence of calcium ions on the toxicity of injected ichthyotoxin. *Gambusia*. Calcium ions facilitate the penetration of the toxin into the circulation.

———. ———. Comparison of toxicity of Ichthyotoxin by different routes of application. *Gambusia*. Subcutaneous administration of the toxin produces the same mortality as intraperitoneal injection within about the same time. With external application, the LD 100 is again of the same order or magnitude as that found by injection.

———. ———. Comparison of toxicity of ichthyotoxin when injected in single or divided doses. *Gambusia*. Has the same effect as administration of the whole quantity in a single dose.

In experiments on roach and white-bait, Liebert and Deerns (1920) observed that the severity of symptoms paralleled the concentration of *Prymnesium*, and that its heat-labile extracellular toxin was most abundant in older cultures (*ergo*, most poisonous in nature in autumn). The toxin seemed to enter through the gills. Anoxia was ruled out by oxygen saturation studies, while bacterial toxicity was excluded by differential light reduction techniques. Liebert and Deerns thought that hemolytic phenomena also played a part, but this was disputed by Otterstrom and Stiemann-Nielsen. The latter, using mostly eels, perch, and pope, also ruled out anoxia and extraneous toxins as causes of fish death.

Reich and Aschner, in Palestine, reached similar conclusions in 1947. They tested carp and *Gambusia* in a variety of ponds and pond waters containing *Prymnesium*. They also found that toxicity could be diminished or abolished by diluting with freshwater or by treatment with ammonium sulfate.

Since 1947 other Israeli investigators (and more recently Asian and southeastern European ones) have been urgently concerned with *Prymnesium* because of its expanding threat to their fish breeding (especially carp) industry.

The idea that *Prymnesium* toxin was hemolytic (as proposed by Liebert and Deerns but denied by Otterstrom and Stiemann-Nielsen) was clearly corroborated by Yariv (1958). Using pure axenic cultures of the alga, he confirmed its toxicity for fish and additionally demonstrated in the culture supernatant the presence of two hemolysins potent against red cells from various species. Yariv also indicated that icthyotoxin activity might increase with certain cofactors. One is the concentration of inorganic salts, divalent cations more so than monovalent ones; another is streptomycin. Significantly, icthyotoxin in the absence of salts or streptomycin does not kill fish, but it does sensitize them to later exposure to salts. In 1961 Yariv, working with Hestrin, suggested that "prymnesin" acts on fish by inducing abnormal permeability of the gills. Shilo and Rosenberger also found both ichthyotoxin and hemolysin in *Prymnesium*.

Many marine fish kills have been mentioned throughout history, but the first direct association with algae was in an episode off the coast of West India in 1849. Carter reported (1858) that *Peridinium* was the probable cause. Since then many incidents have been documented from all over the world (see Table VI).

Manifestations have been generally similar to those reported in fresh and brackish waters. The fish exposed to algae have been variously described as "struggling," "stupefied," "stunned," "lethargic," or "intoxicated." Many appear to have breathing difficulties and spatial disorientation, and they may float belly up before dying. Attention is directed to the widespread geographic occurrence of these fish kills, as well as to the predominant organisms reported: *Peridinium, Gymnodinium, Gonyaulax,* and *Noctiluca.*

Relatively few experiments are reported with algae taken directly from the seas where the fish deaths occurred. Brongersma-Sanders disagreed, believing all the deaths were caused by toxins liberated by dinoflagellates and other planktonic organisms. These appeared to be associated with upwelling waters.

Brongersma–Sanders indicated that these environmental factors favor algal growth and that algal toxins are a principal cause of the fish mortalities. In marine areas she rarely found blue-green algae, rather mostly flagellates and dinoflagellates, with the water often discolored reddish. The noxiousness of such water was variable, depending on chance of escape of the fish, the concentration of toxins, and the specific algal species involved. Most frequent were *Gonyaulax, Gymnodinium, Cochlodinium,* and *Noctiluca.*

Several hypotheses were offered by Brongersma-Sanders on the mechanisms of algal toxicity. Anoxia and high concentrations of hydrogen sulfide may for short periods be harmful to fish, but actual algal toxins are the chief agents.

TABLE VI. FISH INTOXICATIONS DUE TO ALGAE – SALTWATER

Part 1. Fish Kills Associated with Toxic Algae

1849. Porebunder, Khattywar, West Coast of India (Carter, 1858). **Algae:** *Peridinium*. **Victims:** fish. **Manifestations of Toxicity:** the fish were speedily destroyed and were washed up on the beach in large quantities.

1869. Stumpnose Bay, S.W. Africa (Gilchrist, 1914). **Algae:** "red water" (Noctiluca). Geelbek fish. Fish were found swimming, head above water, apparently in a stupefied condition.

1873. East Indian Archipelago. (Veenhuyzen, 1879). **Algae:** *Trichodesmium Erythraeum* (blue-green). Fish. Fish get stunned, floating as if intoxicated on the surface of the water in places where the alga is abundant.

1885. Shetland fisheries, Great Britain (Pearcey, 1885). **Algae:** *Rhizosolenia shrubsolei* (diatom) and *Thalassiosira nordenskioldii* (diatom). Fish. Destroyed.

1890. Saharian coast of North West Africa (Puff, 1948). **Algae:** *Phytoplankton.* Fish. A great mass of dead fish.

1891. Port Jackson, Australia (Whitelegge, 1891). **Algae:** *Glenodinium rubrum* (dinoflagellate). Oysters and mussels. Considerable damage.

1893. Gokasho Bay, Japan (Miyako, 1893). **Algae:** *Gymnodinium* (dinoflagellate). Pearl oysters. Destroyed.

1898. Narragansett Bay, Rhode Island, U.S.A. (Mead, 1898). **Algae:** *Peridinium sp.* Crabs, shrimps, tautog, flatfish, menhaden, and eels. ...the peculiar behavior of the marine animals attracted much attention. Myriad shrimps and blue crabs, and vast numbers of eels, menhaden, tautog and flatfish came up to the surface and to the edge of the shore as though struggling to get out of the noxious water. Indeed, the shrimps and crabs were observed to climb out of the water upon stakes and buoys and even upon the iron cylinders which support one of the bridges and which must have been very hot in the bright sun. In several instances, on these two days, hundreds of blue crabs were caught by a single individual in a few minutes' time, at the mouth of the Seekonk.... several days afterwards,... Along the shore, however, in the same vicinity, cartloads of dead shrimps were piled up in windrows, and among them were strewn great numbers of crabs and fish of various kinds, especially menhaden and eels. This singular behavior and alarming mortality of marine animals was reported from nearly every station at which the red water occurred, and from no other station, which indicates that the two phenomena are related as to cause and effect."

1899. Bay of Toba, Japan (Nishikawa, 1901–1903). **Algae:** *Gonyaulax polygramma* (peridinian). Fish, mollusks, shrimps. Great mortality.

1900. Bay of Agu, Shima Province, Japan (Nishikawa, 1901–1903). **Algae:** *Gonyaulax polygramma* (peridinian). Fish, mollusks, shrimps. Death.

1900. Narragansett Bay, Rhode Island, U.S.A. (Sherwood and Edwards, 1901). **Algae:** *Peridinium sp.* Squeteague. Great numbers were killed by the "red water."

1901. Coast of San Pedro, California, U.S.A. (Torrey, 1902). **Algae:** *Gonyaulax polyhedra* (dinoflagellate and peridinian). Sting ray, guitar fish, dogfish, perch, smelt, octopi, bottom animals. Large numbers of dead and live animals and fish were left on the beach by the "red" tide.

1902. Southern part of Red Sea and Gulf of Aden (Ilg. in Hofer, 1909). **Algae:** *Dinoflagellates.* Fish. A great mortality: fish floated on the surface.

TABLE VI. (Continued)

1904. Gokasho Bay, Japan (Nightingale, 1904). **Algae:** *Gymnodinium.* Pearl oysters. Destroyed.

1907. Coast of Yucatan, Mexico (Brongersma-Sanders, 1948). **Algae:** *Phytoplankton.* Fish. Water had a yellow color and was covered by an immense quantity of dead fish.

1907. Saldanha Bay, South West Africa (Gilchrist, 1914). **Algae:** "red" water (Noctiluca). Fish, mussels, klip-kres. Floating belly upward in a disabled condition.

1907. San Pedro to San Diego, California, U.S.A. (Kofoid, 1907). **Algae:** *Gonyaulax polyhedra.* Fish, shellfish. Mass-mortality.

1907. False Bay, South West Africa (Gilchrist, 1907). **Algae:** *Noctiluca* sp. Fish and other marine animals including shellfish. ... seen floating belly upwards in a disabled condition.

1908. Manila Bay, Phillipines (Smith, 1908). **Algae:** *Peridinium* (dinoflagellate). Fish. Limited mortality.

1908. North Sea (Bullen, 1908). **Algae:** *Phytoplankton.* Herring. It is not worth fishing for herring where the water is stinking. The smell originates from large amounts of phytoplankton.

1908. England (Bullen, 1908). **Algae:** *Phytoplankton.* Mackeral.

1908. South West Coast of India (Hornell, 1917). **Algae:** *Dinoflagellates.* Sardines. Excessively great mortality affecting even large shoals of fish.

1908. In the sea near Mangalore, India (Hornell, 1917). **Algae:** *Flagellates.* Sardine shoals. Excessive mortality, the sea being covered for miles with enormous multitudes of dead sardines.

1910. Gokasho Bay, Japan (Miyako, 1910). **Algae:** *Gymnodinium mikimotoi.* Pearl oysters. Destroyed.

1910–1911. Yokahama Harbour, Japan (Okamura, 1916). **Algae:** *Cochlodinium catenatum.* Fish. Destroyed.

1911. California Coast, U.S.A. (Kofoid, 1911). **Algae:** *Dinoflagellates.* Fish. The products of decay and (metabolism) of these organisms are toxic to many marine organisms.

1911. Gulf of Konsa and in Gokasho and Agu Bays, Japan (Miyajima, 1934). **Algae:** *Gymnodinium splendens, Gymnodinium sanguineum,* and *Gonyaulax catenella.* Pearl oysters. Destroyed.

1915. Red Sea (Carpenter and Wilson, Barker, 0000). **Algae:** *Noctiluca.* Fish. When fish find themselves in one of these brilliant swarms they seem to go quite mad.

1916. Cannore, India (Hornell, 1917). **Algae:** *Flagellates.* Sole, jewfish, catfish, crabs, crayfish, mollusks, Alcyonaria. Mortality lasted three days.

1916. Southwest Coast of Florida, U.S.A. (Taylor, 1917). **Algae:** *Peridinii* (dinoflagellates). Fish, sea urchins, sponges, king crabs. Vast numbers were killed, mullet died in a very short time: as the tide came into the bayou they began to act strangely, coming to the top, whirling around and around, and then sank to the bottom, lying stomach up for a little time, when they turned on their sides, dead.

1917. Malabar and South Kanora coasts, India (Hornell, 1917). **Algae:** *Euglenid flagellate.* Sardines, crabs, soles, catfish. Mortality occurs annually: the first effect of poison is to make the fish sluggish, and boys and men crowd to the shore and make great hauls of dying fish.

1917. Calicut, India (Hornell, 1917). **Algae:** Swarms of certain *flagellates*. Fish, crabs. Mass-mortality.

1917. Santa Barbara, California, U.S.A. (Allen, 1917). **Algae:** *Gonyaulax polyhedra.* Fish, shore fauna. A good deal of injury.

1922. Calicut coast, India (Hornell and Ramaswami, Nayudu, 1923). **Algae:** *Flagellates.* Fish, other marine animals. Dead and dying fish were washed ashore.

1922. Gulf of Konsa and in Gokasho and Agu Bays, Japan (Miyajima, 1934). **Algae:** *Gymnodinium splendens, Gymnodinium sanguineum,* and *Gonyaulax catenella.* Pearl oysters. Destroyed.

1923. East Anglia (Hardy, 1923). **Algae:** *Phaeocystis.* Herring.

1925. Coast of Yucatan, Mexico (Thomson in B.S. 1925). **Algae:** *Phytoplankton.* Fish.

1926. Gokasho Bay, Japan (Miyako, 1926). **Algae:** *Gymnodinium* (dinoflagellate). Pearl oysters. Destroyed.

1928. Walvis Bay, South West Africa (Marchand, 1928). **Algae:** *Noctiluca* (dinoflagellate), *diatoms.* Mullet, massbankers. Shoals of mullet and massbankers were swimming about lethargically on the surface and taking no notice of innumerable sea birds which were catching them by the dozen. The fish were swimming lazily on the surface in shoals, rapidly opening and shutting their mouths as if finding difficulty in breathing. They could be picked out of the water by hand with the greatest ease.

1928. Oakland Bay, Washington, U.S.A. (Nightingale, 1936). **Algae:** *Gymnodinium splendens* (dinoflagellates). Oysters. Losses.

1933. Gokasho Bay, Japan (Miyako, 1933). **Algae:** *Gymnodinium mikimotoi.* Pearl oysters. Great losses.

1933. Gulf of Konsa and in Gokasho and Ago Bays, Japan (Miyajima, 1934). Pearl oysters. **Algae:** *Gymnodinium splendens, Gymnodinium sanguineum,* and *Gonyaulax catenella.* Destruction of the oysters was caused by suffocation of the respiratory organ by masses of dinoflagellates.

1934. , Japan (Miyajima, 1934). **Algae:** *Cochlodinium catenatum.* Shellfish. Destroyed.

1934. (Buckmann, 1934). **Algae:** *Phytoplankton.* Shellfish.

1934–1935. (U.S.A.) (Allison and Cole, 1934–1935). **Algae:** *Dinoflagellates.* Barnacles.

1935. Oakland Bay, Washington, U.S.A. (Nightingale, 1936). **Algae:** *Gymnodinium splendens* (dinoflagellates). Oysters. Losses.

1935. North Sea (Savage and Hardy, 1935). **Algae:** *Phaeocystis, Rhizosolenia styliformis* (diatom), *Biddulphia sinensis* (diatom). Herring. Herring avoids the large amounts of phytoplankton occurring in a certain time of the year.

1935. Madras Coast, India (Aiyar, 1935). **Algae:** *Noctiluca miliaris* (dinoflagellates). Anemones, Cavernularia sipunculids, tetroodons, diodons, fish fry. Large catches of fish, more or less in an exhausted condition, were made. The fish near the coast showed a tendency to swim near the surface, allowing of easy capture.

1935. Texas coast, U.S.A. (Lund, 1935). **Algae:** *Plankton.* Menhaden, mullet. Mass-mortality.

1935. California waters, U.S.A. (Nightingale, 1936). **Algae:** *Gonyaulax.* Sand crabs. Visible effects indicating a pathological condition among these crabs were in evidence in the form of brown spots about the leg joints.

1935. Olympia Oyster Region, Washington U.S.A. (Nightingale, 1936). **Algae:**

TABLE VI. (Continued)

Gymnodinium splendens. Oysters. Losses, especially among the young oysters.

1936. Coast of Peru (Gunther, 1936). **Algae:** *Flagellates*. Fish.

1939. Coast of Peru (Falke, 1939). **Algae:** *Plankton*. Squid. Mass mortality.

1940. Balikpapan, East Coast of Borneo (Mohler, 1940). **Algae:** *Trichodesmium* (blue-green). Fish, crustaceans, worms. Mortality observed in the little pools on the beach.

1942. Krusadai Island, Gulf of Mannar, India (Chidambaram and Unni, Chacko, 1942). **Algae:** *Trichodesmium erythreum* (blue-green). Fish, other marine animals. Mass mortality.

1946–1947. Gulf of Mexico off the Florida Keys, U.S.A. (Davis, 1946–47). **Algae:** *Gymnodinium brevis*. Fish.

1946–1947. Gulf Coast of Southern Florida, U.S.A. (Galtsoff, 1946–47). **Algae:** *Gymnodinium brevis*. Oysters, mullet, horseshoe crabs, other fish. As the fish enters "red" water it begins to act rather strangely, coming to the surface, whirling around, then turning on its side or lying stomach up, then sinking to the bottom. Millions of pounds of dead or dying fish were washed ashore or carried away by the tides: the affected area comprised several hundred square miles. Obviously death was not caused by a lack of oxygen. Schools of mullet surrounded by net fisherman suddenly died when they became excited or disturbed and swam wildly about, strengthening the suggestion that the fishes may have been suffering from some respiratory disturbance which did not become fatal until they were disturbed and their activity was increased under excitement.

1946–1947. West Coast of Florida, U.S.A. (Gunther, Williams, Davis and Smith, 1948). **Algae:** *Gymnodinium brevis*. Mullet.

1947. Venice, South West Florida, U.S.A. (Anderson, 1947). **Algae:** *Gymnodinium brevis*. Horseshoe crabs.

1947. Makaren Island, Red Sea near Coast of Yemen (Thompson in B.S., 1948). **Algae:** *Dinoflagellates*. Fish, crayfishes, crabs, prawns. Hundreds of fish of medium and small sizes were hurling themselves on the beaches, all in a state of what might be termed helpless intoxication.

1948. Walvis Bay, South Africa (Brongersma-Sanders, 1948). **Algae:** *Noctiluca sp.* Fish. Mass-mortality.

1948. Malabar and Kanara Coasts, India (Bhimachar and George, 1950). **Algae:** *Noctiluca miliaris*. Sole. Abrupt and severe setback in the fish. Shoaling of large masses of sole noted just below the surface. In spite of their active movements, the fish could be netted easily.

1949. Bay of Fundy, Canada (Needler, 1949). **Algae:** *Gonyaulax tamarensis* (dinoflagellate).

1949. Portugal (Santos-Pinto, 1949). **Algae:** *Gonyaulax polyhedra* (dinoflagellate).

1949. Offats Bayou, Texas, U.S.A. (Connell and Cross, 1950). **Algae:** *Gonyaulax catenella* (dinoflagellate). Fish. Mass-mortality.

1952–1955. Florida Gulf Coast, U.S.A. (Lackey and Hynes, 1952–1955). **Algae:** *Gymnodinium brevis* (dinoflagellate). Fish—both sport and commercial varieties, fingerlings, crabs, shrimp, scallops, marine worms, copepods, porpoises. Dead fish accumulated in windrows on the beaches.

1954. South East and South West Coasts of India (Subrahmanyan, 1954) [in Ballentine & Abbott]. **Algae:** *Hornellia marina*. Fish.

1955. (U.S.A.) (Davis and Charles, 1955). **Algae:** *Dinoflagellates.* Clams.

1955. (U.S.A.) (Loosanoff, 1955). **Algae:** *Dinoflagellates.* Oysters.

1955. Port Isabel, Texas, U.S.A. (Wilson and Ray, 1956). **Algae:** *Gymnodinium brevis* (dinoflagellate). Fish. Thousands of fish were dying or dead over a 120-mile-length of coast.

1956. Angola, West Africa (Silva, 1956). **Algae:** *Exuriaella baltica.* Fish.

1961. Long Island Sound, U.S.A. (Loosanoff, 1961). **Algae:** Microscopic "red water" organism. Oyster settings.

1962. Offshore near St. Petersburg, Florida (U.S.A.) (Hutton, 1962). **Algae:** *Gymnodinium brevis* (dinoflagellate). Fish.

1963. Gulf Coast of Florida, U.S.A. (N.Y. Times, 1963). **Algae:** *Gymnodinium brevis* (dinoflagellate). Fish.

Part 2. Experiments with Toxic Algae from Areas of Fish Kills

1922–23. Hardy (England). **Algae:** *Phaeocystis*, diatoms. **Subject:** herring. **Procedure:** Plankton disc samples were collected to determine whether the movements of fish are in certain seasons influenced by the occurrence of certain plankton organisms. **Results:** Showed that in the spring and autum green or pale green discs due to *Phaeocystis* or diatoms appeared to indicate water in which fishing was likely to be poor. Reference has already been made to the traditional belief amongst herring fishermen that what they call "weedy" or "stinking" water is bad for fishing and such conditions have been shown to be due to an abundance of phytoplankton (Pearcey, 1885; Bullen, 1908; and Hardy, 1923).

1933. Allison and Cole (U.S.A.). **Algae:** Microorganisms. Barnacles. Experiments designed to identify the causes of almost continuous irregularity of the cirral movements noted during the summertime. The fact responsible for irregularity is some substance in solution in the sea water, perhaps contributed by the disintegration of microorganisms.

1934. Allison and Cole (U.S.A.). **Algae:** Dinoflagellates. Barnacles. To determine why on certain summer days a large percentage of animals in sea water show irregular cirral movements or remain mostly closed. A definite correlation was indicated between percentage closure and the number of dinoflagellates per liter of sea water. Whenever the population of these animals becomes unusually large a correspondingly large percentage of closed barnacles was found. This result is interpreted to mean that some product of metabolism or of decomposition of dinoflagellates causes closure of the barnacle if present in sufficient quantity.

1936. Lucas (England). **Algae:** *Nitzschia closterium* (diatoms). Mysids, copepods. Exclusion experiments to investigate the possible comparative avoidance by animals of illuminated zones of phytoplankton of differing concentration in sea water and brackish water. The adult mysids showed themselves less frequently in the active diatom zone than in diatom-free medium.

_____. _____. Copepods, mysids. Exclusion experiments to investigate the possible comparative avoidance by animals of illuminated zones of phytoplankton of differing concentration in sea water and brackish water. Results were more suggestive than the earlier ones, indicating certain trends in the behavior of the animals in relation to the diatom cultures, i.e., to avoid the illuminated areas of diatom-containing water more than the similarly illuminated areas of water with fewer diatoms or none.

1936. Nightingale (U.S.A.). **Algae:** *Gymnodinium splendens.* Oysters. 10-day

TABLE VI. (Continued)

exposure period to "red water" of progressively higher density. Mucuous formation on gills and much fragmented material in the intestinal tract.

1946. Galtsoff (U.S.A.) **Algae:** *Gymnodinium brevis*. Killifish. Effect of immersion of "red water" extract of the concentration of 1 : 1000. In one hour fish was in distress, lying on side. 20 minutes later was occasionally gulping for air, lying on side. After another 15 minutes was unable to swim even when pushed and respiratory movements slowed down. After another 90 minutes it floated on side with no respiratory movement. Within another 30 minutes, appeared to be dead. Then placed in running sea water. Within 90 minutes respiratory motion starts and fish floats on side. In another hour begins to swim. 12 hours later normal. In review the fish appeared to be dead after about 2½ hours of exposure, but completely recovered after its removal to running sea water.

1947. Corman [in Galtsoff] (U.S.A.). **Algae:** *Gymnodinium brevis*. Killifish. Test toxicity of "red water." Killed fish in 2 hours in 1 : 2 dilution, and in 5½ hours in 1 : 10 dilution.

————. ————. Eggs of the sea urchin *Arbacia*. Studied the effect of "red water" and preserved and concentrated samples on the rate of cleavage. The retardation of cleavage was 9% in 1 : 10 dilution, and 27% in 1 : 5 dilution. Cytolysis resulted from exposure to 1 : 2 dilution.

1948. Galtsoff (U.S.A.) **Algae:** *Gymnodinium brevis*. Killifish. 3 other experiments with a concentration of 1 : 1000 or greater. Gave similar results, namely, a concentration of 1 : 1000 or greater was highly toxic to the fish, while no ill effect was observed in weaker solution.

————. ————. Killifish. Effect of immersion in "red water" extract of the concentration of 1 : 250. Resulted in death of the fish within 1½ hours. Removed from the solution and placed in running sea water in which it was kept for 24 hours, the fish failed to recover.

1950. Bhimacher and George (India). **Algae:** *Noctiluca*. A few live fish. Immersion. A few live fish were kept in the filtered "red water" in glass troughs with separate controls containing sea water taken from an unaffected area. While the fish in the controls were perfectly normal throughout, those in the filtered water from the affected area, though normal at the beginning, showed signs of the toxic effect of the filtrant in 2 hours and died thereafter.

1957. Gunter (U.S.A.). **Algae:** *Gymnodinium brevis*. 8 sheepshead minnows, 2 puffers, 2 majawas, in each aquarium. Florida Bay water containing live dinoflagellates was brought to the laboratory and poured into a glass aquarium. An identical tank with equal amount of Biscayne Bay water was placed side by side with the first: one served as control. Both aquariums were strongly aerated. In the Florida Bay water the minnows died in 22 to 46 hours; both puffers died in 48 hours; and the majawas succumbed—one in 88 hours and another in 118 hours.

————. ————. Controls. One week after the last fish died in the tank containing Florida Bay water, the control fishes were placed in it. They all survived for 3 weeks. From these observations the authors concluded that the "original 'poison'" had been absorbed or taken up by the fishes it killed, or the initial concentration and any which it subsequently produced had been broken down or undergone chemical change rendering it innocuous.

Part 3. Experiments with Toxic Unialgal Cultures

1936. Lucas (England). **Algae:** *Nitzschia closterium* (diatoms). Mysids, copepods. Measuring their length of life when confined to cultures of different strengths to observe toxic effects of differing concentrations of phytoplankton upon animals. There was an optimum concentration of diatoms for a given density of animals, on either side of which an apparently harmful effect might be observed: There was some evidence of ill-effects associated with dense growths of diatoms on the length of life of the animals inhabiting them.

_____. _____. _____. Feeding experiments to investigate rate of consumption of phytoplankton. Given similar food strength, the rates of feeding may be found to vary inversely with the number of feedings.

1935. Parke [in Sieburth] (England). **Algae:** *Phaeocystis pouchetta.* Herring fry. Feeding of culture. Toxic.

1936. Cole [in Davis] (England). **Algae:** *Chlorella.* European oysters. Feeding experiments. The conclusion that the larvae are able to develop on *Chlorella* is not supported by results of well-designed critical experiments.

1947. Loosanoff and Engle (U.S.A.). **Algae:** Mixed cultures of microorganisms. Oysters. Large quantities of food were given under favorable conditions. The oysters failed to show improvement and usually became poorer than the control animal kept in the tank with ordinary sea water. Sometimes, when very large quantities of food organisms were added to the water, the oysters became sick and many died. Examination showed that the stomachs of the oysters that were alive were empty and that the crystalline style was absent.

_____. **Algae:** *Chlorella sp.* (green alga). American oysters. Feeding experiments to determine effect of various types of microorganisms and different concentrations of same. Strong concentrations of *Chlorella* (2 million cells/cc and heavier) depressed the feeding activities of the oysters and changed the character of their shell movements. Light concentrations, e.g., 500,000 cells/cc did not affect the oysters unfavorably. Subjecting the oysters to gradually increasing concentrations of *Chlorella* resulted in further decreases in the rate of pumping. Reversing the procedure and subjecting the oyster to gradually decreasing concentrations resulted in the opposite, i.e., increase in the rate of pumping.

_____. **Algae:** *Nitzschia closterium* (diatom). American oysters. Feeding experiments to determine effects upon the rate of pumping and the character of shell movements. Experiments fully substantiated and corroborated all general conclusions formed during the studies of *Chlorella* (as above).

_____. **Algae:** *Prorocentrum triangulatum* (dinoflagellate). American oysters. Feeding experiments to determine effects upon the rate of pumping and the character of shell movements. Experiments fully substantiated and corroborated all general conclusions formed during the studies of *Chlorella* (as above).

_____. **Algae:** *Euglena viridis* (euglenoid). American oysters. Feeding experiments to determine effects upon the rate of pumping and the character of shell movements. Usually, as soon as the oysters came in contact with a stronger concentrations, the pumping decreased and the type of shell movements changed. As the experiments progressed, we noticed that the oysters became sluggish and their responses to stimuli diminished. For example, if tapped with a glass rod, they would not close their shells as rapidly as under normal conditions. Sometimes the shell would not close at all, as if the tonus of the

TABLE VI. (Continued)

adductor muscle had been partially lost. This condition became more apparent as the experiment progressed, perhaps indicating that the oysters exposed to strong concentrations of *Euglena* became partly paralyzed. Similar observations were made in the previous experiments where forms other than *Euglena viridis* were used. We thought that these conditions might be due partly to purely mechanical causes, such as clogging of the gills with a mass of cells which interfered with the respiration of the oysters, and partly to the toxic effects of the metabolites of the culture. Our experiments gave sufficient evidence to prove that large quantities of microorganisms present in the surrounding water adversely affect the oysters.

————. **Algae:** *Chlorella* (green alga). Oysters. Tests to ascertain the relative importance of the cells and the fluid part of the cultures in affecting the activity of bivalves. ...the filtrate of the culture containing metabolic products of *Chlorella* cells, and the cells, affected the oysters. The rate of pumping was sharply reduced, or even stopped, when the oysters were subjected to either component.

————. **Algae:** *Nitzschia closterium* (diatom). Oysters. A series of similar experiments. Corroborated the results obtained with the *Chlorella*. Each chief component of the culture, the cells, or the filtrate, caused a reduction of the rate of pumping and changed the type of the shell movements of the oysters. Upon return from either one of these components to sea water the oysters soon showed a normal behavior.

————. **Algae:** *Chlorella*. Oysters. Experiments to determine whether the relative quantities of true feces and pseudo-feces formed may be an indication of efficiency of feeding. These experiments showed once more that heavy concentrations of *Chlorella*, containing more than 5 million cells/cc, seriously interfere with the oysters which cease pumping if kept in such a concentration for long periods. In intermediate concentrations ranging from approximately 2 to 00 million cells/cc, the oysters may continue to feed. However, the rate of feeding is low because the activity of oysters is directed primarily to the cleansing of their gills, and results in the formation of a very large quantity of pseudo-feces. If these conditions persist, the oysters may eventually become inactive. Within the scope of our experiments we found that regardless of the type of species, or of their size, the oysters began to show signs of abnormal behavior when, because of the presence of microorganisms, the turbidity of the water, as registered on the microammeter, dropped below the 23 mark. This point corresponded to approximately 2,000,000 *Chlorella*, 70,000 *Nitzschia*, or 3,000 *Euglena* per cc of water.

1948. Gurevich (USSR). **Algae:** *Oscillaria* (blue-green alga). Frogs' eggs. Eggs were placed in algae pond water mixture. ...We were able to establish that the presence of the algae has an impeding effect on the development of the eggs, and that it is undoubtedly related to the excretion of some chemical substances. In a number of experiments, the embryos developed up to the stage of forming external gills and then died: at the same time, in the controlled studies without algae, the embryos developed quite normally. By the 5th day, the controlled dishes have hatched tadpoles: by the same time, the embryos in the experimental dishes (taken from the same egg formation) are in the stage of caudate kidney, and some yet in the stage of neurula or last gastrula. By the 9th day the experimental embryos began to die. When the embryos, after a week's stay in the environment with *Oscillaria*, are removed into the pond water devoid of algae, they do not die: however, their development is markedly retarded.

1949. Gurevich (USSR). **Algae:** *Spirogyra* (green algae). Mollusk embryos. Test influence of the plant life on the animal life. Impede the development.

1949. Korringa (Holland). **Algae:** Flagellates. Oysters. Culture experiments. My own experience makes it highly probable that food, temperature, salinity, pH, and oxygen are not the only factors involved in tank-breeding of oysters. Evidence is adduced to support my hypothesis that many failures in tank breeding may be ascribed to an accumulation of toxic excretions produced by small nanoplanktonic flagellates. Conditions identical to those in a "poisoned" tank have been detected in a fairly stagnant body of water in open communication with the Oostersschelde.

1949. Korringa [in Davis] (Holland). **Algae:** Flagellates. Larvae of the European oyster, *Ostrea edulis*. Feeding experiments. ...water initially containing more than 5,000 flagellates, or a commensurably great number of other phytoplankton, should be mistrusted as it may contain toxic concentrations of phytoplankton metabolites from the first day the tanks are filled.

1951. Loosanoff, Miller, and Smith [in Davis] (U.S.A.). Larvae of *Venus Mercenaria*. Feeding experiments. Noted a lack of uniformity of results in consecutive experiments and considered it possible that at different times the water itself contained certain dissolved substances which, in a manner not yet understood, affected the rate of development of bivalve larvae.

1953. Davis (U.S.A.). **Algae:** Flagellate (an unidentified chrysomonad). Larvae of the American oyster, *Crassostrea virginica*. Feeding experiments. Grew less rapidly than did those in the unfed control culture.

_____. **Algae:** *Chlorella sp.* Oyster larvae. Feeding experiments to determine the effect of the bacteria-free culture on the rate of growth. Repeatedly, the effect on the growth of the larvae during the early stages, although small, is consistently negative.

_____. **Algae:** *Chlorella sp.* (in combination with flagellates). Oyster larvae. Feeding experiments to determine the effect of the bacteria-free culture on the rate of growth. Same as above.

_____. _____. Larva of the American oyster, *Crassostrea virginica*. Feeding experiments. We are probably justified in concluding that with all cultures receiving equal quantities of this food, there is an inverse relation between the concentration of larvae in a culture and their rate of growth, at least after the eighth day.

1954. Davis and Chanley (U.S.A.). **Algae:** Dinoflagellates. Oyster eggs. 12 cultures were started by placing fertilized eggs in cotton filtered sea water to see how many developed into shelled veligers. Only 13.2% of the eggs in the dinoflagellate infested sea water developed far enough to show any shell formation, in contrast to the 73.3% of the eggs in the succeeding experiment that showed shell formation.

_____. _____. _____. Two additional cultures were started in sea water that had been passed through a charcoal filter 3 days before the dinoflagellate bloom appeared. After 48 hours it was found that 57% of the eggs in these 2 cultures had developed normally and that an additional 16.3% had developed some shell but were not normal.

_____. _____. Clams, oysters. Additional attempts to start cultures were made in the infested Harbor water pumped into the laboratory. Virtually none of the eggs developed normally.

TABLE VI. (Continued)

————. **Algae:** *Chlorella.* American oyster, *Crassostrea virginica.* Feeding experiments. Larvae receiving vitamins but no *Chlorella* actually grew faster for the first 6 days than larvae receiving *Chlorella* but no vitamins.

————. ————. ————. ————. All cultures receiving riboflavin throughout the experiment, but the addition of *Chlorella* was delayed until the 2nd, 4th or 6th day. By the 14th day, the larvae in the culture that did not receive *Chlorella* until the 6th day were not only larger, but a higher percentage of them had survived.

————. **Algae:** Dinoflagellates. Clams, oysters. Cultures were started in sea water that was relatively free of dinoflagellates, brought in from a point far out in the Long Island Sound almost midway between Milford and the Long Island Coast. The percentage of eggs developing normally even in this Sound water was comparatively low; only 40.61% for oysters and 36.03% for clams, perhaps indicating that the effects of the bloom extended some distance offshore.

————. ————. ————. Cultures were started in Harbor water. Nevertheless, development in Sound water was considerably better than in Harbor water in which only 4.59% of the oyster eggs and 5.89% of the clam eggs developed normally.

————. ————. ————. Cultures were started about 2 weeks after the onset of the bloom when some abatement in the number of dinoflagellates began. The percentage of eggs developing normally began to increase until, within a few days, cultures could be started with approximately normal success.

————. ————. Clam and oyster eggs. Cultures were started after the development of a bloom. Again we found that the presence of the bloom was correlated with the failure of all but a very small percentage of either clam or oyster eggs to develop into normal straight-hinged larvae. Removal of the dinoflagellates, by filtering the sea water through millipore filters, only slightly increased the percentage of eggs developing normally. We believe, therefore, that the effects noted are attributable to dissolved substances. The abnormal development of clam and oyster eggs may result from the almost complete removal of some substance necessary for normal development, by the rapid increase in numbers of dinoflagellates, or it may result from the toxicity of certain external metabolites liberated by the dinoflagellates. A third possibility is that some substance, by favoring the rapid growth of dinoflagellates and by preventing the normal development of larvae, is responsible for both phenomena.

1957. Guillard (U.S.A.). **Algae:** Flagellates, diatoms. Larvae and adult bivalves. Feeding of pure algal cultures and those grown with bacteria. Whereas pure cultures of many algae are not toxic, if grown with bacteria they are. He recommends feeding of cultures at the peak of their rapid growth before development of appreciable waste products (external metabolites).

1957. Smith (U.S.A.). **Algae:** *Nitschia closterium* (diatoms). Quahogs. Using food organisms grown in radioactive solution, measured rates of clearing the water as a measure of gill efficiency. Addition of diatoms slowed pumpage of water, though clogging of gills. Since diatoms are a major food of quahogs, it is suspected that toxic materials in the culture may have been responsible for fall in pumping rate.

1957. Guillard (U.S.A.). **Algae:** *Amphidinium carteri* (dinoflagellate), *Gymnodinium sp.* (dinoflagellate). Larvae, or juvenile oysters or clams. Food value assay. Useless as food, though they did not kill larvae.

———. **Algae:** *Chlorella A* (green alga). Larvae or juvenile oysters or clams. Using food organisms grown in radioactive solution, measured rates of clearing the water as a measure of gill efficiency. Moderately toxic, particularly to oyster larvae. The fact that a microorganism can be toxic when fed to larvae or juveniles does not necessarily imply that it can prevent the development of eggs to the straight hinge stage. *Chlorella* isolate *A* is an example.

———. **Algae:** *Stichococcus sp.* (green alga). Larvae, or juvenile oysters or clams. Using food organisms grown in radioactive solution, measured rates of clearing the water as a measure of gill efficiency. Moderately toxic, particularly to oyster larvae. It is of interest that two different *Stichococcus*-like organisms, one from Great South Bay and one from the Martha's Vineyard ponds, were also relatively toxic.

———. **Algae:** *Prymnesium parvum* (chrysophyte). Larvae, or juvenile oysters or clams. Using food organisms grown in radioactive solution, measured rates of clearing the water as a measure of gill efficiency. Extremely toxic to all stages of both bivalves. This organism, which unfortunately is widely distributed, produces a toxin of high molecular weight. Exposure to normal feeding concentrations of *Prymnesium* prevented the development of oyster eggs and caused heavy mortality in cultures of larval clams and oysters. In a 17-day feeding experiment with 3 mm oyster spat and 3.8 mm juvenile clams of average sizes, 100% of the oysters and 75% of the clams died.

1955. Wilson and Collier (U.S.A.). **Algae:** *Gymnodinium brevis.* *Mollienesia, Mambras.* Immersion. All fish died.

1957. Roy and Wilson (U.S.A.). **Algae:** *Gymnodinium brevis.* Fish. Immersion to reconfirm toxicity of unialgal culture. Killed.

1957. Abbott and Ballantine (England). **Algae:** *Gymnodinium veneficum.* Mussels. Feeding of toxic cultures to shellfish in attempt to bring about poison concentration in digestive glands. Strong cultures were lethal within a day, and more dilute cultures eventually killed the shellfish without any significant concentration of the toxin by the animals.

———. ———. *Calliactis* (coelenterate). Immersion in culture. Death in 2–3 days (slowly affected).

———. ———. ———. Immersion plus injection of extract. Death in 2–3 days (slowly affected).

———. ———. *Anemonia* (coelenterate). Immersion in culture. Death in 3–4 days (slowly affected).

———. ———. ———. Immersion plus injection of extract. Death in 3–4 days (slowly affected).

———. ———. Ephyrae of *Aurelia* (coelenterate). Immersion in culture. Death in less than 1 minute (rapidly killed).

———. ———. *Nereis* (annelid). Immersion in culture. Not affected.

———. ———. ———. Immersion plus injection of extract. Not affected.

———. ———. ———. Immersion plus incision. Not affected.

———. ———. *Aremicola* (annelid). Immersion in culture. Not affected.

———. ———. *Calanus* (crustacean). Immersion in culture. Death in 1–2 days (slowly affected).

———. ———. *Ciona* (tunicate). Immersion in culture. Death in 3 days (slowly affected).

———. ———. *Amphioxus* (cephalochordate). Immersion in culture. Death in 45 minutes (rapidly killed).

TABLE VI. (Continued)

———. ———. Dogfish (fish). Immersion in culture. Death in 3 hours (rapidly killed).

———. ———. Pollack. Immersion in culture. Death in 18 minutes (rapidly killed).

———. ———. Blenny. Immersion in culture. Death in less than 45 minutes (rapidly killed).

———. ———. Lesser weaver. Immersion in culture. Death in 30 minutes (rapidly killed).

———. ———. Goby. Immersion in culture. Death in 5–15 minutes (rapidly killed).

———. ———. ———. ———. Death in 5–10 minutes (rapidly killed).

———. ———. Plaice. Immersion in culture. Death in 30 minutes (rapidly killed).

———. ———. Wrasse. Immersion in culture. Death in 15–20 minutes (rapidly killed).

———. ———. Frog (amphibian). Injection of extract. Strong, rapid paralysis kills in about 30 hours (rapidly killed).

———. ———. Mouse (mammal). Injection of extract. Death in 2–4 minutes (rapidly killed).

1957. Ballantine and Abbott (England). **Algae:** *Gymnodinium veneficum.* Small fish, mainly gobies. Physiologic effects: investigation of mode of action of the toxin by immersion. Die within 10 minutes in toxic cultures.

———. ———. Frog. Injection of the toxin into dorsal lymph sac. Immediate paralyzing effect.

———. ———. Whelk heart. Effect on isolated tissues. Particularly sensitive; the heart stops in systole and can be used for bio-assay.

———. ———. Frog sartorius muscle. Effect on isolated tissues. Becomes inexcitable both to indirect (nerve) and to direct (muscle) stimulation.

———. ———. Frog muscle fiber. Studies of membrane potentials. Resting potential drops to a very small value within a few minutes of application of toxin, and excitability disappears.

———. ———. *Tigriopus* (crustacean). Immersion in culture. Death in 1–3 days (slowly affected).

———. ———. *Hemimysis.* Immersion in culture. Death in 2–3 days (slowly affected).

———. ———. *Macromysis.* Immersion in culture. Death in 3–4 days (slowly affected).

———. ———. *Palaemon.* Immersion in culture. Death after 4 days (slowly affected).

———. ———. *Eupagurus.* Immersion in culture. Death in 2–3 days (slowly affected).

———. ———. *Carcinus.* Immersion in culture. Death after 4 days (slowly affected).

———. ———. *Cancer.* Immersion in culture. Death in 3 days (slowly affected).

———. ———. *Mytilus* e. (mollusk). Immersion in culture. Death in less than 3 days (slowly affected).

———. ———. *Mytilus* g. (Immersion in culture. Death in less than 3 days (slowly affected).

_____. _____. *Pecten.* Immersion in culture. Death in 1 hour (rapidly killed).

_____. _____. *Lasaea.* Immersion in culture. Death in less than 1 day (slowly affected).

_____. _____. *Buccimon.* Immersion in culture. Death in 1 hour (rapidly killed).

_____. _____. *Aplysia.* Immersion in culture. Death in 1 hour (rapidly killed).

_____. _____. *Eusepia.* Immersion in culture. Death in 3 hours (rapidly killed).

_____. _____. *Asterias* (echinoderm). Immersion in culture. Death in 3–5 days (slowly affected).

_____. _____. *Ophiothrix.* Immersion in culture. Death in less than 3 days (slowly affected).

_____. _____. *Ophiocomina.* Immersion in culture. Death in less than 3 days (slowly affected).

_____. _____. Frog skin. Studies of membrane potentials. Resting potential drops to a very small value within a few minutes of application of toxin, and excitability disappears.

1958. Starr (U.S.A.). **Algae:** *Gymnodinium brevis.* Guppy, mullet, Bioassay of toxin in unialgal culture. Most of our toxin preparations from unialgal mass cultures (1.5 million cells per liter) killed mullet within 2–4 minutes. As the preparations were diluted, the symptoms of distress and time of death were prolonged. Mullet showed the following: within 30 seconds a violent twisting and turning accompanied by corkscrew type movements: then contractions and tail curvature at intervals of 10–20 seconds: within 1–2 minutes equilibrium is lost and fish may turn upside-down or on its side: opercular movements are irregular and slow: little response to probing and they may remain quiescent: immediately before death a violent burst of activity occurs and the fish dies with mouth and opercula opened. Once equilibrium is lost, removal to non-toxic water does not aid recovery. Toxin preparations which kill mullet in 2–4 minutes kill guppies in 8–15 minutes. The response of the guppy is sluggish compared to the mullet, but the symptoms are similar.

Halstead and his colleagues reported (1955) on toxic marine algae off the coast of California and Palmyra Island (960 miles southwest of Honolulu). They made watery extracts of single and mixed species and found them definitely toxic to mice when injected intraperitoneally. Responses included lacrimation, ruffed hair, diarrhea, dyspnea, and weakness with weak toxins; death within thirty-six hours with moderately strong ones and death within an hour with highly potent ones.

Many experiments have been made with suspectedly toxic algae from marine areas. Abbott and Ballantine extracted toxin from cultures of *Gymnodinium veneficum* by dialysis. These cultures were unialgal but not bacteria-free. However, the authors considered the toxin a product of *Gymnodinium* itself, since repeated cultures of the bacteria were nontoxic. They characterized the toxin molecule as probably "large," since it does not pass a dialyzing membrane; soluble in water and the lower alcohols; insoluble in ether and chloroform; unstable in acids, with formation of another toxic product; and decomposed by hot alkali, but rather thermo-stable in neutral solutions. They agree with Sommer and Meyer that this toxin is not the same as paralytic shellfish poison, since they could not render shellfish poisonous with it.

The major Abbott and Ballantine experiments were made with highly susceptible animals, such as *Amphioxus*, fish, frogs, mice, and certain molluscs especially vulnerable because of poor shell closure. The fish *Gobius virescens* was used most extensively for comparison of culture and extract toxicity because of its availability and sensitivity to the *Gymno-dinium* toxin. Its immediate reaction was a violent attempt to swim away (forwards or backwards), intense vasodilatation and chromatophorous color change, equilibrial disturbances, bradypnea, gasping, vomiting, diminished sensory response, paralysis, and death. The fish could recover if removed to clean sea water before its balance was disturbed. In marine animals the gills are the primary site of entry of the toxin, although peroral intake can cause slow toxicity.

As some of you may know, the lead article in a recent *New York Times* Sunday magazine section deals with farming the sea to increase the world's food supply. The article is entitled " Aquiculture is more than a dream."

In closing my section of this presentation, may I add that it can also be a nightmare.

ALGAL TOXICITY IN HUMANS—DAVID SCHWIMMER, M.D.

Most of this symposium is devoted to algal taxonomy, structure, bio-chemistry, and environmental parameters. Dr. Morton Schwimmer has just discussed some algal effects upon animals and fish. I am pleased to talk to you now about algae and what they do to *man*. Man, after all, is the ulti-mate objective (sometimes beneficiary, sometimes victim) at the end of a long chain of scientific observations.

We have elsewhere made ample documentation of the abundant pres-ence of algae in the air, water, soil, caves, plants, animals, and various food products. We also know that algae can enter the human body by inhalation, ingestion, injection, and contact. This means you can breathe them in, either just into the nose, or all the way into the bronchi and alveoli. You can eat them, either *in* or *on* food, or even as the food of the future. You can inject them by design or by contamination or by accidental trauma. Or, if you really want to be efficient, go swimming or fall in when the bloom is on; then you can swallow algae, inhale them, and at the same time achieve ex-cellent direct skin contact.

The effects of toxic algae in man tend to be less acute than in animals because of ingestion of smaller amounts, though this may occur over longer periods of time. This chronicity obtains because man's sensitive olfactory discrimination (and maybe even his intelligence) prevents his swimming in or drinking too large an amount of uncertified water smelly from spoiled algae. Add to this the low index of suspicion of physicians who are unaware of algae, let alone algal toxicity, and the number of diagnosed algal illnesses will be pitifully small.

Human Respiratory Disorders Associated with Algae

Since breathing is a somewhat more constant function than eating, drinking, or swimming, I shall discuss respiratory involvement first. As with animals, respiratory exposure to toxic algae has led to dyspnea, cyanosis, wheezing, choking, and foamy nasal discharge. Pathological lesions have ranged from simple congestion to acute bronchitis to pleural effusion to acute pulmonary edema. These have been reproduced by the administration of toxic algae both in natural state and from unialgal culture. Dead algae can be as noxious as live ones, via either toxicity or allergenicity. And we must remember that inhaled algae can involve other parts of the body besides the respiratory tract. Conversely, respiratory symptoms can result from algal entry through any other portal. Also to be remembered is that respiratory responses to algae can be enhanced by other irritants such as dust, sulfur dioxide, nitrogen oxide, bacteria, viruses, and fungi.

Back in 1917 Taylor reported on fish deaths since 1844 from "poison water" off Florida's west coast. Said he, "Fishes of a great number of species were noted dead and dying; the air was charged with a suffocating gas, which not only occasioned severe discomfort to man and other air-breathing animals, but irritated the air passages, producing the symptoms of colds. This gas, while exceedingly irritating, had no odor." Another observer is quoted, "My attention was called to the action of the dog, which was sneezing violently and seemed to be in acute distress, choking and showing every symptom of asphyxiation. . . . I then noticed that my lungs were feeling sore and that my breathing was labored." There were also many other people with similar respiratory complaints. The same "gas" appeared to affect the live fish and apparently ultimately killed them.

Lund in Texas reported a marine "gas" associated with fish kills, which he associated with "heavy inshore plankton growth." He thought the "gas" might be volatile amines from decaying fish, but he offered no proof.

Gunter et al., writing of Florida fish deaths in 1947, said, "An odorless acrid gas causing stinging of the nostrils and hard coughing made life miserable for the residents of Captiva Island. . . . particularly strong in a sample of yellow water." The yellow discoloration was due to *Gymnodinium brevis*. There was no H_2S or SO_2; and O_2 content of the water was normal, and no undue salinities were present in the water.

Woodcock studied respiratory irritation extensively in Venice, Florida, during an episode of fish deaths associated with "red water" due to *Gymnodinium*. He noted Somner's 1937 observation that high concentrations of certain dinoflagellates produced irritating or poisonous gases. Woodcock cited the presence of "sea water nuclei" from 0.3 to 30.0 micra radius in the overlying oceanic air. These aerosols are formed by bursting bubbles from breaking waves. Woodcock sprayed sea water containing 56×10^6 per liter of *Gymnodinium sp.* (25 micra in diameter) into the nose and throat with a hand atomizer. This produced cough and nasopharyngeal burning comparable to that found on the local beaches during onshore winds. Clear sea water from nearby caused no such symptoms.

Also investigating the winter "red tide" off western Florida, Galtsoff found "spasmic coughing, a burning sensation in the throat and nostrils, and irritation of the eyes. . . . Symptoms resembling those of a heavy cold or hay fever." The ingredients required to achieve this included an off-shore wind, breaking surf, an odorless highly irritating "gas" coming from the water, and—of course—the "red tide." Other toxins, e.g., pesticides, mustard gas, and arsenic, were excluded. Galtsoff incriminated as the cause of these symptoms (and fish deaths) chiefly *Gymnodinium* particles, but also others producing colored waters, e.g., *Gonyaulax, Glenodinium, Mesodinium,* and *Peridinium*. The *Gonyaulax* and *Gymnodinium* have also been implicated in shellfish poisoning, of which we shall speak a little later.

Abbott and Ballantine also produced respiratory symptoms with *Gymnodinium* cultures. They considered the mechanism unrelated to histamine, since the symptoms were not relieved by antihistamines. For whatever it might mean, we can mention here that gobies could be a little protected against *Gymnodinium* by previous exposure to nontoxic flagellates, and also by the addition of cholesterol to the toxic sea water. I knew that someone would rise up to champion cholesterol!

Discussing the same "red tide" in Gulf waters is a rather defensive article by Ingle for the Florida State Board of Conservation. He reviews some of the works mentioned and emphasizes that (1) The respiratory effects are temporary; (2) they occur only when the wind or heat forms aerosols; and (3) these irritating particles do not go far inland, anyway.

The accent is a bit different when federal monies are sought for study of the periodic Floridian menace. As La Cossitt has said, tourist and fishing businesses are badly hit, not only by the massive fish deaths and their stench but also by the resulting human ills. Not only are there the respiratory symptoms previously described; there occur also more severe cases of tracheo-bronchitis and pneumonitis, especially in allergic, asthmatic, or cardiac patients.

A most convincing demonstration that algae were allergenic was made by Herman Heise in Wisconsin. He reported (1949) two cases of hay fever, conjunctivitis, and asthma due to Oscillatoriaceae sensitivity in patients who had swum in a lake when the bloom was on. Intradermal injections produced positive skin tests, passive transfer tests were positive, and desensitization relieved symptoms. He also reported (1951) similar results with *Microcystis* in ten patients susceptible to Oscillatoriaceae. Identical results were obtained for both algae in parallel quantitative skin tests. This led Heise to assume that both these Myxophycae subgroups contained similar antigens.

Inhalant allergy due to airborne green algae was first reported in 1962 by McElhenny and his group in Austin and McGovern in Houston. They utilized unialgal bacteria-free cultures of four strains: *Neochloris sp.* (Hawaii), *Chlorosarcinopsis sp.* (South Dakota), *Bracteacoccus sp.* (Texas), and *Hormidium sp.* (Texas). Testing extracts were made by standard techniques. Of 140 children tested, twenty were non-allergic and 120 were known to have pollen or other inhalant sensitivities, all worse when the wind was blowing. None of the non-allergic children reacted to the algae. Of the 120 allergic individuals, twenty-two also did not react to any of the four algae. The other ninety-eight showed definite positive reactions to intracutaneous injection of one or more of the four green algae. Twenty subjects reacted to one strain, thirty-four to two, thirty-four to three, and ten to all four. The authors suggest that algae thus may well play an important role in many difficult or obscure inhalant allergies. They stress the difficulty of culturing algae, especially the blue-greens, and note that fungi frequently overgrow algae if the culture media contain organic substrates.

A logical follow-up of this study is the report by Bernstein and Safferman (1966) in Cincinnati on the sensitivity of the skin and bronchial mucosa to green algae. They employed bacteria-free cultures of six Chlorococcales that appear to be encountered most often in samples of air, soil, and water: *Chlorella vulgaris, Chlorella pyrenoidosa, Chlorococcum botryoides, Chlorococcum macrostigmastum, Scenedesmus basilensis*, and *Ankistrodesmus falcatus*. They tested seventy-nine atopic patients with well-documented histories of extrinsic allergies, chiefly rhinitis and asthma; all had marked skin reactions for various inhalant allergens. There were twenty-six non-allergic controls. Of the seventy-nine atopic patients, forty-seven gave positive skin reactions to one or more of the six algae. There was no significant cross-reactivity among the algae. Skin sensitivity antibodies could be passively transferred from six of eight patients so studied. Direct bronchial mucosal testing was done in eight asthmatic patients; positive responses were obtained in five. Not only did they have decreases in peak expiratory flow rate, they also actually developed clinical wheezing. Provocative tests with *Chlorella vulgaris* were negative in six asthmatics with negative skin responses to this alga, and also in five non-asthmatics. Since some 20–30 million Americans are afflicted by obvious inhalant allergies, the importance of the subject is evident.

Human Skin Disorders Associated with Algae

Let us now consider the skin. Thick or thin, it is susceptible to direct irritation and to allergenicity, both properties possessed by algae. Fishermen have complained that "red tide" water burned their arms and hands. People generally will not swim in water very heavily infested with algae, but they do sometimes fall in. Or they may swim in an area not obviously infested.

Wiley Sams (1949) described a "seabather's eruption" in sixty-seven patients who had swum off the east coast of Florida. This is an acute itchy erythematous dermatitis with wheals and papules, especially in areas covered by bathing suits, perhaps because of pressure of the causative organism against the skin. Immediate showering after exposure prevents manifestations. Antihistamines help to control the itching and eruption. Sams clearly differentiated this entity from "swimmer's itch," which occurs in freshwater, involves any exposed part, and is definitely due to cercaria of *Schistosoma*. Some of the discussers of Sams's paper thought seabather's eruption might be related to jellyfish or Portuguese man-of-war; others considered some nematocyst, and still others thought microscopic algae such as *Gymnodinium* more likely. Hardin (1961) also described seabather's eruption in Georgians who had been to Florida. He obtained gratifying relief with oral steroids in severe cases.

A far more definitive relationship to algae was that established in Hawaii by Grauer and Arnold and by Banner. They reported a more severe contact eruption, a *dermatitis escharotica*, as being due to direct irritation (not allergy) by *Lyngbya majuscula*, a blue-green alga. This appeared in some 125 swimmers only during the summer months of 1958, 1959, and 1960, and only on the windward side of Oahu. The irritation occurred in the same bathing suit distribution as in Sams's cases and was preventable by washing with soap and water. If not cleansed, the dermal erythema shortly progressed to blistering, peeling, oozing, and ultimately to scarring. There has been no good explanation for the localization of this malady to one island only.

Cohen and Reif demonstrated definite allergy to *Anabaena* in a youngster who developed a papulo-vesicular eruption whenever she swam in a Pennsylvania lake containing the bloom. Sensitivity was chiefly due to the algal phycocyanin. Cohen and Reif also observed acute allergic conjunctivitis in many other people swimming in lakes with blue-green algal blooms. Dr. Sladeckova has also mentioned to me today cases of allergic responses to *Aphanizomenon* noted by co-workers in Prague.

Human Mycoses Associated with Algae

In 1940 Szendy in Brazil reported isolating algae from patients with pleural effusion and pneumothorax, but Mariani in Italy could not confirm this. Another Brazilian, Almeida, isolated *Chlorella* or *Chlorococcum* from three patients with fungus infections. One had renal actinomycosis; one had pulmonary and lingual blastomycosis, and one had dermal and lymphatic blastomycosis. The role of the algae here is unclear—were there contaminants, symbionts, or did they really help to cause disease? If so, did the mycoses, or the therapy for them, permit the algae to grow?

Human Gastrointestinal Disorders Associated with Algae

Now let us look at the human digestive tract. Some algae can be resident therein without creating abnormalities. Kuchenmeister (1885) and Hallier (1886) reported *Oscillaria* parasitic in the intestine. In the 1920's Simons and Fellinger noted them in the mouth, and Langeron noted them in stools. Langeron also found *Anabaenolium* in stools, while Newiadomski and Mariani reported *Blastocystis*. Apparently, none of these algae produced any disorder. In the realm of algae-caused disease, the outstanding and earliest report was that made in 1842 by Farre to the Microscopical Society in London. He described a thirty-five-year-old woman who ". . . suffered lately from slight dyspepsia. Six days ago, after suffering considerable griping pains in the bowels, which continued for 12 hours, she passed *per anum* a number of shreds, which being discharged with some difficulty, and causing an obstruction of the bowel, her attention was thereby attracted, and some of the shreds were pulled away by herself, so that there can be no question as to the source whence they were derived." Farre identified the shreds as *Oscillatoria* and felt they came from drinking water "supplied by the ordinary service-pipes of the metropolis."

Ashford *et al.*, reported a sprue-like syndrome in two Puerto Rican

women, apparently caused by *Prototheca portoricensis*. La Cossit cites
the case of a skin diver who deliberately swam into a Florida "red tide"
(*Gymnodinium*) and swallowed some of the water. He developed numbness, nausea, and abdominal cramps.

Some of the best-documented cases of human algal illnesses are those
presented by Dillenberg in Saskatchewan. These were noted after many
fatal algal poisonings had occurred in the area. The first case was that of a
tourist who developed headache, nausea, vomiting, and diarrhea after
swimming in Gull Lake; his stool contained *Microcystis*, but no other
etiologic agents. The next episode involved ten children who had swum in
Long Lake and developed vomiting and diarrhea; their stools contained
Anabaena. Another episode concerned a physician who fell into Echo Lake
and unwillingly swallowed a half pint (of lake water!); three hours later he
experienced nausea, cramps, vomiting, and diarrhea. The next day he had
a fever of 102°, severe headache, generalized aching, and weakness. His
stool contained many *Microcystis* and some *Anabaena*. Dr. Dillenberg's
own son developed similar manifestations after falling into a lake and
swallowing the water; both his vomitus and stool contained *Aphanizomenon*. Four students also experienced malaise, headache, nausea, and
diarrhea after swimming in a lake containing a heavy growth of *Microcystis* and *Anabaena*. Dillenberg also reported the near-fatal case of a
twelve-year-old boy who developed fever, labored breathing, pneumonitis,
generalized pains, and coma after swimming in water containing *Microcystis aeruginosa*. Dillenberg thought the sudden onset and coma signified
the action of a potent algal toxin.

There was also a series of outbreaks of nearly epidemic proportions of
digestive upsets in the Ohio River valley. These were characterized by
sudden onset of nausea, cramps, vomiting, and diarrhea, and they lasted
one to four days. Tisdale thought they represented algal intoxication from
heavy growths of blue-greens after a severe drought, but others are not
completely convinced. Similar epidemics, without bacterial etiology and
with algae present, have been reported from New Jersey and from Yellowstone National Park.

These algal ingestions have been for the most part involuntary. There
are also some studies of algae intended for use as food. Although the
Orientals and Hawaiians have long eaten some algae, the rest of the world
has scarcely considered them gustatory delicacies. The taste, color, and
tough consistency have diminished the acceptability of algae as food. Attempts have been made, therefore, to modify algae chemically and mechanically. They have been diluted and disguised, but they have not wholly
deceived. This is the substance of reports by Hayami and Shino, who added
30 g. of decolorized *Chlorella* to a basal diet without nutritional benefit.

And when McDowell and his colleagues fed *Chlorella* to five men in significant quantities, they experienced nausea, abdominal fullness and cramping, malaise, and headache, and their stools became green, dry, and hard.

Shellfish Poisoning in Humans

It is clear that one need not ingest algae in pure culture to achieve toxicity. Deleterious effects can also be obtained simply by eating the wrong fish. There have been many reports of illness resulting from eating poisonous fish, one of the earliest being that reported by Meyer as having occurred in the Virgin Islands in 1530. The commonest type is the periodic acute paralytic shellfish poisoning following the eating of clams and mussels.

Manifestations are chiefly neurological, with tingling and numbness of the mouth, face, and fingers, muscular incoordination and paralysis, then respiratory failure. Death may occur in a few hours. It has been observed that the shellfish are usually toxic only when they have ingested large amounts of *Gonyaulax*, generally during the summer months. The poison is now known as "saxitoxin," an alkaloid with effects like those of muscarine, strychnine, and aconitine. It is concentrated mostly in the liver and digestive organs and is not poisonous to the shellfish themselves.

Incidentally, we know that infectious hepatitis can also be transmitted in both sporadic and epidemic form by raw clams and oysters that have grown in presumably polluted estuarial waters. Steaming of the clams has usually been considered sufficient protection against transmission of the hepatitis (whose causative virus or viruses have not yet been isolated). Several proper Bostonians, however, have recently shown that steaming clams only until the shells open is not enough. Most will open during the first minute, whereas four–six minutes are required to heat the inner clam to the 100° C needed to inactivate the hepatitis agent.

Human paralytic poisoning following eating of oysters from Sarasota Bay during a *Gymnodinium brevis* "red tide" was reported as having occurred in 1962. Extracts of the oysters were toxic to mice and kittens; additionally McFarren *et al.*, extracted a *Ciguatera*-like poison from the oysters, and also from clams and *G. breve* cultures derived from the area. Ray and Aldrich also demonstrated that oysters exposed to laboratory cultures of *G. breve* are toxic when fed to chicks. All eight showed marked loss of equilibrium, and six died within six to twenty-two hours. Having proved the potential toxicity of oysters from *G. breve*, Ray and Aldrich attributed its relative infrequency to the fact that commercially exploitable quantities of oysters usually grow in Gulf areas with salinity levels of 25 per 1,000, or less, a concentration which inhibits development of *G. breve.*

Ichthyosarcotoxicosis

Other ichthyosarcotoxicoses occur in all parts of the world. Halstead divided them into four clinical groups: *Tetraedon* (puffer) poisoning, *Gymnothorax* (Moray eel) poisoning, *Ciguatera,* and *Scombroid* poisoning. Randall has modified this to include *Gymnothorax* as a severe form of *Ciguatera,* and to consider *Scombroid* as probably bacterial in origin. Tetraedon poisoning is associated only with the puffer or porcupine fish of the Tetraodontoidae suborder. The poison is chiefly concentrated in the liver, gonads, and skin, some in the viscera, but not in the musculature. The very potent toxin "tetrodotoxin," which is apparently not planktogenic, was crystallized in 1950 by Yokoo. It is fascinating to note that several years ago Buchwald and his group demonstrated that "tarichatoxin," an extraordinarily powerful neurotoxin crystallized from eggs of the California newt *Taricha,* was identical with "tetrodotoxin." The substance is nonprotein, has an action resembling that of local anesthetics, and is being actively studied for its effect on various aspects of nerve transmission.

A large number of fish are capable of producing *Ciguatera.* It has been reported from all seas, but mostly from the Pacific. *Ciguatera* is characterized by gastrointestinal and neurological manifestations, with nausea, vomiting, paresthesias, arthralgias, weakness, and dysequilibrium. Severe cases may progress to coma and death. It is an inconstant disease, occurring in one small area, then another, while neighboring waters may be entirely free. Randall says fish producing *Ciguatera* are not zooplankton feeders, but rather piscivores, feeding on other fish that have fed on toxic benthic blue-green algae. Thus the incidence of toxicity will depend upon the ecological food succession. The actual noxious agent, named "ciguatoxin," has just recently been isolated from *Gymnothorax javanicus* by Scheuer and his group. It is a transparent, light yellow, viscous oil which could not be crystallized. It is relatively unstable and loses toxicity in contact with air, light, and chromatographic adsorbents. It appears to be a lipid containing a quaternary nitrogen atom, one or more hydroxyl groups, and a cyclopentanone moeity. Since ciguatoxin exhibits distinct anticholinesterase activity in animals, it is interesting that it is not a phosphatidic ester.

There are other aspects of algal-human relations that could be discussed, very many that remain to be elucidated. As our chemists identify more substances, as our electron microscopists visualize presently hidden structures, and as our physicians become more algologically aware, so shall we make more progress. A fruitful area would seem to be one involving the interaction of algae with other disease-producing agents, such as bacteria, viruses, and fungi.

REFERENCES

Abbott, B. C., and Ballantine, D., 1957. "The toxin from *Gymnodinium veneficum* Ballantine," *J. Marine Biol.* Ass., U.K., *36*:169.

Aiyar, 1936. "Mortality of fish of the Madras Coast in June 1935," *Current Science* (Bangalore) *4*:488.

"Algae, fish flour, chemical diets tested for therapy, space travel," *Scope Weekly*, Kalamazoo, Mich. May 4, 1960.

Arakawa, S., Tsumuri, N., Murakami, K., Muto, S., Hoshino, J., and Yagi, T., 1960. "Experimental breeding of white leghorn with *Chlorella*-added combined feed," *Japan J. Exp. Med. 30* (3):185.

Arakawa, S., Tsumuri, N., Murakami, K., Hoshino, J., and Nagashima, H., 1960. "Experimental breeding of mice with *Chlorella*-added combined feed and their resisting power against dysentery bacilli," *Yokohama Med. Bull. 11*:186.

Arthur, J. C., 1885. "Second report on some algae of Minnesota supposed to be poisonous," University of Minnesota. Dept. of Agric. Report 1881/86. Biennial Report of the Board of Regents, No. 4, Suppl. No. 1, p. 109, *ibid.*, Bull. Minnesota Acad. Nat. Sc. *3*:97.

Ashford, B. K., Ciferri, R., and Dalmau, L. M., 1930. "A new species of *Prototheca* and a variety of the same isolated from the human intestine," *Arch. f. Protistenkunde 70*:619.

Ashworth, C. T., and Mason, M. F., 1946. "Observations on the pathological changes produced by a toxic substance present in blue-green algae (*Microcystis aeruginosa*)," *Am. J. Path.* 22:369.

Astakhova, T. V., Kun, M. S., and Teplyi, D. L., 1960. "O prichine zabolevaniya sazana nijney Volgi [On the cause of carp disease in the lower Volga]," Doklady Akademii Nauk SSSR (Moscow) *133*:1205.

Ayres, S., 1949. "Discussion of W. M. Sams' Seabather's eruption," Arch. Dermat. & Syph. *60*:236.

Bailey, J. W., 1959. "Algae can poison cattle," *Jersey J. 6*:5.

Ballantine, D., and Abbott, B. C., 1957. "Toxic marine flagellates; their occurrence and physiological effects on animals," *J. Gen. Microbiol. 16*:274.

Banner, A. H., 1959. "A dermatitis-producing alga in Hawaii; preliminary report," *Hawaii Med. J. 19*:35.

Barnum, D. A., Henderson, J. A., and Stewart, A. G., 1950. "Algae poisoning in Ontario," *Milk Producer 25*:312.

Becker, M. J., and Shefner, A. M., 1963. "Research on the chemical composition and digestibility of algal cell walls," United States. 6570th Aerospace Medical Research Laboratories, Wright-Patterson AFB, Ohio. Technical Documentary Report No. AMRL–TDR–63–115.

Bergmann, F., Parnas, I., and Reich, K., 1963. "Observations on the mechanism of action and on the quantitative assay of ichthyotoxin from *Prymnesium parvum* Carter," *Toxicology and Appl. Pharmacol. 5*:637.

Berlin, R., 1948. "Haff disease in Sweden," *Acta. Med. Scand. 129*:560.

Berman, I., 1960. "Formation of toxic principles in concentrated cell suspensions of *Prymnesium parvum*," M. Sc. thesis, Hebrew Univ., Jerusalem, Israel.

Bhimachar, B. S., and George, P. C., 1950. "Abrupt set-backs in the fisheries of the Malabar and Kanara coasts and "red water" phenomenon as their probable cause (Communicated by H. S. Rao)," Proc. Indian Acad. Sci., Sect. B *31*:339.

Bishop, C. T., Anet, E. F. L. J., and Gorham, P. R., 1959. "Isolation and identification of the fast-death factor in *Microcystis aeruginosa* NRC-1," *Canad. J. Biochem. & Physiol. 37*:453.

Bowman, R. O., Middlebrook, J. B., and McDaniel, R. H., 1962. "Nutritional value of algae for mice," *Aerospace Med. 33*:589.

Bowman, R. O., and Thomae, F. W., 1961. "Long-term nontoxic support of animal life with algae," *Science 134*:55.

Braginskii, L. P., 1955. "O toksichnosti sine-zelenykh vodorosley [On the toxicity of blue-green algae]," Priroda (Moscow) *44 (1):117.*

Branco, S. M., 1959. "Algas toxicas—controle das toxinas em aguas de abasticimento [Toxic algae—control of toxins in waste water]," Revista do Departmento de Aguas e Esgatos de Sao Paulo *20* (33):21; *20* (34):29.

Brandenburg, T. O., and Shigley, F. M., 1947. "Water bloom as a cause of poisoning in livestock in North Dakota," *J. Am. Vet. Med. Assoc. 110*:384.

Brongersma-Sanders, M., 1948. "The importance of upwelling water to vertebrate paleontology and oil geology," Verhandel. K. Nederl. Akad. Wetensch. Afd. Natuurkunde, Sect. 2, Deel 45, No. 4, p. 1.

Burlew, J. S., ed., 1953. "Algal culture, from laboratory to pilot plant," Carnegie Institution of Washington, Publication 600.

Carter, H. J., 1858. "Note on the red colouring matter of the sea round the shores of the island of Bombay," Annals and Magazine of Natural History (London) Ser. 3, *1*:258.

"A centre for research in fish diseases, fishbreeders look to the laboratory," *Scopus* (Hebrew University, Jerusalem) Feb. 1965, p. 13.

Chamberlain, W. J., 1948. "Effects of algae on water supply," Univ. of Queensland, Brisbane, Department of Chemistry. Papers, V. 1, No. 29, 60 plates.

Chaput, M., and Grant, G. A., 1958. "Toxic algae. III. Screening of a number of species," Canada. Defence Research Board. Defence Research Laboratories. Report No. 279, Project No. D52-20-20-18. Ottawa, 6 leaves.

Chatton, E., and Perard, C., 1913. "Schizophytes du caecum du cobaye. I. *Oscillospira Guilliermondi* n.g., n. sp. [Schizophytes in the guinea pig cecum]," Compt. rend. Soc. de biol. *74*:1159.

Cohen, S. G., and Reif, C. B., 1953. "Cutaneous sensitization to blue-green algae. *J. Allergy 24*:452.

Collin, B., 1912-13. Sur un ensemble de protistes parasites des batraciens (note preliminaire). d. *Arthromitus batrachorum* n. sp. [Preliminary note on the association of plant parasites and batraciens]." Arch. de zoologie exp. et gen. Notes et revue *51* (3):63-64.

Combs, G. F., 1952. "Algae (*Chlorella*) as a source of nutrients for the chick," *Science 116*: 453.

Connell, C. H., and Cross, J. B., 1950. Mass mortality of fish associated with the protozoan *Gonyaulax* in the Gulf of Mexico," *ibid., 112*:359.

Cook, B. B., 1962. "The nutritive value of waste-grown algae," *Am. J. Pub. Health 52*:243.

Cook, B. B., and Lau, E. W., 1961. "The protein quality of waste-grown green algae alone and in combination with cereal and milk proteins," Federation Proc. *20*:371.

Cook, B. B., Lau, E. W., and Bailey, B. M., 1963. "The protein quality of waste-grown green algae. I. Quality of protein in mixtures of algae, nonfat powdered milk, and cereals," *J. Nutrition, 81*:23.

Cotton, H. L., 1914. "Algae poisoning," *Am. J. Vet. Med. 9*:903.

Covell, W. P., and Whedon, W. F., 1937. "Effects of the paralytic shell-fish poison on nerve cells," *Arch. Path. 24*:411.

Davidson, F. F., 1959. "Poisoning of wild and domestic animals by a toxic waterbloom of *Nostoc rivulare* Kuetz," *J. Am. Water Works Assoc. 51*:1277.

Dawson, E. Y., Aleem, A. A., and Halstead, B. W., 1955. "Marine algae from Palmyra Island with special reference to the feeding habits and toxicology of reef fishes," Allan Hancock Foundation Publ., Univ. So. Calif., Occ. Pap. No. 17.

de Almeida, F., Forattini, O., and da Silva Lacaz, C., 1946. "Consideracoes sobre tres casos de micoses humanas, de cujas lesoes foram isoladas ao lado dos cogumelos responsaveis, algas provavelmente do genero *Chlorella* [Observations on three cases of human mycosis in which algae of the genus *Chlorella*, in addition to the causative mycotic organisms, were isolated from the lesions]," An. Fac. de med. da Univ. de Sao Paulo *22*:295.

Deem, A. W., and Thorp, F., 1939. "Toxic algae in Colorado," *J. Am. Vet. Med. Assoc. 95*: 542.

Dérot, M., 1952. "La nephrite apres ingestion des moules, role de l'allergie [Nephritis after ingestion of mussels, role of allergy]," Presse med. *60*:316.

Dillenberg, H. O., 1961. Case reports of algae poisoning, personal communication.

Dillenberg, H. O., and Dehnel, M. K., 1960. "Toxic waterbloom in Saskatchewan, 1959," presented before the 14th meeting, International Conference on Diseases in Nature Communicable to Man, Washington State College, Pullman, Wash., 1959, *Cand. Med. Assoc. J. 83*:1151.

————, 1961. "Waterbloom poisoning." Fast and "slow death" factors isolated from blue-green algea at Canadian N R C Laboratories. World-Wide Abstr. Gen. Med. *4* (4): 20.

Durrell, L. W., and Deem, A. W., 1940. "Toxic algae in Colorado," *J. Colorado-Wyoming Acad. Sci. 2* (6):18.

Elster, H. J., 1955. "Toxische Wirkungen des Phytoplanktons [Toxic effects of phytoplankton]," Naturwiss. Rundschau *8*:318.

"Farmer tells some news [on stock poisoning in Big Stone Lake]," *Wilmot Enterprise*, Wilmot, S. D., Oct. 1, 1925, *43*.

Farr, W. K., 1963. "Research on the cytochemistry of microorganisms," United States. 6570th Aerospace Medical Research Laboratories, Wright-Patterson AFB, Ohio. Technical Documentary Report No. AMRL–TDR–63–72.

Farre, A., 1844. "On the minute structure of certain substances expelled from the human intestine, having the ordinary appearance of shreds of lymph, but consisting entirely of filaments of a Confervoid type, probably belonging to the genus *Oscillatoria*," Tr. Roy. Microscop. Soc., London *1*:92.

Fink, H., and Herold, E., 1957. "Über die Eiweissqualität einzelliger Grünalgen und ihre Lebernekrose verhutende Wirkung [On the protein quality of unicellular green algae and its preventive action in necrosis of the liver] II," Hoppe Seyler's Ztschr. f. Physiol. Chem. *307*:202.

————, 1958. "Uber die Eiweissqualitat einzelliger Grünalgen und ihre Lebernekrose verhütende Wirkung. III. Über den Einfluss des Trocknens auf das diätetische Verhalten der einzelligen Zuchtalge *Scenedesmus obliquus* [On the protein quality of unicellular green algae and its preventive action in necrosis of the liver. III. On the effect of drying on the dietetic behavior of the unicellular cultured alga *Scenedesmus obliquus*]," *ibid.*, *311*:13.

Fink, H., Schlie, I., and Herold, E., 1954 "Über die Eiweissqualität einzelliger Grunalgen und ihre Beziehung zur alimentären Lebernekrose der Ratte [On the protein quality of unicellular green algae and its relation to alimentary liver necrosis of the rat] XI, Naturwissenschaften *41*:169.

Firkins, G. S., 1953. "Toxic algae poisoning," Iowa State College Veterinarian *15*:151.

Fitch, C. P., Bishop, L. M., Boyd, W. L., Gortner, R. A., Rogers, C. T., and Tilden, J. E., 1934. "Water bloom" as a cause of poisoning in domstic animals. Cornell Veterinarian *24*:30.

Fogg, G. E., 1953. *The Metabolism of Algae*. Methuen, London.

———, 1965. *Algal Cultures and Phytoplakton Ecology*, Madison, Univ. of Wisconsin Press.

Francis, G., 1878. "Poisonous Australian Lake," *Nature 18*:11.

Fraser, I. M., Habekost, R. C., and Halstead, B. W., 1955. "Toxic marine algae and properties of the toxin," read by C. M. Gruber, Federation Proc. *14*:340.

Fritsch, F. E., 1948–52. *The Structure and Reproduction of the Algae*, Cambridge Univ. Press.

Galton, L., 1967. "*Aqui*culture is more than a dream," *New York Times Magazine*, June 18, p. 12.

Galtsoff, P. S., 1948. "Red Tide," U.S. Fish and Wildlife Service; special scientific report, No. *46*.

———, 1949. "The mystery of the red tide," *Sci. Month. 68*:109.

Gates, J. A., and Wilson, W. B., 1960. "The toxicity of *Gonyaulax monilata* Howell to *Mugil cephalus*," *Limnol. Oceano. 5*:171.

Geoghegan, M. J., 1953. "Experiments with *Chlorella* at Jealett's Hill," in *Algal culture: from laboratory to pilot plant*, ed. by J. S. Burlew. Washington, Carnegie Institution, pp. 182–89.

Gilchrist, J. D. F., 1914. "An inquiry into fluctuations in fish supply on the South African coast," Marine Biol. Rep., Province Cape of Good Hope, Union of South Africa *2* (2):8.

Gillam, W. G., 1925. "The effect on livestock, of water contaminated with fresh water algae," *J. Am. Vet. Med. Assoc* (n.s. 20), *67*:780.

Gorham, P. R., 1960. "Toxic waterblooms of blue-green algae," *Canad. Vet. J. 1*:235.

———, 1962. "Laboratory studies on the toxins produced by waterblooms of blue-green algae," Laboratory Sect., Am. Pub. Health Assoc., 89th Meeting, 1961. *Am. J. Pub. Health 52*:2100.

Gorham, P. R., McLachlan, J., Hammer, U. T., and Kim, W. K., 1964. "Isolation and culture of toxic strains of *Anabaena flos-aqua* (Lyngb.) de Berb," Internat. Assoc. Theoret. and Applied Limnology, Congress, U.S.A. 1962, *Proceedings 15*:796.

Gortner, R. A., 1935. [On toxic water bloom], cited in *The algae and their life relations*, by J. E. Tilden, Minneapolis, Univ. of Minnesota Press, p. 473.

Grant, G. A., 1953. "Toxic algae. I. Development of toxicity in blue-green algae," Canada, Defence Research Board, Defence Research Chemical Laboratories, Report No. 124, Project No. D52–20–20–18, Ottawa, 11 leaves.

Grant, G. A., and Hughes, E. O., 1953. "Development of toxicity in blue-green algae," *Canad. J. Pub. Health 44*:334.

Grauer, F. H., 1959. "Dermatitis escharotica caused by a marine alga," *Hawaii Med. J. 19:* 32.

Grauer, F. H., and Arnold, H. L., 1961–62. "Seaweed dermatitis; first report of a dermatitis producing marine alga," *Arch. Dermat. 84:*720; abstracts in, *J. A. M. A. 178:*194, Nov. 18, 1961; *Modern Med. 30:*138, April 2, 1962.

Gunter, G., Smith, F. G. W., and Williams, R. H., 1947. "Mass mortality of marine animals on the lower west coast of Florida, November 1946–January 1947," *Science 105:*256.

Gunter, G., Williams, R. H., Davis, C. C., and Smith, F. G. W., 1948. "Catastrophic mass mortality of marine animals and coincident phytoplankton bloom on the west coast of Florida, November 1946 to August 1947," *Ecological Monogr. 18:*309.

Habekost, R. C., Fraser, I. M., and Halstead, B. W., 1955. "Observations on toxic marine algae," read by J. C. Ewers, *J. Washington Acad. Sci. 45:*101.

Hallier, E., 1886. "*Oscillaria intestini,*" in his, Die pflanzlichen Parasiten des menschlichen Korpers, Leipzig, W. Engelmann.

Halstead, B. W., and Lively, W. M., 1954. "Poisonous fishes and ichthyosarcotoxism," *U.S. Armed Forces M. J. 5:*157.

Hardin, F. F., 1961. "Seabather's eruption," *J.M.A. Georgia 50:*450.

Hardy, A. C., 1936. "The ecological relations between the herring and the plankton investigated with the plankton indicator. Part I. The object, plan and methods of the investigation," *J. Marine Biol. Assoc. U. K. 21:*147.

Hayami, H., and Shino, K., 1958. "Nutritional studies on decolourized *Chlorella* (Part 1). Growth experiments of rats and the digestibility of a diet containing 19% of decolourized *Chlorella,*" Ann. Rept. National Inst. Nutrition, Tokyo.

Hayami, H., Shino, K., Morimoto, K., Okano, T., and Yamamoto, S., 1960. "Studies on the utilization of *Chlorella* as a source of food. Human experiments on the rate of absorption of protein of blanched *Chlorella,*" *ibid.*

Hayami, H., Shino, K., Morimoto, K., and Tsuchida, M., 1960. "Studies on the utilization of *Chlorella* as a source of food (Part 10). Human experiments on the rate of digestion of protein of *Chlorella* dried at low temperature," *ibid.*

Heise, H. A., 1949. "Symptoms of hay fever caused by algae," *J. Allergy 20:*383.

———, 1951. "Symptoms of hay fever caused by algae. II. Mycrocystis," *Ann. Allergy 9:*100.

Hindersson, R., 1933. "Forgiftning av notkreatur genon sotvattenplankton [Poisoning of cattle by fresh-water plankton]," Finsk Vet. Tidskrift *39:*179.

Hocquette, H., 1933. "Cultures d'*Anaboeniolum* Langeron du caecum du cobaye et due lapin [Cultures of *Anaboeniolum* Langeron from guinea pig and rabbit cecum]," Soc. Biol. Lille, Seance, Mai 8, 1933. Compt. rend. Soc. de biol. *113:*779.

Hornell, J., 1918. "A new protozoan cause of widespread mortality among marine fishes." Madras, Fisheries Dept. Bull. *11,* (Rep. No. 2): 53 (1917).

Hornell, J., and Nayudu, M. R., 1924. "A contribution to the life-history of the Indian sardine with notes on the plankton of the Malabar coast," *ibid., 17:*129 (Rep. No. 5, 1923).

Howard, N. J., and Berry, A. E., 1933. "Algal nuisances in surface waters," *Canad. Pub. Health J. 24:*377.

Hughes, E. O., Gorham, P. R., and Zehnder, A., 1958. "Toxicity of a unialgal culture of *Mycrocystis aeruginosa,*" *Canad. J. Microbiol. 4:*225.

Hundley, J. M., and Ing, R. B., 1956. "Algae as sources of lysine and threonine in supplementing wheat and bread diets," *Science 124:*536.

Hutner, S. H., and McLaughlin, J. J. A., 1958. "Poisonous tides," *Scient. Amer. 199:*92.

Ingle, R. M., 1954. "Irritant gases associated with red tide." Univ. of Miami, Coral Gables, Fla., Marine Laboratory. Special Service Bull. No. 9.

Ingram, W. M., and Prescott, G. W., 1954. "Toxic fresh-water algae," *Am. Midland Naturalist 52*:75.

Insalata, N. F., 1952. "Balking algae in beverage water," *Food Engineering 24*:72.

Kafka, J., 1892. "Untersuchungen über dis Fauna der Gewässer Böhmens. II. Die Fauna der böhmischen Teiche [Investigations on the fauna of the waters of Bohemia. II. The fauna of Bohemian ponds]," Archiv d. naturwissenschaftl. Landesdurchforschung von Böhmen (Prag) *8*, No. 2, pp. 51–52, 89–91.

Kristensen, I., 1943. "Mededeeling over massale visch-sterfte [Report on mass mortality of fish]," Aquarium, Nederlandsch, Bond Aquariumvereenig. *14* (2):18.

Kuchenmeister, G. F. H., 1855. *"Oscillaria intestini,"* in his, Die in und an dem Körper des lebenden Menschen vorkommenden Parasiten. 2. Abt. Die pflanzlichen Parasiten. Leipzig, B. G. Teubner. 1855. p. 26.

Kun, M. S., Teplyi, D. L., and Astakhova, T. V., 1963. "The causes of carp disease in the Volga delta," trans. from, *Voprosy Ikhtiologii 17*:159–68, 1961 [Russian] National Research Council of Canada, Ottawa. Technical Translation 1055, NRC TT–1055.

Lackey, J. B., and Hynes, J. A., 1955. "The Florida Gulf Coast red tide," Florida Engineering and Indust. Exp. Station. Bulletin Series, No. 70.

LaCossitt, H., 1954. "The truth about Florida's red tide," *Saturday Evening Post, 227* (7):28.

Lamcke, K., and Kühn, R., 1936. "Discoloration of wall tile by plant organisms," *Chem. Abstr. 30*:1194.

Lampert, K., 1910. *Das Leben der Binnengewässer* [The life of inland waters], 2. Aufl. Leipzig: Tauchnitz.

Langeron, M., 1923. "Les *Oscillariees* parasites du tube digestif de l'homme et des animaux [The parasitic *Oscillatoriae* in the digestive canal of man and animals]," Ann. de Parasit. *1* (1):75, and *1* (2):113.

Larsen, B. A., and Hawkins, W. W., 1961. "Nutritional value as protein of some of the nitrogenous constituents of two marine algae, *Chondrus crispus* and *Laminaria digitata," J. Sci. Food Agric. 12*:523.

Leidy, J., 1849. "Observations," Proc. Acad. Nat. Sci. *4*:225. Repr.: Smithsonian Misc. Collections, *46*, No. 1477, 1904, p. 12.

Leveille, G. A., Sauberlich, H. E., and Edelbrock, J. A., 1961. "The influence of enzyme supplementation on the digestibility of algae," U. S. Army Medical Research and Nutrition Laboratory, Fitzsimons General Hospital, Denver, Col., Report No. 259.

Leveille, G. A., Sauberlich, H. E., and Shockley, J. W., 1962. "Protein value and the amino acid deficiencies of various algae for growth of rats and chicks," *J. Nutrition 76*:423.

Liebert, F., and Deerns, W. M. "Onderzoek naar de oorzaak van een vischsterfte in den polder Workumer-Nieuwland, nabij Workum [Investigation of the cause of fish mortality in the polder Workumer-Nieuland, near Workum]," Verhandel. en Rapporten, Rijksinstituut voor Visscherijonderzoek ('s Gravenhage) deel *1*.

Lindemann, E., 1926. "Massensterben von Fischen infolge einer Hochproduktion von Panzergeisslingen (Peridineen) [Mass fish mortality due to Peridineae]," Kleine Mitt. Ver. Wasserversorgung Abwasserbes, Berlin, *2*:113.

Louw, P. G. J., 1950. "The active constituent of the poisonous algae, *Microcystis toxica* Stephens," with a note on experimental cases of algae poisoning in small animals, by J. D. Smit, South African Industrial Chemist *4*:62.

Lubitz, J. A., 1961. "The protein quality, digestibility, and composition of *Chlorella* 71105," U. S. Air Force, Aeronautical Systems Division, Wright-Patterson AFB, Ohio. Technical Reports ASD–TR 61–535.

————, 1962. "Animal nutrition studies with *Chlorella* 71105," in Biologistics for Space Systems Symposium, May 1962, *ibid.*, Technical Documentary Report No. AMRL–TDR–62–116, pp. 331–56.

————, 1963. "Growth and toxicity studies on rats fed *Chlorella* 71105," in *Medical and biological problems of space flight, proceedings of a conference, Nassau, Bahamas, 1961,* ed. by G. H. Bourne, New York, Academic Press, pp. 245–59.

Lund, E. J., 1934–35. "Some facts relating to the occurrences of dead and dying fish on the Texas coast during June, July and August, 1935," Ann. Rep. Texas Game, Fish, Oyster Comm, p. 47.

MacDonald, D. W., 1960. "Algal poisoning in beef cattle," *Canad. Vet. J. 1*:108.

Mackenthun, K. M., Herman, E. F., and Bartsch, A. F., 1948. "A heavy mortality of fishes resulting from the decomposition of algae in the Yahara River, Wisconsin," Tr. Am. Fisheries Soc. *75*:175 (1945).

MacKinnon, A. F., 1950. "Report on algae poisoning," *Canad. J. Comp. Med. 14*:208.

Marchand, J. M., 1928. "The nature of sea-floor deposits in certain regions on the west coast," Union of South Africa, Fisheries and Marine Biological Survey, Report No. 6.

Mariani, P. L., 1942. "Ricerche sperimentali intorno ad alcune alghe parassite dell'uomo [Experimental researches on some parasitic algae of man]," *Boll. Soc. ital di microbiol. 14*:113.

Mason, M. F., and Wheeler, R. E., 1942. "Observations upon the toxicity of blue-green algae," Am. Soc. Biol. Chemists. 36th Ann. Meeting, Boston, Federation Proc. *1* (12): 124.

McDowell, M. E., and Leveille, G. A., 1963. "Feeding experiments with algae," *ibid.,* 22:1431.

McDowell, M. E., Powell, R. C., Nevels, E. M., Sellars, J. N., and Witt, N. F., 1960. "Algae feeding in humans: acceptability, digestibility and toxicity," 44th Ann. Meeting Fed. Amer. Soc. Exp. Biol., Chicago, Abstracts, *19* (11):319.

McElhenney, T. R., Bold, H. C., Brown, R. M., and McGovern, J. P., 1962. "Algae: A cause of inhalant allergy in children," *Ann. Allergy. 20*: 739.

McFarren, E. F., Schafer, N. L., Campbell, J. E., Lewis, K. H., Jensen, E. T., and Schantz, E. J., 1956. "Public health significance of paralytic shellfish poison: a review of literature and unpublished research," Proc. Natl. Shellfisheries Assoc. *47*:114.

McIvor, R. A., and Grant, G. A., 1955. "Toxic algae. II. Preliminary attempts to prepare toxic extracts," Canada, Defence Research Board, Defence Research Chemical Laboratories. Rep. No. 190. Project No. D52–20–20–18, Ottawa, 7 leaves.

McLaughlin, J. J. A., 1958. "Eurythaline chrysomonads: nutrition and toxigenesis in *Prymnesium parvum* with notes on *Isochrysis galbana* and *Monochrysis lutheri,*" *J. Protozool, 5*:75.

McLeod, J. A., and Bondar, G. F., 1952. "A case of suspected algal poisoning in Manitoba," *Canad. J. Pub. Health 43*:347.

Mead, A. D., 1898. "Peridinium and the "red water" in Narragansett Bay," *Science 8*:707.

Meffert, M. E., and Pabst, W., 1963. "Uber die Verwertbarkeit der Substanz von *Scenedesmus obliquus* als Eiweissquelle in Ratten-Bilanz-Versuchen [On the nutritional value of *Scenedesmus obliquus* as a protein source in rat metabolic studies]," Nutritio et Dieta (Basel) *5*:235.

Messikommer, E., 1948. "Algennachweis in Entenexkrementen [Evidence of algae in duck feces]," Hydrobiologia, Acta Hydrobiologica *1*:22.

Meyer , K. F., Sommer, H., and Schoenholz, P., 1928. "Mussel poisoning," *J. Prev. Med. 2*:365.

Mikhaylev, V. V., and Teplyi, D. L., 1961. "O toksichnosti sine-zelenykh vodorosley reki Volgi [On the toxicity of blue-green algae of the Volga river]" *Zoologicheskii Zhurnal,* Moscow, *40*:1619.

Miyajima, M., 1934. "La question de l'eau rouge, un péril pour les huîtres perlières [The problem of red water, a peril for the pearl-bearing oysters]," Bull. Soc. Centrale d'Aquiculture et de Pêche, Paris, *41*:97.

Müller, R., 1911. "Zur Stellung der Krankheitserreger im Natursystem [On the role of pathogens in nature]," Muenchen. Med. Wchnschr. *58* (Oct.):2246.

Mullor, J. B., 1945. "Algas toxicas [Toxic algae]," Rev. Sanidad, Asistencia Social y Trabajo, Santa Fe, Argentina, *1*:95.

Mullor, J. B., and Wachs, A. M., 1948. "Algunas caracteristicas del alga toxica "*Anabaena venenosa*" [Some characteristics of the toxic alga "*Anabaena venenosa*"]," in Congreso Sudamericano de Quimica, 4th. Trabajos presentados, *1*, pp. 326–27.

Naday, L., 1914. "Az állóvizék virágzása [Water-bloom of stagnant water]," Termeszettudományi Közlöny, K. Magyar természettudományi társulat, Budapest, *46*:432.

Nelson, N. P. B., 1903–1904. "Observations upon some algae which cause water bloom," Minnesota Bot. Studies *3*:51.

Nelson, T. C., 1941. Discussion of "Algae control" paper presented by W. D. Monie, at the New Jersey Section Meeting, *J. Am. Water Works Assoc. 33*:716.

Newiadomski, M. M., 1937. "Blastozystentumoren [Blastocyte tumors]," Zentralbl. f. Bakt. I. Abt. Originale *138*:244.

Nightingale, H. W., 1936. *Red water organisms, their occurrence and influence upon marine aquatic animals, with special reference to shellfish in waters of the Pacific coast*, Seattle, Wash. Argus Press.

Nishikawa, T., 1903. "*Gonyaulax* and the discolored water in the Bay of Aga," Annotations Zoologicae Japonenses, Tokyo, *4*:31.

O'Donoghue, J. G., and Wilton, G. S., 1951. "Algal poisoning in Alberta," *Canad. J. Comp. Med. 15*:193.

Oliveira, L. de, Nascimento, R. do, Krau, L., and Miranda, A., 1956. "Diagnóstico biológico das mortandades de peixes na Lagoa Ridrogo de Freitas; nota prévia [Biological diagnosis of the mortality of fish in the Rodrigo de Freitas Lagoon; preliminary notes]," *Brasil Med. 70*:125.

_____, 1957. "Observacoes hidrobiologicas e mortandade de peixas na Lagoa de Freitas [Hydrobiologic observations and the mortality of fish in the Rodrigo de Freitas Lagoon]," *Mem. Inst. Oswaldo Cruz 55*:211.

Olson, T. A., 1949. "History of toxic plankton and associated phenomena. Algae-laden water causes death of domestic animals; nature of poison," *Sewage Works Engineering 20* (2): 71.

_____, 1951. "Toxic plankton," in *Proc. Inservice Training Course in Water Works Problems*, Univ. of Michigan, School of Public Health, Ann Harbor, Mich., p. 86.

_____, 1952. "Toxic plankton," *Water & Sewage Works 99*:75.

_____, 1955. "Studies of algae poisoning. With special reference to the relationship of this phenomenon to losses of wildfowl and other birds," *The Flicker* (Minneapolis) *27*:105.

_____, 1960. "Water poisoning—a study of poisonous algae blooms in Minnesota," Laboratory Sect. Abstracts, Am. Pub. Health Assoc., 87th Meeting, 1959. *Am. J. Pub. Health 50*:883.

"One hundred twenty-seven hogs, four cows die after drinking water from [Big Stone] Lake, stock stricken last Saturday, all die in short time, lake water sent for analysis," *Wilmot Enterprise*, Wilmot, S. D., Sept. 24, 1925.

Oswald, W. J., 1962. "The coming industry of controlled photosynthesis," *Am. J. Pub. Health 52*:235.

Otterstrom, C. V., and Steemann-Nielsen, E., 1940. "Two cases of extensive mortality in fishes caused by the flagellate *Prymnesium parvum* Carter," Danish Biol. Station, Copenhagen, Rep. *44* (1939).

Pabst, W., Jekat, F., and Rolle, I., 1964. "Die Ausnutzung von Kohlenhydraten, Fett, Phosphor und Stickstoff in walzengetrockneter *Scenedesmus*-Substanz ermittelt im Ratten-Bilanzversuch [The utilization of carbohydrates, fats, phosphorus and nitrogen from roller-dried *Scenedesmus* substance as shown by balance studies in the rat]," Nutrito et Dieta (Basel) 6:279.

Palmer, C. M., 1959. "Algae in water supplies," U.S. Public Health Service. Publ. 657.

Parnas, I., 1963. "The toxicity of *Prymnesium parvum* (a review)," Repr. *Israel J. Zoology* 12 (1–4):15.

Parnas, I., Reich, K., and Bergmann, F., 1962. "Photoinactivation of ichthyotoxin from axenic cultures of *Prymnesium parvum* Carter," *Appl. Microbiol. 10*:237.

Parnas, I., Bergmann, F., and Reich, K., 1963. "Pharmacological effects of the ichthyotoxin of the phytoflagellate *Prymnesium parvum*," Repr. Bull. Research Council of Israel, Section E. Exper. Med. *10 E*, No. 3–4.

Porge, J. F., 1952. "Les nephropathies d'origine alimentaire [Nephropathies of alimentary origin]," Bull. ot mém. Soc. méd. Paris *156*:39.

Porter, E. D., 1881–86. "Investigations of supposed poisonous vegetation in the waters of some of the lakes of Minnesota," Dept. Agric. Biennial Report of the Board of Regents, No. 4, Suppl. No. 1, p. 95.

Powell, R. C., Nevels, E. M., and McDowell, M. E., 1961. "Algae feeding in humans," *J. Nutrit. 75* (1):7.

Prescott, G. W., 1933. "Some effects of the blue-green algae, *Aphanizomenon flos-aquae*, on lake fish," *Collecting Net*, Woods Hole, Mass. *8*:77.

————, 1938. "Objectionable algae and their control in lakes and reservoirs," Repr. *Louisiana Municipal Review*, Shreveport, v. 1, Nos. 2 and 3.

————, 1939. "Some relationships of phytoplankton to limnology and aquatic biology," in, *Problems of lake biology*, Publ. Am. Assoc. Advancement Sci. *10*:65.

————, 1948, "Objectionable algae with reference to the killing of fish and other animals," *Hydrobiol. 1*:1.

Proctor, V. W., 1959. "Dispersal of fresh-water algae by migratory water birds," *Science 130*: 623.

Randall, J. E., 1958. "A review of *Ciguatera*, Tropical Fish Poisoning, with a tentative explanation of its cause," Bull. Marine Science of the Gulf and Carribean, *8* (3):236.

Ray, S. M., and Aldrich, D. V., 1965. "*Gymnodinium breve*: induction of shellfish poisoning in chicks," *Science 148*:1748.

Ray, S. M., and Wilson, W. B., 1957. "Effects of unialgal and bacteria-free cultures of *Gymnodinium brevis* on fish, and notes on related studies with bacteria," U.S. Fish and Wildlife Service. Fishery Bull. V. 57, No. 123, p. 469.

Redaelli, P., and Ciferri, R., 1935. "La patogenicita per gli animal di alghe acloriche coprofite del genere *Prototheca* [Pathogenicity of coprophytic achloric algae of the genus *Prototheca* in animals]," Boll. Soc. ital. biol. sper. *10*:809. Also in French, "Pouvoir pathogene pour les animaux des algues coprophytes achloriques du genre *Prototheca*. Observations sur les protothecaceae [Pathogenicity of coprophytic achloric algae of the genus *Prototheca* in animals. Observations on protothecaceae]," Boll. Sez. ital. Soc. internaz. microbiol. *7*:316.

Rehkemper, J. A., 1962. "Algae feeding in mice: preliminary observations," U.S. Air Force. Arctic Aeromedical Laboratory, F. Wainwright, Alaska. Technical Documentary Report AAL–TDR–62–38.

Reich, K. and Aschner, M., 1947. "Mass development and control of the phytoflagellate *Prymnesium parvum* in fish ponds in Palestine," *Palestine J. Botany*, Jerusalem, Ser. *4*:14.

Reich, K., and Kahn, J., 1954. "A bacteria-free culture of *Prymnesium parvum* (Chrysomonadiniac)," *Bull. Research Council of Israel, 5*:114.

Reich, K., and Parnas, I., 1962. "Effect of illumination on ichthyotoxin in an axenic culture of *Prymnesium parvum* Carter," *J. Protozool. 9*:38.

Reich, K., and Rotberg, M., 1958. "Some factors influencing the formation of toxin poisonous to fish in bacteria-free cultures of *Prymnesium*," Bull. Research Council of Israel *7B*:199.

Remer, F., 1943. Cited in Quin, A. H., "Sheep poisoned by algae," *J. Am. Vet. Med. Assoc. 102*:299.

Robin, C. P., 1853. "*Histoire naturelle des vegetaux parasites qui croissent sur l'homme et sur les animaux vivants* [Natural history of plant parasites growing in man and live animals], Paris, J. B. Bailliere, pp. 359–60, 404–405.

Rose, E. T., 1953. "Toxic algae in Iowa lakes," Proc. Iowa Acad. Sci. *60*:738.

Rotberg, M., 1958. "The thiamine requirements of *Prymnesium parvum*," Bull. Research Council of Israel. *7B*:208.

Roth, L. M., and Willis, E. R., 1960. "The biotic associations of cockroaches," Smithsonian Institution, Miscellaneous Collections, *141*.

Ryther, J. H., 1954. "Inhibitory effects of phytoplankton upon the feeding of *Daphnia magna* with reference to growth, reproduction, and survival," *Ecology 35*:522.

Sams, W. M., 1949. "Seabather's eruption," *Arch. Dermat. & Syph. 60*:227.

Sapeika, N., 1953. "Actions of mussel poison," Arch. internat. de pharmacodyn. et de therap. *93*:135.

Sasaki, R., and Nagai, S., 1960. "Studies on the utilization of *Chlorella* as a source of food (Report 1). Intestinal microorganisms of human subjects fed on blanching *Chlorella* as a source of dietary protein," Ann. Rept. National Inst. Nutrition, Tokyo, p. 63.

Schwimmer, M., and Schwimmer, D., 1955. *The Role of Algae and Plankton in Medicine,* New York, Grune & Stratton.

———, 1962–64. "Algae and Medicine," in, NATO Advanced Study Institute. Louisville, Ky., *Algae and Man,* ed. by Jackson, New York: Plenum Press, pp. 368–412.

Schwimmer, M., 1964. "Human gastro-intestinal, respiratory and skin disorders associated with algae. Tabular data and Special references," in: *Limnological Aspects of Recreational Lakes,* by K. M. Mackenthun, W. M. Ingram, R. Porges, Washington, D. C., U.S. Public Health Service, Division of Water Supply and Pollution Control, pp. 94–96. (U.S. Public Health Service Publication No. 1167).

———, "Algae and disease," in preparation. "A sea of casualties in a killer 'red tide'," *Life 57*:32b.

Selected bibliography on algae, 1955. No. 3. Halifax, Nova Scotia Research Foundation [73] leaves.

Selected bibliography on algae, 1958. No. 4, Halifax, Nova Scotia Research Foundation.

Selected bibliography on algae, 1960. No. 5. Halifax, Nova Scotia Research Foundation.

Senior, V. E., 1960. "Algal poisoning in Saskatchewan," *Canad. J. Comp. Med. 24*:26.

Seydel, E., 1913. "Fischsterben durch Wasserblüte [Fish deaths due to waterbloom]," Mitt. Fischerei-Ver. Brandenburg n.s. *5* (9):87.

Sherwood, G. H., and Edwards, V. N., 1902. "Notes on the migration, spawning, etc. of certain fishes in 1900," Bull. U. S. Fish Commission *21* (2):27 (1901).

Shelubsky (Shilo), M., 1950. "Observations on the properties of a toxin produced by *Microcystis*," Internat. Assoc. Theoret. and Applied Limnology (11th International Limnological Congress, Brussels, 1950), Proceedings *11*:362.

Shilo (Shelubsky), M., and Aschner, M., 1953. "Factors governing the toxicity of cultures containing the phytoflagellate *Prymnesium parvum* Carter," *J. Gen. Microbiol. 8*:333.

Shilo (Shelubsky), M., and Rosenberger, R. F., 1960. "Studies on the toxic principles formed by the chrysomonad *Prymnesium parvum* Carter," Ann. New York Acad. Sci. *90*:866.

Shilo (Shelubsky), M., and Shilo, M., 1953. "Conditions which determine the efficiency of ammonium sulphate in the control of *Prymnesium parvum* in fish breeding ponds," *Appl. Microbiol. 1*:330.

————, 1955. "Control of the phytoflagellate *Prymnesium parvum*," Proc. Intern. Assoc. Theor. Appl. Limn. *12*:233.

————, 1962. "The mechanism of lysis of *Prymnesium parvum* by weak electrolytes," *J. Gen. Microbiol. 29*:645.

————, in press. "Osmotic lysis of *Prymnesium parvum* by weak electrolytes," Proc. Intern. Assoc. Theor. Appl. Limnol. *14*.

Sieburth, J. M., 1959. "Gastrointestinal microflora of antarctic birds," *J. Bact. 77*:521.

Simons, H., 1920. "Eine saprophytische *Oscillaire* im Darm des Meerschweinchens [A saprophytic *Oscillaria* in the guinea pig intestine]. Centralbl. f. Bakt. II. Abt. *50*:356.

Simons, H., 1922. "Saprophytische *Oscillarien* des Menschen und der Tiere [Saprophytic *Oscillaria* in man and animals]. *ibid.*, I agt. Originale. *88*:501.

Simpson, B., and Gorham, P. R., 1958. "Source of the fast-death factor produced by unialgal *Microcystis aeruginosa* NRC-1," Abstract, *Phycol. Soc. Am. News Bull. 11*:59.

Sommer, H., and Meyer, K. F., 1935. "Mussel poisoning," California & West. Med. *42*:423.

————, 1937. "Paralytic shell-fish poisoning," Arch. Path. *24*:560.

Sommer, H., Whedon, W. F., Kofoid, C. A., and Stohler, R., 1937. "Relation of paralytic shell-fish poison to certain plankton organisms of the genus *Gonyaulax*," Arch. Path. *24*:537.

Spencer, R. R., 1930. "Unusually mild recurring epidemic simulating food infection," Pub. Health Rep. *45*:2867.

Sproston, N. G., 1946. "Fish mortality due to brown flagellate," Nature *158*:70.

Stalker, M., 1881–86. "On the Waterville cattle disease," Univ. of Minnesota, Dept. of Agric. Biennial Report of the Board of Regents, No. 4, Suppl. No. 1, p. 105.

Stephens, E. L., 1949. "*Microcystis toxica* sp. nov.: a poisonous alga from the Transvaal and Orange Free State," Read May 16, 1945, Tr. Roy. Soc. South Africa *32* (pt. 1):105.

Stewart, A. G., Barnum, D. A., and Henderson, J. A., 1950. "Algal poisoning in Ontario," *Canad. J. Comp. Med. 14*:197.

Steyn, D. G., 1943. "Poisoning of animals by algae on dams and pans," Farming in South Africa *18*:489.

————, 1944. "Poisonous and non-poisonous algae (waterbloom, scum) in dams and pans," *ibid., 19*:465.

————, 1944. "Vergiftiging deur slyk (algae) op damme en panne [Poisoning by algae on dams and pans]," *South African Med. J. 18*:378.

————, 1945. "Poisoning of animals and human beings by algae," *South African J. Sci. 41*:243.

————, 1945. "Poisoning of animals by algae (scum and waterbloom) in dams and pans," Pretoria, Union of South Africa, Dept. of Agric. and Forestry.

Strodtmann, S., 1898. "Ueber die vermeintliche Schädlichkeit der Wasserblüte [On the supposed injurious effect of waterbloom]," Forschungsberichte, Biologische Station Plön, Stuttgart, Teil 6. Abt. II. pp. 206–12.

Suit, R. F., 1949. "Parasitic diseases of citrus in Florida," Florida Agr. Expt. Sta. Bull. No. 463.

Sunde, M. L., and Madiedo, G., 1963. "Hens fed algae lay eggs with darker yolks," Science News Letter *83*:185.

Taylor, H. F., 1917. "Mortality of fishes on the west coast of Florida," Rep. U.S. Comm. Fish, App. III.

Telitchenko, M. M., and Gusev, M., 1965. "O toksichnosti sinezelenykh vodorosley [Toxicity of blue-green algae]," Doklady Akademii Nauk SSSR *160*:1424.

Tetz, V. I., 1964. "O toksichnosti sinezelenykh vodorosley [Toxicity of blue-green algae]," Gigiena i Sanitariya *29*:106.

"There is no ground for an algae scare. Qu'Appelle Lake tourist trade falls off," *Leader-Post*, Regina, Canada, July 20, 1959, and July 21, 1959.

Thomson, W. K., 1958. "Toxic algae. V. Study of toxic bacterial contaminants," Canada, Defence Research Board, Defence Research Kingston Laboratory, Report No. 63, Project No. D52-20-20-18, Ottawa, 7 leaves.

Thomson, W. K., Laing, A. C., and Grant, G. A., 1957. "Toxic algae. IV. Isolation of toxic bacterial contaminants," *ibid.*, Report No. 51, Ottawa, 9 leaves.

Tiffany, L. H., 1935. "Algae of bizarre abodes," *Sci. Month. 40*:541.

———, 1958. *Algae, the Grass of Many Waters*, 2 ed., Springfield, Ill., C. C. Thomas.

Tisdale, E. S., 1931. "Epidemic of intestinal disorders in Charleston, W. Va., occurring simultaneously with unprecedented water supply conditions," *Am. J. Pub. Health 21*:198.

———, 1931. "The 1930-1931 drought and its effect upon public water supply," *ibid.*, 1203.

Torrey, H. B., 1902. "An unusual occurrence of dinoflagellata on the California coast," *Am. Naturalist 36*:187.

Valentin, G., 1936. "*Hygrocrocis intestinalis*, eine auf der lebendigen und ungestört functionirenden Schleimhaut des Darmkanales vegetirende Conferve [*Hygrocrocis intestinalis*, a Conferva vegetating on the living, normally functioning mucosa of the instestinal canal]," in his: *Repertorium für Anatomie und Physiologie*, Berlin, V. 1, p. 110.

Vanderveen, J. E., Sander, E. G., Speckmann, E. W., Prince, A. E., and Offner, K. M., 1963. "Nutritional value of some microbial foods," *Aerospace Med. 34*:847.

Veenhuyzen, J. C., 1879. "*Trychodesmium erythraeum*," Natuurk. Tijdschr. Nederlandsch Indie, deel *38*, ser. *7*, deel *8*:150.

Veldee, M. V., 1931. "An epidemiological study of suspected water-borne gastroenteritis," *Am. J. Pub. Health 21*:1227.

Vinberg, G. G., 1954. "Toxic phytoplankton," Trans. from Uspekhi Sovr. Biologii *38*, 2 (5) 216. National Research Council of Canada, Technical Translation TT-549.

"Water made children ill," *Saskatoon Star-Phoenix*, Saskatoon, Canada, July 22, 1959.

Weber, A. "Etude sur les algues parasites des paresseux [Study on parasitic algae in sloths]," Natuurk. Verhandel., Holland. Maatsch. Wetensch., Haarlem, ser. 3, *5*. part 1, p. 1.

Weller, C. P., and Sulman, F. G., 1963. "Effect of algae feeding on the development of the albino rat," *Israel Med. J. 22*:189.

Wheeler, R. E., Lackey, J. B., and Schott, S., 1942. "A contribution on the toxicity of algae," Pub. Health Rep. *57*:1695.

Whitelegge, T., 1891. "On the recent discolouration of the waters of Port Jackson," Records, Australian Museum, Sidney *1*:179.

Wilson, W. B., and Collier, A., 1955. "Preliminary notes on the culturing of *Gymnodinium brevis* Davis," *Science 121*:394.

Wilson, W. B., and Ray, S. M., 1956. "The occurrence of *Gymnodinium brevis* in the western Gulf of Mexico," *Ecology 37*:388.

Woodcock, A. H., 1948. "Note concerning human respiratory irritation associated with high concentrations of plankton and mass mortality of marine organisms," *J. Marine Res. 7* (1):56.

Woodcock, E. F., 1927. "Plants of Michigan poisonous to livestock," *J. Am. Vet. Med. Assoc.* (n.s.25) *72*:475.

Yariv, J., and Hestrin, S., 1961. "Toxicity of the extracellular phase of *Prymnesium parvum* cultures," *J. Gen. Microbiol. 24*:165.

Zehnder, A., Hughes, E. O., and Gorham, P. R., 1956. "Giftige Blaualgen [Toxic blue algae]," Abstract in Verh. Schweiz. Naturforsch. Ges. *136*:126.

XVI

Principal Trends and Problems of Soil Algology in the U.S.S.R.

L. N. NOVICHKOVA-IVANOVA

Botanical Institute Academy of Science U.S.S.R.
Leningrad, U.S.S.R.

Soil algology, or phycology, is a science that deals with the low chlorophyllic autotrophic plants, algae growing on and in the soil and mineral substrata, with their upper horizons largely on the very surface of the soil.

If our knowledge concerning algae's use of the soil as a habitat substratum appeared in the last century, soil algology began developing only with the introduction of microbiological methods into research in this field, methods which considerably widened our knowledge about algae in the soil.

Soil algology originated with the merging of three sciences—algology, soil microbiology, and phytocoenology—and became an independent and distinct field of science when it set a number of new problems connected with the soil proper as a specific medium for algae growth.

The keystone of soil algology was laid by the diverse fieldwork of the English researcher Muriel Bristol-Roach, who established the Rothamstead experimental station in 1919–28. The main problems of soil algology have been raised and dealt with in her works: the methods of cultivating soil algae, the composition and quantity of algae in the soil, and their ability to vegetate in the soil, as well as some data on the role played by soil algae.

These studies initiated the development of soil algae investigations in many countries. In the U.S.S.R. the first study to appear on this problem was the paper of A. A. Richter and R. I. Orlova (1928) which, de facto, directly verified Bristol-Roach's quantitative method on the chernozems (black soils) of the Saratov region, a regular research into soil algae starting after the publications of M. M. Hollerbach (1934, 1935, 1936a, 1936b) and K. I. Mayer (1937).

Naturally, at the early stages of research the taxonomy floristic trend in the study of soil algae was the most prominent one, though by that time the physiologic and ecologo-phytocoenological trends were already present. These three independent branches were but quite recently integrated to solve the main problems of soil algology.

The first works of Hollerbach were shortly followed in the U.S.S.R. by diverse and extensive investigations of the soil algae limited mainly by floristic and morphologo-taxonomic studies. These studies formed the basis of future physiologo-biochemical as well as ecologo-phytocoenological investigations into soil algae.

Floristic studies during the last two decades (see Forest bibliography, 1965) have covered a vast territory of our country, and, although somewhat irregularly, at the present time we have a sufficient notion on the principal regularities governing the composition and distribution of soil algae.

Proceeding from the division of soil cover of the Soviet Union into nine regions or facies offered by Gerasimov (1933, 1945), we shall outline the main results of floristic study of soil algae in the U.S.S.R. Soil algae of the Arctic facies have been studied both in the continental (Gromov, 1956; Kosheleva and Novichkova, 1956; Dorogostaiskaya, 1959; Shtina and Roizin, 1966; Dorogostaiskaya and Novichkova-Ivanova, 1967) and the insular varieties (Shirshov, 1935; Novichkova-Ivanova, 1963, 1964).

The algae of East European facies represented by "conditional" normal soils have been those most extensively studied (see, e.g., Hollerbach, 1936; Zauer, 1956a; Vaulina, 1958; Kondratyeva, 1958; Shtina, 1959a), and a significant number of investigations into soil algae has been carried out in central Kazakhstan region with solonetz-steppe, soils (Shtina and Bolyshev, 1960; Sdobnikova, 1959b, 1967) as well as in the Central Asia facies with the desert-solod soils represented in it (Bolyshev and Evdokimova, 1944; Bolyshev and Manucharova, 1946, 1947; Bolyshev, 1955; Melnikova, 1954, 1955, 1962; Mussaev, 1960; Troitskaya, 1957, 1961a, 1961b).* The studies on the soil algae of the Turan facies represented by crabonate-solonchak soils are somewhat fewer (Hollerbach, Novichkova, Sdobnikova, 1956; Sdobnikova, 1958, 1959a). The algae of two vast regions the western Siberia faces with its steppe-solod soils (Popova, 1957; Pivovarova, 1967) and that of eastern Siberia with permafrost podzolic solontrevaty soils have been dealt with but slightly (Novichkova-Ivanova, 1967b). Algologists have studied the Mediterranean podzolic red earth facies on the Crimean peninsula of the Black Sea as well as in Lenkoran (Zauer, 1956b; Matvienko, 1956; Bairamova, 1964, 1965). The algae of the southeast borders of our country represented by the Far East facies (podzolic boggy soils) have not been studied.

Strictly floristic and morphologic systematic investigations are increas-

---

* One should mention that the investigation into the algal flora in the soil and water of the paddy fields stands to a certain degree separately from the studies of soil algae proper, though the former essentially supplements the latter. Naturally these studies lie within the scope of Central Asia, central Kazakhstan, Far East and Mediterranean facies (see Zhurkin, 1956; Obukhova, 1959, 1961; Kuchkarova, 1961a, 1961b; Bairamova, 1967).

ingly rarely met with. Though our knowledge of algal flora of soils in the U.S.S.R. is as yet insufficient, Soviet investigations are concerned with other conjugated problems such as the flora composition of soil algae and the role of algae in the formation of certain soils; comparative characteristics of the algal community in virgin and arable soils; the influence of fertilizers and farming techniques on the floristic composition of the algae; the existence of certain algal communities in definite types of vegetative phytocoenosis, etc. Significantly, many recent floristic studies are supplemented by data concerning quantitative counting and by studies of algal distribution according to soil profile and then elucidating certain aspects of the interrelations between algae and other organisms. Such a many-sided solution of floristic problems became possible because complex research was conducted by algologists in conjunction with specialists in allied fields—pedologists, microbiologists, and geobotanists.

About 160 papers on soil algae in particular have been published in the Soviet Union during the last fifteen years. According to the analysis carried out by Shtina (1967) the taxonomic list of algae contains nearly 1200 species, varieties, and forms; 250 species in it may be considered as common, even dominant, soil forms (See Tables 1 and 2).

Nevertheless, to the present, floristic studies throw insufficient light on the diversity of soil varieties in the U.S.S.R. and provide no possibility for ample correlation from the point of view of plant geography, although the first attempts to generalize in this field have already been made (Shtina, 1956b; 1960a).

Proceeding to the ecologo-phytocoenologic trend in soil algology in the U.S.S.R., one should mention that its progress was secured by advances elsewhere. It is quite natural that the study of soil algae, begun in the twenties, has comparatively quickly outgrown the limits of floristics and become intimately connected with other practical problems. Thus the efforts of investigators to estimate the part played by algae under different specific conditions and to disclose general and partial regularities of their development and distribution in soils are fully comprehensive. Such an evaluation is possible from the point of view of phytocoenology (Novichkova-Ivanova, 1967a).

Soil algae along with other lower plants form a part of nearly every vegetative association or phytocoenosis. They should be considered as one of the structural parts of the phytocoenosis components, being ecologically and phytocoenologically isolated (i.e., a group of certain organisms with a peculiar interrelation inhabiting a definite microecological environment) or, in other words, as a layer or synusium.

Detailed phytocoenological study of soil algae becomes possible provided that direct and indirect methods are applied together.

TABLE 1 Number of Algal Species and Forms in Various Soils in the U.S.S.R. (Shtina, 1967)

Soils	Cyano-phyta	Chloro-phyta	Xantho-phyta	Bacillario-phyta	Other types	Total
Tundra	56	65	22	16	2	161
Podzolic	28	42	17	22	2	111
Soddy-Podzolic	91	88	41	49	7	276
Bogs	86	99	43	64	8	300
Peatbogs	86	128	67	69	3	353
Rendzine	45	32	20	9	—	106
Grey forest	35	31	30	19	—	115
Chernozem typie	44	53	23	21	2	143
Southern chernozem	40	24	10	6	1	81
Dark chestnut	56	24	14	8	—	102
Steppe-solonetz	64	45	12	13	2	134
Meadow-solonetz	44	41	10	30	1	126
Chestnut and light chestnut	28	14	7	5	—	54
Solod	8	37	11	12	—	68
Meadow	62	71	17	38	3	191
Brown desert-steppe	30	19	7	6	—	62
Grey-brown	44	35	12	4	—	94
Grey soil (non-irrigated)	46	29	4	7	—	86
Takyr	92	38	5	12	—	147
Solonchak	39	22	8	3	—	72
Yellow-podzolic	47	47	21	25	—	130
Brown forest	66	61	28	19	—	174
Mountain brown	60	33	12	9	—	114
Total number of species	397	371	112	291	24	1195

TABLE 2 Taxonomic Composition of Soil Algae in the U.S.S.R. (Shtina, 1967)

Types	Number of species and forms	
	Total	Most common
Cyanophyta	397	103
Chlorophyta	371	71
Xanthophyta	112	30
Bacillariophyta	291	23
Euglenophyta	16	—
Pyrophyta	4	—
Chrysophyta	4	—
Total	1195	227

Direct methods involve a thorough study in nature of the surface and the microscopic study of fresh soil samples taken from definite associations during several seasons. The indirect method uses different techniques of cultivating the soil under study. In both cases, apart from determining the species, the frequency encountered and abundance are taken into account. While correlating these observations, one states the role of separate algal species in the structure and composition of the synusium, the dominant and subdominant being distinguished. Comparison of floristic lists for particular synusia enables one to detect the specific and characteristic of algae species. The synusiae will be determined by the dominant species group and their ecologo-biological peculiarities. Data on the productivity of the dominant group (numbers of cells in them per 1 g. of soil or biomass in g.) significantly supplements our knowledge concerning the synusiae.

Relative to widening the scope of our notions concerning special aspects of geobotany and to elaborating definite principles, algal studies are believed to pay more attention to the structure and dynamics of algosynusiae. Seasonal changes, the ecologo-biologic peculiarities of the dominant groups, algal distribution in the profiles of different soils, and their interrelation with the root system of higher plants, as well as the quantitative data, have been more closely followed.

In terrestrial biocoenoses algae often form synusiae, but sometimes independent coenoses are likely to occur. Usually algal coenoses exist in extreme habitat conditions such as mountain areas, arctic deserts, polygonal tundra, as well as in deserts and semi-deserts where they occupy enormous spaces. Relatively independent algal coenoses may be embedded in plant associations if the local ecologic conditions are particularly favorable. These coenoses, which may be called "spotty" as compared with the above mentioned ones, are usually not large but occupy small ecological niches.

Elenkin (1936) was the first to consider the soil algae as being coenoses on studying the field material of Acadamician B. A. Keller collected in the steppes and semi-deserts of the U.S.S.R. Later, many investigators studied in detail the species composition, dynamics, and structural peculiarities of the synusiae in certain territories. Coenoses and synusiae of soil algae have been studied in the Arctic herb-mossy deserts (Novichkova-Ivanova, 1963), in the European and Siberian taiga (Shtina, 1959a; Novichkova-Ivanova, 1967b), in the steppes and semi-deserts (Shtina and Bolyshev, 1963; Sdobnikova, 1967), in the clay and sandy deserts (Troitskaya, 1961b; Melnikova, 1962), and in mountain regions (But, 1967).

Investigations of this type are scanty. In most of these studies, besides, there is no sufficient connection with the concepts and ideas elaborated by the phytocoenologists studying the regularities of coenosis structures. The authors, moreover, do not take advantage of the potentialities of a detailed phytocoenological analysis of algal synusiae.

The third trend in soil algology—the physiologico-biochemical one—embraces a larger field of studies, though work in this field has just begun. One cannot disagree with the fact that experimental techniques are increasing in scope in different branches of biology (see review, ed. by Lewin, 1962), soil algology included. This matter deserves special consideration and will be accordingly treated here but in general terms. The themes and aims of research into this field are many sided. One may mention the following subjects worked out in the U.S.S.R.: (1) twenty-two interrelations between soil algae and bacteria, fungi, soil protozoa, and higher plants; (2) the physiology of separate species; (3) chromatic peculiarities of algae and their connection to the metabolic type; (4) air-nitrogen fixation by blue-green algae; (5) synthesis and utilization of vitamins; (6) extracellular products; and (7) fertilizer and herbicide effect on soil algae.

The data available on the physiology of certain soil algal species is very scanty, including only twelve species which form but 1 per cent of the species composition known. But investigations concerning the other subjects mentioned above are rather numerous. Thus a great deal of significant research into blue-green nitrogen-fixing algae directly isolated from the soil is carried out by various scientific institutions (see, e.g., Shtina, et al., 1966, 1967). Shtina justly mentions a number of soil algae besides the blue-green ones as an interesting subject of physiologic investigation. Investigations concerning the entire cycle of biochemical changes occurring in the soil due to the vital functions of algae and the physiologic studies performed have as yet but insufficiently tackled the problems mentioned above.

One more aspect of this science, namely the agricultural aspect is the most characteristic feature of Soviet algology. Studies in this field were started not so long ago at the Kirov Agricultural Institute and have developed into widespread research. Much research has been done with the aim of learning the vital functions of algae in cultivated soils: changes in soil algal flora in crop rotation under experimental field conditions have been examined; laboratory and field experiments on the effect of soil algae on the growth and yield of agricultural plants are being carried out; interrelations of soil algae to other organisms under various environmental conditions have been studied, as well as the growth of algae in manure-composts and the pesticide effects on algae (Shtina, 1956a, 1956b, 1957, 1960b, 1961, 1964; Shtina and Young, 1963; Shtina, et al., 1964; Bajhina, 1967; Balezina, 1967; Young, 1967). On the other hand, certain physiological processes are being studied here, mainly those connected with air-nitrogen fixation by algae (Shtina, 1965, Shtina, *et al.*, 1966; Pancratova, 1967a, 1967b; Perminova, 1967; Tretyakova, 1967).

Investigators in the agricultural branch of algology naturally have to deal with such tasks as the practical use of algae in providing the fertility of arable soils.

Thus various research carried on in the Soviet Union favors the solving of major problems and tasks set by soil algology such as (1) algal composition in the soils of the U.S.S.R. (floristic-taxonomic studies) and the regularities of the floristic geography of soil algae; (2) the role of algal synusiae in biogeocoenoses, i.e., the phytocoenological studies of algae; (3) the dynamics of algal growth in virgin and arable soils, i.e., the problem of quantitative counting; (4) physiological and ecologo-biological peculiarities of soil algae; (5) the part played by algae in soil life, their interrelations with the microscopic population of soils, and the higher plants; and (6) the view on the practical use of soil algae. The general problem of elaborating methods of qualitative and quantitative studies of direct field and cultural laboratory techniques is still the most important one.

The above-mentioned problems and tasks of soil algology represents the general and particular aspects in this field (Hollerbach, 1967). This enumeration includes both investigations which will be solved by classical methods and those that can be worked out only by the aid of the latest advances of modern science.

The main task of the present day in soil algology is the analysis and generalization of the data obtained which will enable us to detect those sections of this science as yet insufficiently dealt with and which require utmost attention. Ecologobiological and cytological data should be drawn upon for more exact identification of species. In some cases one should probably rely on the findings of experimental physiological research. In phytocoenologic research, a number of new problems arise, the most essential being that of algal interrelation in phytocoenosis and the problem of quantitative counting elaborated on the basis of more exact and objective criteria. Much is to be done in the study of physiological properties of soil algae.

Soil is literally teeming with life. To recognize the laws of biological phenomena—the laws of vital functions of organisms inhabiting the soil—is our aim. Our efforts will eventually result in the possibility of governing soil fertility. Our endeavors to study the regularities of soil biology are directed to this end. Investigations carried out on soil algae are a substantial link in this vast and complex problem.

REFERENCES

Bairamova, L. A., 1964. "Main Features of Algal Flora of Some Soils in the Lenkoran Region," *Izvest. Ak. Nauk Az. SSR, ser. biol. nauk*, 2.

———, 1965. "Algae of Subtropic Soils of Azerbaidjan," abstracts of M. Sc. thesis, Baku.

———, 1967. "Soil Algae of Paddy Fields," Symp. "Sovremen. sostoyan. i perspect. izuchen. pochv. vodoros. v SSR," Kirov.

Bajhina, E. V., 1967. "Interrelations of Certain Soil Algae and Fungi," Symp. "Sovremennoe sostoyanie i perspectivy izucheniya pochvennykh vodorosley v SSSR." Korov.

Balezina, L. S., 1967. "Effect of Certain Fertilizers and Pesticides on the Growth of Soil Algae," *ibid.*

Bolyshev, N. N., 1955. *Origin and Evolution of Takyr Soils*, izdan. Moskov. Uni.

Bolyshev, N. N., and Evdokimova, T. I., 1944. "On the Nature of Takyr Crusts," *Pochvoved*, vol. 8.

Bolyshev, N. N., and Manucharova, E. A., 1947. "Algal Distribution in the Profile of Some Desert Soils," Vestnik Moskov. Uni., 8.

———, 1946. "On the Vegetation of the Takyrs," Vestnik Moskov. Univ., 3–4.

Bristol, B. M., 1919. "On the Retention of Vitality by Algae from old-Stored Soils," *New Phyt.*, *18*, 3–4.

———, 1920. "On the Alga-Flora of Some Desiccated English Soils: An Important Factor in Soil Biology," *Ann. of Bot.*, *34*.

Bristol-Roach, B. M., 1926. "On the Relation of Certain Soil Algae to Some Soluble Carbon Compounds," *ibid.*, *40*.

———, 1927. "On the Algae of Some Normal English Soils," *J. of Agric. Sc.*, *17*, 4.

———, 1928. "On the Influence of Light and Glucose on the Growth of a Soil Alga," *Ann. of Bot.*, *42*.

But, V. P., 1967. "Soil Algae of the West Pamirs," Symp. "Sovremen. sostoyan. i perspect. izuchen. pochv. vodoros. v SSSR," Kirov.

Dorogostoiskaya, E. V., 1959. "Soil Algal Flora of Spotty Tundra of the Extreme North," *Bot. J.*, *3*.

Dorogostoiskaya, E. V., and Novichkova-Ivanova, L. N., 1967. "On the Changes in the Algal Flora in the Tundra Soils Resulting from Their Reclamation," *Bot. J.*, *4*.

Elenkin, A. A., 1936. "Blue-Green Algae of the USSR," general part. Izdan. Akad. Nauk, SSSR., M–L.

Forest, H. S., 1965. "The Soil Algae Community. II. Soviet Soil Studies," *J. of Phycol. 1*, 4.

Gerasimov, I. P., 1933. *On the Soil-Climatol. Plain Facies of the USSR and Bordering Countries*, trudy Pochven. Instit. im. V. V. Dokuchaeva, *8*, 5.

———, 1945. *World Soil Map and General Laws of Soil Geography*, Pochvovedenieye, 3–4.

Hollerbach, M. M., 1934. *New Species and Forms of Blue-green Algae Found in Soil*, trudy Bot. Inst. Ak. Nauk., SSSR, Ser. II, 2.

———, 1935. "Algae and Soil," *Priroda*, 2.

——, 1936a. *The Composition and Distribution of Algae in Soil*, Trudy Bot. Inst. Ak. Nauk, SSSR, II, 3.

———, 1936b. "Adaphon," in Elenkin's monograph "Blue-green algae of the USSR."

———, 1962. "Main Tasks of Modern Algology," *Vestnik Ak. Nauk, SSSR*, 2.

———, 1965. "Main Problems on Taxonomy of Lower Plants on the Present Day," *J. obshchei biolog.*, *26*, 4.

————, 1967. "Algal Taxonomy in the Elaboration of Soil Algological Problems," Symp. "Sovremen. sostoyan. i perspect. izuchen. pochv. vodoros. SSSR," Kirov.

Hollerbach, M. M., Novichkova, L. N., and Sdobnikova, N. V., 1956. "Takyr Algae," in *Takyrs of Western Turkmenia and the Way of Their Agricultural Use*, Ac. Sci. USSR. Mosocw.

Gromov, B. V., 1956. *Observations on Algae of Primitive Soils in Some Northern Districts of the USSR*, Uchen. Zapis. L.G.U. ser. biolog., 216.

Kondratyeva, N. V., 1958. "The Distribution of Algae in Soil Depending on Agricultural Methods," *Ukrainian Bot. J., 15*, 4.

Kosheleva, I. T., and Novichkova, L. N., 1958. "Spotty Tundras of Western Siberia and Their Algal Flora," *Bot. J. 43*, 10.

Kuchkarova, M., 1961a. "On the Algal Flore of Paddy Fields of the Tashkent Region," *Uzbek. biolog. J.*, 2.

Kuchkarova, M., 1961b. "On the Algal Flora of Paddy Fields of the Bostandyk District," *Vopr. Biolog. i krayev. medic.*, 2.

Lewin, R. A., ed., 1962. *Physiology and Biochemistry of Algae.*, New York: Academic Press.

Matvienko, M. A., 1956. "On the Study of Soil Algae of the Crimea and the Northern Caucasus," *Bot. J.*, 9.

Mayer, K. I., 1937. "Algae of the Swampy Soils of the Yakhroma Valley," Trudy Bot. Sada Moskov. Univ. 1.

Melnikova, V. V., 1955. *Algal Flora of Serozems of Southern Tadzhikistan*, Izvest. Otd. esoestven. nauk, Ak. Nauk Tadj. SSR, 13.

————, 1962. "Algal Flora of Serozem Soils of Tadzhikistan," Tr. Bot. Inst. Ak. Nauk Tadz. SSR, 18.

Novichkova-Ivanova, L. N., 1963. "Soil Algae Synusiae Succession of Franz-Joseph Land," *Bot. J., 48*, I.

————, 1964. "Soil Algae of Franz-Joseph Land," *Problemi Severa*, 8.

————, 1967a. "Main Principles and Methods of Phytocoenological Investigation into Soil Algae," Symp. "Sovremen. sostoyan. i perspect. izuchen. pochven. vodoros. SSSR," Kirov.

————, 1967b. "Soil Algae of the Mixed Coniferous-Broad-Leaved Forest Subzone of the Amur-Zeya Watershed," *Amurskaya Taiga*, Izd. Ak. Nauk, SSSR.

Obukhova, V. M., 1959. "Algae of the Rice Fields of Taldy-Kurgan and Ksyl-Ordinsk Districts," *Sbor. rab t po ikhtiolog. i gidrobiolog*, Inst. zoolog., Ak. Nauk, Kaz. SSR, 2.

————, 1961. "Algal Flora of Rice Fields of Some Districts in Kazakhstan, Trudy Inst. Bot., Ak. Nauk, Kaz. SSR, 10.

Pancratova, E. M., 1967. "Nitrogen Compound Influence on the Growth of Blue-Green Algae and on their Fixation of Molecular Nitrogen," Symp. "Sovremen. sostoyan. i perspect. Izuchen. pochv. vodoros. v SSSR." Kirov.

————, 1967. "Extracellular Production of Blue-Green Algae," *ibid.*

Perminova, G. N., 1967. "On the Part Played by Algae in Nitrogen Storage in Soddy-Podzolic Soil," *ibid.*

Pivovarova, J. F., 1967. "Study of Algal Flora of the Solonets-Solonchak Complex Soils of the Barabin Forest-Steppe," *ibid.*

Popova, T. G., 1957. "Soil Algae of Cultivated Virgin Soils of Western Siberia," Tr. Biolog. Inst. Zap.-Siber. fil., Ak. Nauk, SSSR, 3.

Rikhter, A. A., and Orlova, K. E., 1928. "Experience in Algal Flora Counting in Saratov Soils," *Nauchn.-agronom. J.*, 5.

Sdobnikova, N. V., 1959. "Algae which Inhabit the Sands of Middle Asia," Botan. Mater. otd. spor. rasten., Bot. Inst., Ak. Nauk, SSSR, 12.

_____, 1959b. "Algal Flora as the Component of Main Phytocoenoses of the Desert Steppes of Kazakhstan. Materials of First Session of Conference on the Problem." *Biolog. compley rayon. novogo osvoeniya, ikh razional. ispolzov. i obogashch*, Izd. Ak. Nauk, SSSR.

_____, 1967. "Soil Algae of Some Vegetative Communities of Kazakhastan," in symp. *Rastiteln. soobshchest. i zhovotone naselenie step. i pustyn. Centr. Kazakhstana*, Izd. Ak. Nauk, SSSR.

Shirshov, P. P., 1935. "Ecologo-Geographical Review of Freshwater Algae of Noviy Zemli and Franz-Joseph Land." Trudy Arctich. Inst., 14.

Shtina, E. A., 1965a. "On the Effect of Soil Algae on the Growth and Yield of Agricultural Plants," Trudy Kirov. selskhorz instit., XI, 23.

_____, 1959b. "Communities of Algae in the Main Types of Soils of the USSR and Their Diagnostic Importance," *Bot. J.*, 44, 8.

_____, 1960a. "Zonality and Distribution of Communities of Soil Algae," in *Report of Soviet Pedologists to the VII Internat. Congress USA*, Acad. Sci., USSR, M.

_____, 1960b. "Interrelation of Soil Algae and Agricultural Plants in Various Environmental Conditions," *Nauchn. Dokl. vysh. shkoly, I.*

_____, 1961. "On the Part Played by Algae in the Nutrition of Plants," Trud. Inst. Microbiol., 9.

_____, 1964. "On the Role of Algae in Soil Formation Processes," in *Biolog. sinezelen. vodoros*, Izd. MGU.

_____, 1965. "Nitrogen Fixation of Blue-Green Algae," *Ecolog. i physiologx sinezelen. vodoros*, Izd. Ak. Nauk, M.-L.

_____, 1967. "Tasks and Results of Experimental Research into Soil Algology," Symp. "Sovremen. sostoyan. i peerspect. izuchen. pochven. vodoros. v. SSSR," Kirov.

Shtina, E. A., Bairomova, L. A., Perminova, G. N., and Tretyakova, A. N., 1964b. "Interaction of Soil Algae and Plants," Symp. "Phyzika, Khimia, biolog. i mineralog. pochv. SSSR," Izd. Nauk, M.

Shtina, E. A., Balezina, L. S., Pankratova, E. M., Perminova, G. N., Tretyakova, A. N., and Yung, L. A., 1967. "Research into Nitrogen-Fixing Blue-Green Algae in Non-Irrigated Soils," in "Biolog. azot i ego rol' v zemledel," M.

Shtina, E. A., and Bolyshev, N. N., 1960. "The Algae of Solonets Soils," *Bot. J., 45*, 2.

_____, 1963. "Soil Algal Communities in Dry and Desert Steppes," *ibid.*, 5.

Shtina, E. A., Pankratova, E. M., Perminova, G. H. Tretyakova, A. N., and Yung, L. A., 1966. "The Role of Blue-Green Algae in Nitrogen Storage in the Soil," abstracts of reps. to the IX International Microbiol. Congress, Moscow.

Shtina, E. A., and Roizin, M. B., 1966. "Algae of the Podzolic Soils of the Khibins," *Bot. J.,* 4.

Shtina, E. A., and Yung, L. A., 1963. "On the Soil Algae Interrelation With Nitrogen-Fixing Bacteria (azotobacter)," in *Pochven. i selskohoz. microbiolog.*, Tashkent.

Tretyakova, A. N., 1967. "Research into the Active Stratins of Soil Nitrogen-Fixing Algae," Symp. "Sovremen. sostoyan. i perspect. izuchen. pochv. vodoros. v SSSR," Kirov.

Troitskaya, E. N., 1957. "Algal Flora of Cotton Fields of Uzbekistan," Doklady Ak. Nauk, Uz. SSR, 4.

_____, 1961a. "Algae of Some Old-Irrigated and Currently Cultivated Soils of the Bukhara Region," Vop. Biolog. i krayev. medic., 2.

_____, 1961b. "Seasonal Change of Algae of Some Desert Vegetational Formations," *ibid.*

Vaulina, E. N., 1958. "Main Features of Algal Flora of Some Soils of Byelorussia," Vesci. Acad. Nauk Byelor. SSR., ser. biol. nauk.

Yung, L. A., 1967. "Influence of Blue-Green Algae on Soil Micro-Flora," Symp. "Sovremen. sostoyan. iperspect. izuchen. pochven. vodoros. v SSSR," Kirov.

Zhukkina, V. V., 1956. "Algae of Paddy Field, Far East Rice Experimental Station," *Voprosy sel. i lesn. hoz. Dal. Vost.*, vol. I, Vladivostok.

Zauer, L. M., 1956. "A Study of Algae in the Vegetative Associations of the Leningrad Region," Trudy Bot. Instit. im. V. L. Komarova, Ak. Nauk, SSSR, II, 10.

————, 1956a. "Algae of Certain Soils in the Crimean Steppe Relative to the Problem of the Role of Algae in Soil Biology," Uchen. zapisk. Len.-Gos. Univ. 213 ser. geograph. nauk.

XVII

Harvesting and Processing of
Waste-Grown Microalgae

WILLIAM J. OSWALD and CLARENCE G. GOLUEKE

Sanitary Engineering Research Laboratory
School of Public Health, University of California
Berkeley, California

In addition to some fifteen years of laboratory research in applied algal culture, we have designed and operated two relatively large pilot plants for the production of algae from organic wastes (Oswald, Golueke, and Gotaas, 1959; Oswald, Golueke, and Gee, 1959). These large pilot plants were, of course, preceded by several small-scale pilot plants (Oswald, Golueke, Gotaas, and Hee, 1958). The latter totaled one-twentieth of an acre in area and are still used for various outdoor studies. Our larger pilot plants have totaled two and two-thirds acres in area. The largest pilot plant was a temporary, two-acre unit located at the Concord, California, waste disposal plant. It was later abandoned in favor of a more conveniently located permanent unit devoted solely to algae production. The permanent plant has been in operation for the past seven years at the University of California Engineering Field Station, Richmond, California. This two-third-acre system has an active volume of one million liters and is capable of producing a sustained crop of algae of 100 lbs per day. During the operation of this plant we have grown at least 100 tons of algae of which perhaps five tons has actually been separated and dried. The greater part of this material was processed for use in scientific animal feeding tests at the Davis campus of the University of California and elsewhere; some was distributed to researchers who requested it, and, unfortunately, a sizable amount had to be discarded because of the development of molds and actinomycetes from insufficient drying. Under a new and hopefully continuing University of California program, surplus quantities of algae from the plant have been made available at cost for general distribution for experimental purposes. Approximately one-half ton of algae has been sold to experimenters in the United States and abroad under this program.

Several prototype algae growth plants have been built recently in California and Arizona in conjunction with waste disposal plants. Although capable of being operated for algae production, to date they have been operated solely as oxygen generators for waste disposal. Thus, to report on the performance of these units as algae producers, we must await some future symposium.

Before returning to our main subject of harvesting and processing, it is worthwhile to review briefly some of the fundamentals and some of the implications of algae growth on waste. We do this to emphasize the fact that the culture of algae on waste is not only important as a simple way to grow algae, but also that it has important implications in water use, waste disposal, and human environmental control which go far beyond our current and rather superficial accomplishments of producing saleable amounts of algae from wastes. It is also necessary to emphasize that when algae are grown on wastes it is not always possible to consider harvesting, processing, and use independently of growth factors.

Because of the population explosion and the increasing tendency of man to concentrate his populations in urban centers, the problems of pollution of all types are reaching stupendous proportions. Organic wastes of the type most economically transportable in water do not, of course, constitute the only source of pollution, but they do comprise a substantial fraction (perhaps one-half of the total pollution problem).

The weights of water-transmissible wastes are neither definitely known nor constant, but are approximately as indicated in Table 1, where daily

TABLE I.   Estimated Per Capita-Daily Quantities of Liquid-Transmissible Wastes

Agricultural Wastes	Food Processing Wastes	Domestic Wastes	Total
5.5 lbs.	1.1 lbs.	0.22 lbs.	6.82 lbs.
2500 grams	500 grams	100 grams	3100 grams

per capita amounts on a dry weight basis are shown for domestic, organic, industrial, and agricultural wastes in the United States. It should be apparent from Table I that agricultural wastes exceed industrial wastes fivefold, and that industrial wastes in turn, exceed domestic wastes fivefold. Thus, domestic wastes, which at present get almost all of the attention, comprise only 1/30 of the total potential water-carried wastes on a weight basis and 1/60 of the total wastes of an area. Today, water transportation actually is applied in the removal and disposal of perhaps 80 per cent of the domestic wastes and 60 per cent of the industrial wastes. However, only a small fraction (perhaps 5 per cent) of agricultural wastes are transported and disposed of in water at this time. The balance is recovered or remains on the land. Thus, about 1.11 lbs of liquid-carried wastes are now produced

TABLE II. Estimated Daily Quantities of Water-Borne Organic Wastes in the United States

Type of Waste		1967	1990
Agricultural	lbs. $\times 10^6$	55	687
	kilograms $\times 10^6$	25	312
Industrial	lbs. $\times 10^6$	132	220
	kilograms $\times 10^6$	60	100
Domestic	lbs. $\times 10^6$	35	50
	kilograms $\times 10^6$	16	23
Totals	lbs. $\times 10^6$	222	957
	kilograms $\times 10^6$	101	435

per capita per day. As is shown in Table II this amounted to 222×10^6 lbs for the U.S.A. in 1967.

The current trend now increasing rapidly is for animal feeding operations to be concentrated in urban centers, thus making it essential that a larger and larger fraction of agricultural wastes also be disposed of in water. As is also shown in Table II, by 1990 we expect that 90 per cent of the domestic, 80 per cent of the organic industrial, and 50 per cent of the agricultural wastes of the United States will be disposed of in water. Thus, a daily per capita contribution of 3.83 lbs of, or 1.74 kilograms of organic wastes is expected to be disposed of in water by that time, and assuming a U.S. population of 250 million in 1990, liquid-carried, organic wastes will amount to nearly one billion lbs per day. To dilute this quantity of wastes with water to the extent that only one-half of the oxygen normally in water (i.e., 5 mg per liter) were depleted, 2.26×10^{12} gallons of water would be required per day. This is nearly one-half the total average of 4.4×10^{12} gallons of rain which fall daily over the entire United States. It is obvious that the dilution of more than a small fraction of these wastes is impossible and that measures must be taken for their stabilization and disposal. One possible solution would be to aerate the wastes mechanically in special tanks with oxygen obtained from atmospheric reserves. The quantities of oxygen required would be prodigious, amounting to some 6×10^{12} grams, approximately 10 per cent of all the oxygen currently produced daily by all the green plants in the United States.

Another perhaps more reasonable way to satisfy this prodigious oxygen demand, a way which has been the basis for our studies at the University of California (Oswald, 1960, 1962), would be to utilize liquid suspensions of wastes themselves as a substrate for oxygen-producing algae as well as for oxygen-consuming organisms, thus not only satisfying the oxygen demand of the wastes, but simultaneously regenerating much of their elementary substrate into algae. Inasmuch as about 150 lbs of oxygen are produced each day in our pilot system, we believe that approximately only 1.5 million acres of land devoted to algae culture would be required to satisfy the oxygen demand of all liquid-borne wastes in 1967. In 1990 about six million acres would be required. The algae recovered would meet approximately one-quarter the protein needs of the nation's livestock industry, and since the U.S. currently has about 300 million acres devoted to protein production, the savings in water resources normally used to produce protein could amount to 200 million acre-feet each year. Thus, algal culture on waste gives us a great opportunity for multipurpose land use and water savings of substantial proportions.

The fundamental process for algae growth in waste is portrayed schematically in Figure 1. To accomplish this scheme, urban organic wastes

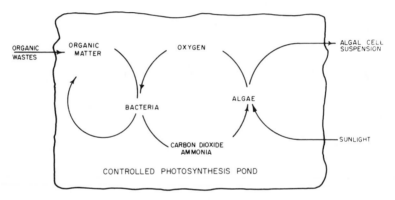

Fig. 1. Cycle of controlled photosynthesis in organic wastes.

transported in water are discharged into a shallow pond and are decomposed by aerobic bacteria in the presence of oxygen into carbon dioxide, ammonia, and other plant nutrients. These nutrients are then assimilated by algae, utilizing sunlight as the energy source for photosynthesis. Oxygen liberated through photosynthesis remains dissolved in the water and is thus available for aerobic bacterial decomposition of additional wastes. Under average conditions, each gram of organic waste entering the system supplies sufficient nutrient for the production of one gram of algae, which, in turn, would result in the production of 1.6 grams of oxygen. In a warm and sunny climate the average time required to complete an entire cycle would be two or three days. The system is continuous.

Major variables upon which a control is imposed in a growth pond system are pond depth, detention period, recirculation, mixing, and waste application. Other factors remaining equal, detention period and pond depth exert the most significant effect on pond yield. In Figure 2 experimentally attained yields in an outdoor pilot plant are shown as a function of various pond depths and detention period. It is evident from the figure that yield is inversely proportional to detention period and attains a maximum when the pond is about twelve inches deep. Yields in excess of twenty tons per acre per year are attained at depths between six and twelve inches and detention periods of two or three days. Subsequent work has indicated that the yield maximum actually occurs when the pond depth is near eight inches (20.3 cm). An optimum amount of mixing is essential to the growth process. Continuous mixing halts the process because suspended sludge excludes light. An absence of mixing is equally detrimental in that it de-

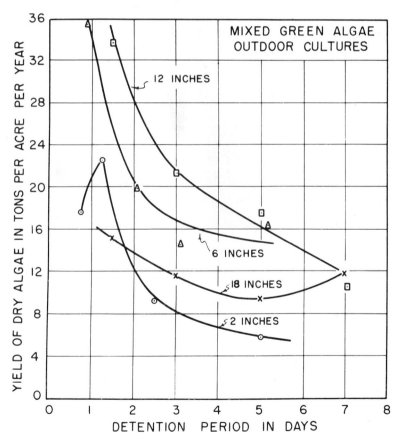

FIG. 2. Pilot plant yields of waste-grown algae in dry tons per acre per year as a function of pond depth and detention period.

prives algae of essential nutrients normally produced by bacteria in sludges near the bottom, and it deprives the bacteria of oxygen which is produced by algae near the pond surface. Mixing approximately two hours out of twenty-four during darkness seems to be near optimum for algae growth in wastes.

HARVESTING THE ALGAE

Harvesting of algae is difficult because algae are normally in dilute suspensions and of a small physical size which precludes simple sedimentation or flotation.

As described in earlier publications of our studies (Gotass, Golueke, and Oswald, 1957; Golueke, Oswald, and Gee, 1965), harvesting the algal crop involves three major steps: (1) initially concentrating the algal suspension; (2) dewatering and concentrating the resulting slurry; and (3) drying the dewatered algae for storage and handling. These three steps are necessary because it is neither technically nor economically feasible to bring the algae from their dispersed state in the culture to a finished dried product in one operation.

Initial Concentration

Experience has shown that among the several methods of removing algae from the pond effluent, centrifugation and coagulation are the most promising. Of the methods, coagulation is least expensive, giving rise to flocculant particles which rise or settle and which are subject to further dewatering. Centrifuging is rapid and easily controlled, although expensive at this time.

Centrifugation

Experiments on removing algae from pond cultures in Concord were conducted with the use of a Dorr-Oliver Merco B-30 industrial centrifuge equipped with a thirty-inch bowl containing disks and having a series of ports around the periphery through which concentrated algae was discharged. The unit, a photograph of which is shown in Figure 3, was designed for continuous operation. A typical experiment involved a determination of the effect of feed throughput rate, cell concentration, disk angle, and rotational velocity of the bowl on algal removal and power re-

FIG. 3. Merco centrifuge installed for algae concentration at Concord, Calif.

quirements. Removal of algae from the influent algal culture (concentration 200 mg/1) ranged from 84 per cent at a throughput rate of 100 gpm to about 64 per cent at 385 gpm at rotational velocities of 3000 and 3300 rpm. The effect of disk angle on degree of removal of algae was not noticeable until throughput rates in excess of 300 gpm were used. Thus, at a throughput rate of 385 gpm, removal with the disk angle at 45° was from 52–64 per cent, while at the 55° angle it was 74 per cent. Power requirement to process a ton of algae varied inversely with culture concentration. For example, at a throughput rate of 300 gpm and the culture concentration at 86 mg/1, 7.64×10^3 KWH were required; whereas, with the cultures concentration at 295 mg/1, the power requirement was only 2.64×10^3 KWH. The effect of throughput rate and the angle of disk and rotational speed of bowl on power requirements are shown in Figure 4.

As can be seen from the data obtained in our studies, the power costs for removal by centrifugation could be relatively high. Assuming that the trend of lower power requirements with increase in disk angle noted at 3300 rpm would be also applicable at 3000, then the minimum power requirement per

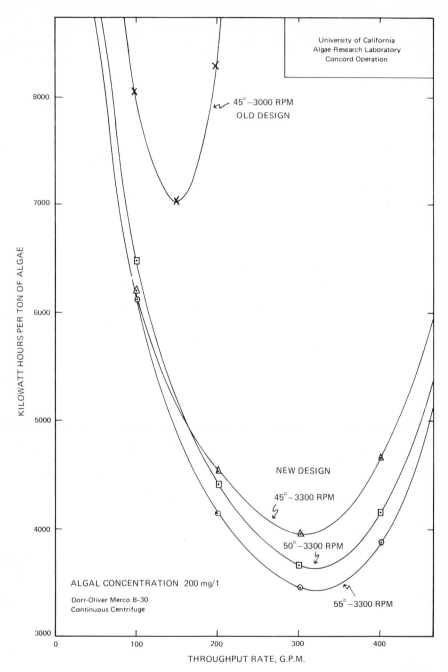

FIG. 4. Influence of speed throughput rate and disc angle on power required to centrifuge algae.

ton (dry weight) would be 2.7×10^3 KWH. If power could be purchased at 7.5 mills per KWH, the cost of power per ton of algae could be about $21.50 per ton dry weight. If the average concentration of the pond culture were increased to 400 ppm, the power requirement would be reduced by one-half and could be only $10.75 per ton dry weight.

Although centrifugation offers the advantage of simplicity and continuity of operation and the production of a material high in quality and devoid of additives reagents, it has certain obvious economical disadvantages. One is the high cost of the centrifuge itself. Machines capable of processing 400 gpm, probably the minimum rate for economical production, range from $40,000 to $50,000 per unit (in 1963–64). A second disadvantage stems from the relatively high demand of electrical power. Although power requirements per ton of algae can be reduced by increasing the concentration of the pond culture, it must be kept in mind that culture concentration is a function of light intensity, nutrient strength, and detention period. Land requirements increase with increase in reactor detention period. Thus the savings in power resulting from increasing the yield by lengthening the detention period could be negated by the rise in cost of land because of the added land requirements. Proposed changes in the design of centrifugal machines, such as enlarging the diameter of the bowl or increasing the machine speed, will contribute greatly to a reduction in power requirements in the future. We are also told that with current advances in nuclear power, power costs will continue to decline. Consequently, the use of centrifuging the algae removal is a definite possibility.

In connection with our permanent pilot plant at Richmond, we have installed a Dorr-Oliver Merco B.H.–20 continuous centrifuge which gives a concentration of ten to one with 80 per cent algae removal at a throughput rate of 100 gallons per minute. This unit has given entirely dependable service with a minimum of attention for more than six years and has been a key to our success in algae production. One major value is its utility with inexperienced personnel who need only push a button to harvest algae from the growth pond.

Flocculation

In algal production, coagulation can be induced by the addition of reagents such as aluminum sulfate (filter alum), lime, or organic cationic flocculents; or through suitable alterations in the chemical and physical constitution of the pond culture.

Chemical Flocculation. When coagulation is induced by the addition of a chemical reagent, the addition of the reagent should be followed by a brief period of rapid mixing, and then by five to ten minutes of gentle stirring to develop floc particles of sufficient size and density to permit rapid sedimentation or air flotation and subsequent removal of the flocculated material.

In optimized aluminum sulfate flocculation, the pH of the culture is first lowered to 7.0 with sulfuric acid and finally reduced to 6.5 with filter alum $(Al_2(SO_4)_3 \cdot 18\ H_2O)$. When lime is used, sufficient material is added to raise the pH of the culture to about 11.3. Because flocculation with lime is a function of change in pH, freshly hydrated lime must be used; otherwise the dosage would be excessive. In the tests, several cationic organic reagents were available, and the most effective were found to be Sondelite 802-OH (Sondel Corp., Palo Alto, Calif.), Puriflocs 601 and 602 (Dow Chemical Co.), and Primafloc C-7 (Rohm and Haas). These four reagents require a pH less than 10.5 for optimum performance.

TABLE III. Effectiveness of Alum and Sondelite as Flocculating Reagents

Item	Sewage	Cent. Super[1]	Alum (100/mg)[4]	Sondel. (2.5 μm)
BOD	130[3] 1	26[3] 18[2]	7.3	13.2
Dis. Solids (ppm)	487[3]	385[3] 558[2]	458	351
S.S. Solids (ppm)	—	0	15.4	7.6
Coliform (MPN)	$1.4 \times 10^{7[3]}$	$2.4 \times 10^{6[3]}$ $6.0 \times 10^{4[2]}$	1.6×10^2	2.4×10^4
Opt. Density (380 mμ)	0.730[3]	0.152[3] 0.124[2]	0.062	0.075
Hardness (mg/1 as $CuCO_3$)	147[3]	128[3]	—	119
Total N	62.5[3]	7.7[3] 6.3[2]	4.9	9.2
NH_4-N (ppm)	42.7[3]	3.2[2] 2.1[3]	3.5	3.2
Na^+ (ppm)	61[3]	—[3] 58[2]	56	58
$SO_4^=$ (ppm)	39[3]	—[3] 108[2]	214	38.1
Cl^- (ppm)	62[3]	—[3] 39	41	53
$PO_4^=$	18[3]	—[3] 8.0[2]	0	4.3

[1]Centrifuge in laboratory at 500 × g for 10 minutes.
[2]Analyses of sewage and centrifuged supernatant at time of experiments with alum.
[3]Analyses of sewage and centrifuged supernatant at time of experiments with Sondelite.
[4]Industrial grade: empirical formula–$Al_2(SO_4)_3 \cdot 18\ H_2O$ product contains 15–17% water-soluble Al_2O_3.

The effectiveness of alum and Sondelite as flocculating reagents is indicated by changes in substrate quality as shown in the date listed in Table III. These data were obtained from pilot plant experiments with filter alum and with Sondelite. Data on lime flocculation are not included because experiments with lime were limited to laboratory tests. Data on flotation are not available at this time.

As the tabulated data show, removal of solids by means of sedimentation following use of the two flocculating reagents was as complete as that accomplished by a laboratory centrifuge at 500 × g for ten minutes at which all of the algae normally are removed from suspension. With respect to certain aspects of water quality, as, for example, coliform removal and optical density of the supernatant, flocculation proved to be much more effective than did centrifugation at the centrifugal forces tested.

Although the dosages of coagulants listed in Table III are the minimum at which complete removal of the algae took place, in practice, the dosage that would be applied would be the one at which the maximum return per unit of reagent could be obtained. The latter dosage is not always identical with that required for complete removal. This is demonstrated in Figure 5, in which curves are plotted showing the effect of alum dosage on amount

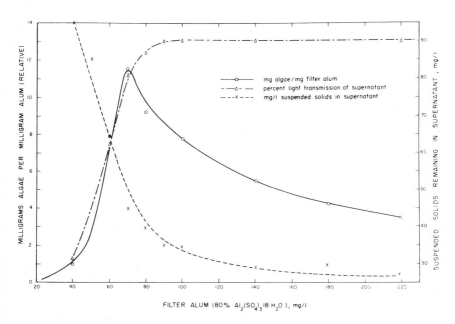

FIG. 5. Relation between dosage and amount of algae harvested per mg of alum added, and that between clarity of supernatant and alum dosage.

of solids precipitated per mg of alum, on the amounts of solids remaining in the liquid, and on the clarity of the supernatant.

Although the cost of coagulating and separating algae with the use of alum ranges from only about $20–25 per ton algae (dry weight), and from as low as $15–20 with lime, the harvested product contains either aluminum or lime. Another disadvantage accompanying the use of lime is the fact that with it the pH of the effluent is raised to a level at which it is unsuitable for direct discharge into a receiving stream or use in industry. On the other hand, the pH generally is too low when alum is used. Consequently, an additional expenditure would be required for waste conditioning. Hydrogen ion level would be less of a problem if cationic polymers were used, but they are less effective than alum and lime in the removal of algae growth potential and coliforms. At the dosages required (on the order of 2 to 10 mg/l) and at present prices, the cost of cationic polymers available commercially would be from $20 to $40 per ton of algae. With the use of modern sedimentation or flotation units and with dosages of reagent geared to maximum yield per unit of reagent, the cost of any of the chemical reagents will be reduced by at least one-third. It thus seems likely that costs on the order of one cent per lb may be assigned for coagulation followed by sedimentation or flotation.

Autoflocculation. A natural process which occurs during the afternoon of sunny days and manifests itself in the clumping and settling of the algae to the pond bottom has been observed repeatedly during the course of our outdoor experiments at Richmond and at Concord, California. This phenomenon of self-separation by the algae is termed "autoflocculation" because it is not induced by chemical additives or other externally applied agents or factors other than natural light. Autoflocculation seems to occur when the temperature of the pond increases several degrees above the morning level; and when, due to algal consumption of CO_2, the pH of the media increases above 9.5. Autoflocculation occurs most rapidly in shallow ponds, and rarely in ponds deeper than two feet. Thus, design conditions taking advantage of the phenomenon would theoretically require that the culture be placed in an autoflocculation pond three to six inches deep during the sunlight hours. After autoflocculation has taken place, the supernatant liquid would be decanted for return to the growth pond or for discharge from the system, while the flocculated algal material would be drawn into a secondary decanting pond for further concentration. Experimental results to date indicate that where conditions permit, autoflocculation would constitute a dependable and extremely low-cost process for concentrating algal material. An intensive systematic investigation of controlled autoflocculation is scheduled to be carried out by our laboratory during the next few years.

Dewatering Algal Concentrates

Separation by centrifugation or by coagulation followed by sedimentation or froth flotation results in a slurry rich in algal cells and having a solids content which may range from 0.5–2.5 per cent depending upon settling time, nature of the flocculent material, characteristics of the algae if separation is by flocculation, and upon underflow rate if it is by centrifugation. The concentrated material is called the "algal slurry" in order to distinguish it from the original primary cell suspension. Because the algal slurry loses some weight and tends to become odorous within twenty-four hours, it is advisable to use it immediately or to preserve its quality by drying it rapidly. Primary algal slurry produced as described above cannot be dried economically by conventional methods without additional concentration because the theoretical cost of energy for water removal would equal or exceed the expected monetary value of the dried algae. Therefore, dewatering the primary concentrate is an essential step in the preparation of algae for final drying.

Some of our earliest efforts to concentrate primary slurry convinced us that algae have properties which render it difficult to dewater. Attempts to dewater slurry using an Oliver vacuum filter were unsuccessful because a large difference in pressure across the filter media caused algae to clog the filter quickly. As a result, a layer could not be formed which would be sufficiently thick to make the cake removal operation feasible. The use of filter-aides did little to improve this situation. Since vacuum filtration proved unfeasible, other methods of dewatering were sought. As a result of our search, three technically and economically feasible methods of dewatering the algal slurry were found: centrifugation in a solid bowl centrifuge; filtration on an industrial gravity filter; and percolation and evaporation from a sand bed. The last-named method combines dewatering and drying into one process.

Centrifugation in a Solid Bowl Centrifuge. Algae are readily removed in a solid bowl centrifuge at 1000 × gravity applied for two to five minutes. According to results obtained in our experiments, the total cost of power, manpower, and machine for dewatering slurry with a solid bowl centrifuge should range from $0.0073 to $0.027 per lb algae, depending on centrifugal force applied, solids content of the slurry, liquid throughput rate, and final solids content. At 1,000 × g the final solids content ranges from 8–10 per cent. The consistency of these solids is indicated in Figure 6.

Gravity Filtration. The use of a gravity filter is an excellent method of dewatering algae. The total cost for dewatering with a gravity filter would range from $0.006 to $0.01 per lb of dry algae, including cost of power, machine and filter paper, operation, and maintenance. Solids content of the

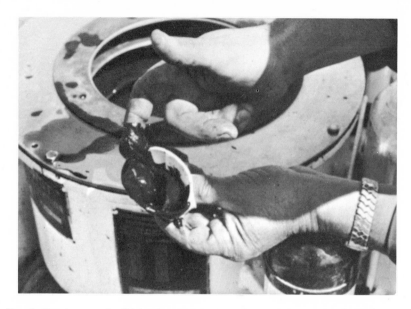

FIG. 6. Consistency of solid bowl centrifuge algal paste when centrifuged at about 1000 × g for two minutes.

paste produced would be 8–10 per cent. The use of nylon or plastic filter media in place of the bonderized cotton filter paper used in our experiment would materially reduce the cost of this method.

A discussion of dewatering algae on sand beds will be treated in the following section on drying.

Drying

For large-scale algal production, drum drying is an excellent method of reducing the moisture content of algae to a level (≃12 per cent) at which the product can be safely stored. Drum drying is a satisfactory method because the dewatered slurry (algae paste) must be dried rapidly and, therefore, as a thin layer. Kiln drying would be unsatisfactory because of the tendency of the algal paste to accumulate in large clumps when rotated in a cylinder. Although these clumps dry rapidly enough on the outside, inside they remain moist and subject to decomposition. It has been found to be virtually impossible to dry the moist centers of clumps to the degree needed to prevent deterioration by biological agents. Judging from our experience at Richmond, California, the drying rate for algae is about two lbs dry weight of algae per square foot of drum per hour. The cost of drum drying should be between one cent and two cents per lb algae depending on the cost of heat energy and the cost of labor. If dual use of labor is possible, as it may be in conjunction with waste disposal systems, the lower figure will prevail. Algae can be stored indefinitely when the moisture content is below about 12 per cent.

A second method of surface drying which appears extremely economical is sun drying. This is applicable where sunlight is abundant and a low-cost method is required. In this method, algae slurry containing 8–10 per cent solids is spread in a layer about ¼ cm thick on a flat, lightly oiled surface exposed to the sun. Spread in this manner, the algae convert light to heat and dry quickly. Usually one day is sufficient to give an 85 per cent solids flake which curls and is easily removed from the bed by scraping. A drying area equal to about 5 per cent of the growing area is required for sun drying a 10 per cent solids algal paste.

Because of the consistency and drying properties of algal slurry, spray drying should be a satisfactory method of drying algae. Unfortunately, because of the large-scale equipment required, no experiments could be run. When algae production plants 100 to 200 acres in extent are in use, spray drying systems can be properly evaluated.

Sand Beds. Our studies on harvesting algae included a combined method of dewatering and dehydration which involved the use of sand beds. Algal slurry was pumped directly from the centrifuge or from the flocculating

FIG. 7. Spreading algal slurry on sand beds for dewatering and sun drying.

chamber to the sand beds. As indicated in Figure 7, the beds were filled to a depth of three to five inches, depending upon the percentage solids of the wet weight. When treated in such a manner, algae were dried sufficiently for indefinite storage within a period of three to five days, depending upon climatic conditions. If sand bed drying were used in regions having a wet climate, a covered bed would be required. When the algal concentrate is dried on open sand beds, a drying area equivalent to 10–15 per cent of the growing area is necessary.

The sand bed method of drying combines simplicity with low cost since only one operation is necessary. The dried algal chips formed during the process are easily raked from the bed, and coarse screening removes most of the adhering sand. The consistency of sun-dried algae flakes are indicated in Figure 8. Of course algae thus harvested have the disadvantage of

Fig. 8. Sack of sun-dried algal flakes showing their chip-like consistency.

being contaminated with some sand. Because of the slow drying and long exposure to light and heat, the vitamin content of the finished product is somewhat lower than of those produced by the more rapid and mechanized methods of dewatering and drying. It has been found experimentally, however, that many of the algal cells remain alive after sun drying and hence must retain a large part of their nutritional value. It is obvious that both sun-dried algae and sand-bed dried algae could transmit agents of disease if not properly sterilized.

PROCESSING ALGAE AS FEED

Regardless of methods of harvesting, dewatering, and drying and in spite of its high nutritional value, the algal product is basically not palatable to most livestock. This problem was overcome almost entirely by Dr. Harold Hintz and Dr. William Weir, at Davis, who pelletized the processed-algae with steamrolled barley prior to feeding them to swine and sheep. The pellets were formed in a conventional pelleting machine. Consequently, when used as an animal feedstuff, algae should be combined and pelletized with the remainder of the dietary constituents.

A 10 per cent level proved to be the optimum concentration of algae in swine-feeding experiments in which algae were pelletized with barley. The addition of small quantities of vitamin B_{12} resulted in weight gains in experimental swine equal to those attained with control swine fed barley and fish meal. Algae at the 10 per cent level has also been found to be an excellent range feed for sheep. Studies of algae fed to cattle have been limited to digestibility trials in which it was found that ruminants were able to digest algae more readily than nonruminants. It should be pointed out at this stage that the wall of the algal cell is extremely resistant to biodegradation and, therefore, that a continued search for ways to improve cell wall digestion is warranted so that algae may be readily accepted by the livestock industry as a basic feed.

ECONOMICS OF THE PROCESS

Obviously, the economics of growing, harvesting, and processing algae depends upon the cost of production and upon the market value of the finished product. The costs of building and maintaining the production pond depend on pond size and financing arrangements. At 1967 levels, the estimated construction cost of a pond should be about $3,000 per acre of pond in a large installation. Annual depreciation and interest may be estimated at 10 per cent of first cost per annum. Because of the simplicity of pond construction and equipment, maintenance and operating costs should not exceed $100 per acre per year. The cost of growing the algae would thus be about $20 per ton, of which $13 represents fixed costs and $7 operational expenses. If the algae were harvested by coagulation with a cationic polymer and the costs of the reagent were as estimated, the cost of initial concentration would be about $20 per ton of algae. Dewatering with a solid bowl centrifuge (Tolhuost model) or with a gravity filter (Delpark type) would amount to about $10 per ton, including cost of machine, depreciation, and interest. If a drum dryer were used for the final drying, the cost would be about $30 per ton. At present cost levels, therefore, the total estimated cost per ton of crude algae would be about $80 per ton. If the dewatering and final drying were done by way of evaporation and percolation on sand beds, about $15 to $20 could be subtracted from this cost estimate, and the reduced cost would be $60 per ton of algae.

In considering the production cost of algae, it should be remembered that the production of algae on sewage or other wastes constitutes complete secondary and partial treatment of the sewage and, therefore, that the equivalent expenditure which would otherwise be necessary in treating sewage should be credited to the cost of algal production. The extent of this credit would vary according to the type of secondary treatment required for the waste, but it should range from $50 to $125 per million gallons of waste. Since an average of one ton of algae can be obtained from a million gallons of waste, each ton of algae produced represents the equivalent of $50 to $125 per million gallons in sewage treatment.

No firm estimate of the market value of the algal product can be made at present. On the basis of protein content and nature, however, it has been predicted by feed experts that the product should have a market value approaching that of soybean oil meal, which ranges from $75 to $85 per ton. The algal product has several nutritional advantages over soybean meal, such as high pigment and vitamin content, which may increase its eventual market value. In areas where water is at a premium, the high quality of water reclaimed in the production of the algae would probably be worth from $10 to $15 per million gallons. Assuming a selling price of $85 per ton for the algae and $10 per million gallons for the water, it may be concluded that a municipality or industry should be able to save a considerable amount by producing algae. Receipts from the sale of the products would pay for producing the algae and reclaiming the water, while the money normally charged for waste treatment could be regarded as profit. Should algae be produced by private enterprise, an arrangement could be made in which the city or industry would pay the producer a fixed sum for treating the sewage. This sum would be the producer's profit. Such an arrangement should theoretically be of mutual advantage to both parties, since the waste discharger would have its wastes treated in a manner satisfactory to water pollution control authorities at less cost and with greater reliability than could be done by means of the conventional methods of waste treatment now used. The entrepreneur would have a profitable business, and, moreover, a public service would be rendered in that valuable water would be reclaimed and nutrients conserved.

Objections to the use of algal culture as a method of combined waste disposal and algae production frequently center around the question of land use. In a growing competition for land use, it is obvious that food production must remain the highest priority for the use of land and that the most efficient methods of using land for food production should prevail. Surely among the 300 million acres of land now used for protein production we should be able to find the six million acres needed for carrying on the algae production process, a process in which wastes are treated, water is reclaimed, and sufficient foodstuff is produced to meet from 30–40 per cent of our protein requirements.

REFERENCES

Golueke, C. G., W. J. Oswald, and H. K. Gee, 1965. "Harvesting and Processing Sewage-Grown Planktonic Algae," *J. Water Poll. Cont. Fed., 37*, No. 4, April.

Gotaas, H. B., C. G. Golueke, and W. J. Oswald, 1957. "Recovery of Algae from Waste Stabilization Ponds, "Univ. of Calif. San. Eng. Res. Lab., Series 44, No. 7, Jan.

Oswald, W. J., 1960. "Light Conversion Efficiency of Algae Grown in Sewage," *J. San. Eng. Div.,* July.

———, 1962. "Coming Industry of Controlled Photosynthesis," *Amer. J. Public Health, 52*, No. 2, Feb.

Oswald, W. J., C. G. Golueke, and H. K. Gee, 1959. "Waste Water Reclamation Through Production of Algae," Univ. of Calif. San. Eng. Res. Lab. and Water Resources Center, Contribution 22.

Oswald, W. J., C. G. Golueke, and H. B. Gotaas, 1959. "Experiments on Algal Culture in a Field-Scale Oxidation Pond," Univ. of Calif. San Eng. Res. Lab., Series 44, No. 10.

Oswald, W. J., C. G. Golueke, H. B. Gotaas, and R. J. Hee, 1958. "Studies of Photosynthetic Oxygenation, Pilot Plant Experiments," *ibid.*, No. 9, Jan.

XVIII

Algal Growth Affected by Degree and Type of Wastewater Treatment

NELSON L. NEMEROW and M. C. RAND

Department of Civil Engineering
Syracuse University
Syracuse, New York

Eutrophication of our streams and lakes has often been linked to the increased contamination reaching these waters both from municipal sewers and through underground percolation from soil treatment systems. It appears that since the world population will continue to increase to the point of doubling in the next seventeen years, contaminants reaching the watercourses will also increase. The problems this will create can only be surmised, but indications exist that all but the largest, swiftest, and coldest bodies of water may be choked with algae in seventeen years. Two schools of thought have emerged on ways to combat the problem. The first school has taken the defeatist attitude and concludes that algae growth prevention is impractical. This decision is based partly on the present paucity of information on exact nutrient and environmental requirements for bloom development and partly on the feelings that nutrients are rather ubiquitous (on land, in the air, as well as in water supplies and wastes) and that natural environmental factors tend to favor blooms. This thinking sometimes suggests control of blooms by physical or chemical removal of the algae after they reach a detrimental level. The other school is more optimistic and proposes to control blooms by limiting nutrients essential for their growth. Members of this school do not agree on either the proper nutrient to remove or how to remove it practically from the wastewater effluents. Nemerow and Rand (1965) reviewed the literature and concluded that the most frequently reported limiting nutrient was organic phosphate. It is repeatedly cited as being the factor most critical for algal growth. The concentration of phosphates in municipal wastewaters is increasing, and removal efficiencies of these contaminants are poor and variable, for good reason. Present treatment practices are not designed to remove phosphates. Other researchers such as Pipes (1961) found that some of the organic compounds commonly found in sewage accelerate the growth of *Chlorella* when CO_2 is limiting, indicating that some of these compounds may serve as additional carbon sources and that some will accelerate the growth when the CO_2 is inadequate. Pipes also found that organic nitrogen will accelerate the growth above that obtained on inorganic media even when CO_2 is not limiting. Saunders (1957) has also found that organic matter can be utilized by certain algae as energy sources.

This audience is certainly familiar with the many various research findings which point to certain trace materials or other elements or compounds which influence the growth of algae.

With reference to wastewater treatment one must consider the contaminants present in raw, untreated wastes as well as those still persisting in waste effluents after treatment by the several methods. Classically we have attempted to reduce or remove as completely as possible from wastes the following major contaminants: (1) suspended solids, (2) colloidal and dissolved organic matter, and (3) pathogenic microorganisms. Table 1 presents the approximate efficiencies of removal of each of these three contaminants.

TABLE 1 Approximate Efficiencies of Removal

	Primary Treatment	Secondary Treatment (% removal)	Tertiary Treatment
Susp. Solids	40–70	70–90	90–100
Organic Matter (as measured indirectly by the BOD test)	25–40	75–90	90–95
Coliform bacteria	90–95	95–99	95–99

In recent laboratory studies Karanik (1965) and Nemerow and Rand (1964) have found that lime precipitation of raw sewage repressed algae growth, especially the blue-green type. Percolation of sewage effluents through certain soils has also given some indication of being an effective method of reducing bloom situations. Some laboratory experimentation appeared warranted to determine the effect of sewage treatment and soil precolation on algae growth.

THEORY OF SOIL ADSORPTION

Adsorption of contaminants commonly found in wastewater effluents is a rather well-known, generally accepted, but seldom used process. Physical adsorption takes place as a result of molecular condensation in the interstices of the filtering media. If the media can be partially activated (by natural or artificial means), then the adsorption and subsequent increase of concentration of contaminant at the interfaces will be followed by a slower diffusion of compounds into the capillaries of the filtering media. The rate-controlling diffusion process varies roughly with the reciprocal of the square of the diameter of the medium, increases directly with the concentration and temperature of contaminant to be removed, and decreases as the contaminant increases in molecular weight. Diffusion also increases with the length of time of contact with the adsorbent. Freundlich developed the empirical relationship

$$\frac{x}{m} = kc^{1/n}$$

where x = weight of contaminant adsorbed
   m = weight of media
   c = concentration of contaminant remaining in solution
   and k and n are constants which vary as the process environmental
   factors vary.

Langmuir developed from theory the linear equation

$$\frac{1}{x/m} = \frac{1}{b} + \frac{1}{abc}$$

where b = amount of contaminant adsorbed to form a complete
   monloayer on the surface of the media
and   a = constant which increases as the molecular size of
   the contaminant increases

It seems important to remember that since both of these formulations were developed for single pure substances, direct application of the equations is not possible for wastewaters having many contaminants subject to adsorption.

In practical treatment processes, filters containing the adsorbing media through which the wastewater is passed have been found to be most effective. Factors which are known to increase the efficiency of removal (lengthen the filter run or breakthrough time; include: (1) greater filter by height, (2) smaller particle size of adsorbent, (3) lower flow rate of wastewater, and (4) higher initial concentration of contaminant.

APPLICATION OF SOIL PERCOLATION

It has been generally presumed that algal growth in a receiving water can be prevented by requiring the adjacent homeowners to utilize properly designed and constructed septic tanks followed by percolation through reasonably porous soil matter. This concept is accepted despite the knowledge of existing algae growths in such carefully protected New York State lakes as Skaneateles and Lake George. Recently the Town of Colonie was faced with a problem with its impounded lake reservoir. A large developer proposed to discharge the secondary treated effluent from about fifty homes through a natural sandy soil before reaching the lake reservoir. In a laboratory investigation, when a small amount of the treated sewage effluent was added to the clear reservoir water, the resulting mixture produced visible algae growth when allowed to stand in a beaker in natural sunlight for a few days. A similar mixture of effluent which had been percolated through some of the native porous soil showed no such algae growth. Soil filtration apparently was effective in removing some material essential

TABLE 2   Analyses of Three Sewage Samples Before

Type of Waste	pH	Alkalinity (ppm $CaCO_3$)	(OH)	(HCO_3) ppm	(CO_3)	(Free) (CO_2)	(Total) (CO_2)	Total Inorganic PO_4 (ppm)
Raw Sewage unfiltered	7.4	292	0	280	0	20	143	49
Primary Sewage unfiltered	7.1	243	0	230	0	34	135	37
Secondary Sewage unfiltered	7.5	217	0	200	0	12	100	28
Raw Sewage filtered 100% sand	7.5	280	0	260	0	15	130	29
Primary Sewage filtered 100% sand	7.3	235	0	210	0	15	107	35
Secondary Sewage filtered 100% sand	7.4	204	0	185	0	13	95	26
Raw Sewage filtered 90% sand	6.7	155	0	145	0	50	113	1.8
Primary Sewage filtered 90% sand	6.8	133	0	125	0	40	95	0.3
Secondary Sewage filtered 90% sand	6.5	79	0	75	0	45	78	0.4
Raw Sewage filtered 85% sand	6.8	132	0	125	0	40	95	0.6
Primary Sewage filtered 85% sand	6.4	93	0	90	0	65	105	1.0
Secondary Sewage filtered 85% sand	6.4	81	0	75	0	55	88	0.8
Bishop's Brook Untreated	7.9	215	—	—	—	—	—	Trace

to the growth of algae. The possibility of the existence of misguided notions, coupled with the experimental evidence of the effects of soil filtration, and the increasing importance of soil percolation as a final treatment of waste-waters influenced a decision to pursue this subject in continued laboratory studies.

The laboratory investigation involved the following three phases:

1. effects of raw, primary, and secondary treated domestic sewages on receiving waters before and after percolation through 100 per cent sand, 90 per cent sand–10 per cent silty-clay, and 85 per cent sand–15 per cent silty clay filters.
2. effects of filtering from one to four volumes of primary treated domestic

and After Percolation Through Three Soil Types

NO_3 (ppm)	Total Solids (ppm)	Total Susp. Solids (ppm)	Total Dissolved Solids (ppm)	Total Inorganic Solids (ppm)	Inorganic Dissolved Solids (ppm)	Organic Dissolved Solids (ppm)	Optical Density at 530 mu after 10 days at 20–30°C and favorable light
<.5	1250	212	1038	996	949	89	0.27
<.5	1312	60	1252	1150	1150	102	0.22
3.6	1278	23	1255	1172	1170	85	0.39
<.5	1106	42	1064	956	946	118	0.18
<.5	1240	37	1203	1094	1089	114	0
4.0	1206	20	1266	1170	1170	96	0
<.5	896	14	882	784	784	98	0.03
<.5	1046	7.5	1039	936	936	103	0.04
3.5	1080	7.0	1073	1008	1008	65	0
<.5	876	5.0	871	774	774	97	0
<.5	1008	4.5	1003	942	942	61	0
3.3	1090	6.0	1084	996	996	88	0
4.5	—	—	—	—	—	—	1.01

TABLE 3   Analysis of Three Soil Types Prior to

Soil Tests	Untreated Samples			RAW		
	Sand	10%CS + 90%S	15%CS + 85%S	Sand	10%CS + 90%S	15%CS + 85%S
Grain Size Analysis (Uniform Coefft.)	1.83	3.8	6.1			
Specific Gravity	2.59	2.71	2.76	2.63	2.73	2.77
Void Ratio	9.51	0.71	0.75	0.67	0.69	0.7
Permeability cm/sec.	1.61×10^{-2}	7.82×10^{-4}	5.35×10^{-4}	2.64×10^{-4}	3.1×10^{-2}	2.39×10^{-3}
Organic Content (Volatile)	0.6%	1.01%	0.8%	0.602%	1.02%	0.900%

sewage effluent through a 90 per cent sand–10 per cent silty clay filter.

3. effects of filtering six different primary sewage effluents through a 90 per cent sand–10 per cent silty clay filter.

RESULTS

The Brookside Treatment Plant at Fayetteville, New York, serves a development of approximately 100 medium-priced homes. It provides primary sedimentation, trickling filtration, and oxidation pond treatment prior to discharge into a small creek. Samples of the raw waste, primary settled effluent, and trickling filter effluent were collected as well as some of the uncontaminated receiving stream, Bishop's Brook. Each of the three wastes and Bishop's Brook was analyzed prior to percolation through the three soils. The soils were also analyzed dry, placed in three-inch cylinders underlaid with a fine screen and saturated with tap water. The three wastes were then allowed to percolate through the soils, and the effluents were collected for analysis. Two samples of each soil effluent were inoculated with a living culture of mixed algae population. The algal growth at 20°–30°C was measured after ten days by measuring the optical density at 530 mu and comparing this with one sample which was not inoculated with the algal culture. The results are presented in Table 2. The physical and chemical analyses of the three soil samples before and after percolation are shown in Table 3.

and Following Percolation of Three Sewages

			Treated Samples			
	PRIMARY			SECONDARY		
Sand	10%CS + 90%S	15%CS + 85%S	Sand	10%CS + 90%S	15%CS + 85%S	
2.61	2.71	2.76	2.59	2.71	2.76	
0.675	0.69	0.69	0.69	0.69	0.695	
2.03×10^{-2}	6.24×10^{-3}	5×10^{-4}	2.28×10^{-2}	5.75×10^{-3}	2.28×10^{-3}	
0.60%	1.01%	0.8%	0.6%	1.02%	0.802%	

PRELIMINARY CONCLUSIONS

1. Algal growth was prevalent in all three sewage samples regardless of treatment; a greater growth occurred in secondary effluent.

2. Algal growth occurred to some extent in primary effluent even after percolation through the 90 per cent sand filter; this growth was greater than that which occurred in uncontaminated Bishop's Brook water but not as great as when raw sewage was filtered through 100 per cent sand.

3. Algal growth did not occur in any samples which had percolated through soils of 85 per cent sand–15 per cent silty-clay, regardless of pretreatment.

4. Algal growth did not occur in any secondary sewage effluents which had been percolated through any of the soils used regardless of sand content.

5. Algal growth can be retarded both by proper pretreatment and percolation through sand as well as by little or no treatment followed by percolation through 85 per cent sand-15 per cent silty clay soil. The results of the physical and chemical analysis of the effluents and soils of the second experiment are presented in Tables 4 and 5, respectively.

The soil column removed 95 per cent of the orthophosphate, 9 per cent of the total inorganic matter, 94 per cent of the total suspended solids, and 38 per cent of the total organic matter, while causing a reduction in pH from 7.7 to 6.8, and a reduction of about 34 per cent in alkalinity. No reduction in nitrate occurred during the filtration. Removal efficiencies de-

TABLE 4   Effect of Filtering Various Volumes of Primary

Sample	pH	Alkalinity (total) (ppm CA CO$_3$)	Ortho-Phosphate (as ppm PO$_4$)	Nitrate (ppm NO$_3$)	Total Solids (ppm)
Primary (unfiltered) (Control)	7.7	234	20	0.9	1581
1 liter volume (filtered)	6.8	153	1.0	1.1	1354
2 liter volume (filtered)	7.1	195	4.0	1.0	1442
4 liter volume (filtered)	7.5	202	6.5	1.0	1516
*Lime precipitated effluent—250 ppm lime (unfiltered)	10.8	186	16	1.0	1405
*Lime precipitated effluent—350 ppm lime	11.0	174	20	1.1	1375

* Used as added information and comparisons of removals.

creased as the volume of effluent applied to the filter increased from one to four liters.

The soil became slightly more permeable and also increased somewhat in void ratio as the quantity of primary effluent passed through increased from one liter to four liters. The reverse effect might have been expected from clogging of the column. A plausible explanation for the increase in permeability might be a slow elution of the clay as it is carried through the column by the flowing effluent.

TABLE 5   Treated Samples

Soil	Effluent Soil Samples		Primary 10% Clayey Silt + 90% Sand
	Effluent Passed		
	1 Liter	2 Liters	4 Liters
1. Specific Gravity	2.72	2.70	2.70
2. Void Ratio	0.71	0.72	0.725
3. Permeability (cm/sec.)	6.5×10^{-3}	7.8×10^{-3}	8.8×10^{-3}
4. Organic Content (Volatile)	No appreciable change observed		

Effluent Through a 90% Sand–10% Silty Clay Soil Mixture

Total Susp. Solids (ppm)	Total Dissolved Solids (ppm)	Total Inorganic Solids (ppm)	Total Organic Solids (ppm)	Inorganic Dissolved Solids (ppm)	Alkalinity Fractions (OH)	(HCO$_3$)	CO$_3$	Free CO$_2$	Total CO$_2$
79	1502	1291	290	1276	0	210	1.5	20	206
5.4	1349	1174	180	1174	0	150	0	45	177
11.0	1431	1227	215	1227	0	180	0	22	180
4.2	1512	1248	268	1248	0	190	0.8	10	178
8.4	1398	1197	308	1197	25	16.5	150	0	147
7.8	1367	1172	203	1172	40	9.0	120	0	114

Eight sewage treatment plant effluents were studied to ascertain the effect of various types of treatment on a receiving water which had already been seeded with an algal culture. Thirty-five ml. of each effluent was mixed with thirty-five ml. of Lake Ontario water (collected at Oswego, New York) seeded with two ml. of an active mixed algal culture and agitated periodically while being exposed to optimum light conditions for algal growth. Controls consisting of seventy ml. of Lake Ontario and distilled water and no sewage effluent plus the two ml. of seed culture were also exposed to identical environmental conditions. Initial turbidity (Hellige Turbidimeter), color (Coleman Spectrophotometer), and microscopic algal counts were determined on May 2, 1967. Similar analyses were made at one point in the growth curve, after one week on May 8, 1967. The source and previous treatment of the eight samples of effluent are shown in Table 6.

The data in Table 7 reveal several important facts. First, and probably most obvious, is that all samples enhanced the growth of algae as evidenced by all three criteria for growth. Direct microscopic counting of algae is, perhaps, the best single indicator of growth. However, turbidity and optical density of the waters provide an indirect measure of the mass of growth associated with these numbers. Often algal mass is even more significant in bloom formation than actual numbers of individual cells. The individual analytical results shown in Table 7 represent the averages of several sam-

TABLE 6   Source and Previous Treatment of Effluent Samples

No. of Sample	Source of Effluent	Prior Treatment of Sewage Effluent
1	Carmel, N. Y.	Activated Sludge & Sand Filtration
2	Alden, N. Y.	Activated Sludge (conventional)
3	Elmira, N. Y.	Activated Sludge (modified aeration)
4	Chemung, N. Y.	Trickling Filtration
5	Cooperstown, N. Y.	Imhoff Tank
6	Cheektowaga, N. Y.	Trickling Filters
7	Chittenango, N. Y.	Primary Sedimentation
8	Sweden, N. Y.	Extended Aeration

ples. For example, the average increase in number of algal cells in four samples of Lake Ontario water, a control, without any added sewage effluent, was from 26,133 to 863,700 in a one-week period; the corresponding increase in turbidity was from 4.4 ppm to 18 ppm, and in optical density at 600 mu wavelength was from .020 to .089. As a comparison, the numbers of cells after one week in Sample No. 3 (an activated sludge effluent) was about double that of the control, 1,600,000, the turbidity increased to 61 ppm (over three times that of the control), and the optical density at 600 mu

TABLE 7   Effect of Sewage Treatment

Sample No.	Treatment Type	Turbidity (ppm) Before	After	Microscop. cts./cc Before	After	450 mu. Before	After
1	Act. Sludge & Sand Filtration	4.55	33	23,625	1,236,375	.0875	.500
2	Act. Sludge (Conventional)	7.95	42.5	17,450	1,774,250	.093	.397
3	Act. Sludge (Mod. Aeration)	11.0	61.0	23,911	1,600,000	.204	.906
4	Trickling Filtration	9.67	79.0	23,308	2,162,500	.114	1.10
5	Imhoff Tank	100	130	46,500	1,218,500	.395	1.84
6	Trickling Filtration	26	79	31,150	1,428,750	.385	1.575
7	Primary Sedimentation	10	30	31,100	744,400	.116	.365
8	Extended Aeration	24	94	30,154	1,789,500	.325	.956
Control	Lake Ontario Water	4.4	18	26,133	863,700	.034	.084
Control	Distilled Water	8.25	47	11,975	270,550	.059	.383

increased to .449 (about six times that of the control). This would point to the activated sludge sewage effluent as responsible for the increased algae growth in Lake Ontario water. Upon closer observation one can separate all the sewage effluents into either primary, activated sludge, or trickling filter types. For comparative analysis this is presented in Table 8.

The two primary treatment plant effluents stimulated algal growth after one week less than half as much as did the six secondary effluents. This observation was borne out by the increase in turbidity after growth of 2.15 for the primary effluents, compared with about 5.5 times for the secondary effluents. Actual microscopic cell counts increased 25 times as compared to 70 times for secondary effluents. The final cell counts were about 1,000,000 per ml. for primary effluents and about 1,700,000 per ml. for secondary effluents. Optical densities increased about 3.5 times in primary effluents and averaged about 6 times in secondary effluents.

There appears to be some similarity between the effects of both the four activated sludge and the two trickling filter effluents on the algae growth in Lake Ontario water. Although algae grew in Lake Ontario water with no sewage effluent, the number of cells reached only 863,700 per cc; distilled water effected a growth of only 270,550 cells per cc. Thus, the final counts

on Stimulation of Algal Growth

		Spectrophotometric Optical Density (%)					
500 mu.		550 mu.		600 mu.		650 mu.	
Before	After	Before	After	Before	After	Before	After
.068	.418	.049	.306	.041	.295	.040	.323
.070	.305	.056	.242	.048	.228	.050	.250
.164	.598	.132	.454	.118	.449	.115	.502
.089	.866	.070	.636	.062	.642	.061	.689
.332	1.24	.286	.93	.274	.92	.268	1.08
.289	1.24	.224	.825	.204	.85	.198	1.04
.085	.307	.068	.229	.062	.226	.062	.251
.270	.784	.231	.597	.198	.586	.193	.644
.027	.076	.017	.062	.020	.089	.020	.055
.049	.411	.037	.344	.033	.329	.032	.346

TABLE 8 Comparative Analysis of Three Types of
Sewage Treatment on Algae Growth

Type of Treatment		Turbidity Measurement		Microscopic Counts		Optical Density	
	Nos.	Ratio of Final to initial	Final (ppm)	Ratio of Final to initial	Final (No./ml.)	Ratio of Final to initial	Final
Primary	5, 7	2.15	80	25	981,450	3.51	.573
Act. Sludge	1, 2, 3, 8	5.54	58	70	1,599,906	4.73	.389
Trickling Filters	4, 6	5.6	79	70	1,795,625	7.2	.746
Control (Lake Ontario)		4.1	18	33	863,700	4.45	.089
Control (Distilled Water)		5.7	47	25	270,550	10.0	.329

after one week of growth showed the following approximate ratios of various effluents to that of distilled water as a control:

Distilled water only	1
Lake Ontario water only	3
Primary effluent	3.5
Activated sludge effluent	6.0
Trickling filter effluent	6.6

Although these results are only preliminary, and at best represent only one point in time on the algal growth cycle, they do show a trend, undeniably apparent, which should be investigated further. They indicate that biological treatment of sewage renders the effluent more stimulating to a given culture for algae growth in a particular receiving water than does primary treatment.

REFERENCES

Karanik, J. M., and N. L. Nemerow, 1965. "Removal of Algal Nutrients from Domestic Wastewaters," *Water and Sewage Works, 112,* 12, 460.

Nemerow, N. L., and M. C. Rand, 1964. "Algal Nutrient Removal from Domestic Wastewaters," Proc. 1st Ann. Water Quality Res. Symp., N.Y. State Dept. Health, Albany, 37–58.

———, 1965. "Removal of Algal Nutrients from Domestic Wastewaters," Report No. 9, Dept. Civil Eng., Syracuse Univ.

Pipes, W. C., 1961. "Algae Growth Rate," *Water and Sewage Works, 108,* 176.

Saunders, G. W., 1957. "Interrelations of Dissolved Organic Matter and Phytoplankton," *Bot. Rev., 23,* 389.

XIX

The Regeneration of Some Large Lakes in Bavaria

H. LIEBMANN

Bavarian Biological Research Institute
Munich, Germany

The content of phosphorus and nitrogen compounds is very high in domestic sewage as well as in industrial wastes. Each inhabitant produces 0.61 g phosphorus by faeces and 0.83 g by urine each day. Domestic sewage contains a mean concentration of 10 g/m^3 phosphorus and 80 g/m^3 nitrogen. The elimination of phosphorus and nitrogen compounds by mechanical and biological purification treatment is not enough. The elimination of phosphorus in the mechanical treatment of a purification plant is only two per cent, and in the biological treatment 23 per cent.

If sewage is discharged in receiving water after mechanical or biological purification alone, the phosphorus and nitrogen content in the effluent can cause a strong development of algae. It is therefore necessary to eliminate these nutritive elements before they come into receiving water. The third of treatment of sewage purification (tertiary treatment) was developed for this purpose. The main problem is the elimination of the phosphorus. Phosphate can be eliminated by chemical flocculation with calcium, aluminum, or tri-valent iron salts. The last is obviously the best method because a sludge with good sedimentation qualities can be obtained. If calcium hydroxide alone is used, there will be a large volume of thin sludge and a high pH development. The salts of aluminum are expensive, but it is possible to combine tri-valent iron with aluminum and calcium hydroxide.

There are two principal methods of chemical flocculation. The first is simultaneous flocculation (Figure 1), and the second is flocculation after the biological step of purification (Figure 2). The first method can be used directly in connection with the activated sludge process, and is therefore practical. If flocculation after biological treatment is used, a separate treatment plant becomes necessary. Figures 3–6 show the placement of such purification plants in Germany (Bavaria) and Switzerland.

There is much discussion today about the influence of the different nutritive elements on algae growth. The special problem is: is it practical to eliminate only the phosphates, only the nitrogen, or both together? Our studies have shown that the elimination of nitrates by ion-exchange is too expensive. At the present time, therefore, we have only the microbiologi-

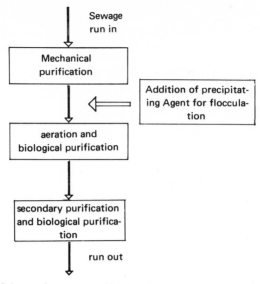

FIG. 1. Scheme of a sewage purification plant with simultaneous flocculation.

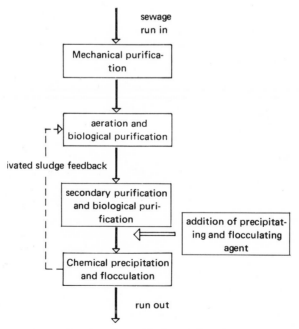

FIG. 2. Scheme of a purification plant with flocculation after the biological step, with activated sludge.

FIG. 3. Aerial photo of a simultaneous system at the biological purification plant of Prien (Bavaria).

FIG. 4. Aerial photo of an activated sludge process with flocculation after the biological step at the city of Moosburg (Bavaria).

FIG. 5. Overlook about the biological purification plant with flocculation after the biological step at Uster, Switzerland.

FIG. 6. The tanks for flocculation material at the purification plant at Uster, Switzerland.

cal methods of eliminating nitrogen. Together with the LURGI Society of Frankfurt we have developed a special plant called the DENIFLOC system at the Sewage Experimental Field of Munich (Figure 7). By the activated sludge process, species of bacteria are developed which can take the oxygen either from the atmosphere or from nitrogen compounds. This is the aerobic phase of a DENIFLOC plant. In the second step, the anaerobic phase, the bacteria use oxygen from nitrates and change it into elementary nitrogen which passes off as gas into the air. At the aerobic phase of the plant a full nitrification is given, which is necessary for the denitrification in the anaerobic phase.

FIG. 7. Overlook about the DENIFLOC plant at the Experimental Field in Munich.

According to our studies of large lakes in Bavaria, the elimination of phosphates is specially important; the treatment plants, therefore, are arranged at first for phosphorus elimination. Phosphates must be eliminated to the extent that the concentrations of phosphorus in domestic sewage and industrial waste effluents are only 0.05–0.5 mg/1. This is not a technical problem because the good flocculation of phosphates from sewage into insoluble compounds is very easy. The technical development to eliminate phosphates is not as great a problem as the elimination of nitrogen. It is possible by simultaneous flocculation to eliminate phosphates by 80–90 per cent. Our studies on the purification plant of Prien, near the large lake Chiemsee, and also in the city of Moosburg, Bavaria, have given good results.

Another possibility for diminishing the algae growth in a lake is to discharge the water into the depths of the lake instead of to the surface water, but this method is only useful at deep lakes which have a small surface area, and cannot be utilized in large lakes. If circumstances are favorable for a strong development of algae they can gather on the surface of a lake, and can be removed by mechanical methods, but this is only a temporary help. Algae can also be destroyed by chemical substances. This method is dangerous for other organisms in the water, however, especially fish. Therefore it is better to develop only those methods which eliminate the phosphates by flocculation and sedimentation. This can be done at a cost of fifty cents per person per year in the area affected.

A good method is to eliminate phosphates and nitrates with biological purification systems when treatment is carried out over a long period of time. We have studied the situation in fish-pond systems, in bio-oxidation channels, and also in oxidation ponds. If the detention time in such a system is more than a few hours, preferably five to ten days, a 60 per cent elimination of phosphate and a 50 per cent elimination of nitrate has been observed.

If drinking water is supplied by a lake with a high rate of eutrophication, the third step of sewage purification is not enough. All sewage must be diverted and a sewage pipeline around the lake must be built. In Bavaria such sewage pipelines have been constructed on the Schliersee (Figure 8) and also on the Tegernsee (Figure 9). At a flow of not more than 20 mph raw sewage can be discharged by means of such pipelines. If the flow is more than 20 mph, such a pipeline systems cannot be used because the

FIG. 8. Sewage pipeline around the Schliersee and at the river Schlierach. After Völk 1960.

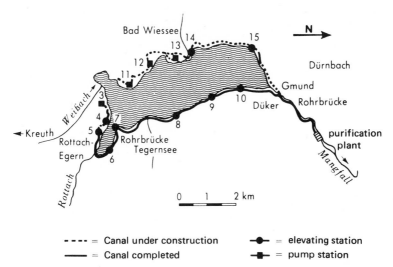

---- = Canal under construction   —●— = elevating station

——— = Canal completed   —■— = pump station

FIG. 9. Sewage pipeline around the Tegernsee Valley. After Völk 1960.

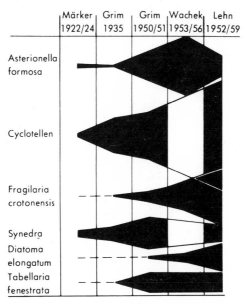

FIG. 10. The increase of phytoplankton caused by high concentration of phosphate fertilizer in Lake Konstanz. After Nümann 1964.

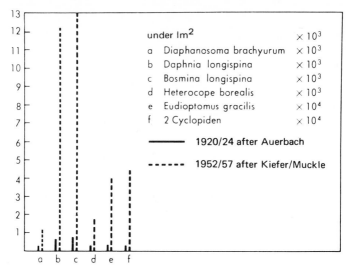

FIG. 11. The increase of zooplankton caused by a strong development of phytoplankton in Lake Konstanz. After Nümann 1964.

sewage will digest. The flow in the lines around the Bavarian lakes of Schliersee and Tegernsee is not more than about 6 mph.

All the sewage transferred by pipelines around a lake is gathered in the outflow, where a large purification plant with both mechanical and biological treatment is built. One of the largest lakes in Europe is the Bodensee (Lake Konstanz), which borders Austria, Germany, and Switzerland. At

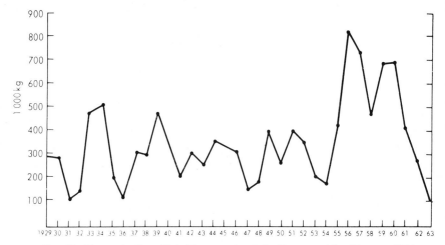

FIG. 12. The production of fish (*Coregones*) at Lake Konstanz. After Nümann 1964.

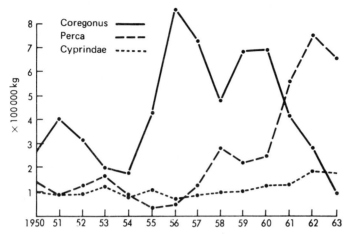

FIG. 13. The production of the fish species *Coregonus*, *Perca*, and the Cyprinidae at Lake Konstanz. After Nümann 1964.

different sites around the Bodensee, various purification plants are located. These plants provide both mechanical and biological treatment. The lake, however, shows that eutrophication is increasing and that the current treatment processes are not enough (Figures 10–15). There are two possibilities to correct this situation: (1) install a third treatment in each of the purification plants, or (2) to build pipelines for the biological purified

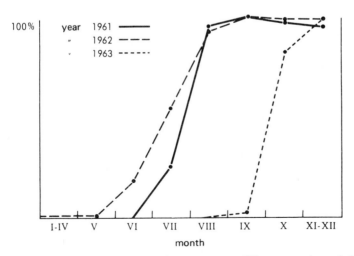

FIG. 14. Composition of stage of life of *Coregones* at different months and different years at Lake Konstanz. After Nümann 1964.

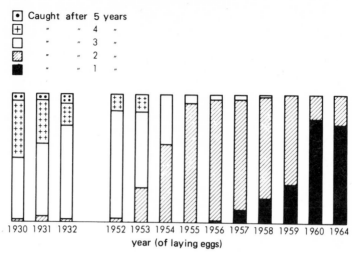

FIG. 15. Changes in the composition of stage of life of all fish caught at Lake Konstanz. After Nümann 1964.

sewage. Because a pipeline for raw sewage around a lake of this size would be more than twenty-five miles long, and would cost more than $300,000, and since this sum is not available, we recommend the second alternative, which would be the submersion of plastic pipes in the lake. The biological purified sewage from different plants can be collected in these plastic pipes and discharged in the outflow of Lake Konstanz. At a later date a plant for phosphorus elimination can be built near the outflow of such a large lake to discharge the effluent, which has been purified, into the receiving running water. This seems to be the only feasible method available at present to help our large lakes from becoming centrophic from wastewater effluence. We do not have the time to waste in waiting while the other two methods of eliminating phosphates and nitrates are fully developed.

XX

Physical and Chemical Removal of Nutrients

NICHOLAS L. CLESCERI

Bio-Environmental Engineering Division
Rensselaer Polytechnic Institute
Troy, New York

In many cases, a major contributor of algal nutrients to receiving waters is the discharge of raw or treated wastewaters. Any program of controlling or retarding eutrophication must consider the removal of these nutrients prior to discharge. The term "nutrients" in present-day usage refers to forms of nitrogen and phosphorus. As comprehension of the complex nutritional requirements of algae in nature increases, the term will be expanded to include items which the algologist deems necessary and noteworthy.

This paper is a compilation of the more pertinent literature regarding physical and chemical means of removing nitrogen and phosphorus from wastewaters. This information will provide the phycologist with a synoptic view of the present technology in and experiences with problems of nitrogen and phosphorus stripping from the liquid wastes of our society.

CHEMICAL FORMS OF NITROGEN AND PHOSPHORUS PRESENT IN WASTEWATERS

Nitrogen is a major component of living matter and, therefore, is a constituent of wastewaters. Nitrogen is found in the following forms:

(1) ammonium ion (NH_3 or NH^+, depending on the pH)
(2) the nitrate ion (NO_3^-)
(3) the nitrite ion (NO_2^-)
(4) organic nitrogen compounds (amino acids, proteins, etc.)
(5) the oxides of nitrogen (N_2O, NO, N_2O_3, NO_2, N_2O_5)
(6) nitrogen gas (N_2).

In wastewater, the predominance of one or more species over the others is dependent upon the chemical and biochemical reactions which have occurred.

413

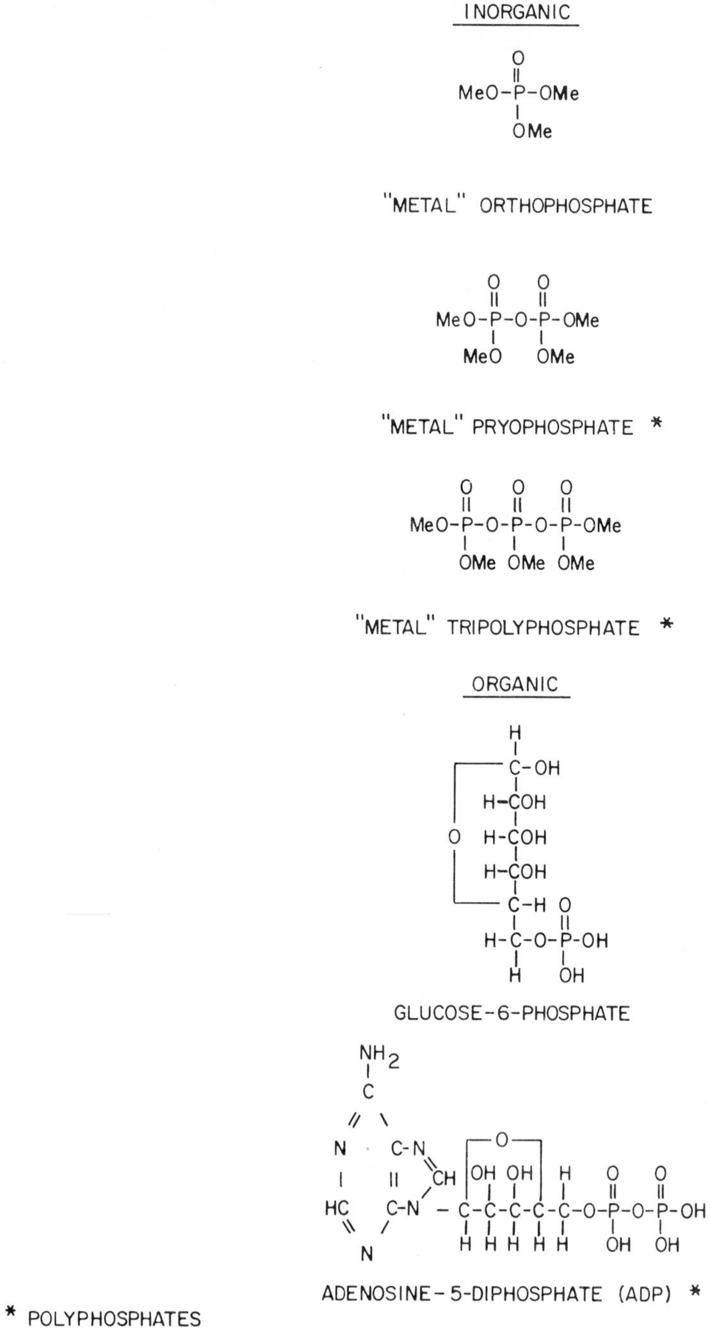

INORGANIC

$$MeO-\underset{\underset{OMe}{|}}{\overset{\overset{O}{\|}}{P}}-OMe$$

"METAL" ORTHOPHOSPHATE

$$MeO-\underset{\underset{MeO}{|}}{\overset{\overset{O}{\|}}{P}}-O-\underset{\underset{OMe}{|}}{\overset{\overset{O}{\|}}{P}}-OMe$$

"METAL" PRYOPHOSPHATE *

$$MeO-\underset{\underset{OMe}{|}}{\overset{\overset{O}{\|}}{P}}-O-\underset{\underset{OMe}{|}}{\overset{\overset{O}{\|}}{P}}-O-\underset{\underset{OMe}{|}}{\overset{\overset{O}{\|}}{P}}-OMe$$

"METAL" TRIPOLYPHOSPHATE *

ORGANIC

GLUCOSE-6-PHOSPHATE

ADENOSINE-5-DIPHOSPHATE (ADP) *

* POLYPHOSPHATES

FIG. 1. Phosphorus Compounds.

There exists a variety of confusing terms to describe the forms in which phosphorus is found in wastewaters. Phosphorus is present either as inorganic or organic phosphates. Typical structures are given in Figure 1. At the present, there are analytical techniques available which can detect both inorganic orthophosphate and total phosphorus, which would include inorganic polyphosphates and organic phosphates, as well as orthophosphate. In the recent past there has been an increase in the inorganic polyphosphate component in wastewaters due to their widespread use in industry.

REMOVAL OF NITROGEN

Various methods have been developed to effect nitrogen removal since it was realized that the discharge of excessive quantities of nitrogen to a receiving body of water might remove any prior limitation to algal growth resulting in a nuisance situation occurring.

Guggenheim Process

In 1933, Gleason and Loonam used the removal of nitrogen as a criterion for the effectiveness of the Guggenheim process which they were developing.

The Guggenheim process, as depicted in Figure 2, consisted of:

(1) Suspended solids removal by coagulation with ferric salts and lime, with sedimentation of the solids.
(2) Sludge disposal by filtration and incineration. The iron was recovered by regeneration as ferric sulfate from the incinerated ash.
(3) Basic nitrogen compounds were removed from the clarifier supernatant by an exchange reaction with zeolite resin.
(4) The zeolite was regenerated with a sodium chloride solution, and the basic nitrogen compounds were concentrated with subsequent recovery of ammonia from this solution.

The authors reported that the total nitrogen in the influent was 24–28 mg/l, and in the effluent from the process it was 2–3 mg/l (approximately 90 per cent removal). The ammonia nitrogen was reduced from the influent concentration of 12–14 mg/l to 0.5.0 mg/l in the effluent (approximately 94 per cent removal).

Air Stripping

Kuhn (1956) studied the feasibility of air stripping in packed towers to remove ammonia nitrogen. It was concluded that it is possible to remove

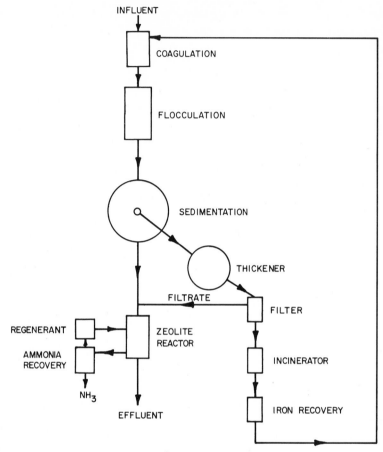

FIG. 2. Flow Sheet for the Guggenheim Process.

ammonia from a sewage effluent by stripping with air. The results indicated that at pH 11, a 7 ft. by 8 in. diameter column packed with ½ in. Raschig Rings and loaded with 52 to 55 cfm of air and 0.10 gpm of effluent could remove 92.3 per cent of the ammonia nitrogen from the sewage effluent.

Culp and Slechta (1966) conducted laboratory and pilot plant studies on the effectiveness of air stripping in removing ammonia nitrogen. Results indicated that approximately 98 per cent removal was obtained by this method.

Ion Exchange Process

Nesselson (1954) investigated the use of ion exchange resin in the removal of nitrate ion and ammonium ion from treatment plant effluents. The results indicated that strongly basic anion exchange resins, in the chloride form, perform satisfactorily for the removal of nitrate ion. Also, strongly acidic cation exchange resins, in the sodium form, effectively remove ammonia nitrogen. A minimum volume of 6 per cent and 7 per cent of the influent feed was required to regenerate the anion resin and the cation resin, respectively.

Eliassen, Wyckoff, and Tonkin (1965) reported on the use of strongly basic anion exchange resins in the chloride form in which removal of nitrate ion was 92 per cent and nitrite ion was 97 per cent from sewage treatment plant effluents. It was noted that fouling of the resin bed with both suspended particulate matter and dissolved organic matter would occur. Filtration of the effluent would obviate one of the sources of fouling. Periodic regeneration with hot sodium hydroxide solution (1N NaOH at 38°C) was thought to suffice in alleviating the problem of dissolved organic matter fouling. The volume of regenerant (10 per cent NaCl) amounted to 3 per cent of the total water processed.

Martinez (1962) also used a strongly basic anion exchange resin in the chloride form for nutrient removal from sewage treatment plant effluents. Nitrate ion removal was approximately 99 per cent.

Culp and Slechta (1966) used a strongly acidic cation exchange resin to achieve 82 to 99.5 per cent ammonia nitrogen removal from sewage treatment plant effluent.

Electrolytic Process

Føyn (1964) has developed a process referred to as the Electrolytic Sewage Purification Method. In this process, raw sewage mixed with 10 to 15 per cent of sea water is conveyed to a cathode chamber, and sea water alone is placed in the anode chamber. After current is applied, the pH increases at the cathode with the concomitant precipitation of phosphorus as a calco-phosphato compound (e.g., hydroxylapatite) and ammonia as a magnesium ammonium phosphate. Magnesium hydroxide, $Mg(OH)_2$, as well as hydrogen gas bubbles are formed at the cathode, thereby aiding in the removal of the insoluble phosphate and ammonia compounds by flotation. This sludge is skimmed off and treated by normal sludge disposal techniques. Chlorine is developed at the anode of the cell and oxidizes and sterilizes the effluent. The treatment, lasting one-half hour with approximately 400KWh per million gallons of sewage being supplied, effects an ammonia nitrogen removal of 70 to 80 per cent.

Although this electrolytic process appears suitable for communities with ready access to sea water, it is difficult to evaluate its usefulness for other communities. Magnesium ions are necessary for successful operation, and these can be supplied from the sea water; however, no information is available on the effectiveness of an artificial supply. Also, only data on the use of this process for raw sewage are published, since Føyn believed that raw sewage gave better flotation and was, therefore, more easily treated than secondary effluent.

REMOVAL OF PHOSPHORUS

Phosphorus has been successfully removed from wastewaters. Chemicals such as lime, aluminum sulfate (alum), ferric chloride, ferric sulfate, ferrous sulfate, and sodium aluminate have been used. In addition, activated alumina, the Føyn process, and ion exchange resins have been used for phosphate removal. Table 1 is a list of some chemical methods for phosphorus removal from wastewaters. Pertinent features of each process are presented to further indicate the environment necessary for effective nutrient removal.

Lime

Rudolfs (1947) studied the removal of phosphates from sewage by the use of lime and indicated the feasibility of the process. Sawyer (1962) also experimented with the use of lime in phosphorus removal and found that approximately 280 mg/1 of $Ca(OH)_2$ reduced the phosphorus level to 0.5 mg/1P for both orthophosphate and added inorganic polyphosphates in sewage. Owen (1953) utilized lime and obtained removals of phosphorus from 6 mg/1P to 0.015 mg/1P (99+ per cent) under laboratory conditions and from 7.4 mg/1P to 1.7 mg/1P (78 per cent) under plant scale tests. The results indicated that approximately three times as much sludge was formed from the sewage treatment scheme (scheme 4, Figure 3) which included phosphate precipitation as compared to the sewage treatment scheme without phosphate removal. Malhotra, *et al*, (1964), used lime to precipitate phosphorus from biochemically treated wastewater effluents. This resulted in the observation that a dose of 600 mg/1 $Ca(OH)_2$ raised the pH of the sample to 11 and removed 99 per cent of the total phosphorus. Karanik and Nemerow (1965) found that 300 mg/1 lime was the optimum dosage yielding a pH of 11 and approximately 95 per cent phosphorus removal from raw sewage. Wuhrmann (1964) experimented with lime precipitation of phosphorus from a sewage treatment plant effluent (scheme 4, Figure 3). He concluded that at a pH of 11, achieved by $Ca(OH)_2$ addition, phosphorus could be reduced to less than 0.5 mg/1P (the criterion

TABLE I. Chemical Methods of Phosphorus Removal

Process	Ref.	Dosage	pH	Initial P mg/1	Final P mg/1	% Removal	Medium
Electrolytic	(6)	—	—	4.0	0.7	83	sewage + seawater
Absorption (Activated alumina)	(28)	—	—	1.63	0.05	99	tap water
Ion Exchange	(20)	—	—	3.57–29.5	0.05–0.32	—	sett. sew.
Ion Exchange	(5)	—	—	7.4–7.6	0.2	95–97	sec. effl.
Lime	(22)	212 mg/1 CaO	—	3.4	0.5	85.4	sewage
Lime	(21)	25 mg/1 CaO	9.6	8.8	0.69	90	sewage
Lime	(19)	600 mg/1 CaO	11.0	6.0	0.01 (filtered)	99+	sec. effl.
Lime	(19)	610 mg/1 CaO	11.0	8.3	1.2	86	sec. effl.
Lime	(14)	488 mg/1 CaO	11.0	7–35	—	99	sec. effl.
Lime	(11 & 20)	244 mg/1 CaO	11.4	9.1	0.59	93.5	sewage
Lime	(1)	—	11.0+	3.7–11.5	0.4–2.0	83.8–90.7	sewage
Alum	(16)	94 ppm alum + 3.4 ppm activated silica	—	—	—	81	—
Alum	(20)	400 mg/1 "alum"	—	8.8	0.26	97	sewage
Alum	(13)	100 mg/1 filter alum	7.1–7.7	4.6	—	66	sec. effl.
		200 mg/1 " "	" "	4.6	—	96	" "
		300 mg/1 " "	" "	4.6	—	99	" "
Alum	(14)	250 mg/1 Al₂(SO₄)₃ · 18H₂O	6.0	7.6	0.5	94	sec. effl.
Alum	(2)	200 mg/1 "liquid alum"	—	8.1–9.8	0.03–0.3	—	sec. effl.
Alum	(3)	200 mg/1 "alum"	—	3.61–4.62	—	96.7	sewage
Alum	(22)	80 mg/1 "alum"	—	3.0	0.3	90	sewage
Iron	(22)	80 mg/1 FeCl₃	—	2.2	0.2	91	sewage
Iron	(13)	200 mg/1 FeSO₄ or Fe₂(SO₄)₃	—	6.0	0.6	99	sec. effl.
Iron	(27)	20–30 mg/1 Fe(III) 10 mg/1 Fe(III) + Ca(OH)₂	8.8	2.2–4.4 1.3–4.8	0.5 0.5	— —	sec. effl. sec. effl.
Alum-Biological	(25)	340 mg/1 Al₂(SO₄)₃ · 18H₂O	5.6	18	1	94	aeration tank effl.
Alum-Biological	(4)	260 mg/1 Al₂(SO₄)₃ · 18H₂O	5.5	13.8	1.04 0.046 (filtered)	93 99+	aeration liquor
Iron-Biological	(27)	30 mg/1 Fe(III)	6.8–7.5	6	0.5–1	88	aeration liquor
Iron-Biological	(26)	20–40 mg/1 FeCl₃	—	—	—	96	aeration liquor

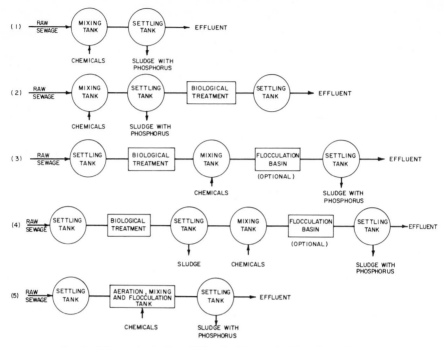

FIG. 3. Schemes in the Use of Chemical Agents for Phosphorus Removal.

used in his work). It was found that a dose of $Ca(OH)_2$ approximately 1.5 times the amount of the carbonate hardness (as mg/l $CaCO_3$) would produce the desired pH (200–300 mg/l $Ca(OH)_2$ was necessary to reach this level). Buzzell and Sawyer (1966) concluded that lime treatment of raw sewage at pH 11 can effect an 80 to 90 per cent removal of total phosphorus with a better than 97 per cent removal of orthophosphate. A relationship between alkalinity and lime dosage to obtain pH 11 was presented. Scheme 2 in Figure 3 illustrates the flow diagram for phosphorus removal prior to biological treatment as used by Buzzell and Sawyer.

The above-mentioned workers concluded that pH 11 was optimum for lime precipitation of phosphorus. However, colloidal chemical studies have indicated that at pH 11, the predominant calco-phosphato compound is hydroxylapatite, which may be mainly microscrystalline particles and, therefore, somewhat difficult to sediment.

Some disadvantages to the use of lime precipitation for phosphorus removal from wastewaters are: (1) the high pH of the effluent (pH 11) is not very acceptable for disposal into receiving waters; (2) the combination of high calcium ion concentration and pH 11 causes precipitation of carbonates as well as phosphates leading to unnecessarily large volumes of sludge;

and (3) the precipitation of calcium carbonate in the receiving water will occur, upsetting the biocoenosis. Wuhrmann (1964) found approximately 1.8 times the sludge was formed from lime treatment as compared to iron-lime treatment of equal volumes of the same wastewater with comparable phosphate removal.

Alum

Aluminum sulfate, alum, or filter alum are terms that have been used to describe Al (III)-containing chemicals. The solubility of AlPO₄ is depicted in Figure 4. The total soluble phosphorus concentration which is

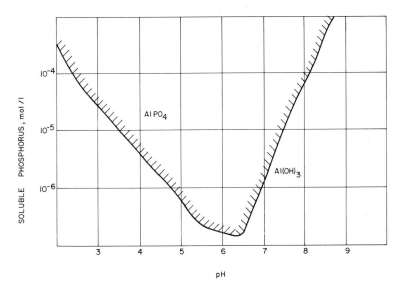

FIG. 4. Solubility Diagram for AlPO₄ (Ref. Stumm, 1962).

in equilibrium with solid $AlPO_4$ is plotted as a function of pH (Stumm 1962). At the pH of least solubility (pH 6), about 18 ug/1 of soluble phosphorus is in equilibrium with $AlPO_4$ (s). At neutral and alkaline conditions, $AlPO_4$ is appreciably soluble. Based upon theoretical considerations, at favorable pH values, the quantity of Al (III) ions needed for phosphate precipitation can be estimated by a consideration of the reaction $Al(III) + H_2PO_4^- = AlPO_4 (s) + 2H^+$ that is, one mole of Al (III) is necessary to precipitate one mole of phosphorus.

Sawyer (1962) found that approximately 1.6 moles of Al (III) were needed to remove one mole of P in the orthophosphate form, and approximately one mole of Al (III) was necessary to remove one mole of P as a mixture of orthophosphate and pyrophosphate or tripolyphosphate. It was concluded by Lea, Rohlich, and Katz (1954) that filter alum appeared to be the most suitable coagulant for removal of soluble phosphates from sewage treatment plant effluents because " . . . (a) The residual phosphate concentration of the effluent following coagulation with 200 p.p.m. of alum is, on the average, 0.06 p.p.m. expressed as P. (b) The optimum pH range for the removal of phosphates through coagulation with alum is 7.1 to 7.7 (c) The concentration of aluminum hydroxide in the effluent of the coagulation process is only approximately 1.0 to 1.5 p.p.m. and represents a loss of only 0.75 per cent of the coagulant. It is assumed that 1.0 to 1.5 p.p.m. of aluminum hydroxide in the effluent is not objectionable. (d) The aluminum hydroxide floc resulting from the hydrolysis of alum may be recovered, purified by removing the adsorbed phosphates in the form of tricalcium phosphate, and re-used for further phosphorus removal in the form of sodium aluminate. This recovery and purification reduces by 80 per cent the cost of chemicals required to remove phosphates from sewage treatment plant effluent." Curry and Wilson (1955) performed preliminary studies which utilized 200 mg/l alum in 4,000-gallon batch treatments with a mixing time of ten minutes and a settling time of two hours. Processing sewage treatment plant effluent having a phosphorus content of 3.6 to 4.6 mg/l gave 96.7 per cent removal of phosphates. In one of the first plant scale experiments in the removal of phosphorus from a primary sewage treatment plant effluent by chemical precipitation using a combination of alum and activated silica, Neil (1957) reported that orthophosphate was reduced by 98 per cent and combined phosphorus by 81 per cent. The average concentrations of alum and silica applied were 94 mg/l and 3.4 mg/l, respectively. Malhotra, *et al.* (1964), in laboratory studies found the optimum pH for alum removal of phosphorus from the effluent of an activated sludge treatment plant was 5.75 ± 0.25. An alum dosage of 250 mg/l at pH 6 removed 94 per cent of total phosphorus from effluent samples. Rand and Nemerow (1965) utilized 400 mg/l of alum for phosphorus removal from raw sewage. This resulted in a 97 per cent removal of phosphorus. Stumm (1962), Stumm and Morgan (1962), Tenney and Stumm (1965), and Henriksen (1962–63) have performed laboratory studies to better define the chemical interactions which occur during phosphorus removal with Al (III). It was concluded that phosphate removal by polyvalent metal ions occurs by precipitation rather than by coagulation or adsorption.

As a possible disadvantage to the use of aluminum sulfate for phosphorus removal, the pH optimum has been described as 6 which in some situations would necessitate pH adjustment. However, Lea, *et al.* (1954), concluded that the optimum pH for alum removal of phosphates is in the range of 7.1–7.7. Possibly, there are other reactions which occur during alum removal of phosphates in the varied chemical milieux of wastewaters which are not yet defined.

Aluminate

Since Lea, *et al.* (1954), described an alum recovery scheme, other workers have investigated the efficiency of the aluminum which was recovered as sodium aluminate for phosphorus removal. Lea, *et al.* (1954), found that the phosphate removal with sodium aluminate varied from 77 to 89 per cent. Sawyer (1962) expressed some doubt as to the effectiveness of the recovered sodium aluminate in removing phosphorus, particularly the complex inorganic phosphates. It was noted that alum or sulfuric acid must be added to reduce the pH to the zone effective for coagulation. The cost of these additional chemicals would nearly nullify the savings realized in the recovery process. Stumm (1962) also noted that aluminate solutions are less efficient in phosphate elimination than acid aluminum salt solutions, even if coagulation is carried out at the same pH levels.

Iron

Iron is a suitable ion for phosphorus removal due to the insolubility of $FePO_4$, as depicted in Figure 5. The total soluble phosphorus concentration which is in equilibrium with solid $FePO_4$ is plotted as a function of pH (Stumm, 1962). At the pH of least solubility (pH 5.3), about 70 ug/1 of soluble phosphorus is in equilibrium with $FePO_4$ (s). At neutral and alkaline conditions, $FePO_4$ is appreciably soluble. Based upon theoretical considerations, at favorable pH values, the quantity of Fe (III) ions needed for phosphate precipitation can be estimated by a consideration of the reaction

$$Fe (III) + H_2PO_4^- = FePO_4 (s) + 2H^+$$

that is, one mole of Fe (III) is necessary to precipitate one mole of phosphorus. Galal-Gorchev and Stumm (1962) reported upon an investigation in which the reaction of ferric ion with orthophosphate was studied. It was concluded that the solubility relations of $FePO_4$ are complicated by the formation of soluble phosphato-ferric complexes.

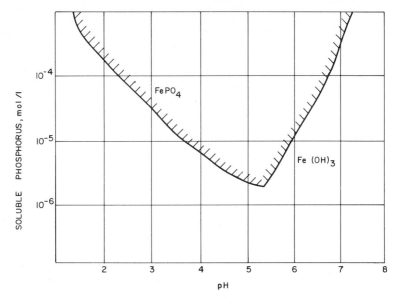

FIG. 5. Solubility Diagram for FePO$_4$ (Ref. Stumm, 1962).

The use of iron compounds for phosphorus removal has been documented in the literature. Sawyer (1962) was able to reduce phosphorus in sewage from 2.2 mg/1 to 0.2 mg/1 (91 per cent) with the use of 80 mg/1 FeCl$_3$. This is approximately 7.5 moles of Fe (III) needed to remove one mole of P in the orthophosphate form. He also noted that approximately 3.7 moles of Fe (III) were necessary to remove one mole of P as a mixture of orthophosphate and pyrophosphate or tripolyphosphate. The pH of these media during phosphorus removal was not specified. Wuhrmann (1964) studied the removal of phosphorus on a plant scale operation. It was concluded that phosphorus elimination with ferric chloride and as much lime as necessary for adjusting the pH to approximately 8.8 might be the most economical solution to the problem, both from the point of view of quantities of chemicals as well as the volume and treatability of the excess sludge. Values calculated from Wuhrmann's work were 110 mgCa(II)/1 and 10 mgFe(III)/1 at pH 8.8 which gave effective phosphate reduction from 3.2 mg/1P total phosphate in the influent to 0.5 mg/1P in the effluent for a removal of 85 per cent (scheme 4, Figure 3). In these experiments, effective phosphate reduction was defined as diminishing the concentration to 0.5 mg/1P in the effluent. The procedure of lime and ferric chloride resulted in 2040 lbs of dry chemical sludge per million gallons of waste treated (245 kg per 1000 cubic meters), whereas similar phosphorus removal for the same wastewater with lime precipitation formed 3300 lbs per million gallons (396 kg per 1000 cubic meters). This represents a sizable decrease in sludge handling and disposal.

Lea, *et al.* (1954), also used ferric sulfate and ferrous sulfate as sources of iron for phosphorus removal. It was noted that either of the iron sulfates gave 99 per cent phosphorus removal.

A disadvantage in the use of ferric ion for phosphorus removal is that the optimum pH for $FePO_4$ precipitation is 5.3 which may necessitate pH adjustment. However, Wuhrmann (1964) concluded that utilizing lime additions for pH adjustment to 8.8 and one-half of the Fe (III) normally required produces a smaller quantity of sludge.

Because of the variety of analytical techniques used for phosphorus detection, the nebulous terms used to describe phosphorus forms, and the varying experimental techniques, such as using distilled water or sewage, raw or treated, and filtered or unfiltered samples, it becomes a monumental task to decide which chemical or procedure is the most efficient for phosphorus removal in any situation without an extensive laboratory investigation. Nesbitt (1966), in summarizing many of the salient features of research work on the chemical precipitation of phosphorus from wastewaters, has noted that the coagulants lime, alum, ferric chloride, ferric sulfate, ferrous sulfate, and sodium aluminate can be expected to produce better than 90 per cent removal of orthophosphate. Although all will also remove some complex phosphates, the aluminum and iron salts gave good results more consistently than did lime.

Activated Alumina

A process which appears to have some advantages over chemical precipitation is phosphorus removal by activated alumina. Yee (1966) studied the removal of mixed phosphates by activated alumina and concluded that "The most efficient mode of operation is by downflow through a packed bed of solid. More than 99 per cent removal is accomplished in this fashion using tap water solutions initially containing 5 p.p.m. and 25 p.p.m. of each type of phosphate. These concentration levels are comparable to those in water streams and in secondary waste treatment plant effluents, respectively. In both cases, then, the process should be directly applicable, provided that solids in the waste solution do not clog the packed bed of alumina.

"Volume reduction factors are high enough to make the process economically attractive, because only small amounts of caustic and nitric acid are required to regenerate and reuse the cheap Type A alumina. Columnar sorption of phosphates using activated alumina does not alter the chemical composition of the treated water in the pH range tested. On the other hand, alum or iron flocculation adds salt to the treated water and lime precipitation increases the pH and calcium ion concentration."

Combined Biological-Chemical Process

A modification of the chemical precipitation process is its combination with high-rate activated sludge. Thomas (1962) described the system (scheme 5, Figure 3) in which the best results were achieved with a dose of 20–40 mg/1 $FeCl_3$ directly into the aeration tank, which would provide sufficient mixing, followed by two hours of settling, yielding orthophosphate removals of up to 96 per cent. Tenney and Stumm (1965) concluded that chemical flocculation methods can complement and substitute for a part of the biological waste treatment process. Figure 3, scheme 3 illustrates the flow system in which phosphate removal was achieved. It was noted at the low activated sludge solids concentration utilized (425 mg volatile solids/1) that aluminum reacts first with the majority of available phosphorus, then with the biomass due to the stronger affinity of Al (III) at pH 5–6 for phosphorus than for the ionogenic groups of the microbial surface. In contrast to this, Eberhardt and Nesbitt (1966), using a system similar to scheme 5, Figure 3, noted that Al/P ratios significantly greater than unity (1.75) were necessary for adequate phosphorus removals at pH 5.5 Since the system was operated at an activated sludge solids concentration of 4000–6000 mg volatile solids/1, it is likely that the sludge exerted a significant coagulant demand. Wuhrmann (1964) noted that 20–30 mg/1 Fe (III) used in a combined biological-chemical treatment scheme gave a phosphorus elimination to 0.5–1 mg/1P in the effluent. This concentration of iron, 20–30 mg/1 Fe (III), when used in scheme 4, Figure 3 (biological treatment followed by chemical treatment), gave a reduction to < 0.5 mg/1P in the final effluent. This is in accord with the results of Eberhardt and Nesbitt that the activated sludge solids exerted a coagulant demand.

Some of the disadvantages of this combined biological-chemical process are: (1) the increased coagulant dosage to effect phosphorus removal due to the coagulant demand of the biological sludge; and (2) the phosphorus-containing sludge should not be treated by anaerobic digestion if Fe (III) is used as a phosphate precipitant, since any phosphate bound to Fe (III) will be released during digestion because of the reduction of Fe (III) to Fe (II). The normal sewage treatment system includes anaerobic decomposition of the excess activated sludge with return of the digestor supernatant to the treatment plant waste flow. However, if this digestor supernatant contains the redissolved phosphate from iron-phosphate removal, no phosphorus elimination has been effected from the wastewater.

Electrolytic Process

The Føyn process (1964), described earlier, attains over 90 per cent removal of phosphorus. The limitations of this process were also discussed previously.

Ion Exchange Process

There has been some work on the applicability of ion exchange resins for phosphorus removal. Eliassen, Wyckoff, and Tonkin (1965) found that 95 per cent of the total phosphorus of filtered activated sludge effluent could be removed with a column made of strongly basic anion exchange resin. Rand and Nemerow (1965) noted 98.5–99.6 per cent removal of phosphorus using a laboratory scale column of strongly basic anion exchange resin. Martinez (1962), also using a strongly basic anion exchange resin, was able to reduce orthophosphate in sewage treatment plant effluent from 7.55 to 0.11 mg/1P for 98 per cent removal. The main problem with the utilization of ion exchange resins for wastewater treatment is the organic fouling of the resin beds which will eventually occur.

Methods are available for removing nitrogen and phosphorus from wastewaters. The selection of the best method for removal cannot be made since there are also some biological methods for nitrogen and phosphorus removal which are not mentioned in this paper but must nevertheless be considered in a comparison of methods. Also, the circumstances surrounding each individual case may dictate which method takes precedence over the other methods. The factor of economics must always enter the discussion since this factor can be more influential than any other. If nitrogen and phosphorus are deemed worthy by algologists as efficient limiting nutrients, the techniques for removal of these elements will be improved and expanded by the environmental engineer and scientist.

REFERENCES

Buzzell, J. C., and C. N. Sawyer, 1966. "Removal of Algal Nutrients from Raw Sewage with Lime," presented at the Missouri Water Pollution Control Association Meeting, Jefferson City, Mo. (March 1, 1966).

Culp, G., and A. Slechta, 1966. "Nitrogen Removal from Waste Effluents," *Public Works*, 97, 90–91.

Curry, J. J., and S. L. Wilson, 1955. "Effect of Sewage-borne Phosphorus on Algae," *Sew. and Ind. Wastes*, 27, 1262–66.

Eberhardt, W. A., and J. B. Nesbitt, 1967. "Chemical Precipitation of Phosphate Within a High Rate Bio-oxidation System," presented at 22nd Annual Purdue Industrial Waste Conference, Lafayette Ind. (May, 1967).

Eliassen, R., B. M. Wyckoff, and D. C. Tonkin, 1965. "Ion Exchange for Reclamation of Reusable Supplies," *J. Am. Wat. Works Assn.*, *57*, 1113–22.

Foyn, E., 1964. "Removal of Sewage Nutrients by Electrolytic Treatment," *Intern. Verein. fuer Theo. U. Angew. Limnologie-Stuttgart*, 569–79.

Galal-Gorchev, A., and W. Stumm, 1963. "The Reaction of Ferric Iron with Orthophosphate," *J. Inorg. Nucl. Chem.*, *25*, 567–74.

Gleason, G. H., and A. C. Loonam, 1933. "The Development of a Chemical Process for Treatment of Sewage," *Sew. Wks. J.*, *5*, 61–73.

Henriksen, A., 1962. "Laboratory Studies on the Removal of Phosphates from Sewage by the Coagulation Process," *Schweiz. Z. Hydro.*, *24*, 253–71.

———, 1963. "Laboratory Studies on the Removal of Phosphates from Sewage by the Coagulation Process (Part 2)," *ibid.*, *25*, 380–96.

Karanik, J. M., and N. L. Nemerow, 1965. "Removal of Algal Nutrients," *Water and Sew. Wks*, *112*, 460–63.

Kuhn, P. A., 1956. "Removal of Ammonia Nitrogen from Sewage Effluent," M. S. thesis, Dept. of Civil Eng., Univ. Wis.

Lea, W. L., G. A. Rohlich, and W. J. Katz, 1954. "Removal of Phosphates from Treated Sewage," *Sew. and Ind. Wastes*, *26*, 261–75.

Malhotra, S. K., G. F. Lee, and G. A. Rohlich, 1964. "Nutrient Removal from Secondary Effluent by Alum Flocculation and Lime Precipitation," *Int. J. Air Water Poll.*, *8*, 487–500.

Martinez, W. W., 1962. "Phosphate and Nitrate Removal from Treated Sewage by Exchange Resins," M. S. thesis, Dept. of Civil Eng., Penn. State Univ.

Neil, J. H., 1957. "Problems and Control of Unnatural Fertilization of Lake Waters," *Proc. 12th Ind. Wastes Conf.*, *94*, 301–16.

Nesbitt, J. B., 1966. "Removal of Phosphorus From Municipal Sewage Plant Effluents," *Eng. Res. Bull. B-93*, Penn. State Univ., 54 pps.

Nesselson, E. J., 1954. "Removal of Inorganic Nitrogen from Sewage Effluent," Ph.D. thesis, Dept. of Civil Eng., Univ. Wisc.

Owen, R., 1953. "Removal of Phosphorus from Sewage Plant Effluent with Lime," *Sew. and Ind. Wastes*, *25*, 548–56.

Rand, M. C., and N. L. Nemerow, 1965. "Removal of Algal Nutrients from Domestic Wastewater," rept No. 9., Dept. of Civil Eng., Syracuse Univ. Res. Inst. 114 pp.

Rudolfs, W., 1947. "Phosphates in Sewage and Sludge Treatment. I. Quantities of Phosphates," *Sew. Wks. J.*, *19*, 43–47.

Sawyer, C. N., 1962. "Some New Aspects of Phosphates in Relation to Lake Fertilization," *Sew. and Ind. Wastes*, *24*, 768–76.

Stumm, W., 1962. *Chemical Elimination of Phosphates as a Third Stage Sewage Treatment; A Discussion*, Int. Conf. Wat. Poll. Res., London, Pergamon Press, New York, 1964. 216–30.

Stumm, W., and J. J. Morgan, 1962. "Chemical Aspects of Coagulation," *J. Am. Wat. Wks Assn.*, *54*, 971–94.

Tenney, M. W., and W. Stumm, 1965. "Chemical Flocculation of Microorganisms in Biological Waste Treatment," *J. Wat. Poll. Cont. Fed.*, *37*, 1370–88.

Thomas, E. A., 1962. "Verfahren zur Entfernung von Phosphaten aus Abwässern," Swiss Patent No. 361543 from April 15, 1962, *Chem. Abstracts*, *58*, Abst. 1237b (1963).

Wuhrmann, K., 1964. "Stickstoff-und Phosphorelimination; Ergebnisse von Versuchen in Technischen Masstab," *Schweiz. Z. Hydrol.*, *26*, 520–58.

Yee, W. C., 1966. "Selective Removal of Mixed Phosphates by Activated Alumina," *J. Am. Wat. Wks Assn.*, *58*, 239–47.

XXI

Virus Diseases in Blue-Green Algae

ROBERT S. SAFFERMAN

Virology Section
Cincinnati Water Research Laboratory
Federal Water Pollution Control Administration
U. S. Dept. of Interior
Cincinnati, Ohio

Viruses have gained increasing acceptance as a promising approach to pest control. Under favorable conditions these viruses provide a valuable alternative to chemical treatment. So successful are some virus pesticides that chemical controls are no longer necessary. The introduction of the myxoma virus into the rabbit population of Australia is a classic example of the effectiveness of this approach (Fenner, 1959). No less dramatic has been the use of viruses in the control of insect pests (Rivers, 1964). It was with this in mind that we approached the problem of virus diseases in algae.

ISOLATION AND HOST SPECTRUM

Waste stabilization ponds have been the focal point of our search for evidence of virus diseases in blue-green algae. These ponds support a wide variety of algal forms that readily undergo fluctuations both in number and species (Fitzgerald and Rohlich, 1958). Thus, they offer a unique opportunity for studying the biological factors which bring about these changes in the algal population. It seems paradoxical that the blue-green algal (BGA) virus that eluded scientists for many years was detected in the first group of samples collected from this environment. At the time there was some doubt as to our interpretation of the data since we were mindful that the BGA virus had remained unnoticed for nearly fifty years after the discovery of the bacteriophage. A subsequent study, however, showed that this virus type is not only frequently observed in waste stabilization ponds, but in some instances the virus is undoubtedly a well-established population (Safferman and Morris, 1967).

A four-acre pond in southeastern Indiana yielded the first example of a BGA virus (Safferman and Morris, 1963). The procedure for isolating the phycovirus is shown in Figure 1. To expedite handling of a greater num-

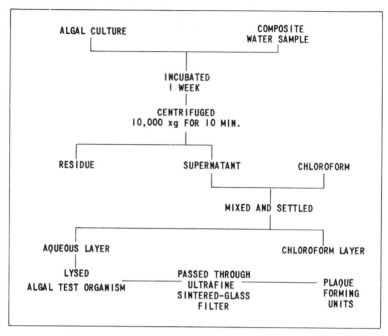

FIG. 1. Outline of procedure for isolating the algal virus.

ber of samples, this method was modified by reducing centrifugation of the pond samples to 2000 x g for five minutes and eliminating the filtration of liquid cultures prior to plating on solid medium. For direct virus counts, samples were immediately centrifuged, treated with chloroform, then plated and plaque counted.

The virus was designated as strain LPP-1 on finding that its host spectrum included members of the genera *Lyngbya, Plectonema,* and *Phormidium.* Of the thirteen strains found susceptible to the LPP-1 virus, all had morphological characteristics that were remarkably similar (Safferman and Morris, 1964b). Personal communications from C. M. Palmer and F. Drouet have confirmed these observations. In accordance with recent revisions in the classification of the Oscillatoriaceae (Drouet, 1963), they have concluded that these strains are ecophenes of a single species and, therefore, their names should be considered synonymous with that of *Schizothrix calcicola.*

PREPARATION OF VIRUS CONCENTRATES

Of the algae susceptible to the LPP-1 virus, *Plectonema boryanum* IU 594 (Starr, 1964) was best suited for studies on this virus-host system.

The culture characteristics of the alga made possible the adoption of methods that are well established in phage investigations (Adams, 1959). The phage plaque-counting method was used in enumerating the relative numbers of virus particles. Experimental data showed the reproducibility of the plaque counts to be within the range of variation observed in phage studies (Safferman and Morris, 1964a). The suitability of this plaque-counting technique was of particular significance in view of the obstacles encountered in quantitating viruses from higher plants.

Large-scale production of the LPP-1 virus was carried out in the fermentor drive assembly shown in Figure 2. Under these culturing conditions,

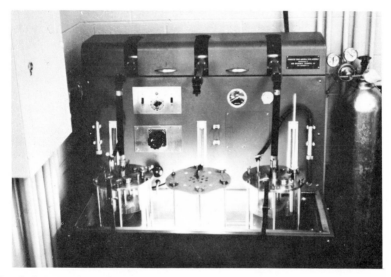

FIG. 2. Large-scale production of BGA virus LPP-1. Fermentor drive assembly with two 14-liter fermentors containing 10 liters each of nutrient medium. A gas mixture of 5 per cent carbon dioxide in air was bubbled through the agitated medium, and continuous illumination of 500–600 ft-c. was provided by a central light source composed of six vertical "cool white" fluorescent tubes.

virus titers of 10^9 to 10^{10} plaque-forming units (PFU)/ml were obtained regularly (Schneider, Diener, and Safferman, 1964). Smith, et al. (1966a), produced 20-liter batches of the virus in 3-liter flasks containing a revised Chu No. 10 nutrient medium. They reported approximate yields of 5×10^{10} PFU/ml from cultures in which *P. boryanum* IU 594 was the host.

The lysates were clarified in a continuous-flow centrifuge. To concentrate the virus to about 10^{12} PFU/ml, either ultrafiltration (Schneider, et al., 1964) or ultracentrifugation (Smith, et al., 1966a) was used.

STABILITY OF VIRUS

The LPP-1 virus was relatively stable when stored in its own lysate. Goldstein (1966) noted that lysates kept at 4°C for as long as three months showed no loss in activity; in a number of instances, he found their titers to be higher after storage. On the other hand, the subjection of the LPP-1 strain to distilled water led to a marked and irreversible loss in its biological activity. This could be prevented by the presence of magnesium ions (Safferman and Morris, 1964a; Schneider, *et al.*, 1964), the removal of which resulted in the disruption of the virus particle and the apparent liberation of DNA (Goldstein, 1966; Luftig and Haselkorn, 1967).

A marked decrease in virus titer was observed above 40°C with a survival rate of less than 0.001 per cent occurring at 55°C. In the alkaline range, the LPP-1 virus had a pH stability significantly greater than that generally noted for bacterial viruses (Adams, 1959). Whereas bacterial viruses are generally reported to have a pH range of 5 to 8, LPP-1 was stable from pH 5 to 11, which is of ecological interest in view of the fact that the algal host *P. boryanum* grows well from pH 7 to 11 (Safferman and Morris, 1964a).

Wu and coworkers (1967) reported that UV damage to the LPP-1 virus could be reversed by suitable illumination of the infected host, *P. boryanum*. Differences in the mechanisms involved in the photoreactivation of virus and algae were suggested since, in the region of 360 mμ, only algal replication was restored.

PLAQUE AND VIRUS MORPHOLOGY

The plaques formed by the LPP-1 virus are clear with regular edges (Figure 3). They vary in size from less than 0.1 mm to more than 8 mm in diameter. This divergence in plaque size was attributed to the presence of variants within the strain (Safferman and Morris, 1964a). Two distinct plaque types with identical host spectra were isolated from the LPP-1 virus; these inevitably reverted to a mixture of both types. Differences in their growth curves were noted, with the large plaque-former multiplying at a somewhat faster rate.

The LPP-1 virus is apparently more closely allied to the bacteriophage than to viruses of higher plants. Morphologically the virus resembles the coliphages T3 and T7 (Figure 4) in that it has a short tail about one-fourth the diameter of the head (Schneider, Diener, and Safferman, 1964; Smith, *et al.*, 1966a). Electron micrographs of the virus revealed icosahedral particles with an average diameter of about 56 mμ. In a more recent report,

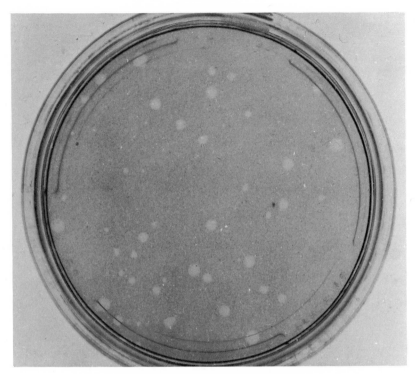

FIG. 3. Plaques of the BGA virus strain LPP-1 on *Plectonema boryanum* culture plate.

Luftig and Haselkorn (1967) stated that the particle had an average edge-to-edge distance of 60 mμ. There is the suggestion that the edges of these particles are made up of dumbbell-shaped subunits which number possibly six per edge (Safferman and Morris, 1963).

Presumably the similarity in the basic structures of the blue-green algae and bacteria reflects the phage-like nature of the LPP-1 virus (Echlin and Morris, 1965). This resemblance was also noted by Goldstein (1966), who suggested a possible taxonomic relationship between LPP-1 and the coliphages. However, data from serological tests with T1, T2, and T3 coliphages (Goldstein, 1966) and from host range studies with T3 and T7 coliphages (Schneider, personal communication) failed to show such a relationship. In a more recent study with plaque-isolated viruses, Smith, *et al.* (1966b), indicated that the LPP-1 virus may in fact have a long tail. Failure to observe these tails in purified preparation has yet to be resolved; it has been suggested, however, that they may fracture or retract during the process of purification. Long-tailed particles were also noted in plaque-isolated viruses by Padan, Shilo, and Kislev (1967). However, Luftig and

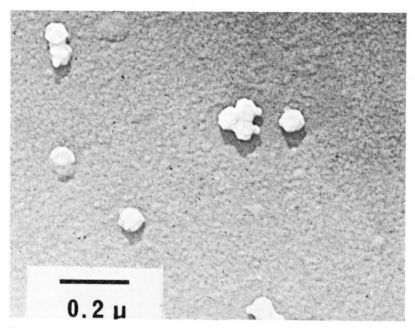

FIG. 4. Electron micrograph of a purified viral preparation of BGA virus strain LPP-1 shadowed with chromium.

Haskelkorn (1967) failed to substantiate these findings. They proposed that the tails observed in crude lysates owe their extra length to adsorption to membrane fragments.

CHEMICAL AND PHYSICAL PROPERTIES

The fact that the LPP-1 virus contains DNA (Schneider, Diener, and Safferman, 1964) lends considerable support to the taxonomic relationship noted in the previous section. Goldstein (1966) has isolated the DNA and shown it to be double stranded with a molecular base composition of 55 per cent guanine plus cytosine. Moreover, he reported that the virus has an apparent molecular weight of $51 \pm 3 \times 10^6$ Daltons. Of this total weight, about 40 per cent was DNA. Luftig and Haselkorn (1967) gave the guanine-cytosine content of the LPP-1 DNA as 53 per cent and the molecular weight of the viral DNA as about 27×10^6 Daltons. By DNA-RNA hybridization, they showed a 0.25 per cent homology between the LPP-1 virus and its host *P. boryanum*. In view of the lack of homology, it has been suggested that LPP-1 is a poor strain for transduction.

The amino acid content of the virus accounted for 52 per cent of the particle weight. The over-all proportions of these amino acids presented a gross pattern which did not differ markedly from the amino acid composition of other viruses (Goldstein, 1966).

PROCESS OF INFECTION

Gross Appearance of Algal Filament

Plectonema boryanum normally forms long filaments that occur either singly or interwoven with one another. In virus-infected cultures, lysis was first noted in cells that were randomly distributed along the length of the filament (Figure 5). As lysis progressed, the filaments fragmented into smaller units until eventually only scattered cells were evident in the preparation (Safferman and Morris, 1964b).

In studying virus-infected filaments, Smith, *et al.* (1967), noted that once lysis began, it progressed rapidly down the length of the filament. To account for this, they suggested that similar concentrations of lytic enzymes must be present in different cells.

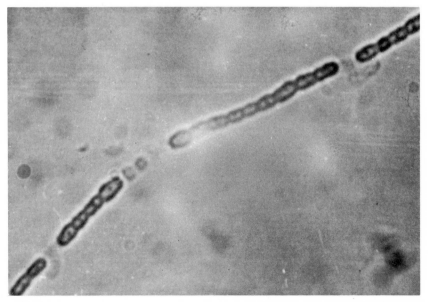

FIG. 5. Photomicrograph of virus-infected culture of *Plectonema boryanum* undergoing lysis ten hours after infection with the LPP-1 virus. Cells randomly lysed along filament with puddling at site of lysis.

Rate of Infection

On studying the adsorption of LPP-1 virus to *P. boryanum,* Goldstein (1966) found that this virus-host system failed to follow the kinetics of first-order reactions. The adsorption rate of the system showed successive decreases with 90 per cent of the virus adsorbed after approximately one hour.

The LPP-1 virus exhibited a one-step growth curve, the pattern of which was typical of that observed with bacterial viruses. Moreover, the multiplication rate of the virus seems consistent with the relatively slow rate of development of the alga. A latent period of about seven hours was recorded, followed by a steady rise in virus counts until a maximum titer was reached approximately ten hours after infection. By calculation, the average burst size was about 100 virus particles per infected algal cell (Goldstein, 1966).

Progression of Virus Disease

Smith and his associates have made a comprehensive study of the growth cycle of the LPP-1 virus (1966a, 1966b, 1967; Brown, *et al.*, 1966). From their findings they indicate that virus replication proceeds according to the following sequence: A virus particle attaches to the outer wall of the host cell by its tail. Presumably the particle remains on the algal surface, whereas its DNA is injected into the cell in the manner described for some phages. Viral DNA appears to be produced in the nucleoplasm. An apparent rearrangement of this region occurred in the early stages of infection. In addition, numerous fine threads, not seen in the nucleoplasm of normal cells, have been observed and indicated as possible viral DNA. It is thought that from the nucleoplasm the DNA migrates to the photosynthetic lamellae since particles are observed between these structures which appear to consist of elongated helices. As virus formation progresses, empty spaces are noted where these particles were contained. From there, the helices apparently move into the virogenic stroma, an area formed by the lateral displacement of the photosynthetic lamellae from their normal position along the perimeter of the cell. This displacement occurs prior to virus formation and is invariably the first indication of infection. In the virogenic stroma, the elongated helices become enclosed in a protein coat and then compressed into the mature particle. At this point in their development, tails were not visible.

Smith and co-workers have also examined the LPP-1 infection process in other species of *Plectonema* as well as several susceptible members of the genera *Lyngbya* and *Phormidium*. Their findings revealed a general pattern of infection which is apparently similar to that described for *P. boryanum*.

ALGAL CONTROL WITH VIRUSES

Virus disease reflects a basic approach to algal control, the effects of which resemble the fluctuations and succession so little understood in the natural environment. In these controls are undoubtedly hidden the clues for efficient treatment of troublesome algal populations.

In laboratory cultures, the disease attains epidemic proportions rapidly and, in three to four days after infection, culminates with lysis of the population and the release of vast numbers of virus progeny. Initial infections of a relatively few cells in a susceptible algal population regularly give rise to a 10^7 to 10^8 increase in virus titers which continue to persist at these levels for some time after lysis of the host (Safferman and Morris, 1964a).

From an economic viewpoint, a virus pesticide is a relatively inexpensive means of treatment. Once established in an algal bloom, virus disease should disseminate naturally from its initial infection, thus reducing the cost of treatment to levels that are comparable, if not lower, than current expenditures for chemical controls. The stability of the LPP-1 virus has been shown to correspond closely to the growth pattern of its algal host, enhancing the prospects that it would be equally effective in any environment that could also support a dense growth of the susceptible algae. Furthermore, this virus showed considerable promise under conditions simulating natural algal blooms. In these laboratory studies, drastic reductions in the algal population were obtained about seven days after infection (Safferman and Morris, 1964b).

OCCURRENCE AND DISTRIBUTION

Viruses of the LPP group have a wide geographic distribution in waste stabilization ponds of the United States. These viruses were readily isolated from ponds in Arkansas, California, Florida, Indiana, Missouri, South Dakota, and Texas (Safferman and Morris, 1967). Twelve ponds were surveyed, and of these only a New Hampshire pond failed to reveal the presence of this virus group. Particularly striking were the high yields obtained in many of the samples. In several ponds these yields were comparable to bacteriophage titers reported in sewage (Anderson, 1957; Ware and Mellon, 1956). The highest titers observed in the course of this study were from a South Dakota pond which gave consecutive bimonthly counts of 270 and 240 PFU/ml. Of the five ponds sampled monthly, one in California and another in Arkansas invariably yielded viruses of the LPP type. In view of these findings, there is little doubt that the ponds support an established BGA virus population.

Although these viruses were related by virtue of their host spectrum, distinct differences were noted in their serological and plaque-forming characteristics. Furthermore, variations in their nature and magnitude could be readily demonstrated in geographically related ponds of similar design. Climatic conditions undoubtedly account for some of the fluctuations noted in several virus populations. However, the marked decrease reported in an Arkansas pond from July through September failed to correspond to the expected development of the algal host (Figure 6). These findings indicated a degeneration in the susceptible algal population, the cause of which is perhaps the effect of the virus itself.

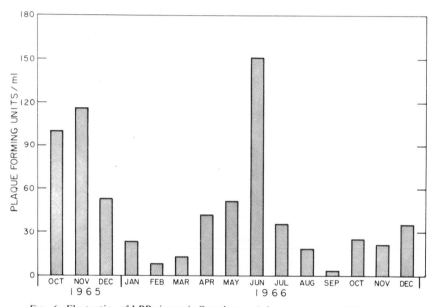

FIG. 6. Fluctuation of LPP viruses in Smackover, Arkansas, waste stabilization pond.

Waste stabilization ponds have provided a highly fertile source of LPP viruses. The high yields obtained in several of the ponds suggest that these viruses may act as a natural control. Considering their distribution pattern, it seems reasonable to assume that the LPP viruses are widely dispersed in nature. Padan and co-workers (1967) recently established their presence in freshwater ponds with the isolation of several LPP viruses from fish ponds in the Beith Shean valley of Israel. From a detailed study made on one of the LPP isolates (GIII), they concluded that it was closely related or perhaps identical to the LPP-1 virus.

So far our knowledge of virus diseases in the blue-green algae has been confined to the LPP group; the newly isolated SM-1 virus (Safferman and Morris, 1967), however, constitutes a new paramater for future studies of BGA viruses.

REFERENCES

Adams, M. H., 1959. *Bacteriophages*, New York: Interscience.

Anderson, E. S., 1957. "The Relations of Bacteriophages to Bacterial Ecology," *Seventh Symp. Soc. Gen. Microbiol.*, 189–217.

Brown, Jr., R. M., Smith, K. M., and Walne, P. L., 1966. "Replication Cycle of the Blue-green Algal Virus LPP-1," *Nature, 212*, 729–30.

Echlin, P., and Morris, I., 1965. "The Relationship Between Blue-Green Algae and Bacteria," *Biol. Rev., 40*, 143–87.

Drouet, F., 1963. "Ecophenes of *Schizothrix calcicola* (Oscillatoriaceae)," *Proc. Acad. Nat. Sci., Phila., 115*, 261–81.

Fenner, F., 1959. "Myxomatosis," *Brit. Med. Bull., 15*, 240–45.

Fitzgerald, G. P., and Rohlich, G. A., 1958. "An Evaluation of Stabilization Pond Literature," *Sew. and Ind. Wastes, 30*, 1213–24.

Goldstein, D. A., 1966. "Some Biological, Chemical and Physical Properties of Blue-Green Algal Virus LPP-1," Ph.D. thesis, Univ. of Pittsburgh.

Luftig, R., and Haselkorn, R., 1967. "Morphology of a Virus of Blue-Green Algae and Properties of Its Deoxyribonucleic Acid," *J. Virol., 1*, 344–61.

Padan, E., Shilo, M., and Kislev, N., 1967. "Isolation of 'Cyanophages' from Fresh-Water Ponds and their Interaction with *Plectonema boryanum*," *Virology, 32*, 234–46.

Rivers, C., 1964. "Virus Pesticides," *Discovery, 25*, 27–31.

Safferman, R. S., and Morris, M. E., 1963. "Algal Virus: Isolation," *Science, 140*, 679–80.

———, 1964a. "Growth Characteristics of the Blue-Green Algal Virus LPP-1," *J. Bact. 88*:771–775.

———, 1964b. "Control of Algae with Viruses," *J. A.W.W.A., 56*, 1217–24.

———, 1967. "Observations on the Occurrence, Distribution, and Seasonal Incidence of Blue-Green Algal Viruses," *Appl. Microbiol., 15*, 1219–22.

Schneider, I. R., Diener, T. O., and Safferman, R. S., 1964. "Blue-Green Algal Virus LPP-1: Purification and Partial Characterization," *Science, 144*:1127–30.

Smith, K. M., Brown, Jr., R. M., Goldstein, D. A., and Walne, P. L., 1966a. "Culture Methods for the Blue-Green Alga *Plectonema boryanum* and Its Virus with an Electron Microscope Study of Virus-Infected Cells," *Virology, 28*:580–91.

Smith, K. M., Brown, Jr., R. M., Walne, P. L., and Goldstein, D. A., 1966b. "Electron Microscopy of the Infection Process of the Blue-Green Algal Virus," *ibid., 30*, 182–92.

Smith, K. M., Brown, Jr., R. M., and Walne, P. L., 1967. "Ultrastructural and Time-Lapse Studies on the Replication Cycle of the Blue-Green Algal Virus LPP-1," *ibid., 31*, 329–37.

Starr, R. C., 1964. "The Culture Collection of Algae at Indiana University," *Amer. J. Bot., 51*, 1013–44.

Ware, G. C., and Mellon, M. A., 1956. "Some Observations on the Coli-Coliphage Relationship in Sewage," *J. Hyg., 54*, 99–101.

Wu, J. H., Lewin, R. A., and Werbin, H., 1967. "Photoreactivation of UV-Irradiated Blue-Green Algal Virus LPP-1," *Virology, 31*, 657–64.

XXII

Algicides—Friends or Foes?

ALENA SLADECKOVA
and VLADIMIR SLADECEK

Department of Water Technology
Prague, Czechoslovakia

The increasing eutrophication process of all types of inland waters has caused the very frequent occurrence of water blooms and heavy growths of filamentous green algae. Therefore, the control of the undesirable mass developments has become one of the most important research problems of applied limnology.

Since 1904 when Moore and Kellerman published the first paper recommending copper sulphate for the algicidal and bactericidal treatment of water supplies, the number of articles and reports on this subject has increased immensely. In most of the textbooks and treatises on general limnology there are usually chapters reviewing the most important literature on algicides, but they are often limited by the nationality, experiences, and interests of the author.

Quite detailed information may be found, for instance, in the books by Whipple, Liebmann, and Beger, and in several reviews and bigger papers on algicides by Bank (1962), Schwarz (1965), Stepanek (1965), and others. The review written in Czech by Moravcova (1965) was extremely useful in preparing the present essay. The author has compiled nearly 300 references mainly concerning the application of algicides in water supplies up to 1962. The *Botanical Review* may soon publish an English version with updated references.

We have tried to compile the most recent literature, particularly from our own sphere of interest—the cooling water treatment. Special attention has been given to European papers which are sometimes not very well known in English-speaking countries.

CRITICAL SURVEY OF USED AND POTENTIAL ALGICIDES

Inorganic Compounds

The most widespread literature deals with the oldest and most common algicide—copper sulphate. The discussion of main advantages and disadvantages connected with its application, e.g., the influence of higher alkalinity on its solubility, may be found in nearly all papers on copper algicides. The tables of effective concentrations of copper sulphate for various genera and species of algae are included in many textbooks on limnology and phycology and in the more extensive papers and reviews mentioned above.

The next group of inorganic algicides comprises halogenic elements, mainly chlorine and its inorganic as well as organic derivatives, e.g., hypochlorites, chlordioxide, chloramines, etc. All these compounds based upon the effect of free chlorine residual are commonly used as disinfectants, bactericides, and agents for removing taste and odor. They are not very convenient for algicidal treatment because of a short-term effect, possibility of adaptation of organisms, and because of their limited effect in alkaline and organically enriched waters.

Silver compounds and colloidal silver function also mainly as bactericides. Their application for algicidal treatment is very limited because of their high cost. Silver nitrate has been successfully utilized as one component in an algicide mixture (see later).

The evaluation of potassium permanganate as an algicide was done recently by Fitzgerald (1964, 1965) and by Kemp, *et al.* (1966). It may be applied successfully in such water bodies where there are algae with varying susceptibilities to copper sulphate. The two main disadvantages of its use are its corrosiveness and formation of precipitates which may sometimes be even more harmful than the nuisance algae themselves.

Sodium arsenite has been applied predominantly for the control of aquatic weeds and filamentous algae.

Other inorganic algicides, e.g., mercury compounds, strong oxidizing agents such as ozone and hydrogen peroxide, sodium sulphate, ammonium sulphate, sulphuric and other acids, etc., have not proved very successful in the control of undersirable algal growths.

Organic Compounds

Much more attention has been given recently to a large number of organic compounds. Some of them have already been put into practice as efficient algicides; the others are still under laboratory examination.

One of the most common organic algicides is natrium pentachlorophenate. It is efficient even in alkaline waters; soluble, stable, and noncorrosive, it does not react with organic pollutants in water, but it has two serious defects. Firstly, it irritates the mucous membranes of eyes and respiratory organs of people operating with it or even bathing in the treated body of water, secondly, it is highly toxic to fish and to fish-food organisms (Weber, 1965). Its usefulness as a component in algicide mixtures will be discussed later.

The effectiveness of quaternary ammonium compounds has been discussed by quite a large number of authors. The summary of positive and negative characteristics of these compounds may be found, for instance, in the review by Moravcova (1965). Several experiences are included in the following chapter.

The derivatives of quinones have been utilized for algicidal treatment quite frequently, too. The most effective compound, 2,3–dichloronaphthoquinone (dichlone), has been found to be one of the most selective algicides controlling blue-green algae even in μg quantities, without any harmful effect on other groups of algae, on aquatic animals, or on macrophytes. Its short-term effect is the only disadvantage. Much data concerning the application of dichlone have been summarized in the papers of Fitzgerald, *et al.* (1952), Fitzgerald and Skoog (1954), Palmer (1956, 1962), Maloney and Palmer (1956), etc.

For the evaluation of another quinone derivative, tetrachlorbenzoquinone (chloranil), see later.

The derivatives of monuron (chlorophenyldimethylurea) have been applied during the recent few years mainly in the U.S.A. and in U.S.S.R. (Palmer, 1956; Maloney, 1958; Braginsky, *et al.,* 1963; Braginsky, 1965; Lisovskaya, 1965). It proved to be an effective control of water weeds and filamentous algae. A special feature of this algicide is its ability to adsorb to the bottom sediments of stagnant bodies of water.

Rosin amines (RADA, RADS), according to Maloney and Palmer (1956), belong to organic compounds with hopeful algicidal properties.

The other organic compounds recommended for the control of algae were introduced originally as fungicides and herbicides. They have been tested by laboratory methods and considered as potential algicides together with a large number of other chemicals selected for their presupposed qualities. The lists of all these preparations may be found, for instance, in Bank 1962), Fitzgerald, *et al.* (1952), Maloney and Palmer (1956), Palmer (1956), Palmer and Maloney (1955), and in the literature reviewed by Moravcova (1965).

Natural Products

The possibility of the application of antibiotics for the control of algae was proposed in 1953 by Foter, Palmer, and Maloney. Since then several authors have tested the effect of commercial antibiotics on various groups of aquatic algae (Palmer and Maloney, 1955; Palmer, 1956; Zehnder and Hughes, 1958, Cervenka, *et al.*, 1959; and Stepanek, *et al.*, 1961).

Safferman and Morris (1962) examined 545 isolates of Actinomycetes and fungi, predominantly from soil, 80 per cent of which showed selective effectiveness on algae. Three of the most hopeful isolates were recommended for further testing.

Toohey, *et al.* (1965), carried out laboratory bioassays with phenazine-1–carboxylic acid and 2-hydroxyphenazine–1-carboxylic acid obtained from cultures of a strain of *Pseudomonas aureofaciens.* They found a relatively high toxicity of these preparations for some species of algae and plants.

Special Mixtures

The original purpose of introducing special mixtures was to keep copper sulphate active in solution, particularly in waters of higher alkalinity. Among the proposed additional compounds functioning as chelates were, for instance, citric acid and several aliphatic hydroxyacids. Some surface active agents have been recommended for the same purpose. Fitzgerald and Faust (1965) pointed out the possibility of bacteriological degradation of organic chelates and recommended the incorporation of bacterial inhibitors.

Cervenka, *et al.* (1959), examined the algicidal properties of various mixtures of algicides and recommended two of them for practical application: CP 310 (300μg $CuSO_4$ and 10 μg Na pentachlorophenate per liter); and CA 350 (300 μg $CuSO_4$ and 50 μg $AgNO_3$ per liter). The effects of both components of the preparations did not interfere; on the contrary, the combined effect of both was much higher than that of individual single compounds, and therefore, μg concentrations were quite sufficient. The mixture CA 350 has been applied very successfully several times since then (Stepanek, *et al.,* 1960, 1963; Hannemann, 1965; Kocurova, 1966).

Other Agents

A special case of the utilization of industrial waste products has been reported from U.S.S.R. Terentiev, *et al.* (1965), applied polymetallic ores and their concentrated manufactured products as algicides. The main advantages of these preparations are as follows: they are not toxic to aquatic organisms and man; they are not degradable by bacteria, and do not hydrolyze in water; their algicidal properties manifest themselves gradually in the course of a longer time period due to their slow leaching rate; and finally, their application is very economical because of their minimum cost.

TECHNIQUE OF THE ALGICIDAL TREATMENT

Laboratory Tests and Bioassays

The most precise procedures of laboratory tests have been worked out in the U.S.A. The methods have been described in several papers by Fitzgerald, Palmer, and Maloney, and recently by Kemp. *et al.* (1966). The main principles of these tests are the application of unialgal cultures, the determination of algicidal or algistatic properties by means of subcultures, the control of effectiveness by filtering the treated algal solutions after a certain period of cultivation through fiberglass filters, photographing the filters, and comparing the results with untreated control samples.

Cervenka, *et al.* (1959), proposed a method for the rapid estimation of the efficiency of algicidal treatment in laboratory conditions, measuring the photosynthetic activity of treated and untreated algae and comparing the courses of their oxygen curves.

Stepanek, *et al.* (1961), when studying the algicidal effect of antibiotics, evaluated the results by means of organism counts and by pigment extraction. The concentrated natural phytoplankton community served as the test material.

Stepanek and Cervenka (1961) proposed for the measurement of the algicidal effect the so-called vitality tests, including the vital staining, plasmolysis and osmolysis, electric conductivity, reaction with phenylendiamine, reduction properties of the cell, titration, and buffer-capacity curves.

Hannemann (1965) utilized fluorescent microscopy for distinguishing living algal cells from dead ones. Shilo (1965) applied the same bacteriological technique as in testing the sensitivity of bacteria to antibiotics.

Braginsky (1965) used the following criteria: visual changes of algae, microscopical changes, reactions with vital stains, falling off of the substrate in case of attached algae, lysis of cells, and the so-called function tests based upon the changes in the photosynthetic activity.

Terentiev, *et al.* (1965), carried out tests with algal cultures and with mixtures of algae from nature, evaluating the results of algicidal treatment by means of direct counting in counting chambers and by chlorophyll extraction.

Shimansky (1965) used a natural plankton community for his laboratory experiments after carefully removing all rotifers and crustaceans. The effect of different algicides has been evaluated by microscopic examination and by measuring the chemical oxygen demand (COD).

The last three papers mentioned in this paragraph refer to the experiments with filamentous algae. Büsscher (1954) exposed glass slides and film strips for four weeks in natural environments. Then he placed the substrates with developed periphyton into test vessels with different concentrations of algicide and estimated the effect both visually and microscopically.

Shimansky (1963) cut the *Cladophora* filaments into small equal pieces and placed them into test tubes with algicide solutions. After different treatment periods he counted living and dead cells within the filament portions. Supplementary tests were carried out with the centrifugated samples of planktonic algae. The effect of treatment has been estimated by counting the cells in the Kolkwitz chamber.

Braginsky, *et al.* (1963), published an extensive study of the effect of two algicides on various genera and species of filamentous algae, namely, *Cladophora fracta, Rhizoclonium hieroglyphicum, Mougeotia viridis, Zygnema* sp., *Ulothrix zonata,* and *Spirogyra* sp. div. He weighed the mats of algae before placing them into test solutions. As the main criteria of the algicidal effect he used the photosynthetic activity (the so-called coefficient of photosynthesis retardation) and the determination of the biochemical oxygen demand (BOD). He described all the morphological changes visible in the filaments, such as the change of color, the production of mucilage, the change of the general appearance of algal filaments and mats as a whole at the end of the experiments. Under the microscope he observed cytological changes such as depigmentation, plasmolysis, and changes of the chloroplast shape and color.

When testing a new compound for algicidal properties many authors have supplemented their results with bioassays on aquatic invertebrates and fish in order to obtain some preliminary information about the influence of the chemical on aquatic biota. They usually carried out common short-term laboratory bioassays (e.g., Fitzgerald, *et al.,* 1952, 1954; Maloney and Palmer, 1956; Maloney, 1958; Cervenka, *et al.,* 1959; and Weber, 1965).

Besides normal bioassays on crustaceans, insect larvae, various species of molluscs, and fish fry, Braginsky (1963) also made more complicated observations. He examined the influence of algicides on the heart function of some cladocerans and on the respiration intensity of some molluscs.

Lisovskaya (1965) published her results of long-term toxicological experiments with laboratory test animals (mammals). The experiments usually lasted four months. In the course of the experiments the effect of algicides was examined to determine the following: blood composition, activity of leukocytes, liver function, and the concentration of the enzymes aldolase and transaminase.

Field experiments

Several authors have supplemented their results of laboratory tests with field experiments before recommending the algicide for further application in practice. For example, Fitzgerald (1962) compared the results of tests on unialgal cultures with the results of tests on a larger scale carried out in an experimental swimming pool.

Stepanek, *et al.* (1960), conducted some experiments with the combined preparation CA 350 (see above) in plastic bags of about 20 cubic meters stretched from the surface to the bottom of a small artificial reservoir in Sedlice, Czechoslovakia. The dose of the algicide was calculated to produce a final concentration of 300 μg/l Cu and 50 μg/l Ag in the whole volume of the bag. One bag served as a control. The solution was applied on the water level of experimental bags by means of a hand-operated sprayer. Several hours after the treatment, the decomposition of *Aphanizomenon* water bloom could be observed, and several days after the spray the quantity of phytoplankton decreased to values adequate for water-works treatment. Four weeks after the treatment the growth pulse of green phytonannoplankton algae (microalgae) was noted. The same phenomenon was described by Rodhe (1949), occurring also about one month after the copper sulphate treatment of Lake Norrviken in Sweden. The development of micron algae in experimental bags lasted approximately two weeks and was followed by a rapid decrease to initial values observed before the experiment. All these results were compared with those of an experiment on a much larger scale. One inflow branch of the same reservoir of an area of about 8 hectares was sprayed from a boat. The control of algicidal effects was done by chemical, microscopical, and bacteriological cultivation methods. The expected pulse of green microalgae appeared earlier, only about one week after the treatment. It was much less conspicuous when compared with that in bags, and it ended in the course of a short time period.

Hannemann (1965) tested the same preparation (CA 350) in a drinking water reservoir in Saidenbach, East Germany, using similar techniques: plastic bags and exposed experimental bottles. Her results were in correspondence with those of Stepanek, *et al.* (1960).

Practical Application

CALCULATION OF THE DOSE   According to the opinion of Cervenka, *et al.* (1959), which is rather different from the literature data, the calculation of the necessary dose should not depend on the volume of the whole body of water. The final concentration of the algicide in the water column is important only secondarily, from the biological and hygienic points of view, i.e., not to exceed the limits of tolerance of aquatic invertebrates and fish and also considering the standards of drinking water.

The algicidal effect itself is not caused by μg quantities of the chemical reached after the subsequent dispersion into the whole body of water but by the short-term influence of mg and even higher doses in the surface water layer in the course of the first few hours after the spray. Therefore, Stepanek and the whole group working at the Institute of Hygiene, Prague, recommend first of all to determine the compensation depth and the volume of the trophogenic layer in all deeper and stratified bodies of water before calculating the dose of algicide. The effective concentration either found in the literature or tested in advance by experiments has to be reached within the whole volume of the trophogenic layer so that the desirable destruction of water blooms is done as completely and quickly as possible without any unfavorable secondary influence. Most of these statements are in correspondence with the experiences of Rodhe in 1949.

PROPER TREATMENT TIME   The main presumption of a successful algicidal treatment is the preventive application. When the mass development of algae has reached its climax, it is usually too late for the treatment. For this reason it is extremely important to know in detail the phytoplankton composition of the particular body of water, the growth curves, and the development stages of organisms which should be controlled. Then some suitable biological test of prognosis of the phytoplankton production may be selected and applied under laboratory conditions, taking into consideration all the individual and specific physical, chemical, and biological factors of the location studied. One of the best prognosis tests has been worked out by Guseva (1952) in U.S.S.R. Other less common but also acceptable tests have been summarized by Moravcova (1965).

METHODS OF APPLICATION   The choice of the method of application of an algicide has to be made according to specific situations. The following circumstances must be taken into consideration: the season of the year, the temperature, the species of algae occurring in blooms, other biota present in water, the kind of particular body of water and the way of its exploitation, etc.

The problem of either continuous or shock treatment has been discussed very often in connection with the algae and slime control in cooling water systems. The most serious objection against the use of continuous treatment is the possible adaptation of organisms to the chemical, resulting sometimes in their total resistance.

Developed water blooms and heavy growths of filamentous algae should be controlled gradually in stages or in smaller sections of the body of water at different times rather than by one big shock treatment—not to upset the biological balance of the ecosystem too much. There is much data in the literature about the undesirably rapid decomposition of treated algae followed by a dangerous oxygen deficiency sometimes even causing fish kills (e.g., Rodhe, 1949; Safferman, 1964; Johnson, 1965; and others).

The techniques of algicide treatment have been summarized by Stepanek, *et al.* (1963), into five possibilities: (1) dosing the algicides into the inflow of the body of water, (2) spraying the chemical in dried state on the surface from a boat or from an airplane; (3) spraying the solution or suspension from a boat or an airplane; (4) the method of drag bag using a boat; and (5) delivering the solution from a pipeline behind a boat. Other modifications may be applied according to local conditions.

LIMITS OF EFFECTIVENESS   The factors limiting the effectiveness of algicides have been gathered into one comprehensive chapter by Moravcova (1965). The most important chemical factors are, for instance, alkalinity, pH, the ability of the algicide to react with organic matter and salts dissolved in water, the influence of hydrogen sulphide and ferrous compounds, etc. Temperature and light are the most important physical factors.

ALGICIDES AS FRIENDS

In the following section are several examples of successful application of algicides in all sorts of aquatic environments or references to the most important papers illustrating the positive aspect of algicidal treatment.

Water Supplies

The literature on the application of algicides in water supplies is extremely comprehensive. The use of algicides in water supplies in general has been discussed in several papers by Palmer, and the survey of algicides used for the control of algae in drinking water reservoirs has been done by Stepanek (1965).

An interesting application of various algicides in water supplies is at present being done at our Department of Water Technology, Prague, by Moravcova. After a series of laboratory tests she has selected a few algicides for the control of filamentous blue-green and green algae growing on the surface of sand infiltration beds. The results were to be presented at the International Water Pollution Congress in Prague, September, 1968.

Swimming Pools

In the U.S.A. several field experiments connected with the control of algae in swimming pools were conducted in 1962 and 1963 by Fitzgerald. In

Europe the most experienced author concerned with algicidal treatment of swimming pools is Cosquino de Bussy in the Netherlands. In 1952 she described a successful treatment of a swimming pool by quaternary ammonium compounds. Doses of 5 to 15 ppm of one of these chemicals prolonged the period of water exchange from fourteen to thirty-six days. The transparency of treated water was nearly 190 cm, whereas it was only 20 of the untreated, maximum 80 cm.

Cooling Water Systems

One successful example of the control of algal growths in a cooling pond of a steam power plant was published in 1946 by Gelfand. After a long period of experiments the author recommended for practical use the mixture of copper sulphate with various aliphatic hydroxyacids as chelates. The most effective concentration of Cu ions was 2.5 to 5 ppm.

In the U.S.S.R. Shimansky (1963, 1965) published his experiences with the application of copper sulphate in cooling reservoirs and discussed the results of his laboratory tests with monuron, diuron, and other herbicides.

For the control of algae in cooling towers, Darragh and Stayner (1954) applied very successfully two quaternary ammonium compounds: for killing existing growths, the dose of 3 ppm per day; for keeping the tower clean, a dose of 2 ppm about twice a week. For the same purpose Williams (1953) used Na pentachlorophenate, Robinson (1953) the polyphosphates of heavy metals, Nemec (1958) and Otto (1958, 1959) the tetrachlorbenzoquinone (chloranil), Distler and Pommer (1965) the ammonium derivative of taurinphenylester and phenylester of the vinylsulphonic acid.

At our department we have tried to introduce those chemicals which are effective in very low concentrations so that their use on a large scale is not too costly. We have conducted laboratory experiments using the slime from condenser tubes as a test material; the effect of the chemical treatment was examined by a bacteriological technique used commonly for the cultivation of mesophilic bacteria and by microscopic observation. As a next step we have also carried out a series of experiments on a model of a cooling system. We tested several chemical preparations and also some waste products from the manufacture of herbicides and fungicides. The most hopeful compound, tetrachlorbenzoquinone (chloranil) proved to be very effective in concentrations of 1 to 10 ppm. Its only disadvantage, the slow and partial solubility, has been slightly improved in several cases by using various types of surfactants.

Recently we have initiated experiments with the mixture of ammonia, hydrogen peroxide, and a special catalyst, a procedure patented a few years ago in Czechoslovakia. The algicidal and bactericidal effect of this mixture is based upon the disinfecting and also physical effect of the nascent and subsequently molecular oxygen. The mechanical decomposition of the slimy material in tubes is the first great advantage of this method. When using other kinds of chemical treatment we have always failed to remove the slime quantitatively from the tubes. Even if it was killed by the treatment, it still adhered firmly to the surface of the tubes. The second great advantage of this method is the total absence of the blowdown pollution problem which may sometimes be the most serious objection against the application of very effective and otherwise convenient preparations. Obviously, the doses must be calculated separately for each cooling system, taking into consideration the quality of cooling water, the material of condenser tubes, and the cooling equipment of towers. If possible, it is highly advisable to examine the influence of the treatment on these materials by means of some laboratory experiments and tests on corrosiveness.

Lakes, Ponds, and Reservoirs

The literature concerning the application of algicides in stagnant bodies of water is very rich. An example of lake treatment is the successful removal of a water bloom from Lake Norrviken, Sweden, as described by Rodhe (1959).

Interesting results of a highly selective effect of ammonium sulphate on the phytoflagellate *Prymnesium parvum* in brackish ponds in Israel have been presented by Reich and Aschner (1947).

The application of the combined preparation CA 350 in several reservoirs in Central Europe may be another good example of a successful algicidal treatment. The chemical solution was generally applied as a spray from the airplane. For detailed descriptions of the treatment see Cervenka, *et al.* (1959); Stepanek, *et al.* (1960); Kocurova, 1966; and Hannemann (1965).

Rivers

A rather unusual nuisance in river water was reported from Czechoslovakia in 1960. A mass development of the green flagellate *Hematococcus droebakensis* in the Ohre River of West Bohemia caused very serious troubles in the water supply of Carlsbad just a few days before the opening of an international film festival. The dangerous nuisance was successfully controlled by spraying a solution of the mixture CA 350 from a cistern (Symon, Cervenka, *et al.* 1960).

ALGICIDES AS FOES

Even at the beginning of the history of algicides several biologists published their experiences with unfavorable secondary effects of copper sulphate treatment. Rodhe (1949) described the mass development of green microalgae after the treatment of a water bloom composed of blue-green algae. The same phenomenon has been observed by other biologists, too.

Fitzgerald, *et al.* (1952), and later on other authors, too, pointed out that one objection to the use of copper sulphate is the possible toxic action of resolubilized copper from the lake mud on the small organisms living in the bottoms of the lakes.

Hasler, in 1949, published a very severe criticism of the copper sulphate treatment. "Copper is not only toxic at the moment, but being a heavy metal it is not destroyed nor made biologically inert even after combining with carbonate or organic substances. It is accumulative—after many years of use concentrations may be built up to a level where many forms of aquatic life cannot exist. . . . Repeated treatment may result in its accumulation to a point where toxic quantities dissolve from the lake bottom just as from a ship-bottom paint." In conclusion he posed a most essential and urgent question: "Why should a permanent poison be employed to combat a temporary nuisance?"

The introduction of modern, mostly organic, algicides seemed to have solved all the problems connected with copper sulphate treatment, but in the course of several years of application, many biologists have realized that the main general objections against the treatment procedures and their consequences have remained valid as before. All this has been summarized by Mackenthun (1962): "The application of a chemical to water involves certain hazards including the short and long range toxicity to all biological life, the deposition and possible deleterious accumulation of the chemical on the lake bottom, the impact resulting from the destruction of too much biological growth at one time, and the possible disturbances of the general aquatic environment."

Moreover, several other dangers arising from the application of algicides have been pointed out. Palmer (1964) stated that "indiscriminate use of an algicide may upset the balance of existing aquatic life and make possible unrestricted growth and dominance of a single kind of alga, causing more serious problems than an inoffensive balanced, mixed growth."

Maloney (1958) discussed the possible danger to littoral macrophytes and to the vegetation on the banks of ponds treated with chlorophenyl-dimethylurea.

Lisovskaya (1965) showed the dangerous effects of the same compound on the course of curves of biochemical and chemical oxygen demand, on the ammonization, nitrification, and, in general, on the whole self-purification process in water.

Hedgepeth (1958) and Dalton (1965) reviewed the cooling tower blow-down pollution problems, particularly the undesirable effects of chloro-phenates applied to the control of algae in cooling water systems. These compounds are not only dangerous to fish and invertebrate animals in receiving streams but also often inconvenient from the hygienic point of view: they may irritate the skin of people bathing in the rivers, and in case of the use of river water for the drinking water treatment, they may cause a very persistent taste and odor even in very low concentrations.

Ihl and Sedlmayer (1965) proved an inhibitory effect of some quaternary ammonium coupounds on the curve of the biochemical oxygen demand of brewery waste water and their negative influence on the whole activated sludge process.

For all these reasons, attempts were made to replace the chemical treatment of undesirable algae by some less harmful procedure. The virological method proposed by Safferman and Morris (1964) is one possible way. The authors criticized the chemical treatment, saying that "neither agent is selectively toxic or completely effective," and that "the treatment is seldom aimed at the specific algae involved but rather at annihilation of the total algal population. . . . This may lead to complete disruption of the biologic community and thereby seriously affect the aquatic environment." The aim should be "the replacement of the nuisance organisms with more desirable species." Unfortunately, the artificial introduction of specific viruses into bodies of water with heavy water blooms is not possible because the viruses which could attack the most common blue-green algae occurring in water blooms have not yet been discovered.

Other potential methods of the biological control of the mass development of algae are, for instance, the elimination of the most important nutrients from the inflows of stagnant bodies of water, the preventive sanitation of the bottoms of newly constructed reservoirs before their impoundment, perfect treatment of all the sewage effluents and industrial wastes discharged into the lakes and rivers, controlled use of fertilizers in the area near to the water body, the elimination of the source of nutrients from the regular leaf fall by planting some evergreen trees on the banks of drinking water reservoirs, and the change of the fish stock in lakes and ponds. A more detailed evaluation of all these possible measures is beyond the scope of our present discussion, but the conclusion may be outlined as follows:

The biological means of control of the undesirable mass developments of algae are the best ones because they have no harmful effects on the whole aquatic ecosystem. But in the present situation, they are more often still a desire than a real method. Where there is the necessity to control algal nuisances frequently, quickly, and economically, e.g., in drinking and industrial water supplies, there is no other possibility at present but the application of some kind of chemical treatment. In lakes, ponds, and other environments where the preservation of natural conditions and of the whole community of aquatic organisms is needed, the algicidal treatment should be realized only exceptionally, and the choice of the chemical preparation should be made with much care.

An Ideal Algicide

Several biologists tried to summarize all the desirable qualities of an ideal preparation for the algicidal treatment (e.g., Gelfand, 1946; Mackenthun, 1962; Braginsky, 1965). Such an ideal algicide should be: (1) selective for the specific nuisance; (2) nontoxic to fish and fish-food organisms; (3) harmless to man; (4) without any negative influence on water quality (no taste, odor, etc.); (5) non-accumulative; (6) easily incorporating into the natural element cycles; (7) non-corrosive and harmless to equipment; (8) effective under any condition; (9) easy and economical to store and handle; (10) of reasonable cost; (11) available for continuous use; and (12) simple in the determination of its presence, both qualitatively and quantitatively in very small amounts, so that its concentration may be accurately and easily controlled.

It is impossible at present to find an algicide of such qualities. But nevertheless, the institutes dealing with applied limnology should search for a preparation which at least corresponds with the ideal to a considerable extent.

REFERENCES

Antonie, C. J., and Osness, W. H., 1963. "Distribution and Accumulation of Copper Following Copper Suphate Application on Lakes," Trans. Wis. Acad. Sci. *52,* 169–75; Water Poll. Abstr. *38 (1),* 11, 1965; Abstr. No. 51.

Bank, O., 1962. "Algen, ihre Bekampfung mit chemischen Mitteln," *Der Fischwirt 12 (9),* 260–69. Literaturberichte 1962/63, *11 (3),* Abstr. No. 436.

Beger, H., 1966. "Leitfaden der Trink- und Brauchwasserbiologie," 2. *Aufl. von Gerloff u. Lüdemann,* Fischer Verl, Jena.

Braginsky, L. P., Grin, V. G., Kostenko, S. V., Lakhin, V. V., and Surkova, L. V., 1963. "Monuron and simasin as algicides in the control of filamentous algae," Trudy Vsesoyuz. Gidrobiol. Obch. *14,* 52–65.

Braginsky, L. P., 1965. "On methods of screening of algicides effective against blue-green algae," *Ekologia i fiziologia sinezelenykh vodorosley* [Ecology and physiology of blue-green algae], Akad. Nauk U.S.S.R.

Büsscher, M., 1954. "Untersuchungen über den Aufwuchs in Wasserbecken und seine Bekampfung mit Kupfersulfat," *Schriftenreihe d. Vereins f. Wasser-, Boden- und Luft-hygiene,* Berlin-Dahlem, (*8*), 1–20.

Cervenka, R., Stepanek, M., Votavova, M., *et al.,* 1959. "Limnological study of the reservoir Sedlice near Zeliv. VII. A contribution to the technique of selecting new algicide compounds," orig. Czech, summary English, Sci. Pap. Inst. Chem. Technol., Prague, Fuel a. Water *3 (1),* 247–88.

Cosquino de Bussy, I. J. le, 1952. "Onderzoek over quaternaire ammoniumverbindingen als bestrijdingsmiddel tegen algen in enoverdekte zwembaden," Afdeling Gezondheits-stechnik T.N.O., Rapport No. 9.

Dalton, T. F., 1965. "Cooling towers: problems . . . and some treatment practices," *Water Works* a. Wastes Engng *2 (12),* 53–56. *Literaturberichte, 14(2),* 47–48, 1966.

Darragh, J. L., and Stayner, R. D., 1954. "Quaternary Ammonium Compounds from Dodecylbenzene. Algae Control in Industrial Cooling Systems," *Ind. Eng. Chem. 46 (2),* 254–57.

Distler, H., and Pommer, E. H., 1965. "Die Bekämpfung des Algenwachstums in Rückkühl-werken mit neuen Mikroziden," *Erdöl u. Kohle 18 (5),* 381–86.

Fitzgerald, G. P., 1962. "Bioassay for Algicidal Chemicals in Swimming Pools," *Water Sewage Wks. 109* (*9*), 361–63.

———, 1963. "Field Tests on the Duration of Algicides in Swimming Pools," *Sanitarian's J. Envir. Health 25,* 319–25. Water Poll. Abstr. 1965, *38* (*4*), Abstr. No. 568.

———, 1964. "Evaluation of Potassium Permanganate as an Algicide for Water Cooling Towers," *Ind. Eng. Chem. 3 (2),* 82–85.

———, 1966. "Use of Potassium Permanganate for Control of Problem Algae," *J. Amer. Water. Wks. Assn. 58 (5),* 609–14.

Fitzgerald, G. P., and Faust, S. L., 1963. "Bioassay for Algicidal vs. Algistatic Chemicals," *Water Sewage Wks. 110 (8),* 296–98.

———, 1963. "Factors Affecting the Algicidal and Algistatic Properties of Copper," *Appl. Microbiol. 11 (4)* 345–51.

———, 1965. "Effect of Bacteria on the Solubility of Copper Algicides," *Water Sewage Wks. 112,* 271–75.

Fitzgerald, G. P., Gerloff, G. C., and Skoog, F., 1952. "Studies on Chemicals with Selective Toxicity to Blue-Green Algae," *Sewage Ind. Wastes 24 (7),* 888–96.

Fitzgerald, G. P., and Skoog, F., 1954. "Control of Blue-Green Algae Blooms with 2,3-dichloronaphthoquinone," *ibid., 26,* 1136–40.

Foter, M. M., Palmer, C. M., and Maloney, T. E., 1953. "Antialgal Properties of Various Antibiotics," *Antibiotics Chemotherapy, 3,* 505–508.

Funk, W. H., and Gaufin, A. R., 1965. "Control of Taste and Odor-Producing Algae in Deer Creek Reservoir," Trans. Amer. Micr. Soc. *84* (2), 263–69; Water Poll. Abstr. 1966, *39 (8),* Abstr. No. 1241.

Gelfand, M., 1946. "Algae Control in Water Supplies," *Power Plant Eng., 50 (1),* 63–65.

Guseva, K. A., 1952. "Water blooms, their causes, prognosis, and control," Trudy Vsesoyuz. Gidrobiol. Obch. *4,* 3–92.

Hannemann, W., 1965. "Versuche über die Anwendung von Algiziden in der Saidenbachtalsperre," *Wiss. Zeitschr.* d. Karl-Marx-Univ., Leipzig, Math.-Nat. Reihe, *14* (2), 315–27.

Hasler, A. D., 1949. "Antibiotic Aspects of Copper Treatment of Lakes," Trans. Wisconsin Acad. Sci. *39,* 97–103.

Hedgepeth, L. L., 1958. "1957 Industrial Wastes Forum. Solving the Cooling Tower Blowdown Pollution Problem," *Sewage Ind. Wastes, 30 (4),* 539–54.

Ihl, A., and Sedlmayer, H., 1965. "Influence of quaternary ammonium bases (quats) on the 5-day biological oxygen demand of brewery waste water, and the biological decomposing ability of quats in brewery waste water," *Brauwelt Ausgabe B, 105,* 1529–33; Water Poll. Abstr. 1966, *39 (8),* Abstr. No. 1370.

Johnson, M. G., 1965. "Control of Aquatic Plants in Farm Ponds in Ontario," *Progr. Fish Cult. 27,* 23–30; Water Poll. Abstr. 1966, *39 (12);* Abstr. No. 2044.

Kemp, H. T., Fuller, R. G., and Davidson, R. S., 1966. "Potassium Permanganate as an Algicide," *J. Amer. Water Wks. Assn. 58 (2),* 255–63.

Kocurova, E., 1966. "The application of the algicide CA 350 in the Lubi Reservoir near Trebic, Czechoslovakia," *Hydrobiologia, 28 (2),* 223–40.

Liebmann, H., 1959. *Handbuch der Frischwasser- und Abwasserbiologie,* Bd. II, Lief. 3, 348–58.

Lisovskaya, E. V., 1965. "On hygienic dosage of monurone contents in water," *Ecology and Physiology of Blue-Green Algae,* Akad. Nauk U.S.S.R.

Mackenthun, K. M., 1962. "A Review of Algae, Lake Weeds, and Nutrients," *J. Water Poll. Contr. Fed. 34,* 1077–85.

Maguire, J. J., 1956. "Biological Fouling in Recirculating Cooling Water Systems," *Ind. Eng. Chem. 48 (12),* 2162–67.

Maloney, T. E., 1958. "Control of Algae with Chlorophenyl Dimethyl Urea," *J. Amer. Water Wks. Assn. 50,* 417–22.

Maloney, T. E., and Palmer, C. M., 1956. "Toxicity of Six Chemical Compounds to Thirty Cultures of Algae," *Water Sewage Wks. 103,* 509–13.

Moore, G. T., and Kellerman, K. F., 1904. "A Method of Destroying or Preventing the Growth of Algae and Certain Pathogenic Bacteria in Water Supplies," Bureau of Plant Ind., U.S. Dept of Agric., *Bull. 64,* 9–44.

Moravcova, V., 1965. "Survey of literature on the Application of Algicides," *Ustav ved. techn. inform.* Praha, No. 2.

———, 1967. "Biological investigations of an infiltration area and experiments with some algicides," *Hydrobiologia,* in press.

———, "Algicides used for water supply purposes," *Bot. Rev.,* in press.

Nemec, J., 1958. "Experiments with the Inhibition of Growth of Filamentous Algae on Cooling Towers," thesis, Inst. of Chem. Tech., Prague.

Otto, W., 1958. "Untersuchungen über die Bekämpfung von Mikroorganismen in einem Kühlwasserkrieslauf," dissertation, Karl Marx Univ., Leipzig.

Palmer, C. M., 1956. "Evaluation of New Algicides for Water Supply Purposes," *J. Amer. Water Wks. Assn. 48 (9),* 1133–37.

———, 1962. "Algae in Water Supplies. An Illustrated Manual on the Identification, Significance, and Control of Algae in Water Supplies," Pub. Health Serv., Wash., D.C.

———, 1964. "Algae in Water Supplies of the United States," in *Algae and Man,* ed. by Jackson, Proceed. of the NATO Advanced St. Inst., New York, Plenum Press, 239–61.

Palmer, C. M., and Maloney, T. E., 1955. "Preliminary Screening for Potential Algicides," *Ohio J. of Science 55 (1),* 1–8.

Prescott, G. W., 1948. "Objectionable Algae with Reference to the Killing of Fish and Other Animals," *Hydrobiologia 1*, 1–13.

Reich, K., and Aschner, M., 1947. "Mass Development and Control of the Phytoflagellate *Prymnesium parvum* in Fish Ponds in Palestine," *Palestine J. of Bot. 4*, 14–23.

Robinson, W. W., 1953. "Treatment of Industrial Wastes," U.S. 2,657,178 and 2,657,179. Chem. Abstr. 1954, *48 (2)*, 918.

Rodhe, W., 1949. "Die Bekämpfung einer Wasserblüte von Microcystis und die gleichzeitige Förderung einer neuen Hochproduktion von Pediastrum im See Norrviken bei Stockholm," Proceedings IAL *10*, 372–76.

Safferman, R. S., and Morris, M. E., 1962. "Evaluation of Natural Products for Algicidal Properties," *Applied Microbiol. 10 (4)*, 289–92.

————, 1964. "Control of Algae with Viruses," *J. Amer. Water Wks. Assn. 56 (9)*, 1217–24.

Schlüter, M., 1966. "Untersuchungen über algizide Eigenschaften von Fungiziden und Herbiziden," *Int. Rev. ges. Hydrobiol. 51 (3)*, 521–41.

Schwarz, D., 1965. "Der Einfluss von Wirkstoffen auf das Wachstum und die Vermehrung von Algen (Literaturübersicht)," *Veröff. d. Hydrol. Forschungsabt. d. Dortmunder Stadtwerke Nr. 8*, 1–206. Literaturberichte 1966, *14 (3)*, Abstr. No. 300.

Shilo, M., 1965. "Study on the Isolation and Control of Blue-Green Algae from Fish Ponds," Bamidgeh, *Bull. of Fish Cult. in Israel 17 (4)*, 83–93.

Shimansky, B. A., 1963. "Active measures in controlling overgrowth in cooler reservoirs," Trudy Vsesoyuz. Gidrobiol. Obch. *14*, 74–114.

————, 1965. "Development of blue-green algae in water reservoirs-coolers of heat power stations and measures of their control," *Ecology and Physiology of Blue-Green Algae*, Akad. Nauk U.S.S.R.

Sladeckova, A., 1961. "Fouling of the cooling equipment of steam-power plants," *Energetika 7*, 327–29.

Sladeckova, A., Sladecek, V., 1958. "Der Aufwuchs auf den Kühltürmen der Dampfkraftwerke und einige einfache Abhilfemassnahmen," *Hydrobiologia 12 (1)*, 43–54.

Stepanek, M., 1965. "Chemische Algenbekämpfung in Trinkwassertalsperren," *Wiss. Zeitschr.* d. Karl Marx Univ., Leipzig, Mat.-Nat. Reihe *14 (2)*, 307–14.

Stepanek, M., Binovec, J., Chalupa, J., Jirik, V., Schmidt, P., and Zelinka, M. D., 1963. "Water blooms in the CSSR," Sci. Pap. Inst., Chem. Technol., Prague, Techn. of Water *7 (2)*, 175–263.

Stepanek, M., Chalupa, J., Masinova, L., Pokorny, J., and Svec, J., 1960. "Application of algicide CA 350 in reservoirs," *ibid., 4 (2)*, 375–402.

Stepanek, M., and Cervenka, R., 1961. "A new method for the determination of the vitality of water algae. Measurement of the effect of algicides," *ibid., 5 (1)*, 189–226.

Stepanek, M., Vlcek, V., and Cervenka, R., 1961. "Algicide effects of some antibiotics," *ibid., 5 (2)*, 333–46.

Symon, K., Cervenka, R., Chalupa, J., and Stepanek, M., 1960. "Acute danger to quality of drinking water in the Karlovy Vary region," *Vod. hosp. 10 (11)*, 491–93.

Terentiev, A. P., Stroganov, N. S., Rukhadze, E. G., and Khobotiev, V. G., 1965. "Polymetallic ores and their working products, applied as algicides," Doklady Akad. Nauk U.S.S.R., *164 (4)*, 928–30.

Toohey, J. I., Nelson, C. D., and Krotkov, G., 1965. "Toxicity of Phenazine Carboxylic Acids to Some Bacteria, Algae, Higher plants, and Animals," *Can. J. Bot. 43*, 1151–55.

Weber, E., 1965. "Effect of sodium pentachlorophenol on fish and fish-food organisms," *Biol. Zbl. 84 (1)*, 91–93; Water Poll. Abstr. 1966, *39 (8)*, Abstr. No. 1408.

Whipple, G. C., 1927. *The Microscopy of Drinking Water,* rev. by Fair and Whipple, New York, J. Wiley & Sons

Williams, A. E., 1953. "Control of Slime and Algae in Cooling Water Systems," *Cheap Steam 37 (4),* 74–75.

Zehnder, A., and Hughes, E. O., 1958. "The Antialgal Activity of Acti-Dione," *Can. J. Microbiol. 4,* 399–408.

XXIII

Algae and Fish Relationships

S. ŻARNECKI

Department of Fisheries
College of Agriculture
Krakow, Poland

In each body of water, great or small, in which fish are living, in the lakes, ponds, and rivers, in the oceans and the seas everywhere the more or less abundant world of algae is present. It is obvious that in such a variety of water habitats the relationship between fish and algae must be differentiated in a high degree. In general, algae, being the first link in the food chain, determinate in a direct or indirect manner the kind and the amount of food for fish. On the other hand they can also exercise an unfavorable influence on them.

This essay is an attempt to summarize what is known in this field based on recent experiments and publications. Not all aspects of this rather complicated problem are discussed and reported here to the same extent. Attention will be given more to those points which seem to be generally less well known, which seem to present a greater biological interest, or which may be more important from the point of view of human management.

ALGAE AS DIRECT, NATURAL FOOD FOR FISH

Nikolsky (1963), in his interesting book about the ecology of fish, also published in English, makes the following general remarks concerning plants as food for fish: "Chlorophyllus plants are very important as food for fish." He goes on to say that it is true that in high latitudes where the vegetative period is short there are no herbivorous fish. But as the lower latitudes are approached there appear first of all facultative phytophages, such as the silver crucian carp and the roach, for which plants have a subsidiary nutritional significance because their main food consists of animals. In still lower latitudes, with longer vegetative periods, plants become even more important as food for fish. Some species of fish feed entirely on plants and have evolved a number of special adaptations for grazing, triturating, and assimilating plant food.

Planktonic algae form the food of such fish as the Amur cyprinoid

459

Hypophthalmichthys molitrix Val., the Pacific sardine *Sardinops sagax melanosticta* Schl., the clupeoid, *Tilapia esculenta* Graham, a cychlid, and many others. Filamentous algae (periphyton) are eaten by *Varicorhinus heratensis* Keys, and *Chondrostoma nasus* L., both cyprinoids. Finally, macrophytes are eaten by the grass carp *Ctenopharyngodon idella* Val. and *Scardinius erythrophthalmus* L.

Herbivorous fish are less numerous in the sea than in fresh water. Many fish use plant detritus as food (*Xenocypris*, lamprey larvae, and certain cychlids).

Several examples can be cited of fish using algae as food.

Reef Fish and Fish from Shallow Tropical Seas

According to Dawson, Aleem, and Halstead (1955), examination of eighty-one samples of eleven phytophagous species of reef fish led to the recognition of sixty-three species of sessile algae, together with five species of dinoflagellates, eighty-six species of diatoms and one silicoflagellate. The list of these species in the paper cited (Dawson, *et al.*, 1955) includes, in addition to the major components of the fish diet, . . . a number of species of *minute epiphytic algae* [including diatoms] such as commonly occur on larger algae and which, therefore, the fish encounter incidentally along with the larger forms. These probably do not contribute appreciably to the nutrition of the fish."

The work of Dawson on the marine algae of Palmyra Island "was indicated by the knowledge that this area harbors a large poisonous fish population and that many poisonous fish are herbivorous. It is believed that fish become poisonous as a direct result of their feeding habits." The idea of such an investigation "was stimulated by the results obtained from a series of screening experiments on the poisonous reef fish of Jalni Saipan (Hiyama, 1953), Phoenix, Line, and Johnston Islands (Halstead and Bunker, 1954).

During the course of some investigations, it was found that a given species of fish may be poisonous in one area and non-toxic in another. This spotty geographical distribution of poisonous fishes leads one to believe that fish become toxic as a result of their feeding habits.

Moreover, studies recently conducted indicate that it is possible to cause a nontoxic California fish to become poisonous by controlled feeding, with no objective symptoms of intoxication. This and other evidence has led to the hypothesis that the poisonous fish problem is basically concerned with the food chain of the fish. Inasmuch as the food cycle must logically be initiated by marine algae (including phytoplankton) which constitute the primary food source of the sea, the desirability of a study of these plants in connection with the fish was indicated. Of further significance is the fact that large numbers of poisonous fish are known to be herbivorous.

A study of feeding habits of reef fish from the Palmyra Islands seems to confirm this hypothesis because it was found that algae were present in a larger number of poisonous fish than any other type of food. Besides, an interesting statement was made. *Lyngbya* (Cyanophyta) was detected in a large majority of the poisonous fish.

Bakus (1964) in his paper concerning the effects of fish grazing on invertebrate evolution in shallow tropical water, enumerates a great number of fish living in such waters and grazing on different species of marine algae which represent the main food for many fish. The fish eating algae from shallow waters from temperate climates were also mentioned.

Fish from Brackish Water Ponds

MILKFISH (CHANOS CHANOS) Ling (1966), from Bangkok, Thailand, states that success in the culture of milkfish depends mostly on the maintenance of an abundant supply of natural food consisting principally of filamentous blue-green algae and diatoms. The paper of Tang and Hwang (1966) from Taiwan gives an excellent review of the whole problem. According to these authors, the brackish water ponds for the culture of milkfish *Chanos chanos* (Forskal) in Indonesia, the Philippines, and Taiwan are situated on alluvial tidal flats of recent deposits with abundant plant nutrients brought by streams running down to them. Algae in the tropics can bloom luxuriantly, and some of them foster the growth of milkfish in pond production, while others are unsuitable as food and harmful for ponds.

Four major groups of algae grow in brackish water ponds: green algae, Chlorophyceae; diatoms, Bacillariophyceae; blue-green algae, Cyanophyceae; and various free-living phytoflagellates. *Chaetomorpha* and *Enteromorpha* dominate in the Chlorophyceae; *Oscillatoria, Lyngbya, Phormidium, Spirulina, Microcoleus,* and probably other genera of Oscillatoriales in the Cyanophyceae; and *Navicula, Pleurosigma, Mastogloia, Stauroneis, Amphor, Nitzschia,* and other unidentified genera. As to the phytoflagellates, *Chlamydomonas, Pyrimimonas, Chlorasarcina, Gymnodinium,* and *Chilomonas* are dominant, as well as a number of unidentified flagellates.

Determination of the amount of digestible nutrient that a particular food supplies to the fish is the most important method of measuring the relative values of foods. A number of digestion experiments were made with the four groups of algae for milkfish of three different sizes—fingerlings 3 to 5 g, juveniles 15 to 20 g, and half-grown fish 60 to 100 g—which are commonly used for stocking ponds in Taiwan.

Feeds of these four groups of algae were given daily at the rate of 20 to 25 per cent of the total body weight of the fish stocked in the pond. The algae in both fresh and detrital forms were given on the basis of wet weight, which contains approximately 88 to 95 per cent water. During the experiments, the faeces excreted by each group of test fish were carefully collected with a glass tube by suction. The results are listed in Table I.

Some following remarks are provided to supplement this information.

THE FILAMENTOUS GREEN ALGAE   Although fresh *Chaetomorpha* contains a relatively high percentage of crude protein, the proportion digested by milkfish of the above-mentioned sizes is extremely low, computed at 0.09 per cent, and it has a high nutritive ratio of 1:33.44. However, *Chaetomorpha* can be used as a feed of relatively high value for milkfish when it dies, since on decomposition its protein content becomes digestible for milkfish. The digestion experiment shows that the *Chaetomorpha*- produced detritus supplies 2.28 per cent digestible protein with a relatively low nutritive ratio of 1:1.66 for milkfish.

THE PHYTOFLAGELLATES   The phytoflagellates were mostly *Chlamydomonas* and *Chilomonas*. The phytoflagellates are the most nutritious feeds for the milkfish as they supply 3.17 per cent digestible protein and 10.41 per cent (including fat × 2.25) total digestible nutrients with a nutritive ratio of 1:2.37.

THE DIATOMS   The diatom sludge formed by various species of bottom-dwelling diatoms is undoubtedly a nutritious food for milkfish as the diatom cells contain a high portion of organic nutrients which can be digested by the fish.

THE FILAMENTOUS BLUE-GREEN ALGAE   The filamentous blue-greens are comprised mainly of various species of the family Oscillatoriaceae. This group of algae is valuable as feed for milkfish. They furnish 1.60 per cent digestible protein with a low nutritive ratio of 1:1.18.

It is believed by some fishery biologists that milkfish are plankton feeders. However, milkfish gill-rakers are not very well adapted to filter planktonic algae from the water. Feeding experiments conducted in concrete ponds indicated that milkfish had little food in their stomachs when they were stocked in ponds containing large quantities of phytoflagellates. This was also found to be the case for fish from plankton-rich earth ponds. With the exception of the planktonic algae that die and accumulate on the pond bottom, the quantity of fresh plankton taken as food by milkfish in ponds is negligible, even by milkfish fingerlings.

Diatoms are found in both planktonic and benthic forms in brackish water ponds. Very common planktonic genera include *Synedra* and *Melo-*

TABLE I Composition of Four Major Algae Groups and Their Relative Nutritive Value as Milkfish Feed Water temperature during digestion experiments ranged from 29° to 33° and the salinity from 24 to 27 ppt (after Yung-An Tang and Ting Lang Hwang, 1966)

Group of algae	Number of samples	Total Composition %						Digestive coefficient[1] %				Digestible[2] protein	Total digestible nutrients[3]	Nutritive[4] Ratio
		Total dry matter	Crude protein	Crude fat	Nitrogen-free extract	Fiber	Mineral matter	Crude protein	Crude fat	Nitrogen-free extract	Fiber			
Chaetomorpha														
Fresh form	15	8.54	2.82	0.91	1.50	1.22	2.09	3	72	87	21	0.09	3.12	1: 33.44
Detrital form	15	10.72	3.46	0.38	3.21	0.98	2.69	66	89	85	37	2.28	6.13	1: 1.66
Phytoflagellates[5]														
Fresh form	5	11.98	3.91	1.32	5.61	0.42	0.72	81	91	78	23	3.17	10.41	1: 2.37
Diatoms[6]														
Fresh form	15	12.87	2.89	0.94	2.25	0.27	6.52	87	96	84	19	2.51	6.48	1: 1.54
Filamentous blue-green algae[7]														
Fresh form	15	9.86	2.32	0.21	1.52	0.70	5.11	69	86	81	38	1.60	3.49	1: 1.18

[1] Digestive coefficient = amount of a class of organic nutrient in the feed–amount of that class of organic nutrient in faeces amount of that class of organic nutrient in the feed × 100.

[2] The percentage of protein in the feed × digestion coefficient of protein.

[3] The sum of digestible protein, fiber, nitrogen-free extract and fat × 2.25.

[4] Percentage of total digestible organic nutrients–percentage of digestible protein ÷ the percentage of digestible protein.

[5] Centrifuged from the pond water where Chlamydomonas and Chilomonas flagellates bloomed predominantly.

[6] Furnished as the diatom sludge.

[7] Collected from the pond bottom where the dominant genera Oscillatoria and Lyngbya grew.

sira. These were found wherever the pond water was examined, but they never grew so abundantly so as to make the pond water turbid as did the phytoflagellates. The benthic diatoms such as *Navicula, Pleurosigma, Mastogloia, Stauroneis*, etc., together with the different species of filamentous blue-green algae, form the algal pasture on the substratum. Since milkfish of various growth stages suck up foodstuffs from the pond floors, these pasture algae furnish the most suitable forms of milkfish food. Milkfish of various sizes often feed on the algal scum floating on the water surface, but show no special preference for food from the upper layers of the water.

Fish from Estuaries–Australian Examples

J. M. Thomsen (1959) has examined the contents of 5,053 gut samples from seventeen species collected in fourteen estuaries or semi-enclosed bays around southwestern Australia. He found that three species of fish—Cobbler, Yellow Eye mullet–Mugil cephalus (Mugiloidei), and Garfish–Strongylura longirostris (Belonidae)—frequently have nothing but masses of algae filaments in the gut, sometimes mixed with polychaetes or chironomids. The majority were filamentous green algae, such as *Enteromorpha sp., Cladophora sp., and Chaetomorpha sp.*

Several species of diatoms were found in the stomachs. Species of *Melosira* and *Cosinodiscus* were common. Garfish and yellow-eye mullet stomachs frequently contain diatoms sometimes by themselves but usually mixed with algal filaments. Cobblers and black bream also take considerable quantities.

Fish from Ponds with Freshwater or Water of Low Salinity

All species of fish cultured in freshwater ponds form a nonpredatory biological group of warm-water fishes.

TILAPIA   Species of *Tilapia* are widely reared in ponds in many tropical and subtropical countries. The following two species are the most common: *Tilapia mossambica* and *Tilapia melanopleura*. The first species is omnivorous; the melanopleura feeds on plants. From the fry stage to a length of three to five cm. it takes phytoplankton and unicellular algae; when bigger it prefers plants such as *Sparganium, Chara, Potamogeton*, etc. (Mann, 1966).

GREY MULLETS   Grey Mullet—*Mugil cephalus* and other species of mullets—are cultured either in freshwater ponds or in brackish waters of low salinity in India, the Philippines, Hong Kong, Taiwan, China, etc. Their natural food consists mainly of unicellular and filamentous algae, diatoms benthic algae, detritus and small pieces of soft vegetable matter (Ling, 1966).

INDIAN CARPS   Under this name one understands the following zoological species: *Catla catla, Labeo rohita* and *Labeo calbasu*, and *Cirrhina mrigala* cultured in ponds in India and Pakistan. The mass production of fry of these species in the so-called nursery ponds is based on rich plankton which presents the necessary natural food. The fry prefer zooplankton, and the role of phytoplankton is till now not sufficiently known.

CHINESE CARP   This group of warm-water fish is endemic in Asia and the Far East and consists of the following species of fishes which may be cultured in ponds: grass carp, *Ctenopharyngodon idella*; black carp, *Mylopharyngodon picens*; silver carp, *Hypophtahnichtys molitrix*; big-head carp, *Aristichthys nobilis*; and common carp, *Cyprinus carpio*. They are reared in mono or in mixed culture. Some of them are also common in Europe, e.g., common carp and crucian carp.

The acclimatization of these species of Chinese carp, which are mostly phytophagous, such as grass carp, silver carp, and big-head, in fish farms of the western part of the U.S.S.R. was started in the late 1930's. The first attempts to introduce these fish in the pond farms of the European part of the U.S.S.R. were not successful owing to the lack of knowledge of their biology and difficulties in transportation over very long distances. The war interrupted further attempts. Fifteen years later, the use of more efficient modern transport such as special live-fish vans and planes, and recently polyethylene bags, allowed a large-scale introduction of young fish, especially grass and silver carp. Both these species are known to occur in the Amur River, the northern boundary of their distribution (Konradt, 1966).

The progeny of grass carp brought from the Amur River and of silver carp brought as young from China were first bred in the U.S.S.R. in 1961 in the Turkman Republic. In the same year the progeny of grass carp was obtained from the pond-reared spawners in the Ukraine (Aliev, 1963). In 1962 a considerable number of young was also produced in the Krasnodar territory. In 1963 from a herbivorous fish hatchery "Goryachy Kluch," Krasnodar, four million young fish of grass and silver carp were obtained.

Here in the same year, for the first time in the U.S.S.R., young of big-head and a viable hybrid progeny of grass carp and big-head were produced (Vinogradov, 1966). Later a commercial production has been developed and now nearly all fish farms of the Northern Caucasus have begun mixed carp cultures.

Three species of herbivorous—grass, silver, and big-head carp—were transferred to different regions of the European U.S.S.R., the Middle

Asian, and Transcaucasian Republics. Large numbers of younger and older groups of these species were released into many natural waters and artificial lakes, e.g., in the Volga Delta, the Kuban system, the Karacum canal, and the Kjubyshev, Tsymlansk, and Novosibirsk reservoirs (Vinogradov, 1966).

In 1964–65 the Experimental State Hatchery "Goryachy Kluch" had already exported about ninety million larvae of grass carp, silver carp, and big-head to Poland, Czechoslovakia, Hungary, and Bulgaria (Vinogradov, 1966).

In that manner before our eyes in the last few years a rapid development and broad distribution of herbivorous species for pond culture also took place in the temperate zone. The problem of a proper utilization of great quantities of heated waters originating from cooling systems of power plants is favorable for the culture of these warm-water herbivorous species and also for common carp.

It is obvious that the whole problem of shortening the food chain between primary production and animal protein, in this case between algae and fish, has a significant importance for man. Thus it is clear that these species of fish which directly eat natural food consisting of algae or higher plants are preferable in the first line for culture purposes. The food chain—algae-fish—is the shortest one we have for this kind of animal protein.

Grass carp, Ctenopharyngodon idella, is a quick-growing fish which can attain more than 30 kg. in body weight in the Amur River. For a month and a half its fry feed on animal food, mostly zooplankton. As soon as fingerlings are three cm. long they become phytophagous. *C. idella* lives on higher aquatic plants, including soft submerged vegetation, young seedlings of semi-submerged water plants, and meadow plants submerged in high floods. In addition to higher plants, the grass carp willingly feeds on filamentous algae. Since the grass carp feeds on aquatic vegetation, it could be used for biological control of aquatic weeds in water cooling reservoirs of power stations and in irrigation reservoirs.

Silver carp, Hypophthalmichthys molitrix, is another rapidly growing fish which may reach the weight of more than 16 kg. Unlike the grass carp, this species feeds on lower aquatic plants, i.e., microscopic planktonic algae, filtered by the gill apparatus. The gill rakers of the silver carp make a fine-meshed sieve which serves to collect the phytoplankton entering the oral cavity.

The fry of the silver carp at first feed on zooplankton, and only when the fingerlings reach the length of 12 to 17 mm. do they become plant-feeders. Adult specimens eat phytoplankton almost exclusively. However, when phytoplankton is not available, they may feed on detritus.

For feeding, phytophagous fishes enter numerous floodplain lakes in the basins of the Amur and some Chinese rivers. In autumn, during the abatement of the river and fall of temperature, both the grass and silver carp migrate toward the river bed where they hibernate and usually do not eat during that time (Verigin, 1963).

Common carp reared in ponds of many European countries are mainly carnivorous in natural conditions of the moderate zone. But in pond culture this species also takes artificially given plant food in great quantities, up to a proportion three parts of the "artificial" plant food (lupin, grains of corn, etc.) to one part of natural animal food.

Recently attempts have been made to find artificial pelleted food already in common use in trout culture for the carp. In the future this kind of food will surely be the basis for European carp farms. Algae are always given as one of the components by producing such pelleted food. One can therefore expect that algae in the near future will see more and more use as food in carp production in the form of pellets.

Freshwater Fishes from Lakes and Running Water of Temperate Zones

This division includes species of the cold-water fish group and species between the cold- and warm-water groups. According to Fott (1959) many algae are found in the alimentary tracts of such very common European species of *Cyprinids* as *Scardinius erythrophtalmus, Abramis vimba,* and *Leuciscus rutilus,* especially in young fish.

Dyk (1945) stated that Phoximus also feed, besides larvae of insects, on many algae in Czechoslovak running montanic waters. In the same genus of fish a Canadian algologist, Irenne-Marie (1938), found that the full content of the stomach was composed of Desmidiacea—*Cosmarium* sp., *Spyrotaenia* sp., and *Spondylosium* sp.

On the basis of our own investigations undertaken in the Department of Fisheries, College of Agriculture, Krakow, Poland, on the alimentary tract of one species of fish dominant in the submontane region of Tatra and Carpathian rivers, *Chondrostoma nasus,* have demonstrated that this species feeds mainly on algae which cover the "free" surface of stones in the river bed. In the alimentary tracts of *Chondrostoma nasus* the larvae of chiromids were found, but these were taken accidentally by the fish together with algae in which the larvae were living. (Prawocheński, 1964; Zarnecki and Miś, 1967)

Chondrostoma nasus has special anatomic features which adapt this species to feed on algae. It is a unique species among European Teleosts which possesses a mouth opening situated on the ventral side of the head in the form of a transverse aperture with sharp edges. This type of structure makes it possible to scrape epiphytic algae overgrowing the stones. This species also has a specific adaptation in the form of enlarged and abundant folds in the alimentary tract which enable the fish to digest plant food consisting mainly of diatoms.

In spite of the fact that this species is common and numerous in the rivers of the European Continent, it was examined relatively rarely till now. No other species among European fish is in such a degree an algae consumer living in cold streams.

One more circumstance which seems to be not quite clear and therefore more interesting from the biological point of view is worth mentioning here: *Chondrostoma nasus* is characteristic for the Barbel region and for the lower part of the Salmonid region. In these places one species, *Chondrostoma nasus*, feeds nearly exclusively on algae; the second species, *Salmo trutta* (Brown Trout and parr of Sea Trout) are carnivorous only. There is undoubtedly no competition for food between these two species. They also occupy two different and separate ecological niches.

Chondrostoma collects its food by scraping periphytic algae from the surface of stones on the river bottom, and the trout takes its food mainly in the current where the drifting organisms of macrobenthos from the upper part of the river (Kalleberg, 1958) flow downstream.

In the above-mentioned observations of the Department of Fisheries of the Kracow Agriculture University many examples of a tendency of *Chondrostoma nasus* to penetrate higher and higher upstream in the Salmonid region were noted. The effect of such a development is always observed in the diminishing number of trout. What factors influence this negative reaction against trout when food competition does not exist?

Nutritive Value of Algal Foods and Some Others
Common in Fish Culture

An evaluation of the nutritive value of foods for pond fish of: (a) some marine algae, (b) fresh plant material, and (c) foods of animal origin is listed in Table II (after Ling, 1966).

Food quotients which allow to calculate how much food is necessary to produce 1 kg of fish were presented for some brackish algae eaten by milk-fish.

For comparison, food quotients of more common foods of animal origin consumed by warm-water fish are presented in Table III (after Ling, 1966).

TABLE II Composition of Some Supplementary Feeds for Pond Fish
(after Ling, 1966)

| | Composition in percentage by weight | | | | | |
	Dry matter	Crude pro-tein	Crude fat	Carbo-hydrates (nitrogen-free extract)	Crude Ash fiber	True pro-tein
Marine algae						
Filamentous blue-green (fresh, mixed)	9.85	2.32	0.21	1.52	0.70	5.11
Oscillatoria spp.	17.10	1.65	0.39	1.37	1.46	12.23
Phormidium spp. (wet) Diatoms (fresh, mixed)	12.87	2.89	0.94	2.25	0.27	6.52
Phytoflagellates (fresh, mixed)	11.89	3.91	1.32	5.61	0.42	0.72
Chaetomorpha						
Fresh	8.54	2.82	0.92	1.50	1.22	2.09
Detrital form	10.72	3.46	0.38	3.21	0.98	2.69
Enteromorpha intestinalis						
Fresh	18.65	3.66	0.48	8.49	—	6.02
Fresh plant material						
Lemna (China)	8.76	1.54	0.73	5.94		0.55
Spirodela (China)	5.63	1.62	0.02	2.85	0.35	0.79
Wolffia (China)	3.62	1.04	0.27	1.75		0.56
Myriophyllum (Minnesota)	13.6	2.4	0.2	6.8	1.8	2.5
Potamogeton (Minnesota)	22.7	3.3	0.4	10.5	4.9	3.7
Ceratophyllum (Minnesota)	14.3	2.4	0.3	6.0	2.0	3.2
Animal Products						
Fish, fresh, trash (Malaya)	28.0	14.2	1.5	—	—	10.7
Silkworm pupae, fresh	35.4	19.1	12.8	2.3	—	1.2
Silkworm pupae, dried	90.0	55.9	24.5	6.6	—	1.9
Silkworm pupae, dried and defatted	91.1	75.4	1.8	8.4	—	5.6
Mussels-freshwater	20.40	18.40	0.80			1.20
Small shrimps	82.80	55.45	5.52	4.37	—	17.65
Liver of cattle	25.0	21.2	0.6	—	—	1.0
Gammarus	85.9	24.7	5.0	—	—	34.6
Neomysis	66.7	35.0	7.0	5.2	—	19.0
Aquatic worms	18.9	8.6	4.4	—	—	1.4
Chironomid, fresh	16.1	9.1	13.6	—	—	7.1

ALGAE AS INDIRECT NATURAL FOOD FOR FISHES

Algae present the first link in the food-chain conducting finally to fish production. The relationship between algae and animals of the zooplankton and benthic world has been the object of many studies.

TABLE III   Food Quotients of Some Supplementary Fish Foods
(after Ling, 1966)

Foods of animal origin		
Daphnids	4	–6.4
Mysis	2	–3.9
Gammarus	3.9	–6.6
Prawn and shrimp	4	–6
Chironomids	2.3	–4.4
Silkworm pupae–fresh	3	–5
Silkworm pupae–dried	1.25	–2.1
Freshwater fish	4	–8
Fresh sea fish (trash)	6	–9
Fresh meat	5	–8

A one-hour lecture is not sufficient even for the shortest review of this field. The phenomenon connected with a mass development of algae and especially in conditions which allow the occurrence of phytoplankton may be of great interest for fishery. Such conditions can be met both in freshwaters and in the sea.

Nikolsky (1963) gives the following example of a relationship of this kind. During the rainy season in India, from June to October, enormous masses of water run into the rivers, carrying great quantities of biogenic materials which cause an enormous development of planktonic algae in the sea and in the vicinity of river mouths, e.g., the Ganges. These algae attract crustaceans even from distant places. Following the crustacean accumulation, a fish, the Bombay duck (*Harpodon nehereus*) of the family Scopelidae also arrives. Local fishermen know the time of appearance of this fish, and as soon as the rainy season sets in, they start to prepare their fishing.

In many freshwater lakes the connection between the more plentiful occurrence of phytoplankton and an adequate abundant development of zooplankton or benthic fauna is also generally known. Edmondson (1963) has presented a study of reproductive rates of rotifers and copepods in lakes. These rates are related to the population density of phytoplankton.

In further consequence one can expect the increasing of individual fish growth and total fish production. The food chain, phytoplankton-zooplankton, is generally valid but not simple. For example, some species of zooplanktonic copepods are carnivorous and use no algae as food; other species of copepods use only some species of algae of a certain size in a selective way. In this connection, Freyer (1957) stated that herbivorous cyclopoid copepods select their food differentiating between diatoms and inorganic particles presumably by means of some sensory perceptive powers. Particles of that kind were never found in the gut of these animals. Copepods probably possess gustatory sense organs near the mouth and may perceive tastes and odors emanating from diatoms. These might be connected with the exudations produced by many species of algae. Other algae, such as *Hydrurus foetidus*, emit some odor which might confirm the hypothesis that diatoms also do the same. These odors are perceived by fish (Walker and Hasler, 1949; Hasler 1954).

Freyer also presented (1957a) studies concerning the interesting feeding mechanism of the herbivorous cyclopoid Copepoda.

Brook (1955) stated that the filamentous diatoms *Melosira varians*, *Fragilaria capucina*, *Diatoma vulgare*, and filamentous Chlorophyceae *Spirogyra* and *Zygnema* spp. may disappear from the slow sand filter bed of waterworks because they are intensively eaten by protozoa.

Certain species of protozoa can eat a considerable number of pennate diatoms, e.g., *Oxytricha* sp. feeding on *Nitschia palea* can eat ninety diatoms in twenty-four hours.

In the studies in Scotch lochs under natural conditions (Brook, 1955) the epiphytic flora of macrophytes, e.g., *Myriophyllum spicatum*, *Eleogiton fluitans*, *Potamogeton natans*, and *Litorella uniflora*, has been examined in relation to the feeding of the caddis larvae *Leptocerus aterrimus*. The disappearance of the diatom *Fragilaria capucina* and the filaments of *Bulbochaete* sp. through the feeding of this larvae have been observed.

The removal of the epiflora by certain larvae can be rapid and complete. Brook (1955) found that ten larvae of the mayfly *Leptophlebia vespertina* can remove a dense algae felt, consisting largely of *Achnarithes*, *Cymbella* sp., *Tabellaria flocculosa*, *Gomphonema*, and *Bulbochaete* spp., from a strand of *Myriophyllum spiceatum* one foot in length in four days.

Thus the author means that physical and chemical properties are not alone responsible for the development and maintenance of algal flora. For example, in two adjoining ponds which appear to be nearly identical in the quality of soil and water, marked differences may occur in the composition of their algal flora. It is reasonable to suggest that the algae-eating fauna of such ponds may be an important and responsible factor controlling the occurrence of algae in them.

All studies of this kind show that the algal flora could be utilized indirectly as food for fish, which primarily belong to carnivorous species, in the shortest way by culture of crustacea or insects larvae feeding on algae which are produced also in monoculture as we now do with *Chlorella* or *Scenedesmus*.

This is undoubtedly the future development for creating a basis for a new branch of fish culture in which great quantities of most valuable fish protein could be obtained most quickly and on a relatively small surface area.

In this light, investigation dealing, for instance, with the growth and survival of *Daphnia* in relation to *Chlorella* medium have a special significance (Dollar and Taub, 1962).

Australian attempts to construct an algal mass culture unit for feeding marine invertebrate larvae should also be mentioned. (Wisby and Purday, 1961).

One can easily imagine what an instrument for the fish feeding problem we can possess after the discovery of a method for a mass culture of chironomids based on an algal mass monoculture.

LETHAL EFFECTS OF ALGAL TOXINS IN SOME FISH KILLS

Certain planktonic species of algae abundant in certain conditions in sea and in freshwater are responsible for lethal effects on fish and also on higher vertebrates.

Often the fish kills are the result of secondary circumstances, such as lack of oxygen in the water resulting from bacterial decomposition of a dense bloom, but it is sometimes evident that specific toxins are produced by algae.

In Lewin's book, *The Physiology and Biochemistry of Algae* (1962), in Fogg's chapter on extracellular products, it is shown that it is not always clear whether these toxins are liberated from living cells. In the extensive literature concerning this subject, Ballantine and Abbott (1957) studied the occurrence and physiological effects of toxic marine flagellates on animals. Dinoflagellates of the genera *Gymnodinium* and *Gonyaulax* dominate here. The toxin of *Gymnodinium veneficum*, specifically acting on the nervous system, is water-soluble, ether-insoluble, acid-labile, with a high molecular weight and can kill molluscs and fish, even mammals. *Prymnesium parvum*, a brackish-water chrysophyte, produces a toxin which is extra-cellular, nondialyzable, acid-labile, and thermo-labile, and it sometimes causes a mass-mortality of fish (Shilo, *et al.*, 1953; Shilo and Aschner, 1953; McLaughlin, 1958).

In the book *Algae and Man*, edited by Jackson (1964), we have Gorham's special report about toxic algae. According to this author, in many cases of fish kill, death is caused by anoxia resulting from decomposition of large masses of algae under shallow water conditions. In other cases fish have been killed while there was still an adequate oxygen supply, a fact which implicates poisonous substances.

There are other kinds, besides blue-green algae, that are poisonous. Fish kills are caused by the yellow-brown alga *Prymnesium parvum* (Otterstrom and Steemann-Nielsen, 1939; and Shilo and Aschner, 1953) and by the dinoflagellates *Gymnodinium veneficum* (Abbot and Ballantine, 1957), *Gymnodinium brevis* (Ray and Wilson, 1957), and *Gonyaulax monilata* (Gates and Wilson, 1960).

ALGAE AND FISH DISEASES

According to the classical handbook of fish diseases of Schäperclaus (1954) and the excellent new handbook of Reichenbach-Klinke (1966), the number of fish diseases caused by algae is very low. Also the extent of such a kind of diseases is usually very limited. In some cases it is even difficult to discern whether algae are present as true parasites or as commensals only. This concerns the mass occurrence of, e.g., *Chlorochytrium pisciolens* Link in carp, tench, and young perch, or *Cladophora glomerata* and diatoms, *Navicula* sp., *Gomphonema* sp., *Achnathes*, and *Diatoma*, living on or in the skin and gills of fish.

On the fry of trout, Schäperclaus (1954) observed kills caused by blue-green algae (probably *Oscillatoria bometi*). In other diseases of trout's fry some species of *Euglena* and *Chroococcacea* were stated. A unicellular species of algae, namely *Mycophilus cyprini* Plehn is—like *Ichthyochytrium vulgare* Plehn—living parasitically, mainly in fish gills.

In the sea and also in different species of warm-water reef fishes, especially living in aquaria, a parasitic algae, *Oodinium ocellatum* Brown (*Branchiophilus maris* Schäperclaus) was discovered and made the object of a detailed study. Only in rather rare circumstances may the algae play a role as a noxious factor in fish diseases.

The indirect influence of algae in fish diseases is seen in the fact that the dangerous occurrence of the fungus *Branchiomyces sanquinis*, which is responsible for the fish kills in pond culture, is usually connected with the blooms of blue-green algae. This relationship is not sufficiently examined till now and needs a basic investigation.

ALGAE BLOOMS IN FISH CULTURE

Fish Kills and Their Prevention

One of the best presentations of the influence of algae blooms on fish kills of fish cultured in ponds is given in Swingle's report discussed in the FAO Warm-Water Fish Symposium in 1966. This report was based on the author's experience with Alabama ponds, but it also explains the mechanism of algae blooms in general and under conditions of the more moderate climate of European waters. According to Swingle, a type of phytoplankton becomes dominant and, under certain conditions, rises to the surface as a dense concentration of scum. These algae usually have vacuoles filled with oil or gas which expand in warm water and rise to the surface. *Microcystis* and *Anabaena* pertain to the scum-forming group, the former associated with most of the fish kills. Algae of the *Trachelomonas* and *Gymnodinium* genera are also held responsible.

Algae rising in dense numbers of the surface or near it rapidly absorb heat from the sun and provoke a sharp rise in the temperature of surface water (Beasley, 1963). A stratification is formed, and light winds stirring the hot surface of the water only prevent the distribution of oxygen from the upper to the lower layers. The dense plankton in the upper layers absorbs and reflects the sunlight causing an inadequate penetration of light to depths greater than 0.3–1.2 meters for photosynthesis. Beasley (1963) stated that oxygen was less than 1 ppm at depths where light had declined to 1 per cent of incident radiation.

After several days or weeks of hot sun and light winds, the surface of 0.3 to 1.2 meters of this shallow stratification contained sufficient oxygen for fish. The surface water was sometimes supersaturated with oxygen, while at greater depths there was no oxygen or only an inadequate amount, and therefore the fish moved into upper waters. But when the oxygen-deficient waters upwelled to the surface, fish of all kinds and sizes were trapped and killed. Sometimes no fish were killed but remained in distress at the surface where top and bottom waters mixed and oxygen became insufficient. This upwelling might be caused by a drop in air temperature, when colder surface water descended to the bottom and oxygenless waters from below rose to the surface. It also was often caused by violent winds blowing surface waters to the opposite bank causing the rise of deeper oxygen-deficient waters to the surface on the windward side. Heavy cold rains also forced deeper waters to the surface, and when they fell on the watershed cold stream water flowed along the bottom of the ponds causing an upwelling of oxygen-deficient bottom waters.

The knowledge of events causing fish kills by phytoplankton blooms suggests ways to prevent them. In some cases, killing a part of *Mycrocystis* with copper sulphate (in two applications) may result in light and oxygen penetration into the deeper layer. It is very important to kill only a part of the algae bloom at any one time. When enough copper sulphate was used to kill all of it, rapid decomposition removed the remaining oxygen and caused total fish kill.

Sometimes a small amount (10–20 kg/ha) of super-phosphate scattered over the surface water may stimulate photosynthesis and a release of oxygen. To prevent the fish kill, Swingle (1966) suggested pumping water from, e.g., 50–70 cm depths and throwing it with force at an acute angle against the pond surface.

A current of oxygenated water moved in the direction of the far bank, underwater circulation went back to the pump, and water containing oxygen broke up the stratification bringing oxygen to vast areas. For a 1-hectare pond a pump delivering 19.000 liter per hour was sufficient.

Our own experience based on many years of observation in the Experimental Carp Farm in Zator (part of the Animal Breeding Institute in Poland), undertaken by myself and Mr. Rychlicki, totally confirms the effectiveness of such mechanical intervention by pumping water.

In Poland we have convenient resources for studying the problem of the control of algae blooms having 63,000 hectare carp ponds with a production of 13,200,000 kg of carp per year. These carp ponds are rather shallow, about 50–100 cm for fry, about 80–150 cm for older fry and market fish, and 150–200 cm for wintering fish.

Some Remarks on Fertilization

Phytoplankton production may be affected by limiting factors other than added fertilizing nutrient elements. Hepher (1962) describes a case where light was a limiting factor. Production increased in the upper layers of water with favorable light conditions when fish ponds were fertilized with large amounts of fertilizers but decreased in the lower layers where shading plankton disturbed the penetration of light. A large dose of fertilizer may provoke a lowering of production per unit area.

From the short review presented here, it can be seen how many interesting aspects, both theoretical and practical, in the field of the algae-fish relationship are waiting for further study. Some seem to be especially important at present, and extensive study in the following points should be undertaken as the result of the exchange of opinions during this symposium: (1) the mechanical method of controlling algae blooms in ponds by water pumping is known from practical experience only, and the problem needs a proper scientific elaboration; (2) endeavors for shortening of the food chain (algae–insect larvae–fish) through mass monoculture of selected suitable algal species like *Chlorella, Scenedesmus*, etc., and through mass monoculture of selected species of insects, e.g., Chironomids, forming mass food for carnivorous fishes should be undertaken; and (3) a detailed study of conditions for further introduction of fish feeding on algal phytoplankton, e.g., silver carp, in ponds, should be made.

REFERENCES

Aliev, D. S., 1963. "The state of prospects of pisciculture of phytophagous fishes in central Asia and Khazakstan," *Problemy rybokhoziaistvennogo ispol'zowaniia rastitiel'noiadnykh ryb v vodocmaku SSSR,*" Ashkobad. Akademia Nauk, Turkmen. SSR, pp. 203–209.

Ballantine, D., and Abbot, B. C., 1957. "Toxic Marine flagellates; Their Occurrence and Physiological Effects on Animals," *J. Gen. Microbiol.,* 16, 274–81.

Bakus, G. J., 1964. "The Effects of Fish-Grazing on Invertebrate Evolution in Shallow Tropical Waters," Allan Hancock Fdtn. Pub., No. 27, Univ. S. Calif. Press, Los Angeles, Calif.

Brook, A. J., 1955. "The aquatic fauna as an ecological factor in studies on the occurrence of freshwater algae," *Revue Algologique,* No. 3.

Dawson, E. Y., Aleem, A. A., and Halstead, B. W., 1955. "Marine Algae from Palmyra Island with Special Reference to the Feeding Habits and Toxicology of Reef Fishes," Allan Hancock Fdtn. Pub., No. 17, Univ. of S. Calif. Press, Los Angeles, Calif.

Dollar, A. M., and Taub, F. B., 1963. "Growth and survival of *Daphnia* in Relation to *Chlorella* medium," Research in Fisheries 1962. Contribution No. 147, March.

Fott, B., 1959. *Algekunde,* Jena.

Freyer, G., 1957a. "The feeding mechanism of some freshwater cyclopoid copepods," *Proc. Zool. Soc. Lond.* Vol. 129, part 1, 1–25.

Hepher, B., 1962. "Primary production in fishponds and its application to fertilization experiments," *Limnol. Oceanogr. 7, 2,* 131–36.

————, 1966. "Some limiting factors affecting the dose of fertilizers added to fish ponds with special reference to the Near East," FAO World Symposium on Warm-Water Pond Fish Culture, Rome 1966.

Jackson, D. F., 1964. *Algae and Man,* New York, Plenum Press.

Kalleberg, H., 1958. "Observations in a Stream Tank of Territoriality and Competition in Juvenile Salmon and Trout (*Salmo salar* L. and *Salmo trutta* L.)," Institute of Freshwater Research, Drottningholm, Report No. 39 Lund.

Konradt, A. G., 1966. "Methods of breeding the grass carp *Ctenopharyngodon idella* (Val.) and the silver carp *Hypophthalmichthys molitrix* (Val.)," FAO World Symposium on Warm-Water Pond Fish Culture, Rome.

Lewin, R. A., 1962. *Physiology and Biochemistry of Algae,* New York: Academic Press.

Ling, S. W., 1966. "Feeds and feeding of warm-water fishes in ponds in Asia and the Far East," FAO World Symposium on Warm-Water Pond Fish Culture, Rome.

Mann, H., 1966 "The profitable use of food and its utilization through *Tilpa melanopleura,*" *ibid.*

Nikolsky, G. W., 1963. *The Ecology of fishes,* New York, Academic Press.

Prawocheński, R., 1964. *Świnka-* "*Chondrostoma nasus L.*" *dorzecza Wisły,* Lublin.

Reichenbach-Klinke, H. H., 1966. *Krankheiten und Schädigungen der Fische.* Stuttgart.

Rychlicki, Z., 1933. "*Świnka-Chondrostoma nasus* L," *Przegl. Ryb. No.* 10.

Schäperclaus, W., 1954. *Fischkrankheiten,* Berlin.

Swingle, H. S., 1966. "Fish kills caused by phytoplankton blooms and their prevention," FAO World Symposium on Warm-Water Pond Fish Culture, Rome.

Thompson, J. M., 1959. "The food of Western Australian estuarine fish," Fisheries Bull. No. 7, pub. by Superintendent of Fisheries, Perth.

Verigin, B. V., 1963. "Modern state and future perspectives of utilization of the silver carp and the grass carp for fisheries in the water bodies of USSR," *Problemy rybokhoziaistven-*

nogo ispol'zovaniia rastitiel'noiadnykh ryb v vodocmakh SSSR, Ashkabad, Akad. Nauk. Turkmen. SSR, 20–39.

Vinogradov, V. K., 1966. "Techniques of rearing phytophagous fishes," FAO World Symposium on Warm-Water Pond Fish Culture, Rome.

Wibely, B., and Purday, C., 1961. "An algal mass culture unit for feeding marine invertebrate larvae," Div. of Fisheries and Oceanogr. Tech. Paper No. 12, Commonwealth Scientific and Indust. Res. Org., Melbourne.

Yun-An Tang, and Ting-Lang Hwang, 1966. "Evaluation of the relative suitability of various groups of algae as food of milkfish in brackish-water ponds," FAO World Symposium on Warm-Water Pond Fish Culture, Rome.

Zarnecki, S., and Miś, J. "*Chondrostoma nasus*, algae consumer in temperate zone," in press.

XXIV

Stream Assimilation Studies in New York State

DONALD R. WASHINGTON

Department of Environmental Engineering
Rensselaer Polytechnic Institute
Troy, New York

With the inception of water-carried waste collection, man has been faced with the problem associated with sewage discharge into receiving streams. The task of evaluating the effects of such discharges has, in modern times, fallen to environmental engineers and, to a lesser extent, aquatic biologists. It has been the environmental engineer's task to reduce the multifactor response of the stream to a limited number of measurable parameters which give a quantitative value of the expected degree of pollution. Starting with rather crude parameters, environmental engineers have taken periodic steps to improve the dependability of their evaluation of stream response to sewage. Streeter and Phelps (1925) published a deterministic equation which related the oxygen balance to the organic load in the stream. This equation has proved most popular with consulting engineers because it enables them to determine the allowable loading which may be imposed on a stream for any desired residual oxygen level with a minimum of field measurements. The allowable load thus determined has been used as a primary consideration in determining the degree of waste treatment for proposed facilities. This approach has been so widely accepted that many consulting engineers use it as the sole appraisal of the stream response to the exclusion of ecological factors not directly affected by the oxygen balance.

A number of scientists and engineers have attempted to show the fallacy in this approach (Hynes, 1960; Patrick, 1950; Dobbins, 1964). The original equation by Streeter and Phelps was itself an oversimplification of the oxygen balance in the stream. A number of environmental engineers have modified the basic equation in order to improve its accuracy or ease of application (Ingram and Bartsch, 1960; Camp *et al.*, 1940; Li, 1962; O'Connor and Dobbins, 1956). Recently, Thomann (1963) has presented a systems approach to prediction of stream response. In his approach, which he used on the Delaware River Basin, essentially the same parameters are considered but as sources and sinks of oxygen for each given reach of stream. This approach gives versatility to the use of the oxygen balance if a large amount of data is available. Using this systems approach, the specific phenomena do not necessarily have to be explicitly defined to determine their effect on the stream.

The engineer's preoccupation with the stream oxygen balance is based upon a desire to prevent odors and to preserve a suitable supply of oxygen to maintain a given fish population. Unfortunately, this procedure gave little consideration to the ecology of the stream environment.

The engineer's analysis of a stream frequently failed to consider the important oxygen sink and/or source created by massive algal growths. In recent years, environmental engineers have attempted to include this factor in their system analysis, but these attempts have met with limited success. This failure stems from the engineer's unwillingness to include in his otherwise straightforward analysis the numerous variables which ecologists insist affect the algal growth. What is needed is a workable compromise between engineers and ecologists which will yield a meaningful expression for algal effects in the engineer's deterministic equations.

The basic question has been and still is: How can one predict the future capacity of a stream to assimilate wastewater discharge? The optimum compromise must be made which will reduce the multivariable stochastic relationship that really exists to a deterministic model which can be used by the practicing engineer to solve the existing problems.

The purpose of this essay is to describe the approach which engineers in New York State have taken and are taking to evaluate the waste assimilation capacity of our streams. The major disadvantages of those approaches will be discussed, and possible future approaches will be presented.

The waste assimilation capacity of a stream is related to the maximum or minimum desirable levels of various physical or chemical characteristics of the stream water which may affect its most beneficial use. In New York State all the streams have been classified as to their most beneficial use. The classifications have resulted from stream surveys followed by public hearings conducted by the New York State Department of Health. The oxygen level in the stream is used almost exclusively as the water characteristic to be optimized. However, with the increase in awareness of the effect of nutrients on algal blooms, some engineers have seen the value of a nitrogen or phosphorus balance in a stream. It may well be that in the future, stream balances will have to be completed on a number of variables in order to predict the future quality of streams and its effect on the ecosystem.

The use of mathematical models is just a means to quantify the systems so that comparisons and extrapolations may be made. A model allows the engineer to quantitatively compare various conditions in a given stream. The currently available models for stream analysis, as will be shown, are not complete deterministic equations describing the phenomena. Much improvement is needed. Scientists may eventually give detailed description to the phenomena taking place in a stream ecosystem. Until such time, however, it is important that engineers be equipped with better tools to solve current problems. It is to these ends that phycologists and engineers should work together.

BIOLOGIST'S APPROACH

Many aquatic biologists have criticized engineers for limiting their stream surveys to physical and chemical characteristics of the liquid wastes and the receiving streams (Edwards and Owens, 1965; Hynes, 1960; Patrick, 1950; Bartsch, 1948; Burlington, 1962; Ingram et al., 1966). Generally speaking, biologists contend that physical and chemical characteristics of the waters or the sediments are not adequate to describe the various effects of pollutants on a stream. They do not show the toxic effect of a given effluent. These tests give general stream characteristics but do not indicate whether or not the plant and animal life is balanced. This is because first, the chemical analysis shows only the conditions at the time of sampling, and second, the tolerance limits of most organisms are not known. For instance, in a study conducted by Patrick (1950), twenty-three stations were found from the biological analyses to be more or less polluted. However, six of these stations showed no signs of pollution from the chemical analyses except that the CO_2 content was high. Similar poor correlation was found between the biological analyses and the BOD determinations.

Biological surveys will become increasingly important in cases of pollution where either adverse effects are not immediately apparent from oxygen balance analyses or in controlling the toxic effects of various effluents on the over-all stream environment (Gaufin and Tarzwell, 1952). Pollution surveys frequently cannot be made during the period of critical conditions, and unfortunately, chemical studies give information on the physical-chemical conditions only at the time of sampling. At this point, the biological survey is superior in that the qualitative and quantitative composition of an aquatic population is determined by recurring critical conditions, even though of short duration, as well as the more stable of long-time environmental factors. The complex of organisms which develops in a given area is in turn indicative of environmental conditions which have occurred during its development. Organisms having life histories of a year or more will thus serve to indicate unfavorable or limiting conditions that occurred several months previously. Thus, the use of biological surveys allow pollution-control agencies to spread their sampling activities over the whole year. Normally, sampling is conducted in the low-flow summer months or otherwise restricted because of other critical conditions, such as the seasonal operation of canneries. Flow may be large, dilution at a maximum, dissolved oxygen near saturation, and visual evidence of pollution at a minimum, but biological studies could delineate former septic areas or indicate previous critical conditions of short duration.

The biologist's approach to stream pollution control is to use the flora and fauna as indicators of pollution. Unfortunately, such an approach is not predictive, i.e., one cannot yet predict what will happen to the stream biology if future changes were to occur in the ecosystem. Nor will their method predict the proper allocation of the stream assimilation capacity.

ENGINEER'S APPROACH

Various researchers have considered the problem of developing a deterministic model which would quantitize the profile of dissolved oxygen along a river reach. These attempts have included various of the factors affecting the oxygen balance in the stream (see Table I). The work

TABLE I   Factors Affecting O_2 Balance

Surface Aeration
Longitudinal Dispersion
Biochemical Oxidation
Waste Assimilation
Benthic Demand
Planktonic Demand
Microbial Respiration
Photosynthesis

of Streeter and Phelps (1925) on the Ohio River marked the beginning of the classical theory. According to this theory, the dissolved oxygen profile along a river reach is given by Equation 1.

$$\frac{dD}{dt} = K_1 L - K_2 D \qquad (1)$$

integration yields

$$D = \frac{K_1 L_A}{K_2 - K_1} (e^{-K_1 t} - e^{-K_2 t}) + D_o e^{-K_2 t}. \qquad (2)$$

In these equations,

L = the first stage BOD at the downstream end of the reach (mg/1)
L_A = the first stage BOD at the upstream end of the reach (mg/1)

D = the dissolved O_2 deficit at the downstream end of the reach (mg/l)

D_o = the dissolved O_2 deficit at the upstream end of the reach (mg/l)

K_1 = the BOD reaction rate coefficient

K_2 = the reaeration rate coefficient

t = the time of flow in the reach (days)

The Streeter-Phelps Equations are based on the assumption that there are only two major processes taking place within an element of a stream; i.e., BOD and oxygen are being removed along the reach by the bacterial oxidation of the organic matter, and oxygen is being replaced by reaeration at the surface. This situation is illustrated for an element of a stream in Figure 1A which shows the input and output from adjacent elements in addition to surface reaeration and waste assimilation. The transfer rates under consideration in this case are as follows:

$$C_1 A_1 = \frac{dx}{dt} = \text{rate of addition of oxygen by the flow into face 1}$$

$$\left(C_1 + \frac{dc}{dx} dx\right) A_2 \frac{dx}{dt} = \text{rate of removal of oxygen by the flow through face 2}$$

$$K_2 (C_s - C) dv = \text{rate of aeration through the water surface}$$

$$K_1 L_t \, dv = \text{rate of waste assimilation in the element.}$$

Equation 2 is usually used to follow the progress of an element of water downstream from a waste discharge, i.e., slug flow. In the case of multi-discharges, Equation 2 is made operative over the reach between the discharges.

In addition to the above factor, some or all of the following processes may be taking place in any given river reach:

1. the removal of BOD by sedimentation or adsorption;
2. the addition of BOD along the reach by the scour of bottom deposits or by the diffusion of partly decomposed organic products from the benthal layer into the water above;
3. the addition of BOD along the reach by the local runoff;
4. the removal of oxygen from the water by diffusion into the benthal layer to satisfy the oxygen demand in the aerobic zone of this layer;
5. the removal of oxygen from the water by purging action of gases rising from the benthal layer;
6. the addition of oxygen by the photosynthetic action of plankton and fixed plants;

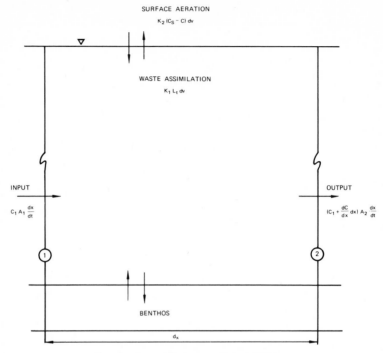

SURFACE AERATION

$K_2 (C_S - C) dv$

WASTE ASSIMILATION

$K_1 L_t dv$

INPUT

$C_1 A_1 \frac{dx}{dt}$

OUTPUT

$(C_1 + \frac{dC}{dx} dx) A_2 \frac{dx}{dt}$

①   ②

BENTHOS

d_x

FIG. 1a Stream Segment—Oxygen Balance

7. the removal of oxygen by the respiration of plankton and fixed plants;
8. the continuous redistribution of both the BOD and oxygen by the effect of longitudinal dispersion.

The classical form of the Streeter-Phelps Equation was used for over two decades without modification in spite of the failure of the formulation to consider the processes listed above. Those factors associated directly with the BOD relationship (Equation 3) could be determined independently of the Streeter-Phelps Equation.

$$L = L_A e^{-K_1 t} \tag{3}$$

Unfortunately, the reaeration rate coefficient (K_2) had to be calculated by substitution of known data into the Streeter-Phelps Equation. In effect, all the errors associated with the omission of the above-listed processes were lumped into the K_2 form. Needless to say, Equation 2 did not necessarily represent the dissolved oxygen profile in a given stream.

The approach to be used in the evaluation of a stream's assimilation capacity is a function of the type of waste to be discharged, the magnitude of the waste discharge to stream discharge, and the availability of funds. In

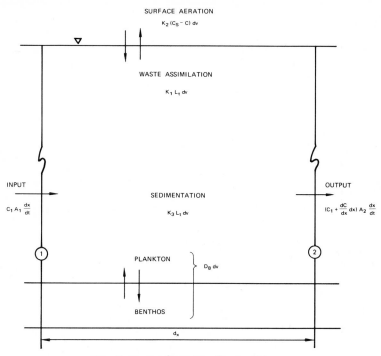

SURFACE AERATION

$K_2 (C_S - C) dv$

WASTE ASSIMILATION

$K_1 L_t dv$

SEDIMENTATION

$K_3 L_t dv$

INPUT

$C_1 A_1 \frac{dx}{dt}$

OUTPUT

$(C_1 + \frac{dC}{dx} dx) A_2 \frac{dx}{dt}$

PLANKTON

$D_8 dv$

BENTHOS

d_x

FIG. 1b Stream Segment—Oxygen Balance

New York State, perhaps most frequently, the proper design of the water pollution control facility does not warrant more than a cursory evaluation of the assimilation capacity of the receiving stream. In the majority of cases where a stream survey is justified, the Streeter-Phelps Model is used without modification. The Streeter-Phelps Model is so widely used that engineers at times seem to have forgotten the circumstances of its applicability. When this approach is taken, gross inconsistencies may develop. An example of a case where such a narrow approach would have proven fallacious was during a stream survey of the Tioughnioga River in New York. The study was conducted by the author for Stearns and Wheler, Sanitary Engineers, Cazenovia, New York, as part of the comprehensive sewerage study for Cortland, New York. The main stream of the Tioughnioga River begins at the northeast portion of the city of Cortland with the confluence of its east and west branches. It flows generally southward for thirty miles to join the Chenango River. A stream survey was conducted on the upper ten miles of the Tioughnioga River in order to gain an estimate of the allowable organic discharge from the Cortland Water Pollution Control Plant. The average flow in the river at the point of municipal dis-

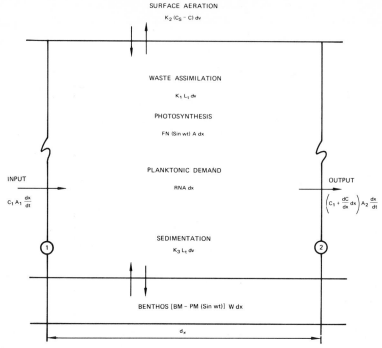

FIG. 1c Stream Segment—Oxygen Balance

charge is 493 cfs (14 cms). However, of more importance to this study is the minimum flow, defined as the average of the minimum seven consecutive days likely to occur once in ten years, of 24 cfs (0.68 cms). In performing a stream survey an effort is usually made to obtain information on the stream during discharges approaching minimum flow as far as time and economic limitations will allow. During this study, two traverses of the reach of the river were made under nocturnal conditions when the average discharge rate was 126 cfs (3.6 cms). Figure 2A shows the dissolved oxygen profiles obtained for the Tioughnioga River. Curve A is plotted from data obtained during the night and early morning while the oxygen demand of the photosynthetic organisms exceeded their oxygen production. Curve B is plotted from data obtained later in the morning with the first three stations reflecting nocturnal conditions and the last station representing intense light conditions. Since the intent of the stream survey was to estimate the stream conditions under the most unfavorable circumstances, Curve B was used in the model analyses from the point of discharge of Hoxie Gorge and Curve A from Hoxie Gorge to Messengerville Bridge.

The river channel was 50 to 70 feet (15.2 to 21.3 m) wide in the reach under study. It had a center depth of from 2.0 feet to 6.0 feet (0.6 m to 1.8 m), with an average depth of 3.0 feet (0.9 m). The river bottom had a moderate cover of aquatic plants which were most numerous near the discharge and diminished with distance downstream from the Cortland Water Pollution Control Plant. Because of this condition, the use of Equation 2 would yield negative values of the reaeration rate coefficient (K_2). Other than being the mathematical consequence of improper assumption, the negative K_2 has little meaning. It is obvious that in this particular case a more sophisticated model is required.

Various modifications of the equations have been proposed in order to take into account some of the processes listed above. Thomas (1948) proposed the introduction of a rate constant, K_3, as a means of accounting for the removal or addition of BOD by deposition of resuspension. The net rate of deposition was assumed to be proportional to $K_3 L$, a positive value of K_3 indicating deposition and a negative value indicating resuspension. O'Connor (1960) introduced the effect of longitudinal dispersion and demonstrated its importance in slow-moving, highly mixed streams, such as estuaries. Since the streams under consideration here are rapidly moving, the effect of mixing will be neglected.

A number of formulae have been presented for the independent calculation of K_2 (O'Connor and Dobbins, 1965; Krenkel, 1962; Churchill, Elmore, and Buckingham, 1962; Dobbins, 1964; Edwards and Owens, 1965). These formulae predict the reaeration coefficient based upon hydraulic and water quality parameters. Most of these equations take the form of

$$K_2 = \frac{CV^n}{H^m} \tag{4}$$

where

C, n, and m are coefficients
V = average stream velocity (ft./sec.) (m/sec.)
H = mean stream depth (ft.) (m)

The effects of algae on the oxygen balance in streams was essentially ignored in stream surveys until recently. Dobbins (1964) presented an oxygen balance equation derived from a consideration of the Streeter-Phelps model and including the other advances mentioned above. In addition, he included a term D_B which he defined as the removal coefficient of oxygen by the benthal demand and the effects of plants. Figure 1 B shows the factors considered for a rapidly moving stream receiving one source of discharge. The additional factors considered in this case are shown as:

$K_3 L_t dv$ = rate of removal by oxygen by
sedimentation and/or adsorption.

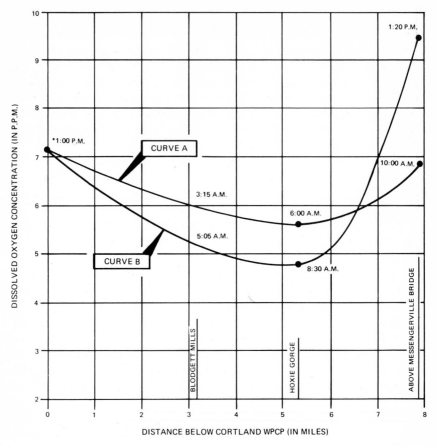

*DENOTES TIME OF SAMPLING

FIG. 2a Observed Dissolved Oxygen Profile of Tioughnioga River, July 10–11, 1963.

$D_B \, dv$ = rate of removal of oxygen by benthal and algal organisms.

The oxygen deficit at any time is given by Equation 5.

$$D = \frac{K_1 L_A}{K_2 - (K_1 + K_3)} \left(e^{-(K_1 + K_3)t} - e^{-K_2 t} \right)$$

$$+ D_o e^{-K_2 t} + \frac{D_B}{K_2} \left(1 - e^{-K_2 t} \right) \tag{5}$$

When K_3 and D_B are set equal to zero, Equation 5 reverts to the familiar Streeter-Phelps Equation.

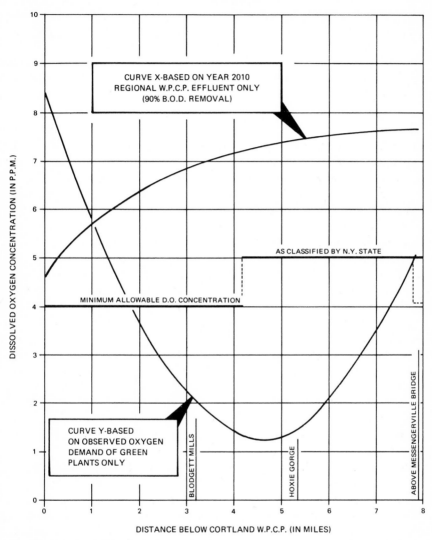

FIG. 2b Calculated Dissolved Oxygen Profile of Tioughnioga River Under Critical Flow Conditions

Assuming the existence of adequate formulae for the determination of the reaeration rate coefficient (K_2), it was possible for Dobbins to incorporate a new term D_B into the deterministic equation. This term could not be determined independently but rather as catch-all for the inadequacies of his modification of the oxygen balance equation.

The shortcomings of this approach are reminiscent of the use of the classical Streeter-Phelps Equation for the calculation of the reaeration rate coefficient. There, too, the gross error of the model was reflected in the calculated coefficient.

Using Equation 5 with the data obtained from the Tioughnioga River Survey, it was possible to determine the quantity of oxygen used by the bottom plants. In this case, field observations had indicated a negligible quantity of benthos in the river channel which made it possible to ignore that aspect of the factor of D_B . Following the above procedure, the portion of the oxygen demand which would be contributed to the discharge of organic matter in the effluent from the water pollution control plant was separated from the effects of the algae and green plants. Figure 2B shows the calculated DO profile of the Tioughnioga River under critical flow conditions as it would result from both these sources separately. It can easily be seen from this improved analysis (Dobbins' Model) that the river could adequately handle the treated municipal waste were it not for the algae and green plants. Further, the river conditions would become critical due to the algae and plants alone during minimum flow conditions. This statement should not be construed that the effluent has minor effect on the stream. On the contrary, although this was not substantiated by the study, the algae and plant growth in the river may have been supported to a great extent by the nutrients carried in the effluent.

Dobbins' Model (Equation 5), although representing a great improvement over previous models, reveals a lack in that it is conceptually too simple with respect to factors affecting metabolic processes.

Other approaches have been used by engineers studying New York State streams. Mr. Mt. Pleasant and his staff, of the Water Pollution Control Section of the New York State Department of Health, have devised a graphical method for eliminating the effects of algae on the stream. In their method, one first determines the times of the day at which the maximum and minimum DO occur at the point of waste discharge. Typical values would be 3:00 P.M. and 5:00 P.M., respectively. Then, preferably during low-flow conditions, samples are collected and analyzed for a "slug" of river water which passed the discharge point at each of the predetermined times. If the time of travel over the reach of stream under study exceeds one day, sinusoidal-type curves will occur on the DO profiles. The assumption is made that the algae affect an equal fluctuation of DO concentration on either side of the mean value occurring at a given station due to their maximum respiration and photosynthesis. Thus, using points where the curves intersect and midpoints between intersections, a curve of the expected DO sag in the absence of algae is obtained. A typical graph is shown in Figure 3 for an analysis of Elliot Creek at Amherst, New York, taken on October 6, 1964.

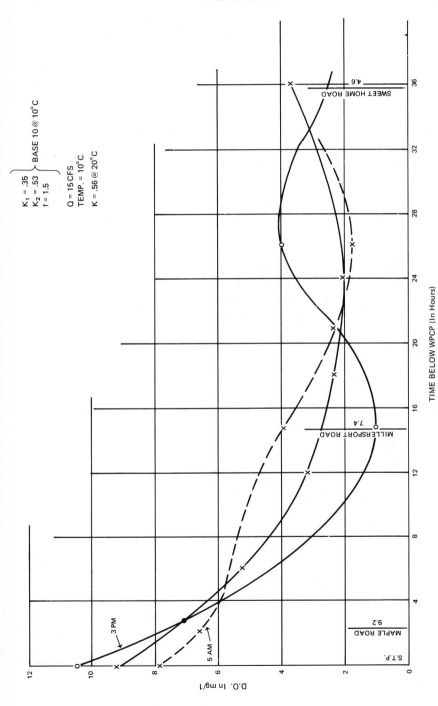

K₁ = .35
K₂ = .53 } BASE 10 @10°C
f = 1.5

Q = 15 CFS
TEMP. = 10°C
K = .56 @ 20°C

FIG. 3 Ellicott Creek Dissolved Oxygen Profiles, October 6, 1964

There is great doubt about the validity of the assumption made by these engineers. Further, it is not realistic to ignore the effects of algae as this procedure does. It is hoped, however, that their continued thinking on this problem will produce an improved analytical procedure for estimating the future conditions of streams.

Two major stream studies are presently under way in the state under contract with the New York State Department of Health. Hydroscience, Incorporated, is analyzing the response of the Mohawk River to existing sources of pollution under various environmental circumstances. In this study, the engineers are using a modification of Dobbins' Model which includes sinusoidal variations in the oxygen requirements of algae. The Mohawk River is a major navigational stream in New York State. As such, it is receiving considerable attention, including continuous monitoring of a number of chemical and biochemical characteristics. The large amount of data being collected on this river should yield a good test of the Dobbins' Model. The study may produce an improved approach to stream analyses.

The second major study currently under way is on the Hudson River. It is being conducted by the firm of Quirk, Lawler and Matusky. These engineers are collecting data which will be used in a system analysis of the capacity of the river. This approach is quite similar to that used by Thomann (1963) on the Delaware River. It is too early to determine whether any sink for algae will be significant in this analysis. The systems approach has considerable merit, however, the concepts involved are beyond the special limitations of this paper. The reader is referred to other writers (Dorrestein, 1959; Thomann,1963; Leeds and Bybee, 1967).

It is doubtful that any of these approaches will be a panacea to the estimation of assimilation capacities. The approach to be used will continue to be a function of the circumstances of the particular discharge and receiving stream. However, these efforts hopefully will lead to better approaches. Rational expressions for the various sources and sinks of oxygen resulting from the planktonic and benthal organisms are needed, as well as expressions for benthal oxygen demand, and the production and/or demand of oxygen from both attached plants and phytoplankton. The factors which affect these sources and sinks of oxygen are indeed numerous. Some of these are included in Table II.

The importance of many of these factors and the need for considering them in evaulating the oxygen balance in a stream has been mentioned by critics of the current engineering approach to stream assimilation studies. However, the conclusion invariably reached by critics is that in streams where benthic respiration and photosynthesis of plants are important, *it is*

TABLE II   Factors Affecting the Oxygen Balance in Streams

Incident Light	Concentration
Cloud Cover	Algae
Turbidity	Rooted Plants
Size Distribution	Larvae
Water Depth	Bacteria
Water Salinity	Specific Respiration Rate
Stream Discharge	Specific Surface
ORP	Photosynthesis Rate
Deposit Density	Genera, Species
Areal Density	

not yet possible to calculate changes in the oxygen concentration of a river from measurements of environmental parameters (Edwards and Owens, 1965).

Impossible is an incorrect word as applied to evaluation or prediction of the stream assimilation capacity. Practicing environmental engineers have for years been faced with making such evaluations. The task must be done today; therefore, these engineers are in no position to wait for others to develop tomorrow's improved formula. They must and do make do with the tools, or models, that are currently available.

It should fall to a team of phycologists and engineers to cooperate in development of improved models using rational expressions which are a workable compromise of significant factors that can be reasonably used within our economic structure to better predict stream assimilation capacity. A number of models have been proposed which incorporate one or more of the biological relationships associated with benthos and/or photosynthesis (Edmondsen, 1956; Ryther, 1956; Talling, 1957; Vollenweider, 1965; Westlake, 1966). Westlake (1966) developed a graphical approach to the quantitative study of the photosynthesis by higher plants in streams. His approach considered a good number of those factors affecting the stream. Unfortunately, the approach was not directly applicable as part of an extended deterministic model. Also, the procedure may well be too cumbersome to be within the budget of the practicing engineer except in special cases.

As a result of teaching and consulting activities, members of the Environmental Engineering staff at Rensselaer Polytechnic Institute developed an interest in the oxygen sources and sinks associated with attached and planktonic photosynthetic plants. In line with their belief that the models must be kept as simple as possible while remaining within the realm of scientific truth, they proposed that the following rate terms be incorporated (integrated) into the classical Streeter-Phelps type expression.

SINKS: Oxygen Demands

Attached Plants

$$\frac{\delta D}{\delta t} = B\,M\,W\,dx$$

Phytoplankton

$$\frac{\delta D}{\delta t} = R\,N\,A\,dx.$$

SOURCES: Oxygen Production

Attached Plants

$$\frac{\delta D}{\delta t} = -P\,M\,(\text{Sin }\omega t)\;W\,dx$$

Phytoplankton

$$\frac{\delta D}{\delta t} = -F\,N\,(\text{Sin }\omega t)\;A\,dx$$

where

$A\,dx$ = volume of element $(\text{ft}^3)(\text{m}^3)$.

B = Respiration rate of the specific attached algae and/or plant culture (Lb. O_2/(Lb. algae-day))(gm/(gm-day)).

F = Maximum photosynthesis rate of phytoplankton (Lb. O_2/(Lb. algae-day)) (gm/(gm-day))

M = Average areal density of bottom algae (Lb. algae/ft^2)(gm/m^2)

N = Concentration of phytoplankton (Lb. algae/ft^3)(gm/m^3)

P = Maximum photosynthesis rate of attached plants (Lb. O_2/(Lb. algae-day))(gm/(gm-day))

R = Respiration rate of phytoplankton (Lb. O_2/(Lb. algae-day))(gm/(gm-day))

t = Time which must be related to a specific daily occurrence, such as noon (days).

$W\,dx$ = Area element with attached plant growth $(\text{ft}^2)(\text{m}^2)$

These expressions consider all the important processes taking place in the stream segment as shown in Figure 1c.

Substitution of these expressions into Dobbins' rate equations for D_B and integrating

$$D = D_0 e^{-K_2 t} + \frac{K_1 L_A}{K_2 - K_r} (e^{-K_1 t} - e^{-K_2 t}) +$$

$$\frac{RNQt}{K_2} + \frac{BMA}{K_2} \quad 1 - e^{-K_2 t} - \frac{PMA + FNQt}{K_2^2 - \omega^2} \tag{6}$$

$$- \frac{PMA + FNQT}{(K_2^2 - \omega^2} (K_2 \sin \omega t - \omega \cos \omega t + \omega e^{-K_2 +})$$

where

K_r = Field measurement of BOD rate coefficient
Q = Rate of stream discharge (ft^3/day)
A_s = Stream bottom area (ft^2)

It is proposed that this model may be sufficiently accurate for engineering evaluation of stream assimilation capacity if one uses the average respiration and photosynthesis rates of the predominant species of both the attached and planktonic algae and/or plants. The assumption was also made that the rate of photosynthesis can be described by a sinusiodal relationship. These R.P.I. engineers ask the phycologists their opinion on the reasonableness of assumptions used in deriving Equation 6. Considering this question, it should be kept in mind that the desire for improvement over the existing models is tempered by the practical necessity for economy. Perhaps a more important question to these engineers is whether the factor included in Equation 6 can be predicted for future critical flow conditions. It is their hope that comments from phycologists will be forthcoming prior to the initiation of field studies designed to determine the validity of this model.

REFERENCES

Bartsch, A. F., 1948. "Biological Aspects of Stream Pollution," *Sewage Works J.*, *20*, 292–302.

Burlington, R. F., 1962. "Quantitative Biological Assessment of Pollution," *J.W.P.C.F.*, *34*, 179–83.

Camp, Dresser, and McKee, 1949. "Clarion River Pollution Abatement," Pa. Dept. Health, Harrisburg, Pa.

Churchill, M. A., Elmore, H. L., and Buckingham, R. A., 1962. "The Prediction of Stream Reaeration Rates,"*Int. Jr. Air and Water Poll.*, *6*, 467–504.

Dobbins, W. E., 1964. "BOD and Oxygen Relationships in Streams," *San. Eng. Div. J.*, ASCE,SA3, *90*, 53–78.

Dorrestein, R., 1959. "The Use of a Matrix-Function for Describing the Longitudinal Transfer of Matter in a Steady-State Estuary," *Internat. Oceanog. Cong. Reprint,* ed. by Sears, AAAS, 585–687.

Edwards, R. W., and Owens, M., 1965. "The Oxygen Balance of Streams," *Ecology and the Indust. Soc.,* 149–72.

Gaufin, A. R., and Tarzwell, C.. M., 1952. "Aquatic Invertebrates as Indications of Stream Pollution," *Pub. Health Rep., 67,* 57–64.

Hynes, H.B.N., 1960. *The Biology of Polluted Waters.* Liverpool: Liverpool Univ. Press.

Ingram, W. M., and Bartsch, A. F., 1960. "Graphic Expressions of Biological Data in Water Pollution Reports," *J. W.P.C.F., 32,* 297–310.

Ingram, W. M., Mackenthun, K. M., and Bartsch, A. F., 1966. *Biological Field Investigative Data for Water Pollution Surveys,* U.S. Dept. of Int., FWPCA.

Krenkel, P. A., and Orlob, G. T., 1962. "Turbulent Diffusion and the Reaeration Coefficient," *San. Eng. Div. J.,* ASCE, SA2, *88,* 53.

Leeds, J. V., and Bybee, H. H., 1967. "Solution of Estuary Problems and Network Programs," *ibid.,* SA3, *93,* 29–36.

Li, W. H., 1962. "Unsteady Dissolved Oxygen Sag in a Stream," *ibid., 88,75.*

O'Connor, D. J., 1960. "Oxygen Balance of an Estuary," *ibid., 86,* 35–55.

O'Connor, D. J., and Dobbins, W. E., 1956. "The Mechanism of Reaeration in Natural Streams," *ibid.,* SA6, Paper 1115.

Patrick, R., 1950. "Biological Measures of Stream Conditions," *Sew. and Indust. Wastes, 22,* 926–38.

Ryther, J. H., 1956. "Photosynthesis in the Ocean as a Function of Light Intensity," *Limnol. Oceanogr., 1,* 61–70.

Streeter, H. W., and Phelps, E. B., 1925. "A Study of the Pollution and Natural Purification of the Ohio River," *Pub. Health Bull. 146.*

Talling, J. F., 1957. "The Phytoplankton Population as a Compound Photosynthetic System," *New Phytol. 56,* 133–149.

Thoeman, R. V., 1963. "Mathematical Model for Dissolved Oxygen," *San. Eng. Div. Jr., ASCE, 89,* SA5, 1–32.

Thomas, H. A., Jr., 1948. "Pollution Load Capacity of Streams," *Water and Sew. Works, 95.*

Vollenweider, R. A., 1965. "Calculation Models of Photosynthesis-depth Curves and Some Implications Regarding Day Rate Estimates in Primary Production Measurements," *Memorie Inst. ital Idrobiol., 18,* 425–57.

Westlake, D. F., 1966. "A Model for Quantitative Studies of Photosynthesis by Higher Plants in Streams," *Air and Water Poll., 10,* 883–96.

XXV

Organic Production in Moriches Bay, New York

JOHN P. BARLOW

and MADELYN A. STAFFORD

Division of Biological Sciences

Cornell University

Ithaca, New York

The lagoons that border the south shore of New York's Long Island are singularly suited for the growth of plankton algae. They are shallow enough to be well illuminated, and they are abundantly supplied with nutrients. The physical conditions are therefore similar to those that produce the spring phytoplankton blooms. The immense populations that have been discribed by Ryther, *et al.* (1958), Lorenzen (1963), Lackey (1964), and Barlow, *et al.* (1963) give testimony for the unique fitness for phytoplankton of this environment.*

Even this environment will not, of course, allow the phytoplankton to increase indefinitely, but what ultimately limits their growth is not immediately evident. Since the physical and chemical features are so favorable, one is lead to look for biological limiting factors. In many aquatic environments herbivore grazing seems to act as the principal biological control. Here, however, it appears that during the summer period of maximum abundance planktonic grazers are so scarce that it is difficult to believe that they could be effective in limiting the growth of the phytoplankton. Other biological controls may exist in the physiological responses of the growing algal populations. In previous studies (Barlow, *et al.,* 1963) it has been shown that there are large variations in the photosynthetic rates of these populations. It was suggested then that these may have been the result of nutrient limitation, and Williams and Murdoch (1966) have since suggested that they may have instead been the result of temperature differences. It is now evident that neither explanation is wholly correct. What is more important is that these variations appear to be related to the size and state of growth of the populations.

---

* Studies now under way (summer, 1968) indicate that there has been a great reduction in algal populations in Moriches Bay and its tributaries since 1967. Size and species composition of existing populations have not been determined exactly, nor have probable causes of changes been determined.

The purpose of the present essay is to describe these variations in photo-synthetic activity in more detail, and to consider their relation to the growth and limitation of the population. It is based on studies in the Mo-riches Bay area made in 1965 and 1966 which were supported by grants from the Federal Water Pollution Control Administration. We also wish to acknowledge the assistance of several students, including William R. Schaffner, Richard S. Laub, Randolph L. Ferguson, and Bruce E. Frey, who have assisted both in the field and laboratory, and the able technical assistance of Mrs. Patricia J. Barton and Mrs. Susann S. Hogger.

Materials and Methods

Moriches Bay is situated near the center of the south shore of Long Island, with great South Bay to the west and Shinnecock Bay to the east. Figure 1 shows the western half of the bay. It has a maximum land-sea width of about 3 km, and a maximum depth in the open bay outside the dredged channels of 2–3 m. The several embayments along the land-ward margin are considerably shallower.

The Forge River, near the western end of the bay, is about 4 km long and has maximum depths outside a dredged channel of about 1 m. Several large duck farms are located along the margin of the estuary and its river. Although wastes from these farms are not now discharged directly into the river or its estuary, substantial amounts of both N and P do nonethe-less reach the estuary. Concentrations of over 150 μgm-at 1^{-1} of nitrogen (combined and inorganic) and 90 μgm-at 1^{-1} phosphorus (total) have been measured in the river water. During the summer of 1966, for example, when river flow averaged about 0.3 M^3 sec^{-1}, the concentration of nitrogen in the river was such that the inner half of the estuary would have received about 6mgm-at nitrogen 1;1 per day. Although it can readily be shown that this is probably but a small fraction of the total daily requirements of the usual summer algal populations, this addition does serve to maintain very high total nutrient levels within the estuary. Total nitrogen may exceed 300 μgm-at 1^{-1}, and total phosphorus 50 μgm-at 1^{-1}.

Senix Creek is not only narrower and shorter than Forge River, but it also has a much smaller supply of fresh-water. There are no obvious large supplies of nutrients from farms or domestic sources. Both Forge River and Senix Creek support very large populations of planktonic algae. Tut-hill Cove, to the east, is shallower and, in contrast to the preceding, has dense stands of benthic algae and correspondingly small populations of plankton. The smallest plankton populations, however, were always found in Moriches Inlet.

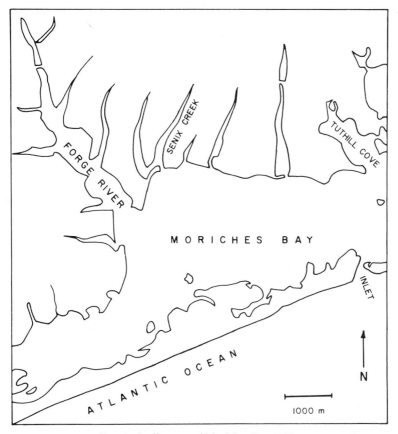

FIG. 1. Outline map of Moriches Bay, N.Y.

This region was visited at various times in the summers of 1965 and 1966. During these visits measurements were made of abundance, composition, and photosynthetic activity of samples of the planktonic algal populations taken from various places in the bay and the small estuaries. An effort was made on each trip to make observations on as wide a range of population sizes as was available in the region. Samples were nearly always taken between 8:00 and 10:00 A.M. to avoid having to begin an experiment with water supersaturated with oxygen. At the time of sampling transparency was measured with a Clarke submarine photometer, which uses a selenium barrier-layer sensing element. Extinction coefficients, k, computed from these measurements have been used to estimate mean illumination, $\bar{I}$, in the water column by means of the following expression: (1) $\bar{I} = \dfrac{I_0(1 - e^{-kz})}{kz}$, in which I_0 is the surface solar radiation, k the extinction coefficient, and z the depth in meters. I_0 was measured with a Belfort radiometer at the field-laboratory.

On returning to the field laboratory aliquots of the sample were dispensed into 125 ml glass stoppered bottles for dark-and light-bottle photosynthesis experiments. Two light bottles were left clear, and two were covered with a neutral density monel or nylon-mesh screen which reduced the light by one quarter or one third. These bottles were secured to the hub of a wooden wheel which could accomodate eight bottles on either side of a large central disc. The wheel was lowered into a tank which was illuminated by 400-watt G.E. quartz iodine-vapor lamps beamed through the plate glass sides. One side of the tank was illuminated with one lamp, the other with six. The distance of the lamps from the tank was adjusted so that the illumination on the side with one lamp was one-fifth that with six lamps. Hence, by placing a screened and unscreened bottle on each side of the wheel, the sample from a single station could be exposed to four different intensities.

Illumination in the tank was measured with a selenium cell with maximum sensitivity in the yellow-green part of the spectrum. This cell was compared with an Eppley pyrheliometer at Ithaca, New York, over a range of intensitites. On the basis of these comparisons, measurements of illumination in the tank were converted into units of energy flux, g cal $cm^{-2}hr^{-1}$.

The central disc on the "wheel" served as a light shield to separate the two sides and as a pulley by which it was rotated about a horizontal axle at *ca.* 1 rpm. through a belt drive. The rotation ensured uniform light for all the bottles and provided some mixing within the bottles. A 1 cm glass ball was placed in each bottle to enhance the mixing.

A dark bottle was prepared by wrapping it in aluminum foil or black cloth and placed in the tank. An extra light bottle was prepared on cloudless days when solar radiation could be measured readily over short periods. It was exposed to natural light at about 1 meter below the surface.

Samples were usually incubated for 2–3 hours, but sometimes for less than an hour. The experiments were always terminated as soon as bubbles indicating supersaturation appeared in the light bottles. Even with this precaution, final concentrations of oxygen were sometimes well above saturation. There was no evidence, however, of any inhibition of photosynthesis at high oxygen levels. Initial pH was sometimes measured, the values usually falling below 8.2. Final pH was not measured then, but subsequently in 1967 pH changes in experiments were measured. Even with high rates of photosynthesis they did not usually exceed 0.5 pH units, and final pH was less than 9.

Changes in oxygen were determined by Winkler titration using 0.0035

N thiosulfate. Reproducibility of measurements of oxygen production at a given light intensity was usually very good, differences between replicate bottles in most cases being barely more than the titration error.

Because of the limited capacity of the wheel, replicates were not usually run at each light intensity. Photosynthesis at the two highest light intensities was usually nearly the same, and the average rate at these two intensities is taken as the saturation rate, symbolized by Pmax. The rates at the three lower intensities, including the dark bottle, usually indicated a linear increase with light. The slope of an eye-fitted line through these points was taken as the light-dependent rate of photosynthesis, symbolized by P/I. The intersection of this line and a straight line representing the saturation rate (Pmax) defines the saturation intensity, I_k, as used by Talling (1961), Yentsch and Lee (1966), Ichimura (1967), and others.

One of us (MAS) has conducted special studies on the effect of illumination on pigmentation and photosynthesis of populations from the Forge River. In these studies samples were impounded in five-gallon carboys which were left clear, shaded with cloth, or made opaque by wrapping with layers of black cloth, and resuspended in the estuary. The populations in these carboys were sampled at two–three day intervals, and photosynthesis was measured by the methods outlined above.

Algal abundance was determined by cell counts and pigment assays. Counts were made with an inverted microscope on samples preserved with neutral formaldehyde. Samples for pigment assay were filtered onto glass fiber filters at a pressure differential of one-third atmosphere, stored in a desiccator in the dark until analysis. There was no evidence of deterioration of filters stored for periods up to two weeks. The filters were ground with a tissue homogenizer, and extracted with 90 per cent acetone for one-helf to one hour in the dark. Extraction appeared to be complete in that time; no pigment could be eluted by reextraction with acetone, ether, or methanol. Concentrations were determined by the method of Richards with Thompson (1952). Attempts were made to determine relative amounts of phaeophytin fluorometrically by the method of Yentsch and Menzel (1963), but, as Schaffner (1966) has shown, chlorophyll b of the dense chlorophyte populations interferes with the determination. Therefore, in 1966 phaeophtin was determined spectrophotometrically by the method of Lorenzen (1967). Although large amounts did appear in the populations impounded in carboys, significant amounts were not found in the natural populations.

During June, 1966, the concentration of chlorophyll in the Forge River was determined directly by measuring fluorescence of estuary water as it circulated from a submersible pump through the continuous flow cell of a Turner model 111 fluormeter. (Lorenzen, 1966). The instrument was equipped with a Corning CS-5-60 excitation filter and CS-2-60 emission filter, and the standard Turner F4T4-B1 lamp and S-4 photomultiplier tube.

Results

Changes in Abundance

Previous studies by Barlow, *et al.* (1963), and other unpublished works have shown that there is a general increase in abundance through the spring and early summer to high levels in midsummer. Although July and August are the periods when one can expcet to find the greatest populations, there are frequent large changes in abundance. These are especially striking in the inlets such as Forge River, where we have observed as much as ten-fold changes in the course of a week.

A typical sequence of changes was followed in detail in June, 1966, when the estuary was sampled with the recording fluorometer over a four-day period. There was an excellent linear relation between fluorometer readings and pigment samples such that each fluorometer unit was approximately equal to 2 mgm chlorophyll a M^{-3}. Figure 2 is a repli-

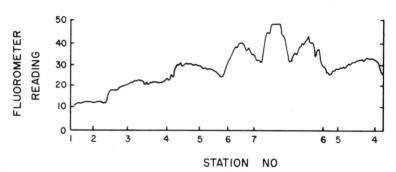

STATION NO

Fig. 2. Replica of record from fluorometer survey of Forge River June 27, 1966. Station 2 is at connection with Moriches Bay, Station 7 about 2,500 meters landward. At the peak value, which was reached about 50 meters landward of 7, the course was reversed. Each fluorometer unit is approximately equal to 2 mg chl a M^{-3}.

cate of the record obtained on June 27. It will be noted that there were several abrupt changes in fluorescence along the long axis of the estuary. These correspond to changes of 20–30 mgm chlorophyll a M^{-3} in ca. 100m. These changes occurred at about the same place near the marked constrictions which can be seen in Figure 1. These were also noted on the other days. They may possibly be associated with more intense tidal streaming in these constricted areas.

Since the other records were interrupted by vertical profiles, or were complicated by changes in speed or direction of the boat, they have all been simplified and redrawn in Figure 3. On two days, June 23 and 27,

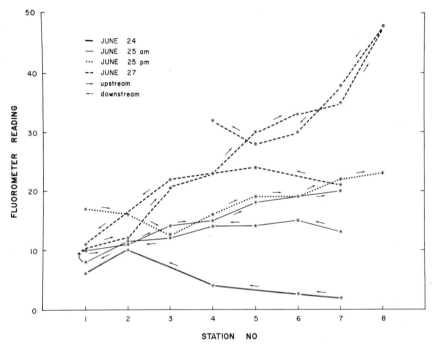

FIG. 3. A simplified representation of the several fluorometer traces made in June, 1966, in the Forge River. Stations as in Figure 2 are located along a long axis from Station 1 in Moriches Bay to Station 8 about 2,600 meters landward. Each fluorometer unit equivalent to about 2 mg chl a M^{-3}.

recordings were made continuously on a complete round trip, giving some indication of reproducibility. Differences in up-and-down estuary traces may be due to small differendes in the boat's course or the effect of tidal displacement of patches of plankton. However, the larger day-to-day differences give clear evidence of a regular increase in the population in the inner part of the estuary. The first run on June 24 was not in very good agreement with the pigment samples, but the four- to fivefold increase in fluorometer readings from June 25 to 27 corresponds very well with the increase in chlorophyll a from 44 to 181 mg M^{-3} at the innermost station.

Although the short period changes observed above are fairly typical of those in other summers, the maximum populations attained have often been far greater. Pigment concentrations of 300 to 400 mgm M^{-3} and cell counts of 10^7–10^9 per liter are frequent. The maximum pigment concentration observed was 1,900 mgm chlorophyll a M^{-3} in August 1965 in the inner Forge River. Unfortunately no sample was kept for counting. Maximum cell counts at nearby stations were over 10^9 cells per liter, consisting mainly of small chlorophytes.

Relation of Abundance to Radiation

It has been evident from previous observations that some changes in abundance may be related to changes in solar radiation. A good example is the marked increase in abundance depicted in Figure 3, which occurred during a week of continuous clear sunny weather when daily radiation was about 500 gm-cal cm^{-2}. Some other conspicuous blooms have been ovserved to follow periods of bright sunny weather. Yet it is difficult to establish any direct correlation between plankton abundance and the radiation in the period immediately preceeding. In fact, at times the relationship seems to be negative.

This difficulty is in part a result of the significant effect on available light of self-absorption by the algae. Measurements of transparency show a strong relation with plankton abundance. At lower concentrations there is a linear relation between pigment and extinction, but at higher concentrations, above about 300 mg M^{-3}, the relationship becomes nonlinear. A least-squares line fitted to the 1965 data (which had the greater range of pigment concentrations) had the equation (2) $k = 0.068 + 0.0159\ C - 0.000006\ C^2$, in which k is the extinction coefficient, and C is the Chlorophyll a concentration in mg M^{-3}.

As a consequence of this strong self-absorption the amount of light available for the entire population in the water column is strongly dependent on the population size. Changes in abundance may lead to larger changes in average light in the water column than most day-to-day changes in solar radiation at the surface. As a result there is a negative relation between plankton abundance as measured by chlorophyll a and the light available for photosynthesis for the whole population. This is shown in Figure 4. Note that in this figure the column intensity I, is averaged over a period of two days preceeding the time of sampling. This particular averaging scheme was chosen because it will be used later in another connection.

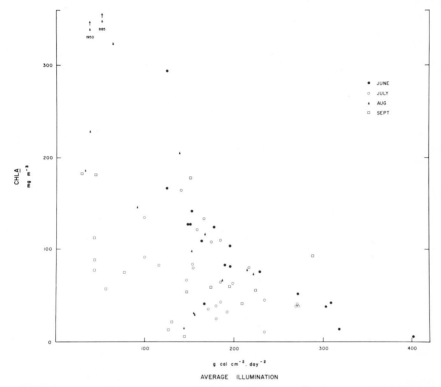

Fig. 4. Relation between mean illumination in water column, $\bar{I}$, and chlorophyll concentration. Based on data from 1965 and 1966. Mean illumination for day of and day preceding sampling.

Relation Between Photosynthesis and Radiation

There was a large variation in the photosynthetic activity of the population, the saturation rate (Pmax) ranging from over 50 to less than 5 g O_2 g^{-1} chlorophyll a hr^{-1}. There does not appear to be any consistent correlation with time or space in the distribution of these photosynthetic rates. The maximum range of values was observed in midsummer at a time of relatively constant temperature and light. Although the largest variation was found in the Forge River, where the greatest number of observations was made, the range in nearby Senix Creek was nearly as great, and was substantial, though smaller, in Moriches Bay.

Yentsch and Lee (1966) have pointed out that such changes in Pmax might result from changes in saturation intensity (I_k) and in the slope (P/I) of the light dependent part of the photosynthesis-light curve. The examples presented by these authors suggest that changes in Pmax usually result from changes in I_k. This was not the case here. In 1965, when measurements were made at several light intensities, variations in Pmax were not correlated with I_k which, in fact, remained nearly constant throughout the summer. Rather, as shown in Figure 5, there was a strong correlation between Pmax and P/I.

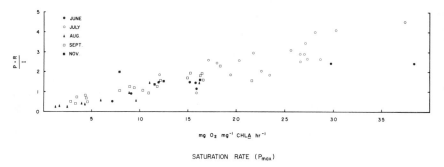

SATURATION RATE (P_{max})

FIG. 5. Relation between light-saturated rate of photosynthesis, Pmax, and light-dependent rates, $(P + R)I$.

As Yentsch and Lee have pointed out, changes in the slope P/I may result from changes in either the dark or light reactions; hence there could be several factors acting simultaneously to produce these variations in Pmax. There is some evidence for the possible effects of both nutrients and light on Pmax here.

Unpublished studies have shown that the summer phytoplankton in the Forge River and adjacent Moriches Bay are frequently limited by available nitrogen. Levels of available nitrogen, i.e., $(NH_4^+ + NO_2^- + NO_3^-)$, frequently fall to less than 10 μg-at 1^{-1}. Numerous nutrient enrichment experiments similar to those of Ryther and Guillard (1959) have shown that the populations are often nitrogen limited. Additions of either nitrate or ammonia, but especially nitrate, in relatively low concentrations sometimes caused almost a twofold enhancement of photosynthesis in just a one–two-hour exposure. No other tested nutrient, including P, Si, Fe and other trace metals, and vitamins is apparently limiting. The response of the populations in these experiments suggest that at levels below about 10–15μg-at N 1^{-1} Pmax is supressed.

Despite this strong evidence of nitrogen limitation the relation between Pmax and available nutrients, either phosphorus or nitrogen, as shown in Figure 6 is so poor that some other factor or factors must be affecting Pmax. Among these, available radiation may play an important part.

The effect of radiation on the activity of the populations in the Forge

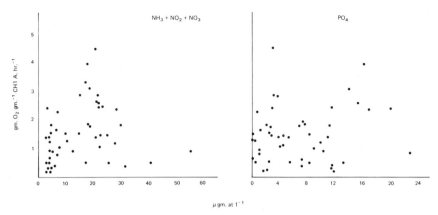

FIG. 6. Relation between photosynthetic rates and nutrient concentrations in Moriches Bay, 1965.

River has been studied experimentally by impounding populations in carboys. This work is reported fully elsewhere (Stafford, 1967), hence will only be summarized here. As others have demonstrated, changes in light effected various changes in pigment. The total pigment and pigment per cell decreased in the clear bottles and increased in the shade. This is of special interest because the algae in the unshaded carboys were held above the upper half-meter, and therefore were exposed to considerably higher intensities than in their normal environment. In contrast the algae in the shaded carboys were usually at illumination levels somewhat below the average to which they had previously been exposed. Accompanying these changes in pigmentation, Stafford has also found significant changes in photosynthetic activity per unit pigment, or P/chl a. In spite of the increase in pigment per cell in the shade bottles exposed to the lower light, there was a decrease in P/chl a, whereas in the light bottles there were consistent increases in P/chl a. Here it should be noted that she also found that changes in P/chl a were correlated with changes in P/I as was pointed out above for the unimpounded populations.

These experiments have led us to look for relations between photosynthetic rate and illumination in the natural populations. In order to do this we have estimated the average illumination in the water column in the period immediately preceeding the time samples were taken for measurement of photosynthesis, using equation (1). Extinction coefficients were almost always determined at the time of sampling, and in a good many cases there were observations for one or two days preceding. When no direct observations of transparency had been made, the extinction coefficient k was estimated from the pigment concentration using the regression equation (2), or estimated from the preceding or following day. By trial and error it was found that the best relation was obtained by averaging the column illumination for the day of sampling and the day before sampling. The relation found is shown in Figure 7. It appears to be fairly strong at lower intensities, with the P/chl a increasing with increasing intensity. At higher intensities there is more scatter, with some suggestion that there might be some depression at the highest intensities. Despite this scatter at the higher light, the linear correlation coefficient r = 0.43 is significant at the 5 per cent level.

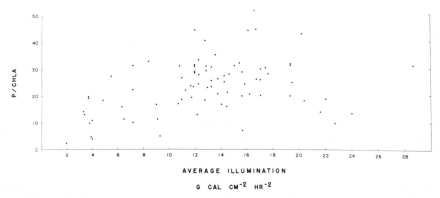

FIG. 7. Relation between photosynthesis and illumination. Photosynthesis is g O_2 g chl a^{-1} hr^{-1} at light saturation; average illumination is average column illumination for day of and day preceding sampling.

Since the average illumination in the water column is so strongly influenced by the amount of pigment, one might hope to find a correlation between pigment concentration and P/chl a. There does not, however, appear to be any such relation, except that very high pigment concentrations, those exceeding 250 mgm M^{-3} all had very low P/chl a.

DISCUSSION

Although the pigment assay has often been used by ecologists as a measure of the photosynthetic potential of natural populations, there are a number of studies that have shown large variations in the photosynthetic activity of pigments of both marine and freshwater phytoplankton, as for example those of Steemann-Nielsen and Hansen (1959), Williams and Murdoch (1966), Hepher (1962), Ichimura (1967), Ichimura and Aruga (1964), Curl and Small (1965), and others. The range in individual investigations is often as great as 5 g C g^{-1} chl a hr^{-1}. In the data compiled by Strickland (1960) the total range is from 1–10 g C g^{-1} chl a hr^{-1}. The range met in the present studies seems to be substantially greater. Net photosynthesis converted to units of carbon assimilated (assuming P. Q. = 1.25) varied from 1–20 g C g^{-1} chl a hr^{-1}. It should be pointed out here that this range is not determined by singular and possibly erroneous values; there were several observations very near both the upper and lower limits.

What produces these large variations is not known. Ichimura (1967), Curl and Small (1965), and others have suggested that such variations may be an effect of nutrient deficiency. Curl and Small have gone so far as to define rates that they consider characteristic of nutrient poor water (1–3 g C g^{-1} chl a hr^{-1}) and recently upwelled, nutrient-rich water (over 5). The possible significance of nutrients has also been shown in laboratory studies of McAllister, Shah, and Strickland (1964), who found large differences in rates between nutrient-deficient and nutrient-rich cultures.

However, the effect of factors other than nutrients cannot be ignored. Williams and Murdoch (1966) gave evidence that a large part of the variations in photosynthetic activity that they observed in the Beaufort Channel, North Carolina, was due to the effect of temperature. It seems likely that a good part of both seasonal and regional variations may be ascribed to the effects of temperature. However, only a small part of the differences in photosynthetic activity encountered in the present studies can be a direct effect of temperature. This is, for example, clearly seen in Figure 5, where the maximum range in rates occurred in the period July–September, when the temperature range was only 6°C; in fact, in the data for both years one can find variations in a single survey at essentially the same temperature that cover as much as two-thirds the maximum observed range.

In the present study we have found correlation between photosynthetic activity and the previous light-history of the populations. On a physiological basis it seems reasonable that illumination should have such consequences on photosynthetic activity, if only for the fact that light is known to be important in synthesis and destruction of pigments. However, the fact that illumination is itself strongly influenced by the plants makes it immediately apparent that these correlations could be the result of one of several density-dependent factors, such as nutrients or CO_2 availability, metabolite accumulation, etc. That we were unable to demonstrate any clear relation between abundance, as measured by pigment concentration, and activity, does not, of course, rule out such possibilities. However, the effects produced by varying light in the carboy experiments, although not wholly free from possibly density-dependent effects either, do lend support to the hypothesis that prior illumination may have significant effects on photosynthetic activity.

Whatever the mechanism that produces them, the variations in photosynthetic activity do appear to be to some degree density-dependent. This conclusion leads us to ask what consequences these variations may have on total production and growth of these populations. Translation of measurements of photosynthesis in the light-tank to those that might be expected in the natural environment is, however, not an easy matter. Two problems are particularly thorny here:

First, the quality of light in the tank was different from that in the natural environment since the quartz-iodine vapor lamps that were used to illuminate the tank are rich in red-energy compared to sunlight. There is too little understanding of effects of differences in light quality to do much more than speculate about their consequences. However, some empirical estimate of effects in this particular set-up were obtained from the comparison of photosynthesis in replicate samples in the light tank and in natural light. In order to do this, the rate of photosynthesis per unit light in the sample exposed to natural light was determined from measurement of oxygen production and by estimating the amount of light reaching the bottle during the period of exposure. The latter was determined from the pyrheliometer records and measurements of water transparency. Next the intensity at which the same rate occurred in the tank was interpolated from a light vs. photosynthesis curve drawn up for that particular experiment. The relative effectiveness of artifical vs. natural light could then be expressed as a ratio of one to the other. There was a good deal of variation in this ratio, but as would have been expected, the artificial light was usually less effective than natural light. The difference was not very great: a least squares line fitted to the data indicated that the artificial light was about 77 per cent as effective as natural light.

The second problem that has to be met is presented by the complex relationship between photosynthesis measured at constant light intensity and the rate exhibited by a population subjected to the normal diurnal variation in light in the water column. A number of workers have wrestled with the conceptual and mathematical problems involved in attempting to estimate total daily photosynthesis in a natural population. All the practical solutions necessarily involve some simplifications. We have adopted the solution proposed by Talling (1961) principally because it offers certain conveniences in application.

For each of the observations in 1965 for which there were complete data (i.e., pigment concentration, Pmax, incident radiation, day length, I_k, and transparency) we have calculated the total daily photosynthesis using Talling's equations 5 and 8. Because of the considerable uncertainty about the relation between "inside" and "outside" light as discussed above, which would affect the value of I_k, we did not attempt to make any correction for it. If our inferences from the outside bottle experiments about the differences in light are correct, the value of I_k would be decreased by about one fourth. This would result in a relatively small but not uniform increase in total photosynthesis. Talling's equation assumes that the water is infinitely deep. In most cases here the water is so turbid that little light reaches the bottom, and this assumption leads to no serious error. Where significant light was found at the bottom, i.e., more than 10 per cent of the surface light, we have calculated the amount of photosynthesis that would have occurred below the bottom in infinitely deep water, and subtracted this. Total daily respiration was estimated simply from the rate of oxygen consumption in dark bottles.

The ratio of total photosynthesis to total respiration is plotted against chlorophyll concentration in Figure 8. The most striking feature of the

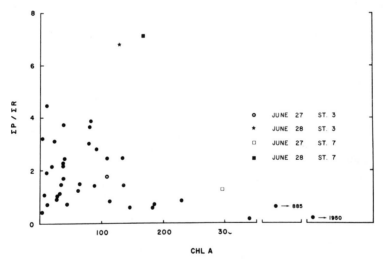

FIG. 8. Photosynthesis:respiration ratio is influenced by pigment concentration. Photosynthesis and respiration are total daily rates estimated from light tank measurements.

behavior of the ratio that is revealed in this plot is that the maximum ratio at any pigment concentration falls sharply with increasing pigment concentration except for two unique observations. For both observations there was, fortuitously, another measurement of photosynthesis the day preceeding or following. These, as shown in the plot, fell in with the main body of the data. Also, in each case there was a larger amount of available nitrogen, relative to the amount of chlorophyll on the day of high ratio.

Figure 8 suggests that most of the populations with pigment concentrations above about 150 mgm M^{-3} had a ratio close to or below 1, at the prevailing conditions of solar radiation.

Although the uncertainties involved in the calculations ot total daily photosynthesis are great, it seems likely that these large populations are approaching the density at which their growth is limited by available radiation. However, it is important to recognize that this limitation is imposed not only by reduction of light, but also by reduction of photosynthetic efficiency at these high concentrations. This is illustrated by the fact that if the populations had the average observed Pmax (18.1 g O_2 g^{-1} chl a hr^{-1}) and average observed respiration rate (4.2 g O_2 g^{-1} chl a hr^{-1}) they would not be limited by self-shading on even a very dull summer day (11 g-cal hr^{-1}) until they reached concentrations of 250 mg chl a M^{-3}. On an average summer day (37 g-cal hr^{-1}) self-shading would reduce the P:R to 1 at 660 mg chl a M^{-3}, and on a bright day (57 g-cal hr^{-1}) it would occur at populations of 980 mg ch l a/M^{-3}. It is largely the very low Pmax characteristic of the denser populations that reduces the P:R ratio to the levels at which the populations may be no longer self sustaining.

Because of these large changes in the P:R ratios with changes in concentration, it is evident that maximum net production will occur at some concentration considerably below the concentration at which self-shading occurs. The observed maximum net daily production of 33 g O_2 g chl a $^{-1}$ m^{-2} day^{-1} was in one of the anomalous samples, that of June 27 at the "Marina" where there was a population of 128 Mg chl a m^{-3}. In the main body of the data the highest production was in populations with pigment concentrations well below 100 mg M^{-3} but at high P:R ratios. The highest of these was a net production of 22 g O_2 M^{-2} day $^{-1}$ at a pigment concentration of only 87 mg M^{-3}. Hence the maximum size of these populations appears to be regulated in some degree by internal mechanisms.

REFERENCES

Barlow, J. P., C. J. Lorenzen, and R. T. Myren, 1963. "Eutrophication of a Tidal Estuary," *Limnol. Oceanogr. 8*, 251–62.

Curl, H., and L. F. Small, 1965. "Variations in Photosynthetic Assimilation Ratios in Marine Phytoplankton Populations," *ibid., 10*, (Supplement) R67–R73.

Hepher, B., 1962. "Primary Production in Fish Ponds and its Application to Fertilization Experiments," *ibid., 7*, 131–36.

XXVI

Onondaga Lake, New York—An Unusual Algal Environment

DANIEL F. JACKSON

Department of Civil Engineering
Syracuse University
Syracuse, New York

BACKGROUND

Geographic and Morphometric Data

Onondaga Lake is characterized by the New York State Department of Health as P 154 or the one hundred and fifty-fourth lentic environment in the Oswego River system. Onondaga Lake is one of two major lakes located near the northern edge of the Limestone Belt. The other major lake is Fayetteville Green Lake, which is located in Green Lake State Park.

The New York State Department of Health, in the Oswego River Drainage Basin Survey Series Report No. 1 (1951), describes seven tributary streams contributing to Onondaga Lake. It is reported that the Onondaga Lake drainage basin is 240.84 square miles in area, and the lake proper has an area of 4.51 square miles. The volume of the lake is estimated to be 32.96×10^9 gallons, assuming an average depth of thirty-five feet. The lake was formerly a part of the Glacial Lake Iroquois, and its drainage is northerly into the Seneca River.

The lake is approximately five miles long and one mile wide. Its southeastern half extends into the city of Syracuse. It is the center of a drainage basin comprising twelve communities that contain 80 per cent of Onondaga County's population and most of its heavy industry.

Historical Review

The first white man to reach Onondaga Lake was Father Le Moyne. He reported in his diary on August 16, 1653, " . . . we arrived at the entrance of a small lake [Onondaga]. In a large basin, half dry, we tasted the

515

water of a spring, which the Indians are afraid to drink, saying that it is inhabited by a demon who renders it foul. I found it to be a fountain of salt water, from which we made a little salt, as natural as from the sea, some of which we shall carry to Quebec" (Clark, 1849). In 1788 the State of New York made a treaty with the Onondaga Indians, which permitted the state to manage the salt springs that covered about ten square miles. In 1803 the salt industry was developed on a major scale. Salt production in Syracuse reached its peak by 1862, at which time there were fifteen different companies producing nine million bushels of salt per year. Until about 1870 the salt business was the dominant industry, and Syracuse was the principal source of supply for the United States. The last commercial salt production in Syracuse was in 1926. Competition from other areas, deterioration of the quality of the brine, and the lack of access to high-quality saturated solutions were principal factors in the decline of the salt industry.

The rapid increase of population in Syracuse due to the development of the salt industry brought with it the associated problems of urban life, including waste disposal. As long as the population was small, dispersed privies could be used, but as the homes were built closer together, this type of waste disposal was no longer feasible. By the year 1896, sewers carried the raw sewage into Onondaga Creek, which eventually deposited its noxious burden in Onondaga Lake. When the suspended raw sewage from Onondaga Creek entered the south end of the lake, it sank to the bottom and formed sludge deposits.

As the city's population grew, so did the sludge deposits on the lake's bottom. Through the process of decomposition of these various, vast quantities of organic matter, the dissolved oxygen in the deeper section of the lake became depleted, and hydrogen sulfide gas became abundant. Both of these chemical processes resulted in the destruction or modification of the biota.

Until 1907 the city of Syracuse discharged its sewage directly into Onondaga Creek and Harbor Brook—the two main tributaries of Onondaga Lake (Figure 1). Originally, there were underground conduits to carry excess surface drainage and runoff into the lake. When inside sanitation facilities were established, sewer lines were connected to storm drains. In 1907 the state legislature created the Syracuse Intercepting Board which proceeded to construct two trunk sewers parallel to Harbor Brook and Onondaga Creek. These two intercepting systems carried the sanitary flow to the sewage treatment plant on Hiawatha Boulevard. The plant was constructed in 1924 and was nothing more than a sedimentation system (primary treatment). This plant was about 35 per cent efficient in dry weather and of little use during rainstorms.

The development of industries in the Ley Creek area forced the con-

struction of a secondary treatment plant in 1940 on Ley Creek, another
tributary to Onondaga Lake. This plant operated successfully for several
years only; then it became defunct. In the meantime, the Hiawatha plant
became overloaded, and by 1950 Onondaga Lake was receiving only im-
properly treated wastewaters from the city of Syracuse and Onondaga
County. The current primary treatment plant was not completed until 1961.
It is thus apparent that Onondaga Lake, except for very short periods, has
been continuously and seriously abused with man's domestic and industrial
wastes.

Water Quality

Table 1 compares the contaminants found at site A (Station 2 in
Nemerow, 1964) in Onondaga Lake (Figure 1) with those found in a

TABLE 1   Mean Values of Contaminants in Onondaga Lake (1959–1962).
Nemerow (1964).

	Site A (Station 2)	Typical Clean Lake
Coliform Bacteria (MPN)	5,300–180,000	0–50
Alkalinity (ppm)	120–149	50–200
Chlorides (ppm)	1,700–1,960	0–5
Carbon Dioxide (ppm)	5.1–10.0	0–5
NO_3–N (ppm)	0.27–1.60	0–Trace
NH_3–N (ppm)	0.013–0.14	0–Trace
Organic–N (ppm)	0.27–1.01	0–.10
Phosphates (Total) (ppm)	0.36–1.54	0–.10
Suspended Solids (ppm)	11.9–18.4	0–2
Dissolved Oxygen (ppm)	1.5–7.4	More Than 6.0
B.O.D. (ppm)	8.5–11.3	1.0
pH	7.4–8.0	6–8

clean water lake. The larger number of coliform bacteria in Onondaga
Lake is a direct result of the sewage. Table 2 compares Onondaga Lake
chemically with four other Onondaga County lakes. The chloride value of
1,460 mg/1 is the highest found in any lake in New York State. It is my
opinion that stratified layers of salt waters exist in Onondaga Lake, thus
making it meromictic. Since adequate studies have never been made on the
conductivity or even water temperature, only an opinion can be offered.
It is estimated that Onondaga Lake receives from sixty to ninety tons of
calcium chloride and carbonate daily via Nine Mile Creek. These materials
are by-products from the Allied Chemical Corporation, whose plant is
located near the western shores of Onondaga Lake.

TABLE 2   Some Chemical Constituents in Selected Lakes in Onondaga County.
Results expressed as ions (mg/l). Berg (1963).

	Onondaga Lake	Fayetteville Green Lake	Oneida Lake	Otisco Lake	Skaneateles Lake
Calcium	472	400	31	40	36
Magnesium	13	62	7.2	8.5	6.2
Potassium + Sodium	538	0.6	4.9	2.3	2.9
Chloride	1,460	24	4.5	5.7	3.6
Sulphate	167	1,050	42	19	16

There has never been a comprehensive biological survey made of Onondaga Lake. The New York State Conservation Department long ago wrote off the Lake as a lost cause. Algal blooms have been reported to occur annually in Onondaga Lake since 1962. The blooms are formed usually in late June or early July and are composed of members of the Chlorophyta or Euglenophyta. Diatoms are abundant throughout the year. Hohn (1951), in his survey of the diatoms of western New York, recorded twenty-eight genera from Onondaga Lake (Table 3).

In relation to attached algal forms. Onondaga Lake's flora are distributed in two uneven sections. The division line is near the outlet of Nine Mile Creek. South of this outlet, *Enteromorpha intestinalis* is the dominant attached form. *Cladophora* replaces *Enteromorpha* along the shorelines north of the Nine Mile Creek outlet. *Cladophora* is especially noticeable along the eastern shoreline. The sodium to calcium ratios in Onondaga Lake may provide an insight as to the distribution of these attached genera. The ratio between sodium and calcium expressed on a

TABLE 3   Genera of Diatoms in Onondaga Lake,
reported by Hohn (1951).

Cyclotella	*Neridium*
Coscinodiscus	*Navicula*
Stephanodiscus	*Pinnularia*
Fragilaria	*Stauroneis*
Opephora	*Tropidoneis*
Synedra	*Gomphonema*
Diatoma	*Amphora*
Eunotia	*Cymbella*
Cocconeis	*Epithemia*
Rhoicosphenia	*Rhopalodia*
Caloneis	*Nitzschia*
Mastogloia	*Cymatopleura*
Diploneis	*Surirella*
Anomoeoneis	*Amphiprora*

weight basis of the surface waters on September 19, 1966, in Onondaga Lake near site A was 5.04; at the outlet of Nine Mile Creek the ratio was 1.20, and at site B, the ratio was 1.49 (Figure 1). It appears that *Clado-phora* favors a more equally balanced ratio between sodium and calcium ions than does *Enteromorpha*.

Why the Current Investigation?

The above introduction provides some understanding of the unusual environmental conditions present in Onondaga Lake. Because of the large quantities of nutrients entering the lake, it should be a huge stinking mess of unsightly filamentous or blue-green algae. Instead it is a huge stinking mess of unsightly fecal brown-green water. There are several reasons, perhaps, why the algal populations in the past have been below expectation and for the lack of blue-green species. These are salinity, calcium inhibition, or the lack of adequate mineralization of the allochthonous organic matter. It also may be a result of the interactions of two or more of these factors.

Due to recent legislation by the State of New York, every wastewater treatment facility must be of a secondary type. The effluent from such a facility will have a higher degree of mineralization and will be significantly different chemically from a primary effluent (Jackson, 1967). The exact effects of secondary treatment on algal growth are currently controversial. Since a secondary treatment plant must be constructed for Onondaga Lake, the following experiment was designed to determine what effect the present wastewater effluent has on unicellular cultures of algae. After the secondary plant is constructed and operating, the same type of algal cultures and laboratory conditions can be used to evaluate the quality of this new effluent. A comparison of the results from the two sets of data will be, to my knowledge, the first recorded information using controlled experiments to evaluate *in situ* the differences in the effects of primary and secondary treatment on the algal flora of a large lentic environment. These experiments will illustrate the theme of this symposium, "Algae, Man, and the Environment."

EXPERIMENTAL DESIGN

Procedures

WATER SAMPLES The Onondaga Lake water used in the following set of experiments was obtained from site A, which is near the outlet of effluent from the Metropolitan Syracuse Treatment Plant (Figure 1). The water samples were always collected from a depth of .5 meter and were filtered through "angel hair" to remove large particulated materials. Previous tests showed no significant differences in algal growth between filtered and nonfiltered samples. The major difference was in the ease of recording the algal growth when the lake water was filtered. Lake water samples were collected every twelve days from September 16, 1966, until October 22, 1966. Sufficient lake water was obtained to permit growth determinations of all the algal forms in one group.

ALGAL CULTURES AND MEDIA   Twenty-five algal cultures were procured from the culture collection of algae at Indiana University. Of this quantity, five cultures were members of the Cyanophyta, eight cultures from the Chrysophyta; there were ten Chlorophyta cultures and two Euglenophyta genera. The cultures were obtained three days prior to the

TABLE 4   Average Growth of Algal Cultures Expressed in Cells/l
After 10 days of Inoculation

	Bristol's Solution	Per Cent Filtered Onondaga Lake Water			
CHLOROPHYTA		25	50	75	100
LB 762 *Carteria* sp.	2.5×10^3	3.7×10^4	2.1×10^2	1.6×10^2	0.6×10^2
LB 796 *Chlamydomonas* sp.	1.8×10^5	1.7×10^6	1.9×10^6	2.1×10^6	2.9×10^6
LB 805 *Gonium pectorale*	1.2×10^3	2.5×10^4	1.6×10^2	0.3×10^2	0.1×10^2
LB 107 *Ankistrodesmus spiralis*	1.7×10^4	2.9×10^4	2.8×10^4	1.7×10^3	0.9×10^3
820 *Chlorella* (Milford strain)	0.5×10^3	1.1×10^3	9.5×10^3	6.3×10^3	4.7×10^3
260 *Chlorella vulgaris*	4.4×10^4	1.7×10^4	0.8×10^3	2.2×10^2	1.5×10^2
LB 472 *Microspora* sp.	6.7×10^5	3.9×10^3	2.1×10^3	1.7×10^2	0.4×10^2
LB 470 *Pediastrum duplex*	4.2×10^4	4.9×10^5	3.1×10^3	2.2×10^3	1.7×10^2
LB 1490 *Halochlorococcum marinum*	3.1×10^4	4.7×10^5	4.9×10^6	8.9×10^6	4.7×10^5
LB 1358 *Scenedesmus abundans*	9.9×10^4	7.8×10^4	5.4×10^4	3.1×10^4	0.2×10^3
EUGLENOPHYTA	Difco's *Euglena* Medium				
LB 367 *Euglena gracilis*	11.7×10^6	10.3×10^5	7.2×10^5	4.7×10^5	9.1×10^4
LB 523 *Lepocinclis buetschlii*	2.3×10^6	8.3×10^5	5.2×10^5	6.1×10^5	7.3×10^3

time they were used in the experiment. The individual cultures used are listed in Tables 4 and 5.

The following standard media were used as controls to grow the following types of algae: Chlorophyta, Bristol's solution; Chrysophyta, Bristol's solution and soil water; Euglenophyta, Difco's *Euglena* medium; and Cyanophyta, Gorham's ASM medium.

REGIMEN The following method described for *Carteria* was followed with each of the other twenty-four algal cultures. Only the nutrient medium was varied. Ten ml of *Carteria* culture were placed in each of four 250 ml Erlenmeyer flasks containing 200 ml of Bristol's solution. The same quantity of *Carteria* was added to each of four Erlenmeyer flasks containing 150 ml of Bristol's solution and 50 ml of filtered Onondaga Lake water. The same procedure was used for four flasks containing 100 ml of

TABLE 5   Average Growth of Algal Cultures Expressed in Cells/l
After 10 Days Inoculation

CYANOPHYTA	Gorham's ASM Medium	Per Cent Filtered Onondaga Lake Water			
		25	50	75	100
1444 *Anabaena flos aquae*	43×10^6	21×10^3	8×10^2	0.1×10^2	—
LB 1538 *Anacystis aeruginosa*	39×10^5	14×10^2	0.1×10^2	0.1×10^2	—
LB 1303 *Gloeotrichia echinulata*	19×10^6	9×10^3	0.7×10^2	0.2×10^2	—
LB 795 *Gloeocapsa* sp.	35×10^5	8×10^2	0.4×10^2	0.2×10^2	—
LB 1191 *Synechococcus cedrorum*	93×10^5	40×10^4	9.6×10^3	2.2×10^2	—
CHRYSOPHYTA	Bristol and Soil-Water Medium				
1269 *Cyclotella* sp.	2.6×10^4	5.8×10^4	8.1×10^4	3.7×10^5	3.1×10^6
1268 *Navicula incerta*	5.8×10^5	3.7×10^2	2.7×10^2	2.1×10^2	0.9×10^2
686 *Nitzschia* sp.	4.7×10^5	3.9×10^4	3.1×10^2	2.1×10^3	0.7×10^3
679 *Pinnularia* sp.	3.9×10^6	1.8×10^4	0.3×10^3	1.9×10^2	0.6×10^2
644 *Gomphonema parvulum*	4.7×10^4	3.9×10	2.8×10^2	1.6×10^2	0.9×10^2
1276 *Amphora coffaeiformis*	7.1×10^6	4.7×10^4	3.4×10^2	1.9×10^2	1.6×10^2
670 *Eunotia* sp.	8.1×10^5	5.9×10^3	3.7×10^2	2.1×10^2	1.9×10^2
1264 *Stauroneis amphoroides*	12.1×10^6	8.3×10^4	0.7×10^2	0.9×10^2	0.6×10^2

Bristol's solution and 100 ml of filtered Onondaga Lake water, as well as four flasks containing 50 ml of Bristol's solution and 150 ml of filtered Onondaga Lake water. The last set of four flasks to which 10 ml of *Carteria* was added contained 200 ml of filtered Onondaga Lake water only. The *Carteria* stock culture was shaken thoroughly each time a 10 ml sample was withdrawn. It is assumed that each flask received approximately the same number of *Carteria* cells. A 10-ml sample of *Carteria* was counted microscopically and recorded as number of cells per liter (cells/l).

All twenty flasks were placed in a constant temperature chamber at 25°C and were illuminated for fourteen hours and kept dark for ten hours. The illumination at the water surface in the flasks was about 400 lux and was provided by a battery of Gro-Lux bulbs. The flasks were each shaken by hand once each day and were distributed randomly under the battery of lights to prevent favoring any particular flask. The flasks were kept in the environmental chamber for ten days. At the end of this period, the contents in each flask were centrifuged in a Foerst centrifuge and the filtrate was reconstituted to a 5 ml volume with distilled water and placed in a vial. Each of the twenty vials was examined microscopically within eight hours of being centrifuged. The results were reported as cells/l. The average growth of the four flasks containing *Carteria* for the ten-day period, minus the original number of cells/l, is given in Table 4.

The flasks and media were sterilized before use. Neither the algal cultures nor the filtered Onondaga Lake water was sterilized, although aseptic techniques were used in handling them.

Discussion and Results

The results of the twenty-five different experiments are reported in Tables 4 and 5. Of the cultures examined, four forms had more growth in the flasks containing only filtered Onondaga Lake water than in the flasks containing their respective nutrient enriched media. These forms were *Cyclotella, Halochlorococcum marinum, Chlorella* (Milford strain), and *Chlamydomonas*. The most outstanding of these was *Cyclotella*, which grew over 100 times more cells in just filtered Onondaga Lake water. All the flasks containing both *Cyclotella* and filtered Onondaga Lake water had greater growth than the *Cyclotella* cultured in only the Bristol and soil-water medium. *Halochlorococcum marinum* also exhibited better growth in the flasks containing filtered Onondaga Lake water than those in Bristol's solution alone. The greatest growth of *Halochlorococ-*

cum marinum was in the flasks containing 75 per cent filtered Onondaga Lake water. Here the growth was 300 times greater than that observed in the flasks containing only Bristol's solution. The *Chlorella*, Milford strain, was also better in the flasks with filtered Onondaga Lake water than in cultures containing only Bristol's solution. The growth of the *Chlorella* cells in the filtered Onondaga Lake water, however, was not as spectacular as that manifested by the *Halochlorococcum* and *Cyclotella*. The *Chlorella*, Milford strain, had the best growth in the 50 per cent filtered Onondaga Lake water. It is of interest to compare the *Chlorella*, Milford strain, with the *Chlorella vulgaris* cultures. The latter grew better in the Bristol's solution and did not develop as well in any of the flasks containing filtered Onondaga Lake water. The greater growth of *Chylamydomonas* in the flasks containing filtered Onondaga Lake water in comparison with that of *Chlamydomonas* in the Bristol's solution was expected. This algal form is one of the current bloom species. Its association with organically polluted water is known also. Although each of the other twenty-one algae grew better in flasks which contained only nutrient medium, all forms except the blue-green species survived in only filtered Onondaga Lake water. *Synechococcus* in the 25 per cent filtered Onondaga Lake water flasks was the only blue-green algal species studied which tended to show significant growth in flasks containing filtered Onondaga Lake water.

It is undoubtedly true that the environmental conditions to which all of the twenty-five cultures were exposed was not optimum for many of the species. It is also acknowledged that it is difficult to culture many of the Chrysophyta by means of liquid media. The significant part of the results, however, is the comparison of the algal growth in the nutrient medium compared to growth in the medium containing varying amounts of filtered Onondaga Lake water.

Conclusions

Currently, filtered Onondaga Lake water alone will not support planktonic blue-green algae. This laboratory result supports the observations made in the lake for the past three years. *Chlamydomonas* and *Cyclotella*, both of which normally occur in abundance in Onondaga Lake, are stimulated by some component part of the lake's water. The same is true of *Chlorella*, although the species found in Onondaga Lake tends to be more like the Milford strain than like *Chlorella vulgaris*. *Halochlorococcum marinum* has never been observed in Onondaga Lake, although it has been collected from nearby ponds. It is of interest that both *Chlorella*

(Milford strain) and *Halochlorococcum marinum* have been reported to be toxic (Dangeard, 1965; Starr, 1967).

Since the algae are just becoming of nuisance quantity in Onondaga Lake, it will be of interest to observe how the flora will change with secondary treatment of the wastewater effluent. Will this sanitary improvement accelerate eutrophication or curtail it? The experiment just described will help provide a scientific method for evaluating the answer to this question.

Some of the financial support for this study was provided by the New York State Department of Health under contract number C-19638. The assistance of my wife, Bettina, in all phases of this investigation, was indispensable.

REFERENCES

Berg, C. O., 1963. "Middle Atlantic States," *Limnology in North America*, ed. by Grey, University of Wisconsin Press, 191–239.

Clark, J. V. H., 1849. *Onondaga*, Stoddard and Babcock, Syracuse, N.Y.

Dangeard, P., 1965. "Sur Deux Chloroccales marines," *Botaniste ser XLVIII* (Fasc. I–VI): 65–74.

Hohn, M. H., 1951. "A Study of the Distribution of Diatoms (Bacillarieae) in Western New York State," Memoir 308 Cornell Univ. Agric. Exper. St., Ithaca, N.Y., 39 pp.

Jackson, D. F., 1967. "Management of Wastewater Effluents in Relation to Algal Problems," Proc. 4th Ann. Water Qual. Res. Symp., N.Y. State Dept. of Health, Albany, 37–72.

Nemerow, N. L., 1964. "Onondaga Lake—A Lake That Was," in *Some Aquatic Resources of Onondaga County*, ed. by Jackson, Onondaga Co. Dept. of Pub. Wks., Onondaga Co., N.Y., 22–29.

New York State, 1951. "Onondaga Lake Drainage Basin," Oswego River Drainage Basin Survey Series Report No. 1, N.Y. State Dept. of Health, Albany, 151 pp.

Starr, R. C., 1967. Personal communication.

XXVII

Review of the Algal Literature
For New York State*

JOHN M. KINGSBURY

Division of Biological Sciences and
New York State College of Agriculture
Cornell University, Ithaca, New York

EARLY STUDIES

New York State is unique among states in its aquatic resources. It is the only state having an open shoreline on both the Great Lakes and the Atlantic Ocean. With Michigan alone, it borders on more than one Great Lake. The central part of the state is dominated by the Finger Lakes, of unusual depth, and Oneida Lake (1) (see Figure 1 for letters and numerals), of nearly opposite characteristics. The latter is one of the most productive lakes of North America. Fayetteville Green Lake (2) presents a textbook example of chemical stratification. Pristine mountain lakes of the Adirondacks in the east contrast with eutrophic Chautauqua Lake (3) at the western end of the state. Cayuta Lake (4) grows *Cladophora* balls that are as large as any reported in the world (Clovis, 1955). The state's largest rivers are the St. Lawrence, shared with Canada, and the Hudson, entirely within the state. The Great Lakes, Oneida Lake, Lake Champlain (5), Seneca (6) and Cayuga Lakes (7), the St. Lawrence, and the Hudson are interconnected by the state barge canal system.

Limnological investigations of the waters of New York State have been comprehensively reviewed by C. O. Berg (1963). This essay, therefore, emphasizes investigations relating particularly to algae. Literature citations include pertinent major papers, but they are not intended to present a complete bibliography.

To 1850

The early history of the study of algae in New York State parallels the development of the subject nationally and internationally. Particularly

* The literature survey on which this summary is based was supported in part by a grant from the New York State Department of Health.

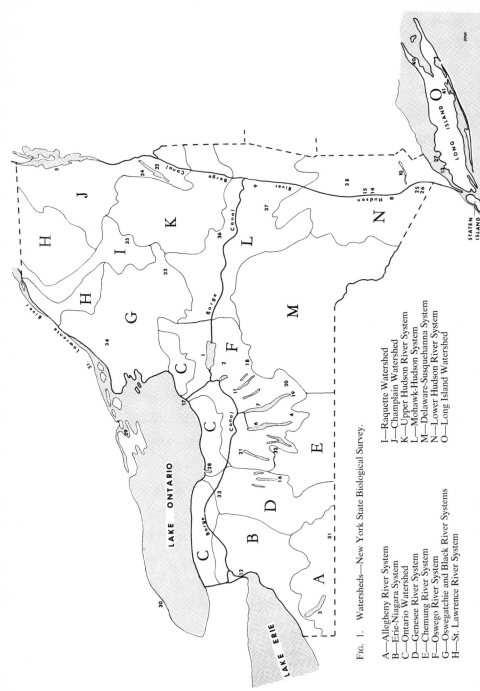

Fig. 1. Watersheds—New York State Biological Survey.

A—Allegheny River System
B—Erie-Niagara System
C—Ontario Watershed
D—Genesee River System
E—Chemung River System
F—Oswego River System
G—Oswegatchie and Black River Systems
H—St. Lawrence River System

I—Raquette Watershed
J—Champlain Watershed
K—Upper Hudson River System
L—Mohawk-Hudson System
M—Delaware-Susquehanna System
N—Lower Hudson River System
O—Long Island Watershed

Figures refer to locations identified in text.

attractive topics which initially received greater attention than others included the desmids and diatoms, the stoneworts, and marine algae.
Desmids and diatoms attracted the enthusiastic attention of microscopists
both because of their intrinsic beauty and also by virtue of the fact that
they took the measure of optical equipment then becoming available.
Stoneworts were conspicuous and unusual members of the freshwater
environment, while the seaweeds were equally conspicuous along the
shores. A fourth topic not so much attracted as required attention from
time to time—blooms of undesirable algae in domestic water sources.

Microscopist Jacob Whitman Bailey (1811–57) spent most of his productive life at the West Point Military Academy (8) on the Hudson River.
There, successively from 1828 to his premature death at the age of forty-
six, he was student, assistant professor, and professor of chemistry, min-
eralogy, and geology. Bailey had discontinued his formal education at the
age of twelve for financial reasons. He went to work in a bookstore in
Providence, Rhode Island, where his diligence in improving himself came
to the attention of John Kingsbury, secretary of Brown University, who
took Bailey into his home that he might study Latin and French. As a
youth, Bailey had obtained a Chevalier microscope, one of the best then
available in the United States. By applying it to the study of unicellular
algae, Bailey became the first person in this country to pay close attention to the algae of fresh water (Brunel, 1944; Coulter, 1888). Bailey was
led to this application of his microscope through initial discovery and investigation of unicellular fossil forms (also a first in America) during the
course of his interest in geology. The result was the publication of several
papers commencing in 1841 (1841, 1842, 1846) dealing with desmids and
diatoms and other unicellular algae. This led in turn to an assignment
to discuss the algae and some other cryptogams in John Torrey's monumental catalog of the flora of New York. Torrey made available to Bailey
his own collections of algae including many specimens obtained from or
authenticated by the leading European phycologists (Agardh, Greville,
Harvey, Mrs. Griffiths).

Bailey never contributed directly to Torrey's catalog (Torrey, 1843),
but instead presented his collected observations several years later as a
series (1847, 1848) in the *American Journal of Arts* (*Silliman's Journal*).
In contrast to the earlier papers, patterned after Ehrenberg, which had
concentrated on unicellular freshwater algae, these summary papers dealt
with phycology broadly and included notice of marine forms, many previously undescribed for America. They were dependent on the collecting
of others as well as his own. Despite his earlier preoccupation with desmids
and diatoms, Bailey thus developed extensive personal knowledge of
marine algae and other flora. West Point is situated at a location on the

Hudson River where freshwater and marine influences meet. Bailey's footnoted comments on the mixture of freshwater and marine forms of plants and animals at West Point in his paper of 1842 might prove sufficiently detailed to invite instructive comparison with the present situation in that much-discussed river.

Just as Bailey was the first to investigate microscopic algae of the United States, C. F. Durant (1805–73) is said (Hollick, 1915; Kelley, 1927) to be the first to publish a book on American algae (1850). Durant was a man of many firsts, most of them spectacular. He was the first United States citizen to make a profession of aeronautics, the first to construct and fly a balloon on this side of the Atlantic, and the first American to make silk (using silkworms imported from China). His book on algae also was spectacular. It was a finely detailed list and discussion of the green, red, and brown seaweeds (and some animal forms) in New York Harbor and bay, illustrated by actual specimens. Very few copies were printed. Copies may now be found at the New York Botanical Garden, the Brooklyn Botanical Garden, Rutgers, Jersey City Library (his home town), and the Farlow Library of Harvard University. This publication could serve as a base line for demonstrating changes in flora of the now heavily polluted harbor, the more so since actual specimens are at hand, and thus can reduce the uncertainties of changes in taxonomy.

1850–1900

In the period from 1850 to about 1900, except for sporadic attention to water supply problems (see later), the story of algal collecting and research in New York State is largely the story of three men, Charles Horton Peck, Francis Wolle, and Timothy Field Allen.

Charles Horton Peck (1833–1917) was born, educated, and employed throughout his long and productive life at institutions within a fifteen-mile radius of Albany (9). Although largely self-educated as a botanist, he developed a keen interest in the subject which brought him to the attention of the Honorable G. W. Clinton, a botanist, and soon led to his appointment (1867) to the staff of the New York State Cabinet of Natural History (after 1870, the New York State Museum) which he served until his retirement in 1913. Peck's first report (for 1867, but delayed in publishing until 1871, therefore antedated in appearance by his report for 1868) states that ninety-eight species of seaweeds had been collected from Peconic Bay (Long Island) by a Mrs. M. A. Bush. These appear to have been the first algal specimens acquired by the State Museum. These specimens, together with others from other collectors, and including specimens of Charales and other freshwater algae, were listed with some collection data in Peck's report for 1868 (appearing in 1869). Unfortunately for phycology, this fine start toward an algal flora for the state of New York was not realized as Peck's interests turned increasingly toward fungi. Additional records for algae appear in subsequent reports with decreasing frequency. An index to genera and species appears in the report published in 1888. Specimens referred to in Peck's reports are currently housed in the State Museum Herbarium, Albany.

The Reverend Francis Wolle (1817–95), who patented the first machinery for making paper bags, did not begin publishing on freshwater algae until 1876, at which time the first of a series of notes appeared in the *Bulletin of the Torrey Botanical Club*, and his major contributions came only after his retirement as principal of the then famous Moravian Seminary for Young Ladies at Bethlehem, Pennsylvania, at the age of sixty-four and for reasons of health. Nevertheless, three books appeared in the decade following 1881, concerned respectively with the desmids (1884), the freshwater algae (1887), and the diatoms (1894) of the United States. Collections from New York State are cited in the papers and books published by Wolle. Drouet (1939) has reviewed Wolle's filamentous blue-green algae.

Timothy Field Allen (1837–1902), educated as a physician, was attracted to the study of botany by association with D. C. Eaton, John Torrey, and others of that distinguished company of botanists then active in New York City. It is said that the suggestion for the formation of a formal group (which soon became the Torrey Botanical Club) is owed to Allen. Allen's early papers dealt with a variety of topics concerning higher plants, but he was particularly attracted to the stoneworts, and papers on that special group began appearing in 1871, continuing until 1900 (bibliography in Britton, 1903). Allen's privately published monographs on the Characeae of America (1880, 1888, 1892–96) became the standard references for their time. In both papers and monographs, collections from the waters of the state are frequently cited. Whereas many botanists of the time were educated as physicians and came to a study of botany later in life, Allen reversed this pattern. He was early attracted to botany by Horatio Wood's (1872) beautifully illustrated volume on the freshwater algae of North America (which included New York data and a geographic index), but later gave himself increasingly to the practice of medicine (Brunel, 1944). Dr. Allen was an indefatigable collector both of specimens and of literature on Charales. His collections are now part of the herbarium of the New York Botanical Garden (Howe, 1908).

Water Supply Investigations, 1860–1905

The majority of papers dealing with the algae of New York State that appeared from 1860 to shortly after 1900 were more or less directly related to incidence and effects of algae as nuisance organisms in public water supplies. New York's contribution to this developing literature was second only to that of Massachusetts, where trouble had appeared as early as 1851, almost immediately after water from Lake Cochituate was introduced into Boston.

The public water supply for New York City was initiated with the damming of the Croton River to form a reservoir (10) about five miles long, the construction of an aqueduct spanning the forty miles to the city, and the construction of water mains in the city. It went into service in late 1842. The investigation of a musty odor in the system in 1859 was the first such investigation in the state and one of the first in the country. Professor John Torrey, who was pressed into service, visited the reservoir in August, collected water there and at hydrants in the city, and reported (1860) that the musty odor and bad taste existing for the previous two weeks, which had caused general complaints throughout the city, appeared to be associated with the wind-driven accumulation of a bright green substance at the Croton dam. The water was then particularly low. Microscopic examination revealed that the water was "loaded" with small, straight filaments which Dr. Torrey (out of his realm) tentatively identified as *Nortoc* (*sic.*), but which, on the basis of his relatively careful description appear probably to have been *Anabaena planctonica*.

Although suspected earlier, the ability of water to cause disease was laid open to scientific investigation with the proof of the germ theory of disease by Koch's demonstration in 1876 of a bacillus as the cause of anthrax. Much interest was thus aroused in the microbiology of public water supplies, and the public soon came to demand and expect water of proven sanitary quality. Increase in interest was intensified by the growing number of communities served by public supplies over the same years. Consequently much literature exists of investigations into water microbiology between 1870 and 1900, and papers on problems caused by algae are not infrequent. Algae were not generally considered capable of causing disease, though they might well produce odors and tastes. Filtration was not generally used in those decades; water appeared at the tap more or less as it left the reservoir. Some surveys were initiated solely for the purpose of following seasonal populations of microorganisms in public water supplies, and often as not, the collecting locale was a domestic faucet. Literature on algae as nuisance organisms diminished greatly after 1904, when the first demonstrations of the effectiveness of copper sulfate in con-

TABLE I. Algal Investigations in New York Water Supplies, 1860–1905.

City	Water	Notes	References
Albany (9)	—	Unidentified troubles in 1853, 1865, 1872 and 1875	Rafter, 1890b Lattimore, 1877
Auburn (11)	—		Lattimore, 1877
Brooklyn	Ridgewood Prospect Heights	No troubles; these are general algal surveys	Lewis, 1870 Jeliffe, 1893a, 1893b, 1894
Buffalo (12)	Niagara River	No troubles; general algal surveys	Killicott, 1878 Mills, 1882 Smith, 1882
Cleveland*	Lake Erie	No troubles; general algal surveys	Vorce, 1880–82
Glen Cove† (13)	L. I. Sound	Effect of starch pollution on marine and freshwater algae	Britton, 1884
Newburgh (14)	Hudson River		Lattimore, 1877
New York	Croton Res. (10)	*Anabaena* (?), 1859 Survey; no troubles	Torrey, 1860 Lewis, 1870
		Coelosphaerium and *Anabaena*	Hitchcock, 1881a
		Survey; no troubles	Hitchcock, 1881b Wolle, 1882
		Meridion circulare, 1881	Hyatt, 1882
	Central Park Reservoir	"Foul," but no specific trouble	Gratacap & Woodward, 1884
Poughkeepsie (15)	Hudson River	Diatom bloom	Hyatt, 1882 Rafter, 1890b
Rochester	Hemlock Lake (16)	Late summer trouble, 1876; found *Botryococcus* and others	Lattimore, 1877
		No trouble; survey	Lattimore, 1878
		Volvox globator; fishy	Mallory & Rafter, 1889
		No trouble; survey	Rafter, 1890a

* Lake Erie as contiguous to New York State
† Not a public water supply

trolling algal growths were publicized. During the thirty-five-year period in question, algal investigations in New York water supplies (so far as they are recorded in the scientific literature) may be outlined as in Table 1. The literature for this time and subject has been reviewed by Jeliffe (1893, 1894), Lattimore (1877), Moore (1903), Moore and Kellerman (1904), Rafter (1890b), and Whipple (1914), among others. In several of the general algal surveys of public water supplies, enough detail may be found to effect useful comparisons with the present, a century later.

Copper sulfate had been used for many years as a fungicide when it was first investigated for controlling algae. G. T. Moore deserves (Whipple, 1914) the credit for its introduction in the latter capacity. His well-documented review of the problems caused by algae, which was accomplished in part by means of a survey of 500 prominent water works engineers, and of the use and effects of copper sulfate were followed by the rapid, general adoption of this technique wherever troubles occurred. This was followed in turn by a marked diminution in reports of trouble from algae in water supplies. Moore (1905) reported a number of before and after examinations of bodies of water treated with copper sulfate, including those at Cambridge (New York), Elmira, Fieldhome, Glen Cove, Middletown, Rhinebeck, Scarboro, and Water Mill (Southampton). See also Jackson (1905) and Caird (1905) for reports of the effects of copper sulfate as first employed in this state.

1900–1925

State government has sponsored two major compilations of the state's natural resources. The first, including geological and biological surveys, commenced in 1836, and included John Torrey's two volumes on the botany of the state mentioned above. The second, initiated in 1926, examined the biological resources of particular watersheds. Algal work published between 1900 and the start of the second survey is reviewed geographically below, and for uniformity of later comparison, on the basis of watersheds as defined in the watershed survey publications. The major drainage basins of New York State are presented in Figure 1.

From 1900 to 1925, the majority of these watersheds remained entirely or mostly uninvestigated for their algal flora. Investigations of the others were conditioned primarily by the availability of persons and institutions that could accomplish or support such an endeavor. Principal foci of activity included the Oswego watershed (F) or Finger Lakes region (Cornell and Syracuse Universities), Lower Hudson watershed (N) (New York City and the area immediately north), Long Island (O), Staten Island, and the marine waters of the state. Major investigations included the following:

Under the administration of the U.S. Fish Commission, a survey of the aquatic vegetation of western Lake Erie was undertaken. Boats and laboratory space were made available at the U.S. Fish Hatchery at Put-in-Bay. Pieters (1902) published a list with collection data for attached and planktonic species in some twenty-five genera. Julia Snow (1903) expanded the list to some 102 genera and extensively applied the then new technique of culturing in the laboratory to determine the full life cycle. She chose to concentrate on the unicellular and colonial green algae for the latter, and may have been the first person to apply culture techniques for algal taxonomy in America. These studies gave a good starting point for review of eutrophication in Lake Erie in later years.

The Geological Survey of Canada sponsored a transect study of the bottom sediments of Lake Ontario published in 1925 (Kindle, 1925). Two transects were taken across the western end of the lake and one northward from Oswego (17) toward the eastern end. Algae were especially emphasized in the latter and were submitted to F. S. Collins and the diatoms to Albert Mann for comment.

In the Oswego watershed, F. C. Baker, of the New York State College of Forestry at Syracuse University, was responsible for a detailed study of molluscs and fish in Oneida Lake (1), and the resulting publications (e.g., 1918) contain considerable information concerning algae present in the lake at that time. Baker enlisted the help of E. N. Transeau, who described a new species of *Mougeotia* (1918) from the lake.

W. L. Bray (1915) presented some semi-quantitative data on the considerable growths of *Rivularia* in the plankton of Oneida Lake and of several filamentous algae in Tully Lake (18).

Cornell University (19) pioneered in the development of aquatic biology as a science in the United States, sharing with Wisconsin the honor of initiating formal instruction in limnology. Some of the early faculty were remarkably acute generalists who recorded and integrated into their own special subjects observations on the local algal flora or particular components of it. Such persons included J. G. Needham, W. W. Rowlee, R. Hitchcock, and G. F. Atkinson. The latter published observations on freshwater red algae (1890, 1931) and further incidentally (1909) on the distribution of algae as hosts of the fungi, his primary object of interest. O. A. Johannsen and J. T. Lloyd developed (1915) a key to genera of planktonic organisms of the Cayuga Lake basin for use in classes. Emilie Platt (1915) surveyed the mat-forming algae and associated organisms from about twenty temporary and permanent ponds near the university. Over a period of years, the university's scientific staff cooperated in a

relatively thorough examination (Members . . . , 1926) of the Lloyd-Cornell
Reservation, more popularly called the McLean Bogs (20). The reservation
encompasses in relatively small area a number of bogs of quite different
character, and some open water. In close proximity are bogs with basic
water and marl underneath, and soft-water bogs underlain by peat. The
resulting survey included passing references to the algae, though this
group of organisms is perhaps the most important of the groups not specifically covered. At that time no one at Cornell had made the algae the object
of his special interest.

Following their initial work in Wisconsin, E. A. Birge and Chauncy
Juday turned their attention to the Finger Lakes of New York (1914, 1921).
While primary emphasis was placed on physical factors, net (and later
centrifuge) collections of plankton were made in eleven lakes and handled
in part quantitatively at the generic level. Nineteen genera are named,
and distributions with depth are given. The presence of algal "water bis-
cuits" in one of these lakes [Canandaigua (21)] is mentioned by J. M.
Clarke (1919).

In the Adirondacks, Lake George (22) came under study by a group
from Cornell University (Needham et al., 1922) charged by the New York
State Conservation Commission with surveying all factors that might
be of significance in determining fish populations and productivity in the
lake. Shore vegetation (including Charales) and major phytoplankton (by
genus) were discussed by J. G. Needham (1921) and the plankton in more
detail by C. Juday. Marshall Howe, from material sent him, had reported
earlier (1903) on annual summer blooms of Cyanophyta in Honnedaga (23)
Lake (western Adirondacks) and Chilson Lake (24) (eastern Adirondacks).
Howe believed that his was the first report of blooms in lakes of eastern
North America.

With one notable exception, the papers dealing with algae of the lower
Hudson watershed are minor notes. They deal with Van Cortlandt Lake
(New York City) (Merriman, 1922), ponds of Central Park (Anonymous,
1913), Grassy Sprain Reservoir (Yonkers) (Hastings, 1921), Bronx Park,
Bear Mountain–Harriman (25) lakes (Hastings, 1924), and Long Lake at
the New York Botanical Garden which bloomed with *Oscillatoria prolifica* (Howe, 1921). The exception was an investigation of twenty-six lakes
in the Palisades Interstate Park (26) by Gilbert Morgan Smith (1924)
who did the necessary field work in July and August of 1918. Dr. Smith's
services were requested by the Parks Commission as the result of conflicts
between the use of copper sulfate to enhance recreational and aesthetic
values and its effects on fish populations. In his usual fashion, Dr. Smith
made a thorough survey of American and world literature dealing with
algal blooms (more than seventy-five literature citations) and abstracted

a long list of algae known to cause blooms. Similarly, he looked closely into the literature dealing with the effects of copper sulfate on algae. Finally he presented an illustrated tabulation of some 165 species of algae with some estimate of quantity that he collected from the lakes. This remarkably thorough study was somewhat buried by being published in the *Roosevelt Wildlife Bulletin*.

For some reason (perhaps because it is an island), persons who worked on the flora of Long Island, contrary to usual practice, included the algae. Jelliffe's *Flora of Long Island* (1899) and additions (1904) name nearly 400 species of freshwater and marine algae with brief collection data. Burnham and Latham's series of papers on the flora of Southold (eastern Long Island) commencing in 1914, (1917, 1921, 1923, 1925), include a large number of marine algae together with some freshwater species. These authors were able to draw on a considerable literature dealing with the marine algae of that area. In addition to the reports of J. W. Bailey mentioned above, F. W. Hall (1876), W. G. Farlow (1893), N. Pike (1886; Martindale, 1889), and others had described collections of marine algae from Long Island waters in the years between 1875 and 1900.

Establishment of the Biological Laboratory at Cold Spring Harbor (27) in 1890 soon gave a focus in teaching program and research facilities for investigations of the algae of the vicinity. A list of local organisms appeared as early as 1898 (Davenport). It was followed by increasingly more detailed lists through the efforts of Copeland (1901) and Grier (1908–25). Detailed study of the inner harbor from 1905 to 1913 by D. S. Johnson and H. H. York (1915) resulted in the publication of a major report on the relation of plants to tide levels, encompassing hundreds of species including higher plants, fresh, salt marsh, and marine algae. At about the same time, E. N. Transeau (1913) discussed in a more general way plant associations of the seashore of Long Island Sound based mainly on observations also made at Cold Spring Harbor. These surveys were accompanied by occasional papers on particular algal topics that came to attention at the laboratory.

The plankton of coastal waters off Long Island were explored in cruises of the U.S. Fisheries schooner, *Grampus*, and reported in publications of H. B. Bigelow (1915, 1922). Marine and freshwater diatoms were described from collections on Staten Island by E. A. Schultze in 1889.

NEW YORK STATE BIOLOGICAL SURVEY, 1927–1940

Results of the state's biological survey dominated its algal literature for the next quarter-century. This was the first, and remains one of the most comprehensive, of such surveys in any state. The pattern of this work was set by the Lake George survey described above. Emphasis was on aquatic biology with particular reference to the major factors influencing sports and commercial fisheries and stocking policies of the New York State Conservation Department, which supported the survey. Thus close attention was given to characteristics and sources of pollution and the organisms of major significance in food chains and in other ecological relationships. Physical and chemical data were also obtained. The survey was begun in the summer of 1926 with fourteen competent scientists working in the field throughout the Genesee River watershed. A separate watershed was surveyed by an increasingly larger staff for each of the thirteen following summers until all waters of the state had been surveyed. Although there was some evolution in pattern, the reports give relatively uniform coverage to the principal factors. In each, attention is given to planktonic algae, and results are expressed quantitatively. W. C. Muenscher provided the plankton analyses for the Genesee (D), Oswego (F), Champlain (J), and St. Lawrence (H) studies. J. P. Young reported separately on diatoms of the Genesee area. P. R. Burkholder reported on the plankton of Lake Erie (B), Upper Hudson (K), and Oswegatchie and Black River watersheds (G). W. L. Tressler was associated in the latter and became the principal author for surveys of the remaining watersheds (with R. Bere). These were given somewhat greater limnological emphasis compared with the earlier surveys.

W. C. Muenscher, my predecessor at Cornell, also provided an enumeration of the higher aquatic plants for most of the watersheds. In these surveys he included mention of Charales, and often of blooms of conspicuous mat algae. Saline algae, particularly *Enteromorpha*, are found in certain locations in the Genesee and Oswego basins at points where fossil marine salt deposits are exposed to freshwater sources. Dr. Muenscher made particular note of such occurrences in the reports dealing with these watersheds and also in a separate paper (1927). I have retraced his footsteps to many of the places cited. Some have been destroyed by construction, but luxuriant *Enteromorpha* is still to be found in several. Rogers McVaugh and R. T. Clausen surveyed the higher plants and Charales of the Allegheny (A) and Chemung (E), and the Ontario (C) watersheds, respectively.

These are the obvious places to expect algal data in the reports of the Biological Survey, but much additional information is contained in less conspicuous places such as reports dealing with effects of pollution, food habits of fish (stomach analyses), bottom organisms, and the like.

No attempt was made in the Biological Survey to enumerate the flora of attached algae. Likewise, the surveys of plankton algae were of necessity confined to a relatively small number of sampling stations in each region. Field work was done during summer months, and seasonal records are not available.

1925–1965

The concerted effort of the Biological Survey has not again been achieved. Pursuit of knowledge concerning algae of the state during this period fell again to those few individuals who were motivated, appropriately located, and reasonably supported. The review in the next paragraphs, organized by watersheds from west to east, shows much the same pattern of geographic strengths and weaknesses as was evident in the period 1900 to 1925.

New York shares the shoreline of Lake Erie with Pennsylvania, Ohio, Michigan, and Ontario. Lake Erie is for its size the most thoroughly studied of the Great Lakes. Centers of investigation have been at Erie, Pennsylvania; Cleveland, Ohio; and Put-in-Bay, Ohio (Franz Theodore Stone Laboratory). In sharp contrast, the eastern or New York end of the lake has remained nearly unexamined. Those contributing importantly to algal topics associated with the western part of the lake include E. H. Ahlstrom, D. C. Chandler, C. C. Davis, R. Y. Gottschall, C. E. Taft, L. H. Tiffany, and J. Verduin. Major papers on phytoplankton and limnological relationships have resulted.

At the eastern end of the lake, Burkholder's study of the plankton, mentioned above as part of the Biological Survey, was also reported in greater detail elsewhere (1929, 1960). J. L. Blum (1965) has followed the algal flora of the Buffalo River (12) as it enters the lake. C. C. Davis (1966) and A. M. Beeton (1966) have provided reviews of the plankton of the Great Lakes and indices of eutrophication in the Great Lakes, respectively.

Compared with Lake Erie, Lake Ontario has had little attention, either from New York or Ontario. Tressler and associates (1941, 1953) investigated seasonal distribution of phytoplankton in Irondequoit Bay (28), and A. Tucker (1948) surveyed the phytoplankton of the Bay of Quinte (29) on the Ontario side of the lake, due north of Oswego. Neither bay is a good measure of conditions in the lake itself, particularly Irondequoit, which Tressler showed to be highly polluted and to have little mixing with the waters of the lake. Despite the paucity of data bearing on Lake Ontario, Schenk and Thompson (1965), using data from the records of the Toronto (30) water system, have been able to show that the plankton level approximately doubled from 1923 to 1954, thus that Ontario is undergoing rapid eutrophication in a fashion similar to that demonstrated for Lake Erie.

New York beaches along Lake Ontario have been increasingly bothered by accumulations of *Cladophora* in summer months. D. F. Jackson (1966) has investigated photosynthetic rates of *Cladophora* as related to fertility of the water and presented evidence that phosphorus is normally the limiting factor preventing even greater growths of this plant in the lake.

Chautauqua Lake (3) was investigated by Tressler *et. al.* (1940), over a three-year period in a study which extended that of the Biological Survey. Plankton are handled quantitatively to genus, and seasonal distributions are given. Another seasonal study has been made more recently in the southeastern end of the lake (Giebner, 1951). At the southern border of the state, the New York State Museum has sponsored a study of the biology of the Allegheny Indian Reservation (31) and vicinity. G. J. Schumacher reported (1961) finding 148 taxa in 65 genera from 46 stations sampled in the month of August. This area is particularly noted for its rich flora of freshwater red algae; *Batrachospermum, Chantransia, Bangia,* and *Tuomeya (Lemanea)* have been reported (Gordon, 1934; Matthews, 1932; Palmer, 1942). Lying at the northern edge of the Chemung watershed, the Italy Hill swamp is one of the few remaining areas of the state relatively untouched by man. J. F. Clovis (1955) surveyed its algal flora of 97 species with notes on distribution, habitats, and ecology.

In 1936 about 100 persons joined to form the Bergen Swamp Preservation Society. Through their efforts and those of their successors, funds have been raised enabling most of the area in the Genesee watershed, known to naturalists and botanists from the earliest history of the state as the Bergen Swamp (33), to be preserved in its wild condition. This area is noteworthy for the large number of unusual plants and animals that inhabit it. Beyond that, several marshes and a marl bog form conspicuous and unusual features. From efforts made in connection with its preservation came an inventory of its biological characteristics. Stewart and Merrell (1937) discussed the ecology of the swamp with particular attention to the marl bog and its algal deposition. A decade later, W. C. Muenscher (1946, 1951) and a number of his students undertook a survey of the vegetation. Algae are mentioned in several sections of the survey, and are emphasized in papers by Hotchkiss (1950), on the algae he found in collections made over a four-year period, and M. H. Hohn (1950), who listed 240 species of diatoms.

Studies in the Oswego watershed (F) in recent years have been dominated by an interest in Cayuga Lake (7) and environs, Oneida Lake (1), and Fayetteville Green Lake (2). P. R. Burkholder (1931) conducted a seasonal survey of the phytoplankton on the Cayuga Lake basin, and H. H. Howard (1963) has investigated primary production in the lake. Barlow and Bishop (1965) have followed phosphorus in relation to phytoplankters of the lake, while D. H. Hamilton (1966) has investigated the principal algal nutrients of both Cayuga and Seneca (6) lakes as related to the chlorophyll a:phaeophytin ratio. C. P. Mason (1965) has investigated the ontogeny and some of the factors controlling growths of floating mats of *Cladophora* in farm ponds of the Ithaca area (19). One of the few studies reported on the effects of herbicides on algae was conducted by A. W. Eipper (1959), also using farm ponds in this area.

In the last few years, ninety-six equal quarter-acre ponds have been constructed in an experimental facility at Cornell University (19) that will be used for basic studies in the ecology and control of aquatic weeds. The algae present in the soil from which one group of forty ponds was constructed have been enumerated by Lanciani and Kingsbury (1965).

Because of its remarkable characteristics as a chemically stratified lake, Fayetteville Green Lake (2) has been repeatedly studied both limnologically and biologically (Eggleton, 1956, with algal identifications by W. R. Taylor; Bradley, 1929; Howe, 1932). It contains large marl ledges (bioherms) of algal origin, and it supports a highly discrete layer of purple photosynthetic bacteria (*Lamprocystis*). Its dominant phytoplankters have been compared with the dominant flora of nearby lakes by Jackson and Dence (1958).

Ten green algae, eight blue-greens, and two chrysophytes were collected and identified by Gilbert Morgan Smith on a trip to Oneida Lake (1) in August of 1918, at a time of major interest in this lake on the part of fisheries (see above), but the results were not published for a decade as part of another fisheries investigation (Adams and Hankinson, 1928). Dence and Jackson (1959) reviewed earlier observations and discussed changes that have taken place over the years in the algal flora of the lake. More recently, D. F. Jackson and others from Syracuse University have concerned themselves with measuring and interpreting the biological significance of certain limnological parameters and characteristics of pollution in this lake (Mt. Pleasant et. al., 1962). Hastings (1940) has reported on algal communities in Tully Lake (18) to the south.

At Payne Lake (34), cattle mortality associated with a blue-green algal bloom led to an enumeration of the algae by W. C. Muenscher (Evans, 1936). To the east, in the center of the Adirondacks, H. F. Heady (1942) conducted a detailed survey of the shoreline vegetation of five lakes on the Huntington Forest Reservation (35) of the New York State College of Forestry, including Charales but not other algae in his observations. Nutrients in one of these ponds have been investigated by Brun (1960). At the southern edge of the Adirondack State Park, Maloney and Tressler (1942) investigated the diurnal migration of zooplankton in Caroga Lake (36), giving passing attention to phytoplankters. In the same watershed, (Mohawk-Hudson), M. S. Markle (1950) followed the algal populations of ponds and a stream in the Edmund Niles Huyck Preserve near Rensselaersville (37). Tests (Greeley, 1960) in the Mohawk River of 2,4-D to control water chestnut (*Trapa natans*) were successful in killing the higher plant but often resulted in the replacement of water chestnut by dense mats of filamentous algae tangled in the dead chestnut.

Starting in 1958 (–1961), Madeline Pierce has tested the immediate and longer term effects of 2,4-D and other weed killers on aquatic vegetation in Long Pond (38), lower Hudson watershed. She paid particular attention to effects on phytoplankton, which for the most part were transitory.

With few exceptions, interest in algae in the Staten and Long Island area has centered in recent years on marine forms. As one exception, diatoms and other microscopic algae of the Wm. T. Davis Refuge on Staten Island were enumerated by Burke (1957) and Cooper (1957). From Cold Spring Harbor, H. S. Conrad (1935) examined the plant associations of central Long Island, but as far as the algae were concerned, observations were limited primarily to marine forms. W. R. Taylor (1940) listed sixty-four species of marine algae from twenty-four stations on the shores of Long Island. Bouck and Morgan (1957) recorded the initial occurrence of *Codium* on North American shores, at Orient Point (40). It has now spread to New Jersey and in the other direction to beyond Chatham on Cape Cod. Much detailed work on the plankton of Long Island Sound and other coastal waters has come from the Bingham Oceanographic Station of Yale University. Persons principally associated with algal aspects of this work include S. A. M. Conover (1956) and G. A. Riley (1959).

Approximately half the ducks consumed in the United States originate in a small number of duck farms in eastern Long Island. Effluent from the water courses utilized by these farms discharges into shallow bays on the south shore of Long Island—especially Moriches Bay (41)—and causes problems for recreational uses and shell fisheries. The resulting bloom of phytoplankton has been studied in some detail, first by J. H. Ryther (1954) and more recently by J. P. Barlow and students (Barlow *et. al.*, 1963; Barlow and Myren, 1961; Lorenzen, 1963). B. Patten (1961) has looked into plankton relationships of Raritan Bay, just south of New York City.

In comparison with studies of algae of particular bodies of water as enumerated in the paragraphs above, studies of particular groups of algae from wider geographic areas have been fewer in number. The Vaucherias and Zygnemataceae of western New York won the attention of J. L. Blum (1951, 1953, 1956). R. D. Wood and W. C. Muenscher published a memoir on the Characeae of New York (1956). The diatoms have been surveyed in western New York by M. H. Hohn (1951, 1952) and the Hudson, St. Lawrence, and Niagara Rivers as part of the sampling by the National Water Quality Network by L. G. Williams and C. Scott (1962). Stoneworts have been included in transect studies of succession in a number of experimental marshes constructed by the Conservation Department in western New York (Dane, 1959).

New York State has participated responsibly in the development of knowledge of algae in America from the beginning. Its Biological Survey remains a model for emulation. Nevertheless the resulting body of information is not adequate to the demands presently placed on it by the problems and concerns of increasing human populations and resulting uses and abuses of water. What we know is colored too much by accidents of geography, opportunity, season, personality, and institution; results are unscientifically non-methodical and lacunae clearly greater than the accumulation.

This pattern will change; it is changing.

REFERENCES

Adams, C. C., and T. L. Hankinson, 1928. "The Ecology and Economics of Oneida Lake Fish," *Roosevelt Wildl. Ann. 1*, 239–548, and map.

Allen, T. F., 1871. "Characeae," *Bull. Torrey Bot. Club 2*, 9–10.

————, 1880. *The Characeae of America*, S. E. Cassion, Boston, pp. 1–14, plus 6 colored pl.

————, 1888. *The Characeae of America*, part I, pub. by author, New York, pp. 1–64.

————, 1892–6. *The Characeae of America*, part II, pub. by author, New York, pp. 1–28, plus 36 pl.

Anonymous, 1913. "Destruction of Fishes by Algae," *Zoological Soc. Bull. 16*, 1048.

Atkinson, G. F., 1890. "Monograph of the Lemaneaceae of the United States," *Ann. Bot. 4*, 177–229.

————, 1909. "Some Fungus Parasites of Algae," *Bot. Gaz. 48*, 321–38.

————, 1931. "Notes on the Genus *Lemanea* in North America," *ibid., 29*, 225–42.

Bailey, J. W., 1841. "American Bacillaria. I. Desmidiacea," *Am. J. Sci. and Arts 41(2)*, 1–24, plus 2 pl.

————, 1842. "American Bacillaria. II. Naviculacea," *ibid., 42(1)*, 1–20, plus 2 pl.

————, 1846. "On Some New Species of American Desmidiaceae, from the Catskill Mountains," *ibid., 1(2)*, 126–27.

————, 1847, 1848. "Notes on the Algae of the United States," *ibid., 3(2)*, 80–85, 399–403; *6(2)*, 37–42.

Baker, F. C., 1918. "The Productivity of Invertebrate Fish Food on the Bottom of Oneida Lake, with Special Reference to Molluscs," N.Y.S. Col. Forestry at Syracuse Univ., Tech. Publ. *9*, 11–264.

Barlow, J. P., and J. W. Bishop, 1965. "Phosphate Regeneration by Zooplankton in Cayuga Lake," *Limnol. Oceanogr. 10*(suppl.), R15–R24.

Barlow, J. P., C. J. Lorenzen, and R. T. Myren, 1963. "Eutrophication of a Tidal Estuary," *ibid., 8*, 251–62.

Barlow, J. P., and R. T. Myren, 1961. "Oxygen Resources of Tidal Waters," *Water & Sewage Works, 108*, 68–71.

Beeton, A. M., 1966. "Indices of Great Lakes Eutrophication," Univ. Michigan Gt. Lakes Res. Div. Publ. *15*, 1–8.

Berg, C. O., 1963. "Middle Atlantic States," *Limnology in North America*, ed. by D. G. Frey, Univ. Wisconsin Press, Madison, pp. 191–237.

Bigelow, H. B., 1915. "Exploration of the Coast Water between Nova Scotia and Chesapeake Bay, July and August, 1913, by the U.S. Fisheries Schooner *Grampus*, Oceanography and Plankton," Bull. Mus. Comp. Zool., Harvard, *59*, 149–359, plus 2 pl.

———, 1922. "Exploration of the Coastal Water off the Northeastern United States in 1916 by the U.S. Fisheries Schooner *Grampus*," *ibid., 65(5)*, 85–188.

Birge, E. A., and C. Juday, 1914. "A Limnological Study of the Finger Lakes of New York," *Bull. U. S. Bur Fisheries 32*, 524–609, and 6 pl.

———, 1921. "Further Limnological Observations on the Finger Lakes of New York," *ibid., 37*, 209–52.

Blum, J. L., 1951. "Notes on Vaucheriaceae with Particular Reference to Western New York," *Bull. Torrey Bot. Club 78*, 441–48.

———, 1953. "The Racemose Vaucheriae with Inclined Pendent Oogonia," *ibid., 80*, 478–97.

———, 1956. "Zygnemataceae of Western New York," I. *Papers Mich. Acad. Sci., Arts, and Letters 41*, 3–11.

———, 1965. "Interactions between Buffalo River and Lake Erie," Univ. Michigan, Gt. Lakes Res. Div. Publ. *13*, 25–28.

Bouck, G. B., and E. Morgan, 1957. "The Occurrence of *Codium* in Long Island Waters," *Bull. Torrey Bot. Club 84*, 384–87.

Bradley, W. H., 1929. "Algae Reefs and Oolites of the Green River Formation," U.S. Geol. Surv. Prof. Paper *154*, 203–92, plus pl. 70–76.

Bray, W. L., 1915. "Development of the Vegetation of New York State," N.Y.S. Col. Forestry at Syracuse Univ., Tech. Publ. *3*, 1–186, plus map.

Britton, N. L., 1884. "[Report on] Microscopical Examination of the Wastes [of the Starch Works of the Glen Cove Manufacturing Company, Glen Cove, N.Y.]," *Ann. Rept. N.Y. State Bd. Health 4*, 378–80.

———, 1903. "Timothy Field Allen," *Bull. Torrey Bot. Club 30*, 173–177.

Brun, B. S., 1960. "Investigation of Four Nutrient Elements in Rich Lake," MS. thesis, N.Y.S. Coll. Forestry, Syracuse, N.Y.

Brunel, J., 1944. "Les grandes etapes de l'algologie americaine," *Rev. Trim. Canad. 30*, 71–72.

Burke, J. F., 1957. "Diatoms [of the Wm. T. Davis Refuge]," *Proc. Staten Island Inst. Arts & Sci. 19*, 56–59.

Burkholder, P. R., 1929. "Microplankton Studies of Lake Erie," In Preliminary Report on the Cooperative Survey of Lake Erie, *Bull. Buffalo Soc. Nat. Sci. 14*, 73–93.

———, 1931. "Studies in the Phytoplankton of the Cayuga Lake Basin, New York," *ibid. 15*, 15–181.

———, 1960. "A Survey of the Microplankton of Lake Erie," U. S. Fish and Wildlife Serv. Sp. Sci. Report—Fisheries, No. 334, 123–44.

Burnham, S. H., and R. A. Latham, 1914. "The Flora of the Town of Southold, Long Island and Gardiner's Island," *Torreya 14*, 201–25, 229–54.

———, 1917. *Ibid., 17*, 111–22.

———, 1921. *Ibid.*, Second supplementary list, *21*, 1–11.

———, 1923. *Ibid.*, third supplementary list, *23*, 3–9.

———, 1925. *Ibid.*, fifth supplementary list, *25*, 71–83.

Caird, J. M., 1905. "The Copper Sulphate Treatment for Algae at Middletown, N.Y.," *Engineering News 53*, 33–34.

Clarke, J. M., 1919. "The Scientific Reservations under Control of the Museum," *N.Y.S. Museum Bull. 219*, 16–20.

Clovis, Jesse F., 1955. "Ecological Association Types in the Italy Hill (N.Y.) Swamp Area," Ph.D. thesis, Cornell Univ., Ithaca, N.Y.

———, 1955. "A New Record for *Cladophora* Balls," *Am. Midl. Nat. 54*, 508–509.

Conrad, H. S., 1935. "The Plant Associations of Central Long Island—A Study in Descriptive Plant Sociology," *ibid., 16*, 433–516.

Conover, S. A. M., 1956. "Oceanography of Long Island Sound, 1952–1954. IV. Phytoplankton," *Bull. Bingham Oceanogr. Coll. 15*, 62–112.

Cooper, I. C. G., 1957. "Microscopic Life [of the Wm. T. Davis Refuge]. I. Algae," *Proc. Staten Island Inst. Arts and Sci. 19*, 60–62.

Copeland, E. B., 1901. "Cryptogamic and Physiological Botany at Cold Spring Harbor in 1901," *Torreya 1*, 127–30.

Coulter, S., 1888. "Jacob Whitman Bailey," *Bot. Gaz. 13*, 118–24.

Dane, C. W., 1959. "Succession of Aquatic Plants in Small Artificial Marshes in New York State," *N.Y. Fish and Game J. 6*, 57–76.

Davenport, C. B., 1898. "The Fauna and Flora about Coldspring Harbor, L.I.," *Science 8*, 685–89.

Davis, C. C., 1966. "Plankton Studies in the Largest Great Lakes of the World," *Univ. Michigan, Gt. Lakes Res. Div. Publ. 14*, 1–36.

Day, D. F., 1882. "The Plants of Buffalo and Vicinity," *Bull. Buffalo Soc. Nat. Sci. 4*, 65–290.

Dence, W. A., and D. F. Jackson, 1959. "Changing Chemical and Biological Conditions in Oneida Lake, New York," *School Sci. & Math. 59*, 317–24.

Drouet, F., 1939. "Francis Wolle's Filamentous Myxophyceae," Field Mus. Nat. Hist., Bot. Ser. (Publ. 460) *20*, 17–64.

Durant, C. F., 1850. *Algae and Corallines of the Bay and Harbor of New York Illustrated with Natural Types,* Narine and Co., Geo. P. Putnam, New York, 43 pp, plus 42 pl.

Eggleton, F. E., 1956. "Limnology of a Meromictic, Interglacial, Plunge-Basin Lake," *Trans. Am. Microscop. Soc. 75*, 334–78.

Eipper, A. W., 1959. "Effects of Five Herbicides on Farm Pond Plants and Fish," *N.Y. Fish and Game J. 6*, 46–56.

Evans, W. M., 1936. "Report of Investigations of Cattle Poisoning around Payne Lake, Jefferson County, New York," *Cornell Vet. 26*, 337–41.

Farlow, W. G., 1893. "Notes on Some Algae in the Herbarium of the Long Island Historical Society," *Bull. Torrey Bot. Club 20*, 107–109.

Giebner, B. M., 1951. "The Plankton Algae of the Southeast End of Chautauqua Lake," *Proc. Rochester Acad. Sci. 9*, 409–20.

Gordon, R. B., 1934. "*Lemanea grandis* (Wolle) Atk. Rediscovered after Forty Years," *Bull. Torrey Bot. Club 61*, 437–39.

Gratacap, L. P., and A. Woodward, 1884. "The Freshwater Flora and Fauna of Central Park," *Sci. Am. Suppl.* Dec. 27, 1884, 480–81.

Greeley, J. R., 1960. "A New 2,4-D Amine Pellet for Eradication of Water Chestnut," *Proc. Northeast. Weed Contr. Conf. 14*, 488–95.

Grier, N. M., 1908. "The Native Flora of the Vicinity of Cold Spring Harbor, L.I., New York," *Am. Midl. Nat. 9*, 1–265.

———, 1924. "The Native Flora of the Vicinity of Cold Spring Harbor, L.I., N.Y. Schizophyta, Myxomycetes, Dinoflagellatae, Bacillariophyta," *ibid.*, 245–56, 283–318, 550–63.

———, 1925. "Unreported Plants from Long Island, N.Y. II. Cryptogams Exclusive of Pteridophyta. *Torreya 25*, 5–11, 29–35.

Hall, F. W., 1876. "List of Marine Algae Growing in Long Island Sound within 20 Miles of New Haven," *Bull. Torrey Bot. Club 6*, 109–12.

Hamilton, D. H., 1966. "Eutrophication of Water Resources of New York State," Cornell Water Res. Ctr. Publ. 14 (processed), 24 pp.

Hastings, G. T., 1921. "Succession of Algae in the Grassy Sprain Reservior," *J. N.Y. Bot. Gard. 22*, 64–66.

———, 1924. "Water Plants of the Kanawauke Lakes," *Torreya 24*, 93–97.

———, 1940. "Algal Communities in Tully Lake," *ibid., 40*, 33.

Heady, H. F., 1942. "Littoral Vegetation of the Lakes on the Huntington Forest," *Roosevelt Wildlife Bull. 8*, 4–37.

Hitchcock, R., 1881a. "Croton Water in August," *Am. Mon. Microscope J. 2*, 156–57.

———, 1881b. "Report on Croton Water," *ibid.*, 238.

Hohn, M. H., 1950. "The Vegetation of Bergen Swamp. V. The Diatoms (Bacillariae)," *Proc. Rochester Acad. Sci. 9*, 265–76.

———, 1951. "A Study of Distribution of Diatoms (Bacillarieae) in Western New York State," *Cornell Univ. Agr. Expt. Sta. Mem. 308*, 1–39.

———, 1952. "Contributions to the Diatoms of Western New York State," *Trans. Am. Microscope Soc. 71*, 270–71.

Hollick, A., 1915. "A Quaint old Work on Seaweeds," *Proc. Staten Island Assoc. Arts and Sci. 5*, 85–91.

Hotchkiss, A. T., 1950. "The Vegetation of Bergen Swamp. IV. The Algae," *Proc. Rochester Acad. Sci. 9*, 237–64.

Howard, H. H., 1963. "Primary Production, Phytoplankton, and Temperature Studies of Cayuga Lake, New York," PhD thesis, Cornell Univ., Ithaca, N.Y.

Howe, M. A., 1903. "A Note on the Flowering of the Lakes of the Adirondacks," *Torreya 3*, 150–54.

———, 1908. "The Collections of Algae," *J. N.Y. Bot Gard. 9*, 123–30.

———, 1914. "Some Midwinter Alage of Long Island Sound," *Torreya 14*, 97–101.

———, 1921. "The Working of Long Lake," *J. N.Y. Bot Gard. 22*, 156–59.

———, 1932. "The Geological Importance of the Lime-Secreting Algae with a Description of a New Travertine-Forming Organism," *U.S. Geol. Surv. Prof. Paper 170*, 57–64, plus pl. 19–23.

Hyatt, J. D., 1882. "Sporadic Growth of Certain Diatoms and the Relation thereof to Impurities in the Water Supply of Cities," Proc. Am. Soc. Microscopists *4*, 197–99.

Jackson, D. D., 1905. "Purification of Water by Copper Sulphate," *Municipal Engineering 29*, 245–46.

Jackson, D. F., 1966. "Photosynthetic Rates of *Cladophora refracta* from Two Sites in Lake Ontario Under Natural and Laboratory Conditions," *Univ. Michigan, Gt. Lakes Res. Div. Publ. 15*, 44–50.

Jackson, D. F., and W. A. Dence, 1958. "Primary Productivity in a Dichothermic Lake," *Am. Midl. Nat. 59*, 511–17.

Jelliffe, S. E., 1893a. A preliminary report upon the microscopical organisms found in the Brooklyn water supply. *Brooklyn Med. J. 7*, 593–617.

———, 1893b. "A Preliminary List of the Plants Found in the Ridgewood Water Supply of the City of Brooklyn, King's County, N.Y.," *Bull. Torrey Bot. Club 20*, 243–46.

_____, 1894. "A Further Contribution to the Microscopical Examination of the Brooklyn Water Supply," *Brooklyn Med. J. 8*, 588–604.

_____, 1899. *The Flora of Long Island*, New Era Printing Co., Lancaster, Pa., 160 pp.

_____, 1904. "Additions to 'The Flora of Long Island'," *Torreya 4*, 97–100.

Johannsen, O. A., and J. T. Lloyd, 1915. "Genera of Plankton Organisms of the Cayuga Lake Basin," Limnol. Lab. Dept. Entomology, Cornell University, Ithaca, N.Y., 27 pp.

Johnson, D. S., and H. H. York, 1915. "The Relation of Plants to Tide-levels," Carnegie Institution of Washington, Publ. 206, 162 pp.

Kelley, A. P., 1927. "An Early Book on Algology," *Science 65*, 472–73.

Kellicott, D. S., 1878. "Notes on Microscopic Life in the Buffalo Water Supply," *Am. J. Microscopy and Pop. Sci. 3*, 250–52.

Kindle, E. M., 1925. "The Bottom Deposits of Lake Ontario," *Trans. Royal Soc. Canada* 19 (3, sect. 4), 47–102, plus 3 pl.

Lanciani, G. D., and J. M. Kingsbury, 1965. "Soil Algae of Forty Ponds under Construction at Ithaca, New York," *Rhodora 67*, 242–54.

Lattimore, S. A., 1877. "Report on the Recent Peculiar Condition of the Hemlock Lake Water Supply," *Ann. Rept. Exec. Bd. Depts. Water Works, Fire, Highway and Street Improvements, City of Rochester, N.Y.*, 1876, 108–19.

_____, 1878. "Report ... on the Water Supply of the City of Rochester," *ibid.*, 2 (1877), 71–97.

Lewis, W. B., 1870. "Report on the Microscopical Examination of the Croton and Ridgewood Waters," *Ann. Rept. Metropol. Bd. Health, State of N.Y. 4* (1869), 422–25.

Lorenzen, C. J., 1963. "Diurnal Variation in Photosynthetic Activity of Natural Phytoplankton Populations," *Limnol. Oceanogr. 8*, 56–62.

Mallory, M. L., and G. W. Rafter, 1889. [Causes of fishy tastes and odors in Hemlock Lake waters.] *Proc. Exec. Bd. City of Rochester, N.Y.*, 1889, 82–84.

Maloney, M. T., and W. I. Tressler, 1942. "The Diurnal Migration of Certain Species of Zooplankton in Caroga Lake, New York," *Trans. Am. Microscop. Soc. 61*, 40–52.

Markle, M. S., 1950. "The Algae of the Edmund Niles Huyck Preserve," *Proc. Indiana Acad. Sci. 59* (1949), 80–81.

Martindale, I. C., 1889. "Marine Algae of the New Jersey Coast and Adjacent Waters of Staten Island," *Mem. Torrey Bot. Club 1*, 87–109.

Mason, C. P., 1965. "Ecology of *Cladophora* in Farm Ponds," *Ecology 46*, 421–29.

Matthews, V. D., 1932. "The Aquatic Vegetation of Quaker Run," *J. Elisha Mitchell Soc. 47*, 74–84.

Members of the Scientific Staff of Cornell University, 1926. "A Preliminary Biological Survey of the Lloyd-Cornell Reservation," *Lloyd Library Bot. Pharm. & Mat. Med., Bull. 27*, 247 pp.

Merriman, M. L., 1922. "A new Species of *Spirogyra* with Unusual Arrangement of the Chromatophores," *Am. J. Bot. 9*, 283–84.

Mills, Henry, 1882. "Microscopic Organisms in the Buffalo Water Supply and in Niagara River," *Proc. Am. Soc. Microscopists 4*, 165–75.

Moore, G. T., 1903. "The Contamination of Public Water Supplies by Algae," U.S.D.A. Ybk. of Agr. 1902, 175–86.

Moore, G. T., and K. F. Kellerman, 1904. "A Method of Destroying or Preventing the Growth of Algae and Certain Pathogenic Bacteria in Water Supplies," U.S.D.A., Bur. Plant Ind., Bull. 64, 44 pp.

_____, 1905. "Copper as an Algicide and Disinfectant in Water Supplies," *ibid.*, 76, 55 p.

Mt. Pleasant, R. C., M. C. Rand, and N. L. Nemerow, 1962. "Chemical and Microbiological Aspects of Oneida Lake, New York," *N.Y.S. Dept Health Res. Rept. 8*, 1–95.

Muenscher, W. C., 1927. *"Spartina patens* and Other Saline Plants in the Genesee Valley of Western New York," *Rhodora 29,* 138–39.

———, 1946. "The Vegetation of Bergen Swamp. I. The Vascular Plants," *Proc. Rochester Acad. Sci. 9,* 64–117.

———, 1951. "The Vegetation of Bergen Swamp. IX. Supplement," *ibid.,* 339–47.

Needham, J. G., 1921. "A Biological Examination of Lake George, N.Y.," *Sci. Monthly 12,* 434–38.

Needham, J. G., C. Juday, E. Moore, C. K. Sibley, and J. W. Titcomb, 1922. "A Biological Survey of Lake George, N.Y.," Rept. N.Y.S. Conservation Comm., 78 pp.

Palmer, C. M., 1942. "Lemanea herbarium Packets Containing More than One Species," *Butler Univ. Bot. Stud. 5,* 222–23.

Patten, B., 1961. "Plankton Energetics of Raritan Bay," *Limnol. Oceanogr. 6,* 369–87.

Peck, C. H., 1869. "Species Growing Spontaneously in the State and Not Before Reported," *Rept. Regents Univ. State N.Y. 22* (1868), 52–106.

———, 1871. "Report of the (State) Botanist," *Report Regents Univ. State of N.Y. on Cabinet of Nat. Hist. (State Museum) 21* (1867), 23–24.

———, 1888. "Botanical Index to New York State Museum Reports—Twenty-two to Thirty-eight," *Rept. Trustees (previously Regents) State Mus. Nat. Hist. (Ann. Rept. N.Y.S. Mus. Nat. Hist) 41* (1887), 94–122.

Pierce, M. E., 1958. "The Effect of the Weedicide Kuron upon the Flora and Fauna of Two Experimental areas of Long Pond, Dutchess County, N. Y.," *Proc. Northeast. Weed Contr. Conf. 12,* 338–43.

———, 1959. "Further Study of the Effect of the Weedicide Kuron upon the Flora and Fauna of Long Pond, Dutchess County, N.Y.," *ibid., 13,* 310–14.

———, 1960. "Progress report of the Effect of the Kuron upon the Biota of Long Pond, Dutchess County, N.Y.," *ibid., 14,* 472–75.

———, 1960. "A Study of the Effect of the Weed Killer, 2,4-D Granular on Three Experimental Plots of Long Pond, Dutchess County, N.Y..," *ibid.,* 483–87.

———, 1961. "A Study of the Effect of the Weed Killer, 2,4-D Aqua Granular on Six Experimental Plots of Long Pond, Dutchess County, N.Y.," *ibid., 15* 539–44.

———, 1961. "Progress Report on the Effect of Kuron Applications after One and Two Years at Long Pond, Dutchess County, N.Y.," *ibid.,* 545.

Pieters, A. J., 1902. "The Plants of Western Lake Erie, with Observations on Their Distribution," *Bull. U.S. Fish Commission (for 1901),* 57–79, plus 8 pl.

Pike, N., 1886. "Check List of Marine Algae," *Bull. Torrey Bot. Club 13,* 105–14.

Platt, E. L., 1915. "The Population of the 'Blanket-algae' of Freshwater Pools," *Am. Nat. 49,* 752–62.

Rafter, G. W., 1890a. "Biological Examination of Potable Water," *Proc. Rochester Acad. Sci. 1,* 34–44.

——— 1890b. "Deterioration of Water in Reservoirs, its Causes and Prevention," Ann. Rept. N.J. Bd. Health *14* (1890), 11–122.

Riley, G. A., 1959. "Oceanography of Long Island Sound 1954–1955," *Bull. Bingham Oceanogr. Coll. 17,* 9–29.

Ryther, J. H., 1954. "The Ecology of Phytoplankton Blooms in Moriches Bay and Great South Bay, Long Island, New York," *Biol. Bull. 106,* 198–209.

Schenk, C. F., and R. E. Thompson, 1965. "Long-term changes in Water Chemistry and Abundance of Plankton at a Single Sampling Location in Lake Ontario," *Univ. Mich., Gt. Lakes Res. Div. Publ. 13,* 197–208.

Schultze, E. A., 1889. "A Descriptive List of Staten Island Diatoms," *Bull. Torrey Bot. Club 16,* 98–104.

Schumacher, G. J., 1961. "Biology of the Allegany Indian Reservation and Vicinity. I. The Algae," *N.Y.S. Mus. & Sci. Serv. Bull. 383*, 5–18.

Smith, G. M., 1924. "Ecology of the Plankton Algae in the Palisades Interstate Park, Including the Relation of Control Methods to Fish Culture," *Roosevelt Wildlife Bull. 2*, 93–195.

Smith, H. L., 1882. *"Rhizoselenia gracilis*, n. sp.," *Proc. Am. Soc. Microscopists 4*, 177–78.

Snow, J. W., 1903. "The Plankton Algae of Lake Erie with Special Reference to the Chlorophyceae," *Bull. U.S. Comm. Fish & Fisheries 1902*, 369–94, plus 4 pl.

Stewart P. A., and Merrell, W. D., 1937. "The Bergen Swamp: An Ecological Study," *Proc. Rochester Acad. Sci. 7*, 209–62.

Taylor, W. R., 1940. "Marine Algae from Long Island," *Torreya 40*, 185–95.

Torrey, J., 1843. *A Flora of the State of New York . . .*, Vol. I., Carroll & Cook, Albany.

———, 1860. "Report on Cause of Disagreeable Quality of Water," *Ann. Rept. Croton Aqueduct Dept.* 1859, 28–33.

Transeau, E. N., 1913. "The Vegetation of Cold Spring Harbor, Long Island, I. The Littoral Successions," *Plant World 16*, 189–209.

———, 1918. "A New Species and a new Variety of Algae from Oneida Lake," N.Y. S. Col. Forestry at Syracuse Univ., Tech. Publ. *9*, 237–38.

Tressler, W. L., 1941. "Seasonal Variation of Some Limnological Factors in Irondequoit Bay, New York; Specific Conductivity of New York and Maryland Lakes," *Ybk. Am. Philosoph. Soc. 1940*, 260–63.

Tressler, W. L., T. S. Austin, and E. Orban, 1953. "Seasonal Variation of Some Limnological Factors in Irondequoit Bay, New York," *Am. Midl Nat. 49*, 878–903.

Tressler, W. L., L. G. Wagner, and R. Bere, 1940. "A Limnological Study of Chautauqua Lake. II. Seasonal Variation," *Trans. Am. Microscop. Soc. 59*, 12–30.

Tucker, A., 1948. "The Phytoplankton of the Bay of Quinte," *ibid. 67*, 365–83.

Vorce, C. M., 1880. "The Minute Forms of Life in the Waters of the Lakes," *Am. J. Microscopy & Pop. Sci. 5*, 263–65.

———, 1881. "Forms Observed in the Water of Lake Erie," *Proc. Am. Soc. Microscop. 3*, 51–60.

———, 1882. "Microscopic Forms Observed in Water of Lake Erie," *ibid., 4*, 187–96.

Whipple G. C., 1914. *The Microscopy of Drinking Water*, 3rd ed., Wiley, New York. 409 pp., plus 19 pl.

Williams, L. G., and C. Scott, 1962. "Principal Diatoms of Major Waterways of the United States," *Limnol. Oceanogr. 7*, 365–79.

Wood, H. C., 1872. "A Contribution to the History of the Fresh-water Algae of North America," *Smithsonian Contrib. Knowl. 241*, 1–262, plus 21 pl.

Wood, R. D., and W. C. Muenscher, 1956. "The Characeae of the State of New York," *Cornell Univ. Agr. Expt. Sta. Mem. 238*, 1–77.

Wolle, F., 1876. "Fresh Water Algae Collected during the Past Three Years, mostly within a Circuit of about Twenty Miles around Bethlehem, Penn.," *Bull. Torrey Bot. Club 6*, 121–23.

———, 1882. "Freshwater Algae," *ibid., 9*, 25–30.

———, 1884. *Desmids of the United States . . .*, Moravian Pulb. Office, Bethlehem, Pa., 168 pp, plus 53 pl.

———, 1887. *Freshwater Algae of the United States*, Vol. II, pub. by author, Bethlehem, Pa., 364 pp, plus 210 pl.

———, 1894, *Diatomaceae of North America*, pub. by author, Bethlehem, Pa., 47 pp, plus 122 pl.

INDEX